CW00801791

£29.99

CONTENTS

ROB DANTER
DONALD THOMSON
Music Setters

RICHARD WEAVER
LOUISE SELFE
MATTHEW LOCKWOOD
Text Setters

HUBERT J. RICHARDS
JANET SIMPSON
ANNE GILBERT
Indexes

GEOFF PEACHEY
ELISABETH BATES
HELEN ELLIOT
KATE GALLAHER
HELEN GOODALL
RACHEL JUDD
GEOFFREY MOORE
Proof Readers

JONATHAN STROULGER
Cover Design

JANE RAYSON
Copyright Manager

JANET SIMPSON
Project Manager

FOREWORD

The first edition of *Hymns Old and New* appeared in 1977. The principle underlying its production was simple: to offer in one, single, conveniently sized book, a selection of the hymns most used by Catholic communities in Britain and Ireland. The contents ranged from the stalwart songs of the traditional pre-Vatican II hymnals to the best of the new as discovered and tested by the series of *20th Century Folk Hymnals*.

By 1984 it was clear that a major revision of this basically sound idea was needed. Very little adjustment to the 'old' traditional material was needed, but by now the repertoire of 'new' material had broadened. This was largely due to the work of people like the late Brother Damian Lundy in encouraging young people to be brave enough to express their faith in song, and which had made the influential *Songs of the Spirit* series possible. There was also the papal visit of 1982, where the various public celebrations had opened the eyes of many parishes to the role that music could and should play in their liturgy. Not only did parishes and other communities seem to have developed an immense appetite for music for their celebrations, but they were demanding a wider repertoire of material, and expecting higher standards from the words. As a response to these pastoral demands, *Hymns Old and New with Supplement* was published. It was the first popular hymnal to offer a scriptural index, and to equip parishes to be able to sing the Responsorial Psalm for every Sunday and major feast. This edition soon became, and for many years has remained, Britain's best-selling hymnal.

A decade later seemed an opportune moment to offer a new edition. There was, of course, the need to include the good new material that had been emerging in the rest of Europe and the United States. The result, *Hymns Old and New, New Century Edition*, was also a far more elegant product, thanks to the improvements in computer-based music-setting which did not exist ten years earlier. The somewhat summary scriptural index of its predecessor was now far more generous, matching the growing realisation that scripture should be the primary source for what we proclaim in song in our liturgies. This edition's main innovation, though, was to try and serve those parishes whose musical repertoire was almost exclusively traditional material by offering 'hymns for the Lectionary': a comprehensive range of new texts, explicitly constructed on the scripture readings for the Sundays and feasts – but all singable to traditional hymn-tunes.

The need so clearly felt to renew the material for our celebrations is a healthy one, because it is a sign of the Church's vitality. Quite naturally, parishes and communities are now looking for the pastoral tool that will take them and their celebrations forward into the third millennium. This latest edition of the series is designed to serve that purpose. It has consciously taken the best insights and initiatives of its predecessors, and added another very important one. The basic title *Hymns Old and New* has gained the significant adjective 'Liturgical'. Parishes are now more discerning in the material they choose for their celebrations: they are demanding songs that have clear and coherent connections with the scripture texts that are proclaimed; the people are reclaiming the parts of the Mass and the celebration of the sacraments that belong to them by wanting – as they should – to sing them; it is, happily, becoming standard practice for the Responsorial Psalm to be sung. These are all profoundly 'liturgical' aspirations, and this book is designed to satisfy them.

Robert Kelly
Sister Sheila McGovern SSL
Kevin Mayhew
Father Andrew Moore
Sister Louisa Poole SSL

Editorial Note

The keyboard arrangements of many of the newer songs in *Liturgical Hymns Old and New* are based on the guitar chords. This allows both instruments to be played together.

LITURGICAL

HYMNS OLD & NEW

1 A New People's Mass (Gregory Murray)

Penitential Rite

Gloria

take a - way the sins of the world, have mer - cy on us; you are seat-ed at the right hand of the Fa - ther, re-ceive our prayer. For you a -lone are the Ho - ly One, you a -lone are the Lord, you a -lone are the Most High, Je - sus Christ, with the Ho - ly Spi - rit, in the glo - ry of God the Fa - ther. A - men.

Sanctus

Text: from the Roman Missal
Music: Gregory Murray (1905-1992)

LITURGICAL

HYMNS OLD & NEW

2 A Simple Mass (Andrew Moore)

Penitential Rite

Lord, have mer-cy. Lord, have mer-cy. Christ, have mer-cy.

Christ, have mer-cy. Lord, have mer-cy. Lord, have mer-cy.

Gloria

Glo - ry to God in the high - est, and peace to his peo-ple on earth. Lord God, heav'n-ly King, al - migh - ty God and Fa - ther, we wor-ship you, we give you thanks, we praise you for your glo - ry, we praise you for your glo - ry. Lord Je-sus Christ, on - ly Son of the Fa - ther, Lord God, Lamb of God, you take a-way the sins of the world: have

Sanctus

Ho - ly, ho - ly, ho - ly Lord,

God of pow - er and God of might, hea - ven and earth are

full of your glo - ry. Ho - san - na in the high - est. Ho -

san - na in the high - est. Bless-ed is he who comes in the name of the

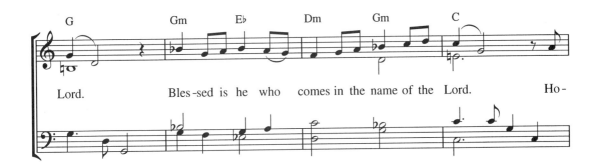

Lord. Bles-sed is he who comes in the name of the Lord. Ho-

san - na in the high - est, ho - san - na in the high - est.

Memorial acclamation

Unison

Dy - ing, you de - stroyed our death,

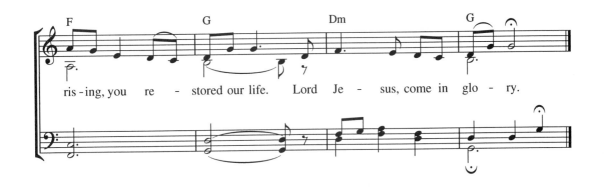

ris - ing, you re - stored our life. Lord Je - sus, come in glo - ry.

Agnus Dei

Lamb of God, you take a-way the sins of the world: have mer – cy on us.

Lamb of God, you take a-way the sins of the world: have mer – cy on us.

Lamb of God, you take a-way the sins of the world: grant us peace.

Text: from the Roman Missal
Music: Andrew Moore (b.1954)

3 Mass of the Spirit (Kevin Mayhew)

Penitential Rite

Lord, have mer- cy. Lord, have mer- cy. Lord, have mer- cy.

Christ, have mer - cy. Christ, have mer - cy. Christ, have mer - cy.

Lord, have mer - cy. Lord, have mer - cy. Lord, have mer - cy.

Gloria

Glo - ry to God in the high - est, and peace to his

peo - ple on earth. Lord God, hea - ven - ly

King, al - migh - ty God and Fa - ther, we wor - ship you, we

Sanctus

Text: from the Roman Missal
Music: Kevin Mayhew (b.1942)

4 Mass of the Bread of Life (Margaret Rizza)

Penitential Rite

Gloria

Con gioia ($\textstyle\quad$ = c. 84)

Glo - ry, glo-ry to God, glo-ry to God in the high - est;

peace to his peo-ple on earth, peace to his peo-ple on earth.

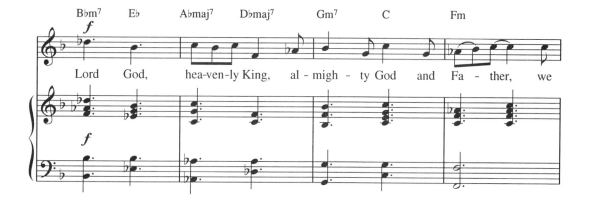

Lord God, hea-ven-ly King, al - migh - ty God and Fa - ther, we

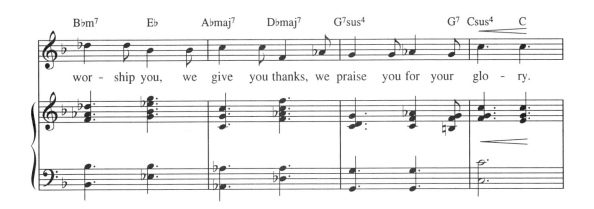

B♭m⁷   E♭   A♭maj⁷   D♭maj⁷   G⁷sus⁴   G⁷ Csus⁴   C

wor - ship you,   we   give   you thanks, we praise   you for   your   glo - ry.

Optional Descant

Glo - ry,   glo-ry to God,   glo-ry to God in the high - est;

Glo - ry,   glo-ry to God,   glo-ry to God in the high - est;

F   Gm¹¹   Fmaj⁷   Gm¹¹   F   Gm¹¹   Fmaj⁷   Gm¹¹

rit.

peace   to   his peo-ple on earth,   peace to his peo-ple on   earth.

peace   to   his peo-ple on earth,   peace to his peo-ple on   earth.

F   Gm¹¹   Fmaj⁷   Gm¹¹   F   Gm¹¹   Fmaj⁷ Gm¹¹   F
rit.

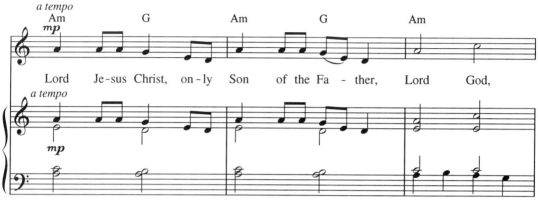

Lord Je-sus Christ, on-ly Son of the Fa – ther, Lord God,

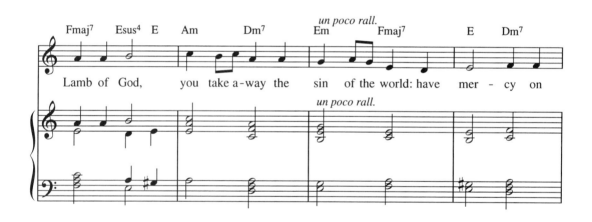

Lamb of God, you take a-way the sin of the world: have mer – cy on

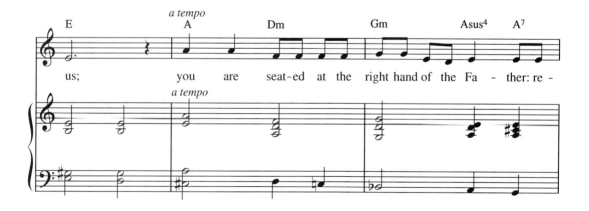

us; you are seat-ed at the right hand of the Fa – ther: re –

Sanctus

Ho - ly, ho - ly, ho - ly Lord, God of pow'r and God of might,

hea-ven and earth are full of your glo-ry. Ho - san - na in the high - est; ho-

san - na, ho-san - na, ho-san - na in the high - est; ho-

Memorial Acclamation

Great Amen

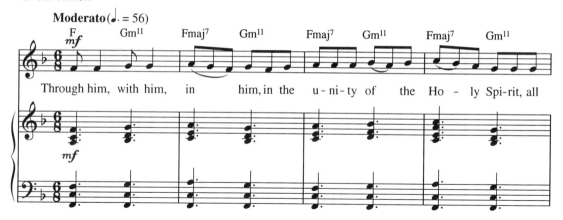

Through him, with him, in him, in the u-ni-ty of the Ho - ly Spi-rit, all

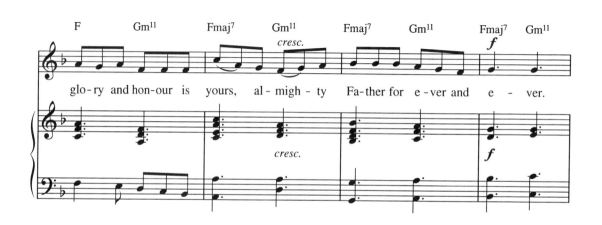

glo-ry and hon-our is yours, al - migh - ty Fa-ther for e -ver and e - ver.

Optional Descant

A - men, a - men, a - men,

A - men, a - men, a - men,

Agnus Dei

Text: from the Roman Missal
Music: Margaret Rizza (b.1929)

LITURGICAL

HYMNS OLD & NEW

5 Missa de Angelis (Plainsong)

Penitential Rite

Unison

Ky-ri - e, e - le-i-son.

Chris-te, e - le-i-son.

Ky-ri- e, e - le-i-son.

Ky-ri-e, e - le-i-son.

Gloria

Unison

Glo-ri - a in ex-cel-sis De - o, et in ter-ra pax ho-mi-ni-bus

in glo-ri-a De-i Pa - tris. A - men.

Sanctus
Unison

San - ctus, san-ctus, san - ctus

Do - mi-nus De-us sa - ba - oth.

Ple-ni sunt cæ-li et ter - ra glo-ri-a tu - a.

Ho-san - na in ex-cel - sis.

Be-ne-di - ctus qui ve - nit in no-mi-ne Do - mi-ni.

Text: from the Roman Missal
Music: Plainsong, accompaniment by Andrew Moore (b.1954)

6 Mass XVIII (Plainsong)

Penitential Rite

Ky - ri - e, e-le - i - son. Chris-te, e - le - i - son.

Ky - ri - e, e-le - i - son. Ky - ri - e, e - le - i - son.

Sanctus

San-ctus, san-ctus, san-ctus Do-mi-nus De-us sa-ba-oth.

Ple-ni sunt cæ-li et ter-ra glo-ri-a tu-a. Ho-san-na in ex-cel-sis.

Be-ne-di-ctus qui ve-nit in no-mi-ne Do-mi-ni. Ho-san - na in ex-cel - sis.

Agnus Dei
Unison

A - gnus De - i, qui tol - lis pec - ca - ta mun - di:

mi - se - re - re no - bis. A - gnus De - i,

qui tol - lis pec - ca - ta mun - di: do - na no - bis pa - cem.

Text: from the Roman Missal
Music: Plainsong, accompaniment by Andrew Moore (b.1954)

7 The 'American' Eucharist

Penitential Rite

2. Christ, have mercy; Christ, have mercy;
   gift from heaven, Christ, have mercy.
   Light of truth and light of justice,
   Christ, have mercy; Christ, have mercy.

3. Lord, have mercy; Lord, have mercy;
   on your servants, Lord, have mercy.
   God almighty, just and faithful,
   Lord, have mercy; Lord, have mercy.

Gospel acclamation

Alleluia, alleluia,
let us praise Christ, our Lord Jesus.
Alleluia, let us praise him,
now among us in his Gospel.

Sanctus

1. Holy, holy, holy, holy,
   Lord of hosts. You fill with glory
   all the earth and all the heavens.
   Sing hosanna, sing hosanna.

2. Blest and holy, blest and holy,
   he who comes now in the Lord's name.
   In the highest sing hosanna,
   in the highest sing hosanna.

Memorial acclamation

When we eat this bread you give us,
and we drink this cup you left us,
we proclaim your death, Lord Jesus,
till you come again in glory.

Agnus Dei

1. Jesus, Lamb of God, have mercy,
   bearer of our sins, have mercy.
   Jesus, Lamb of God, have mercy,
   bearer of our sins, have mercy.

2. Saviour of the world, Lord Jesus,
   may your peace be with us always.
   Saviour of the world, Lord Jesus,
   may your peace be always with us.

Text: Kyrie, Sanctus, Agnus Dei adapted from the Liturgy by Sandra Joan Billington (b.1946)
Gospel acclamation and Memorial acclamation adapted from the Liturgy by Robert B. Kelly (b.1948)
Music: traditional American melody arr. Andrew Moore

8 The 'Hopwood' Mass

2. Saviour of all, O Christ, have mercy.
   Saviour of all, O Christ, have mercy.
   Saviour of all, have mercy on us.
   Saviour of all, be ever near us.

3. Spirit of all, O Lord, have mercy.
   Spirit of all, O Lord, have mercy.
   Spirit of all, have mercy on us.
   Spirit of all, be ever near us.

Sanctus

1. Holy are you, Lord of creation!
   Holy are you, Lord God of angels!
   Holy are you, God of all people!
   Heaven and earth proclaim your glory.

2. Glory to you! Your name is holy.
   Blessèd is he who comes in your name!
   Glory to him! We sing his praises.
   Heaven and earth proclaim your glory.

Agnus Dei

   O Lamb of God, you bore our sinning.
   O Lamb of God, you bore our dying.
   O Lamb of God, have mercy on us.
   O Lamb of God, your peace be with us.

Text: adapted from the Liturgy by Terence Collins (b.1938)
Music: Welsh melody adapted by Terence Collins (b.1938) and David Bentley

9 The 'Israeli' Mass

Penitential Rite

1. Lord, have mer-cy. Lord, have mer-cy. Lord, have mer-cy on us all.

Lord, have mer-cy. Lord, have mer-cy. Lord, have mer-cy on us all.

2. Christ, have mercy. Christ, have mercy.
   Christ, have mercy on us all.
   Christ, have mercy. Christ, have mercy.
   Christ, have mercy on us all.

3. Lord, have mercy. Lord, have mercy.
   Lord, have mercy on us all.
   Lord, have mercy. Lord, have mercy.
   Lord, have mercy on us all.

Sanctus

1. Holy, holy, holy, holy,
   Lord of pow'r, Lord of might.
   Heav'n and earth are filled with glory.
   Sing hosanna evermore.

2. Blest and holy, blest and holy,
   he who comes from God on high.
   Raise your voices, sing his glory,
   praise his name for evermore.

Agnus Dei

1. Lamb of God, you take away the sin,
   the sin of all the world:
   give us mercy, give us mercy,
   give us mercy, Lamb of God.

2. Lamb of God, you take away the sin,
   the sin of all the world:
   give us mercy, give us mercy,
   give us mercy, Lamb of God.

3. Lamb of God, you take away the sin,
   the sin of all the world:
   grant us peace, Lord; grant us peace, Lord;
   grant us peace, Lamb of God.

Text: adapted from the Liturgy by Anthony Hamson
Music: traditional Iraeli melody collected by Anthony Hamson

10 Lord, have mercy (Missa de Angelis)

Text: from the Roman Missal
Music: Alan Rees (b.1941) adapted from Plainsong

11 Lord, have mercy (Orbis Factor)

King e-ter-nal, cre-a-tor of the world, have mer-cy. Lord, have mer-cy.

Christ, light of the world, be-stow-er of life, have mer-cy. Christ, have mer-cy.

Lov-ing Sa-viour, take a-way our sins and have mer-cy. Lord, have mer-cy.

Text: from the Roman Missal
Music: Alan Rees (b.1941) adapted from Plainsong

12 Lord, have mercy (Alme Pater)

Cantor You were sent to heal the con - trite. *(All on repeat)* Lord, have mer - cy.

Cantor You came to call sin - ners. *(All on repeat)* Christ, have mer - cy.

Cantor You are seat-ed at the right hand of the Fa - ther. *(All on repeat)* Lord, have mer - cy.

Text: from the Roman Missal
Music: Alan Rees (b.1941) based on Plainsong
© Copyright 1999 Kevin Mayhew Ltd.

13 Kyrie eleison (Haugen)

Text: adapted from the Liturgy by Marty Haugen (b.1950)
Music: Marty Haugen (b.1950)

14 Lord, have mercy (Archer)

Text: from the Roman Missal
Music: Malcolm Archer (b.1952) from 'The Halesworth Setting'
© Copyright 1995 Kevin Mayhew Ltd.

15 Lord, have mercy (Rock)

2. Christ, have mercy on us all.
   Christ, have mercy on us all.
   Christ, have mercy,
   Christ, have mercy,
   Christ, have mercy on us all.

3. Lord, have mercy . . .

Text: from the Roman Missal
Music: Gordon Rock from 'The Pilgrim's Mass' arr. Andrew Moore

16 Kyrie eleison (Rizza)

17 Kyrie (Mawby)

Ky - ri - e, Chri - ste,

Ky - ri - e, e - le - i - son.

Or

Lord, have mer - cy. Christ, have mer - cy.

Lord have mer - cy, have mer - cy.

Text: from the Roman Missal
Music: Colin Mawby (b.1936)
© Copyright 1991 Kevin Mayhew Ltd.

18 Kyrie 7

Ky - ri - e, Ky - ri - e, e - le - i - son.

Ky - ri - e, Ky - ri - e, e - le - i - son. *(hum under the invocations)*

* ad lib. 2nd time only

Text: from the Roman Missal
Music: Jacques Berthier (1923-1994)

LITURGICAL

HYMNS OLD & NEW

19 Lord, have mercy (Filitz)

CASWALL 65 65

1. Lord, have mer - cy on us, hear us as we pray;

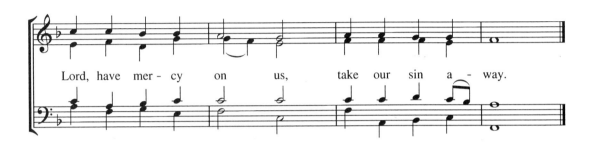

Lord, have mer - cy on us, take our sin a - way.

2. Christ, have mercy on us,
   hear us as we pray;
   Christ, have mercy on us,
   take our sin away.

3. Lord, have mercy on us,
   hear us as we pray;
   Lord, have mercy on us,
   take our sin away.

Text: Michael Forster (b.1946)
Music: Friedrich Filitz (1804-1876)
Text © Copyright 1997 Kevin Mayhew Ltd.

20 Coventry Gloria

Glo - ry to God, glo - ry in the high - est,

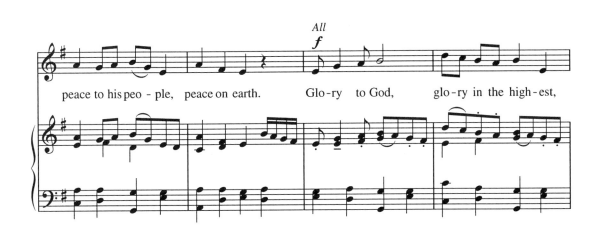

peace to his peo - ple, peace on earth. Glo - ry to God, glo - ry in the high - est,

peace to his peo - ple, peace on earth. For you a - lone are the Ho - ly One,

glo-ry in the high - est, peace to his peo - ple, peace on earth.

glo-ry in the high - est, peace to his peo - ple, peace on earth.

Choir

A - men, a - men.

ff

ff

ff

Text: from the Roman Missal
Music: Peter Jones

21 Gloria (Rees)

a tempo

Optional Descant

in the glo-ry of God the Fa - ther.

Cantor

All

with the Ho - ly Spi - rit, in the glo-ry of God the Fa - ther.

a tempo

A - men, a - men. A - men, a - men.

Cantor

All

rit.

A - men, a - men. A - men, a - men.

rit.

Text: from the Roman Missal
Music: Alan Rees (b.1941)

22 Glory to God (Archer)

Text: from the Roman Missal
Music: Malcolm Archer (b.1952) from 'The People's Setting'

LITURGICAL

HYMNS OLD & NEW

23 Gloria 3

This setting may be sung as a canon with entries as indicated.

Glo - ri - a, glo - ri - a in ex-cel - sis De - o!

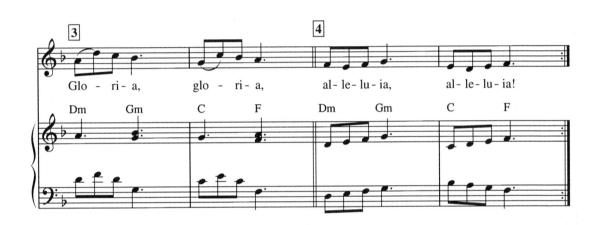

Glo - ri - a, glo - ri - a, al - le - lu - ia, al - le - lu - ia!

Text: Taizé Community, from the Roman Missal
Music: Jacques Berthier (1923-1994)

24 Glory, glory in the highest

Bright. joyful feel

Glo - ry, glo-ry in the high - est; glo - ry

to the Al - migh - ty; glo-ry to the Lamb of God, and

glo-ry to the liv - ing Word; glo - ry

Text and Music: Danny Daniels

25 Gloria (Anderson)

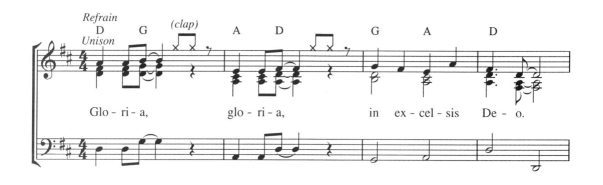

Refrain
Unison

Glo-ri-a, glo-ri-a, in ex-cel-sis De-o.

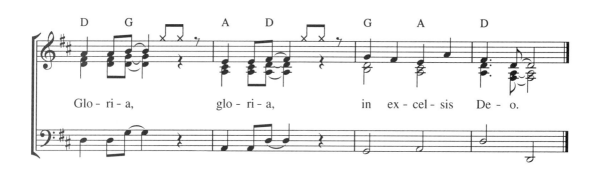

Glo-ri-a, glo-ri-a, in ex-cel-sis De-o.

1. Lord God, hea-ven-ly King, peace you bring to us; we

wor-ship you, we give you thanks, we sing our song of praise.

2. Jesus, Saviour of all, Lord God, Lamb of God,
   you take away our sins, O Lord, have mercy on us all.

3. At the Father's right hand, Lord receive our prayer,
   for you alone are the Holy One, and you alone are Lord.

4. Glory, Father and Son, glory, Holy Spirit,
   to you we raise our hands up high, we glorify your name.

Text: Mike Anderson (b.1956) adapted from the Liturgy
Music: Mike Anderson (b.1956)

26 Gloria (Salazar)

2. Son of the Father, all glory and worship;
   praise and thanksgiving to you, Lamb of God.

3. You take away the sin of the world;
   have mercy on us, receive our prayer.

4. Seated in pow'r at the right of the Father,
   Jesus alone is the Lord, the Most High.

5. And with the Spirit of love everlasting,
   reigning in glory for ever. Amen.

Text: George Salazar trans. Paul Inwood
Music: George Salazar arr. Paul Inwood

Original text and music © Copyright 1984 George Salazar.
English translation and arrangement © Copyright 1984, 1993, Paul Inwood.
Published by OCP Publications, 5536 NE Hassalo, Portland OR 97213, USA.

27 Gloria (Duffy)

Text: from the Roman Missal
Music: Francis Duffy

28 Lourdes Gloria

Text: from the Roman Missal
Music: Jean-Paul Lécot (b.1947)

29 Sing to God a song of glory

1. Sing to God a song of glo-ry, peace he brings to all on earth. Wor-ship we the King of hea-ven; praise and bless his ho-ly name. *Refrain* Glo-ry, glo-ry, sing his glo-ry. Glo-ry to our God on high.

2. Sing to Christ, the Father's loved one,
Jesus, Lord and Lamb of God:
hear our prayer, O Lord, have mercy,
you who bear the sins of all.

3. Sing to Christ, the Lord and Saviour,
seated there at God's right hand:
hear our prayer, O Lord, have mercy,
you alone the Holy One.

4. Glory sing to God the Father,
glory to his only Son,
glory to the Holy Spirit,
glory to the Three in One.

Text: Francesca Leftley (b.1955) based on the 'Gloria'
Music: Francesca Leftley (b.1955) arr. Christopher Tambling

LITURGICAL

HYMNS OLD & NEW

30 Peruvian Gloria

Cantor
1. Glo-ry to God, glo-ry to God, glo-ry to the Fa - ther.

All
Glo-ry to God, glo-ry to God, glo-ry to the Fa - ther.

Refrain
Cantor   *All*
To him be glo-ry for e - ver. **To him be glo-ry for e - ver.**

Cantor   *All*
Al-le-lu-ia, a-men, **al-le-lu-ia, a-men,** al-le-lu-ia, a-men, al-le-lu-ia, a -men.

2. Glory to God, glory to God,
Son of the Father.
Glory to God, glory to God,
Son of the Father.
To him be glory for ever.
To him be glory for ever.
Alleluia, amen.
Alleluia, amen,
alleluia, amen,
alleluia, amen.

3. Glory to God, glory to God,
glory to the Spirit.
Glory to God, glory to God,
Son of the Spirit.
To him be glory for ever.
To him be glory for ever.
Alleluia, amen.
Alleluia, amen,
alleluia, amen,
alleluia, amen.

This is best sung accompanied only by bongos or a similar percussion instrument.
The optional harmony notes give added effect, but those singing the tune should
remain on the lower notes.

Text and Music: traditional Peruvian, collected and arr. John Ballantine (b.1945)
© Copyright 1976 Kevin Mayhew Ltd.

31 Glory to God, to God in the height
Country Gardens Gloria

1. Glo - ry to God, to God in the height, bring - ing

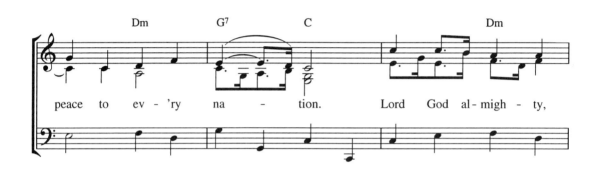

peace to ev - 'ry na - tion. Lord God al - migh - ty,

Fa - ther and King, and the au - thor of sal - va - tion.

'Glo - ry!' let the peo - ple sing, let the whole cre - a - tion ring,

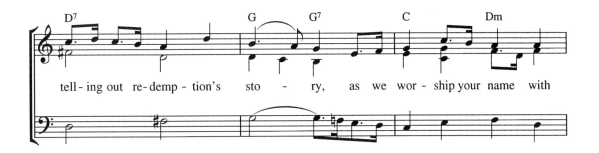

tell - ing out re - demp - tion's sto - ry, as we wor - ship your name with

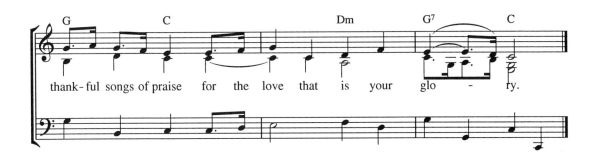

thank - ful songs of praise for the love that is your glo - ry.

2. Jesus, the Father's one holy Son,
   all creation bows before you.
   You are the God, the God we acclaim,
   and we worship and adore you.
   Lamb of God, to you we pray,
   you who take our sin away,
   mercy, grace and truth revealing.
   At the right hand of God, receive our humble prayer
   for forgiveness, hope and healing.

3. You, Jesus Christ, alone are the Lord,
   by your own eternal merit;
   sharing by right the glory of God
   in the presence of the Spirit.
   You alone are Lord Most High,
   you alone we glorify,
   reigning over all creation.
   To the Father, the Son and Spirit, Three in One,
   be eternal acclamation!

Text: Michael Forster (b.1946) based on the Gloria
Music: traditional English melody arr. Keith Stent

32 Sing glory to God
Ash Grove Gloria

1. Sing glo-ry to God in the height of the hea-vens, sal-va-tion and peace to his peo-ple on earth; our King and our Sa-viour, our God and our Fa-ther, we wor-ship and praise you and sing of your worth. Cre-a-tion u-nites in the power of the Spi-rit, in praise of the Fa-ther, through Je-sus, the Son. So

com - plex, so sim - ple, so clear, so my - ste - rious, our
God e - ver three, yet e - ter - nal - ly one.

2. Lord Jesus, the Christ, only Son of the Father,
   the Lamb who has carried our burden of shame,
   now seated on high in the glory of heaven,
   have mercy upon us who call on your name.

3. For you, only you, we acknowledge as holy,
   we name you alone as our Saviour and Lord;
   you only, O Christ, with the Spirit exalted,
   at one with the Father, for ever adored.

Text: Michael Forster (b.1946) based on the 'Gloria'
Music: traditional Welsh melody arr. Keith Stent

33 Advent Alleluia

Al - le - lu - ia, al - le - lu - ia, al - le - lu - ia, al - le - lu - ia!

Pre-pare the way of the Lord, make straight his paths:

all peo-ple shall see the sal - va - tion of God.

Or

A vir-gin will give birth to a Son; a vir-gin will give birth to a Son; his name will be Em-ma-nu-el: God is with us.

Text: from the Lectionary
Music: Michael Joncas (b.1951)

34 Alleluia (Lloyd)

Unison

Al - le-lu - ia, al - le-lu-ia, al - le-lu - ia, al - le-lu - ia!

Either:

Speak, Lord, your ser-vant is lis-ten-ing: you have the mes-sage of e - ter - nal life.

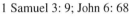

1 Samuel 3: 9; John 6: 68

Or:

The Word was made flesh and lived a-mong us; to all who did ac -

cept him he gave pow-er to be-come chil - dren of God.

John 1: 14,12

Text: from the Lectionary
Music: Richard Lloyd (b.1933)

35 Scottish Alleluia

Refrain
Harmony

Al - le - lu - ia! Al - le - lu - ia! Al - le -

lu - ia! Al - le - lu - ia!

Fine

Cantor *All* *Cantor* *All* D.S.

Praise to you, Lord Je - sus Christ! Al - le - lu - ia! You bring us heal-ing! Al - le -

Other texts may be substituted for 'You bring us healing'
to reflect the Gospel reading:

Light for our darkness!

Way to the Father!

Shepherd eternal!

Strength in our weakness!

Word here among us!

Text and Music: Frances M. Kelly
© Copyright 1998, 1999 Kevin Mayhew Ltd.

36 Irish Alleluia

This may be sung unaccompanied as a round

Sing al - le - lu – ia! Sing al - le - lu – ia! Sing

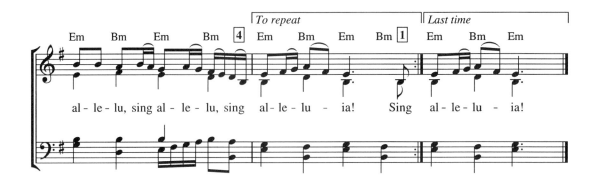

al - le - lu, sing al - le - lu, sing al - le - lu – ia! Sing al - le - lu – ia!

Psalm tone for the Proper text

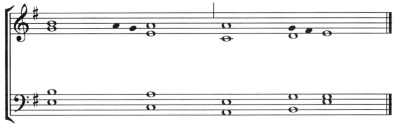

Music: Response – traditional Irish arr. Robert B. Kelly (b.1948) and Frances M. Kelly
Psalm tone – Gregory Murray (1905-1992)
This arrangement © Copyright 1984 Kevin Mayhew Ltd.
Psalm tone © Copyright Downside Abbey. Used by permission.

37 Celtic Alleluia

Al - le - lu - ia, al - le - lu - ia,

al - le - lu - ia, al - le - lu - ia.

Psalm tone for the Proper text

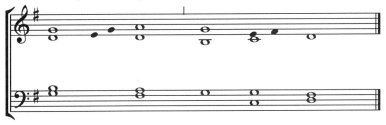

Music: Response – Fintan O'Carroll
Psalm tone – Gregory Murray (1905-1992)

LITURGICAL

HYMNS OLD & NEW

38 Eightfold Alleluia

1. Al-le-lu-ia, al-le-lu-ia, al-le-lu-ia, al-le-lu-ia, al-le-lu-ia, al-le-lu-ia, al-le-lu-ia, al-le-lu-ia.

Psalm tone for the Proper text

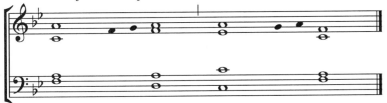

Music: Response – unknown arr. Andrew Moore
Psalm tone – Gregory Murray (1905-1992)

39 Easter Alleluia

Al-le-lu-ia, al-le-lu-ia, al-le-lu-ia.

Psalm tone for the Proper text

Music: Response – Plainsong arr. Andrew Moore
Psalm tone – Gregory Murray (1905-1992)

40 Alleluia 7

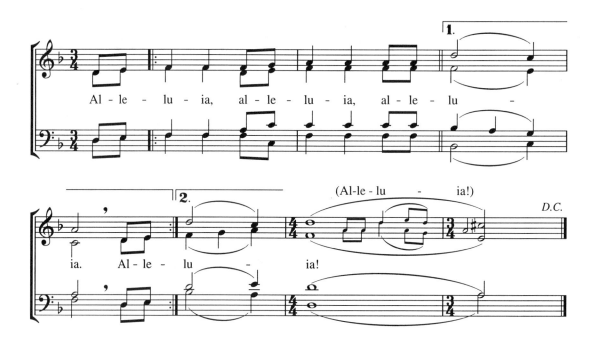

41 Alleluia (Archer)

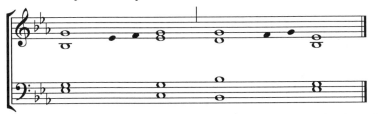

Music: Response – Malcolm Archer (b.1956)
Psalm tone – Gregory Murray (1905-1992)

42 Alleluia (Plainsong)

Unison

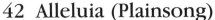

Al - le - lu - ia, al - le - lu - ia, al - le - lu - ia.

Psalm tone for the Proper text

Music: Response – Plainsong arr. Andrew Moore (b.1954)
Psalm tone – Gregory Murray (1905-1992)

43 Alleluia (Moore No. 1)

Unison

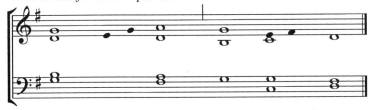

Al - le - lu - ia, al - le - lu - ia, al - le - lu - ia.

Psalm tone for the Proper text

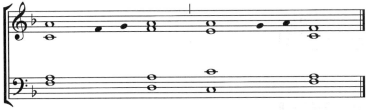

Music: Response – Plainsong arr. Andrew Moore (b.1954)
Psalm tone – Gregory Murray (1905-1992)

44 Alleluia (Moore No.2)

Optional Introduction

Unison

Al - le - lu - ia, al - le - lu - ia, al - le - lu - ia.

Psalm tone for the Proper text

Music: Response – Plainsong arr. Andrew Moore (b.1954)
Psalm tone – Gregory Murray (1905-1992)

45 Alleluia (White)

Unison

Al - le - lu - ia. (Al - le - lu - ia)   Your word is   true,   help

us   to   lis - ten,   Lord.

Text and Music: Estelle White (b.1925)

46 Alleluia (Moore No. 3)

47 Alleluia (Bevenot)

48 Alleluia (Lundy)

Unison

Al - le - lu - ia, al - le - lu - ia, al - le - lu - ia. *Fine*

Easter

1. Lord Je - sus, you are ri - sen from the dead: you are our com -

pan-ion on the road of life, and we know you in the break-ing of the bread. *D.C.*

Advent and Christmas

2. Lord Jesus, Word of God made man for us,
   you reveal your glory to our broken world,
   and we worship you. Come again in glory!

Pentecost

3. Lord Jesus, you are at the Father's side:
   you have sent your Spirit to renew our joy,
   and we praise you. Come again in glory!

Text: Damian Lundy (b.1944-1997))
Music: adapted from Plainsong arr. John Ballantine
© Copyright 1979 Kevin Mayhew Ltd.

49 Alleluia! Magnificat!

A good way to sing this is as follows: The 'Alleluia' is sung by a cantor then echoed by the congregation;
the congregation continue to sing the 'Alleluia' while the cantor sings the verse; all then sing the 'Alleluia'.

50 Alleluia: We will hear your Word

Text and Music: Joe Wise (b.1939)

51 Halle, halle, halle

Text: traditional
Music: unknown arr. John Ballantine

52 Sing praises to the Lord

Alternatively, everyone may sing throughout

2. God's truth can set us free, alleluia,
Christ Jesus is the key, alleluia.
Our ears hear the Word,
but it lives in our hearts,
alleluia, alleluia.

3. We listen to your voice, alleluia,
we praise you and rejoice, alleluia.
Your Spirit is with us,
she breathes in your Word:
alleluia, alleluia.

4. Sing praises to the Lord, alleluia,
sing praise to greet the Word, alleluia.
Creator and Son
with the Spirit adored:
alleluia, alleluia.

Text and Music: Christopher Walker (b.1947)

53 Lent and Holy Week Gospel Acclamation (Lundy)

Praise to you, Lord, praise to you, Lord, praise to you, Lord.

Lord Je - sus, o - be - dient to the Fa - ther's will, you be - came a

slave, en - dur - ing death for us. Now you reign as Lord. Come a - gain in glo - ry!

Text: Damian Lundy (1944-1997)
Music: adapted from Plainsong arr. John Ballantine

LITURGICAL
HYMNS OLD & NEW

54 Lent and Holy Week Gospel Acclamation (Walsh)

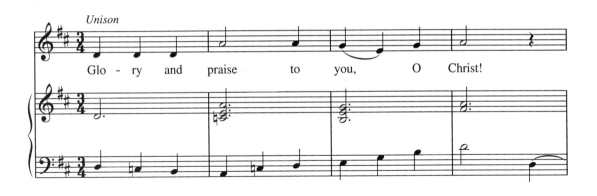

Glo - ry and praise to you, O Christ!

Glo - ry and praise to you, O Christ!

Psalm tone for the Proper text

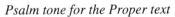
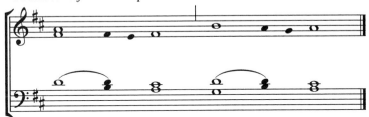

Music: James Walsh
© Copyright Rev. James Walsh. Used by permission.

55 Lent and Holy Week Gospel Acclamation (Moore)

Holy Week

Text: Matthew 17:5; Philippians 2:8-9
Music: Andrew Moore (b.1954)

56 Credo 3

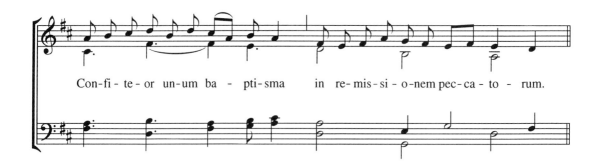

Con-fi - te - or un-um ba – pti-sma   in re-mis-si - o-nem pec-ca - to - rum.

Et ex - spe - cto   re - sur - re - cti - o - nem mor - tu - o - rum.

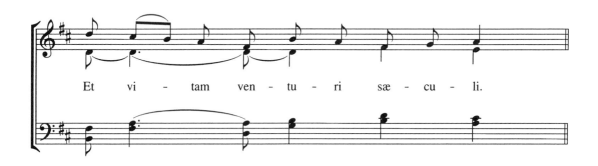

Et vi   –   tam ven - tu - ri sæ - cu - li.

A -   -   -   -   men.

Text: from the Roman Missal
Music: Plainsong, arr. Andrew Moore

57 Lourdes Credo

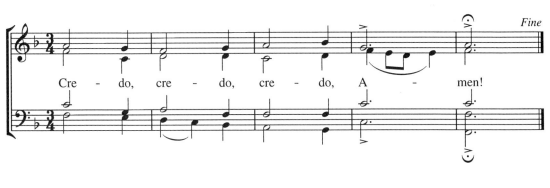

Cre - do, cre - do, cre - do, A - men!

Unaccompanied

I believe in God the Fa - ther, Cre - ator of heaven and earth

I believe in Jesus his Son, who was made man, who died and rose a - gain.

I believe in the Ho - ly Spirit, who gives life to the Church.

Text and Music: Jean-Paul Lécot (b.1947)

© Copyright Jean-Paul Lécot, 'Espélugues', 1 Ave. Mgr. Théas, 65100 Lourdes, France. Used by permission.

58 We believe (Fitzpatrick)

Text: from the Roman Missal
Music: Gerry Fitzpatrick (b.1940)

59 Holy, holy, holy (MacMillan)

Moderato

Unison

Holy, ho-ly, ho-ly Lord, God of pow'r and might. Heav'n and earth are full of your glo-ry. Ho-san-na in the high-est. Bles-sed is he, O

bles - sed is he who comes in the name of the Lord.

Ho - san - na in the high -

est. Ho - san - na in the high - est.

Text: from the Roman Missal
Music: James MacMillan from 'St. Anne's Mass'

60 Holy, holy, holy (Celtic Liturgy)

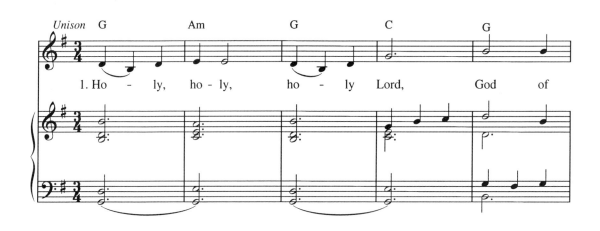

1. Ho - ly, ho - ly, ho - ly Lord, God of

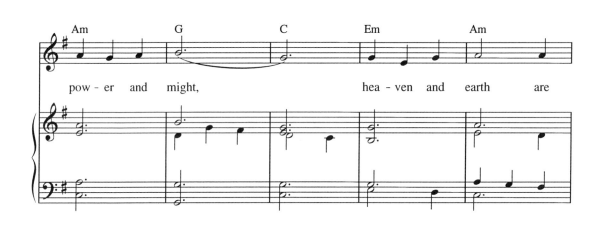

pow - er and might, hea - ven and earth are

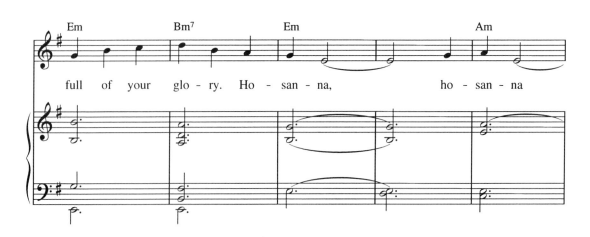

full of your glo - ry. Ho - san - na, ho - san - na

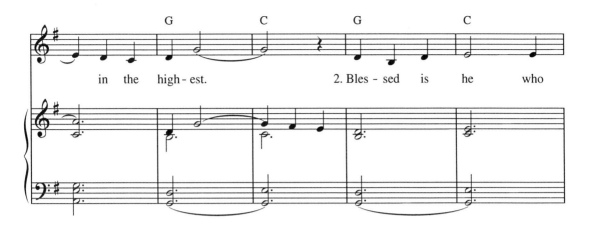

in the high - est. 2. Bles - sed is he who

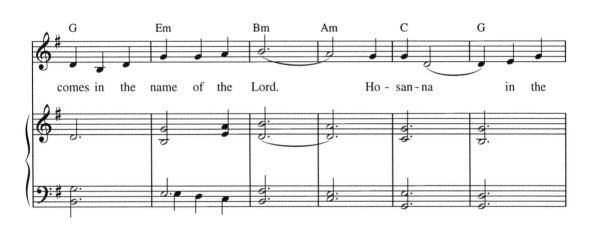

comes in the name of the Lord. Ho - san - na in the

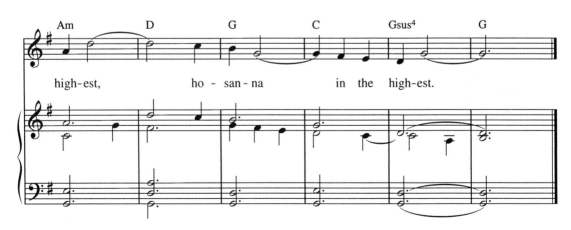

high-est, ho - san - na in the high-est.

Text: from the Roman Missal
Music: Christopher Walker (b.1947) from 'A Celtic Liturgy'

LITURGICAL
HYMNS OLD & NEW

61 Sanctus (Donnelly)

To be sung unaccompanied. A Cantor may sing each phrase first.

Ho - ly, ho - ly, ho - ly Lord, God of pow'r and

might, hea - ven and earth are full of your glo - ry. Ho -

san - na in the high - est. Bles - sed is he who

comes in the name of the Lord. Ho - san - na in the high - est.

Text: from the Roman Missal
Music: Noel Donnelly (b.1932)
© Copyright 1986 Kevin Mayhew Ltd.

62 Holy, holy, holy (Deutsche Messe)

Text: from the Roman Missal
Music: Franz Schubert (1797-1828) adapted by Richard Proulx

63 Sanctus (Taizé)

*Choose either part.

Text: from the Roman Missal
Music: Jacques Berthier (1923-1994)

64 Lourdes Sanctus

Text: adapted by W.R. Lawrence (1925-1997)
Music: Jean-Paul Lécot (b.1947)
© Copyright 1988 Kevin Mayhew Ltd.

65 Holy, holy, holy is the Lord

Unison

1. Ho - ly, ho - ly, ho - ly is the Lord, ho - ly is the Lord God al - migh - ty! Ho - ly, ho - ly, ho - ly is the Lord, ho - ly is the Lord God al - migh - ty! Who was and is, and is to come; ho - ly, ho - ly, ho - ly is the Lord.

2. Blessèd, blessèd, blest is he who comes,
   blest is he who comes in the Lord's name.
   Blessèd, blessèd, blest is he who comes,
   blest is he who comes in the Lord's name.
   Hosanna in the heights of heav'n.
   Blessèd, blessèd, blessèd is the Lord.

Text: John Ballantine (b.1945)
Music: Unknown arr. Colin Hand

66 Holy, most holy, all holy the Lord
Slane Sanctus

1. Holy, most holy, all holy the Lord, in power and wisdom for ever adored. The earth and the heavens are full of your love; our joyful hosannas re-echo above.

2. Blessèd, most blessèd, all blessèd is he
whose life makes us whole, and whose death sets us free:
who comes in the name of the Father of light,
let endless hosannas resound in the height.

Text: Michael Forster (b.1946) based on the Sanctus
Music: traditional Irish melody arr. Keith Stent

67 O holy, most holy
Ash Grove Sanctus

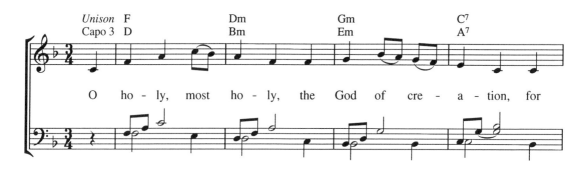

O ho - ly, most ho - ly, the God of cre - a - tion, for

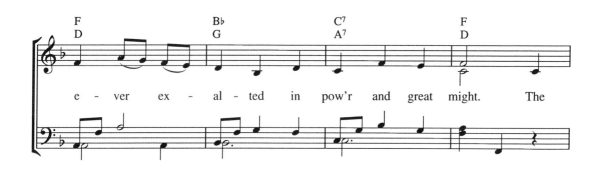

e - ver ex - al - ted in pow'r and great might. The

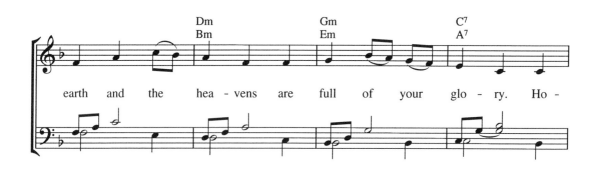

earth and the hea - vens are full of your glo - ry. Ho -

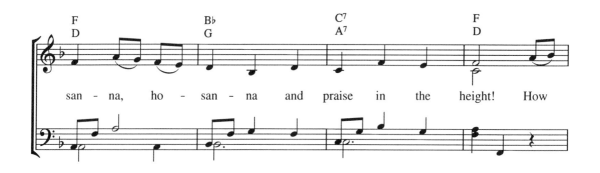

san - na, ho - san - na and praise in the height! How

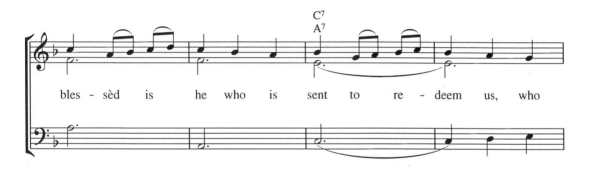

bles - sèd is he who is sent to re - deem us, who

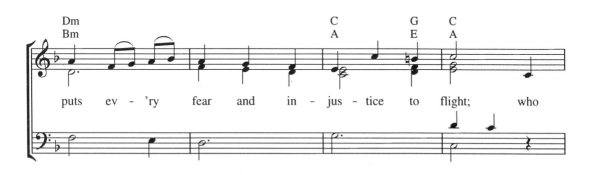

puts ev - 'ry fear and in - jus - tice to flight; who

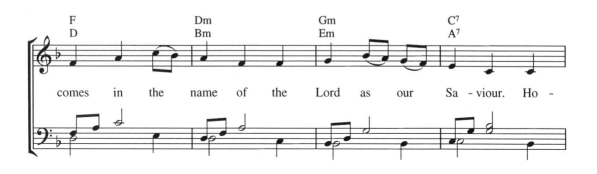

comes in the name of the Lord as our Sa - viour. Ho -

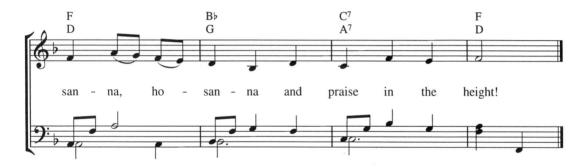

san - na, ho - san - na and praise in the height!

Text: Michael Forster (b.1946) based on the 'Sanctus'
Music: traditional Welsh melody arr. Keith Stent

68 Christ has died (Celtic Liturgy)

Christ has died, Christ has died, Christ is ri-sen, Christ will come a-gain, Christ will come a-gain.

Celebrant
Let us pro-claim the my-ste-ry of faith.

Text: from the Roman Missal
Music: Christopher Walker (b.1947) from 'A Celtic Liturgy'

69 Christ has died (Duffy)

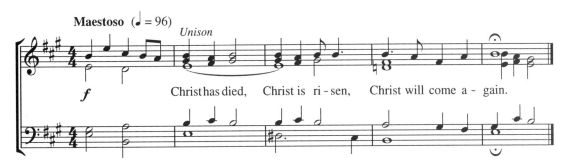

Maestoso (♩ = 96)

Unison

f

Christ has died, Christ is ri - sen, Christ will come a - gain.

Text: from the Roman Missal
Music: Philip Duffy
© Copyright 1979 Philip Duffy. Used by permission.

70 Christ has died (Donnelly)

Celebrant   *All*

Let us pro-claim the mys-t'ry of faith. Christ has died, al - le - lu - ia.

Christ is ri - sen, al - le - lu - ia. Christ will come a - gain.

Text: from the Roman Missal
Music: Noel Donnelly (b.1932)
© Copyright 1986 Kevin Mayhew Ltd.

71 Christ has died (Hill)

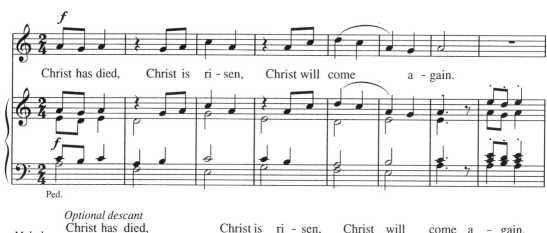

Christ has died, Christ is ri-sen, Christ will come a-gain.

Optional descant
Christ has died, Christ is ri-sen, Christ will come a-gain.

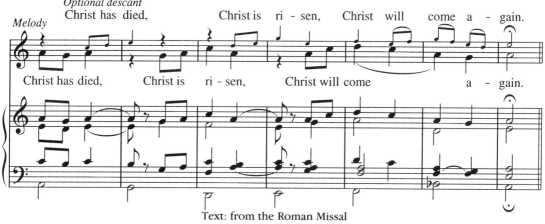

Melody
Christ has died, Christ is ri-sen, Christ will come a-gain.

Text: from the Roman Missal
Music: David Hill
© Copyright 1999 Kevin Mayhew Ltd.

72 Christ has died (Wise)

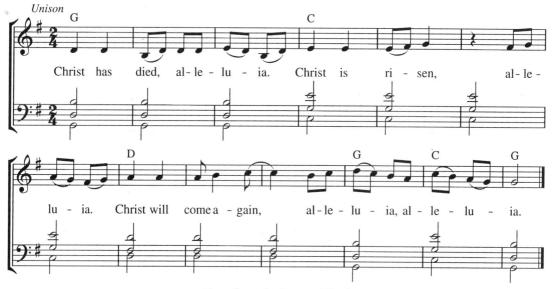

Unison
Christ has died, al-le-lu-ia. Christ is ri-sen, al-le-lu-ia. Christ will come a-gain, al-le-lu-ia, al-le-lu-ia.

Text: from the Roman Missal
Music: Joe Wise (b.1939)

73 Dying you destroyed our death (Duffy)

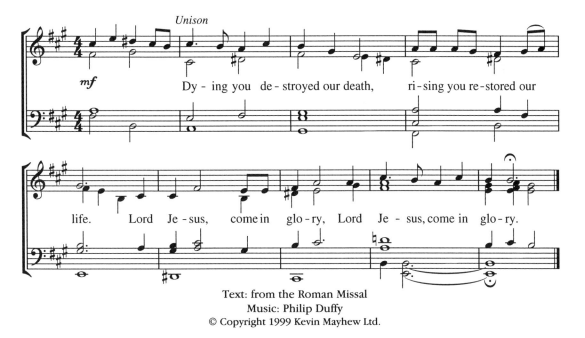

Dy-ing you de-stroyed our death, ri-sing you re-stored our life. Lord Je-sus, come in glo-ry, Lord Je-sus, come in glo-ry.

Text: from the Roman Missal
Music: Philip Duffy
© Copyright 1999 Kevin Mayhew Ltd.

74 When we eat this bread (Irish melody)

When we eat this bread and drink this cup, we pro-claim your death, Lord Je-sus, un-til you come in glo-ry, un-til you come in glo-ry.

Text: from the Roman Missal
Music: Irish melody (Petrie Collection)
This arrangement © Copyright 1999 Kevin Mayhew Ltd.

75 When we eat this bread (MacMillan)

Text: from the Roman Missal
Music: James MacMillan from 'St. Anne's Mass'

76 When we eat this bread (Proulx)

Text: from the Roman Missal
Music: Richard Proulx (b.1937) from 'A Festival Eucharist'

77 Great Amen (Mayhew)

To be sung unaccompanied

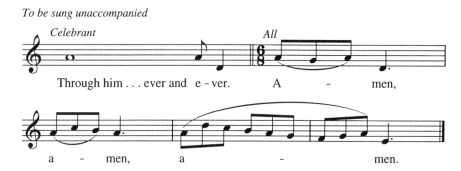

Through him . . . ever and e-ver. A - men, a - men, a - men.

Music: Kevin Mayhew (b.1942)
© Copyright 1986 Kevin Mayhew Ltd.

78 Great Amen (Lourdes)

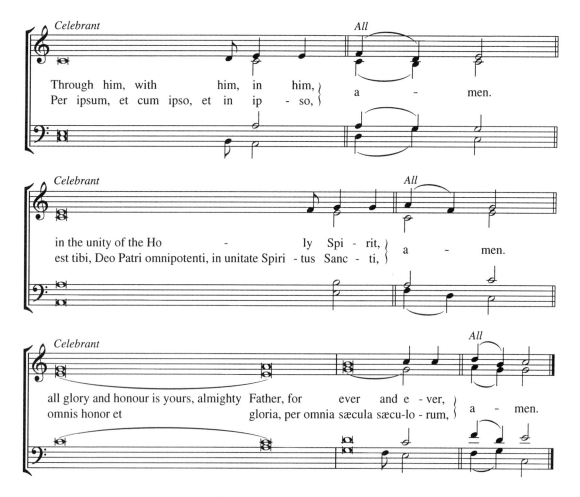

Through him, with him, in him, a - men.
Per ipsum, et cum ipso, et in ip - so,

in the unity of the Ho - ly Spi - rit, a - men.
est tibi, Deo Patri omnipotenti, in unitate Spiri - tus Sanc - ti,

all glory and honour is yours, almighty Father, for ever and e - ver, a - men.
omnis honor et gloria, per omnia sæcula sæcu-lo - rum,

Text: from the Roman Missal
Music: Jean-Paul Lécot (b.1947)
© Copyright 1988 Kevin Mayhew Ltd.

79 Great Amen (Plainsong)

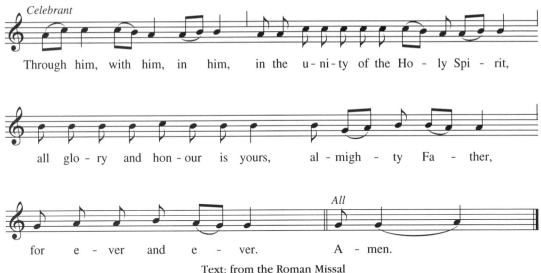

Through him, with him, in him, in the u-ni-ty of the Ho-ly Spi-rit,

all glo-ry and hon-our is yours, al-migh-ty Fa-ther,

for e-ver and e-ver. A-men.

Text: from the Roman Missal
Music: adapted from Plainsong

80 Great Amen (Hill)

A - men.

Optional descant A - men.

Melody A - men.

Text: from the Roman Missal
Music: David Hill

81 Great Amen (Proulx)

Text: from the Roman Missal
Music: Richard Proulx (b.1937) from 'A Festival Eucharist'

82 Great Amen (South African)

Ho-nour and glo-ry, a - men! Ho-nour and glo-ry, a -

a - men, a - men! a -

A - men! A - men!

men! A - men! A - men! A - men! A - men!

men, a - men! A - men! A - men! A - men!

Ho - nour and glo - ry, a - men!

a - men, a - men!

Text: Robert B. Kelly (b.1948)
Music: traditional South African melody arr. Robert B. Kelly (b.1948)

83 Our Father (White)

ta - tion, but de - liv – er us from e - vil.

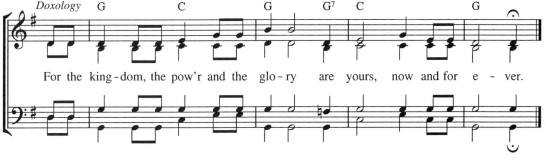

Doxology

For the king - dom, the pow'r and the glo - ry are yours, now and for e - ver.

Text: Matthew 6:9-13 and Luke 11:2-4
Music: Estelle White (b.1925)

84 Our Father (Wiener)

Text: Matthew 6:9-13 and Luke 11:2-4
Music: Julian Wiener arr. Keith Stent

85 Our Father (Rimsky-Korsakov)

Our Fa-ther, who art in hea-ven, hal-lowed be thy name; thy king-dom come; thy will be done on earth as it is in hea-ven. Give us this day our dai-ly bread; and for-give us our tres-pas-ses as we for-give those who tres-pass a-gainst us; and lead us not in-to temp-ta-tion, but de-li-ver us from e-vil.

Doxology

For the king-dom, the pow'r, and the glo-ry are yours, now and for e-ver. A-men.

Text: traditional based on Matthew 6:9-13 ; Luke 11:2-4
Music: Nicholai Rimsky-Korsakov (1844-1908) based on traditional Russian Orthodox sources,
adapted by Joseph Gelineau and Robert B. Kelly (b.1948)

86 'Echo' Our Father

Words: Matthew 6:9-13 and Luke 11:2-4
Music: Jacqueline Emery arr. Donald Thomson

87 Our Father (Caribbean)

2. On earth as it is in heaven,
   hallowed be thy name.
   Give us this day our daily bread,
   hallowed be thy name,
   hallowed be thy name.

3. Forgive us our trespasses,
   as we forgive those who trespass against us.

4. Lead us not into temptation,
   but deliver us from all that is evil.

5. For thine is the kingdom, the power, and the glory,
   for ever, and for ever and ever.

6. Amen, amen, it shall be so.
   Amen, amen, it shall be so.

Text: traditional Caribbean based on Matthew 6:9-13 and Luke 11:2-4
Music: traditional Caribbean arr. Keith Stent

88 Lamb of God (Fitzpatrick)

Text: from the Roman Missal
Music: Gerry Fitzpatrick (b.1940)
© Copyright 1986 Kevin Mayhew Ltd.

89 Lamb of God (Archer)

Lamb of God, you take a-way the

sins of the world: have mer - cy, have mer - cy on us.

Lamb of God, you take a - way the

sins of the world: grant us, grant us peace.

Text: from the Roman Missal
Music: Malcolm Archer (b.1952) from 'The Halesworth Setting'

90 Lamb of God (Rees)

Lamb of God, you take a-way the sins of the world: have mer - cy on us. Lamb of God, you take a - way the sins of the world: grant us peace.

Text: from the Roman Missal
Music: Alan Rees (b.1941)

91 Jesus, Lamb of God (Inwood)

Text: adapted from the Liturgy by Paul Inwood (b.1947)
Music: Paul Inwood (b.1947)

92 Jesus, Lamb of God (Duffy)

Calmly and peacefully

Cantor

Je-sus, Lamb of God, have mer-cy on us.

All

Je-sus, Lamb of God, have mer-cy on us.

Cantor

God's be-lov-ed Son, Sa-viour of us all.

All

Je-sus, Lamb of God, have mer-cy on us.

Cantor

Bear-er of our sins, have mer-cy on us:

All

Shep-herd of the flock: Je - sus, Lamb of God, have mer-cy on us.

Cantor

Hope of those who fail,

All

rest for those who toil; Bear-er of our sins, have mer-cy on us.

Cantor

So-lace of the sick, com-fort in dis-tress:

All

Bear-er of our sins, have

Text and Music: Philip Duffy

93 O Lamb of God

REPTON 86 88 6

1. O Lamb of God, come cleanse our hearts and take our sin a-
way. O Lamb of God, your grace im-part, and
let our guil-ty fear de-part, have mer-cy, Lord, we
pray, have mer-cy, Lord, we pray.

Another arrangement of this melody will be found at No. 234

2. O Lamb of God, our lives restore,
   our guilty souls release.
   Into our lives your Spirit pour
   and let us live for evermore
   in perfect heav'nly peace,
   in perfect heav'nly peace.

Text: Michael Forster (b.1946) based on the 'Agnus Dei'
Music: Hubert Parry (1848-1918) arr. Keith Stent

Hymns and Songs

94 Abba, Abba, Father

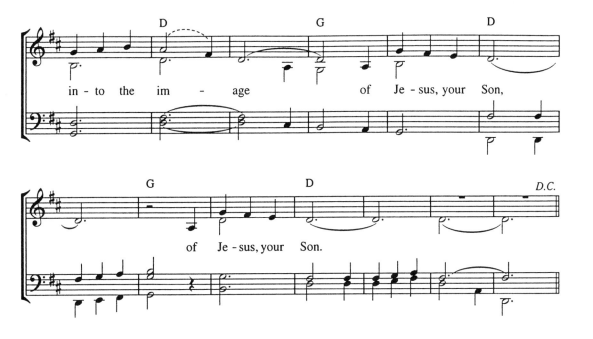

in - to the im - age of Je - sus, your Son,

of Je - sus, your Son.

2. Father, may we be one in you,
   as he is in you and you are in him,
   and you are in him.

3. Glory, glory and praise to you,
   glory and praise to you for ever, amen,
   for ever, amen.

Text: Carey Landry
Music: Carey Landry arr. Andrew Moore

95 Abba, Father, from your hands

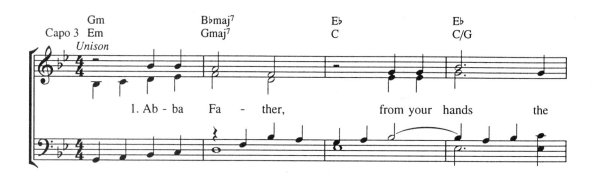

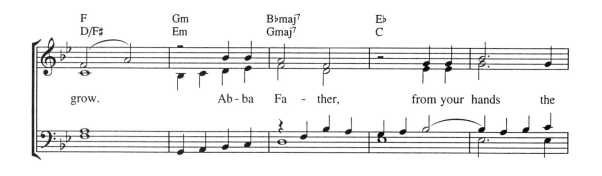

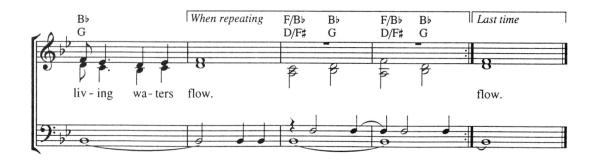

2. Jesus, Saviour, from your wounds
   the living waters flow.
   In your love you give me peace,
   peace so I may grow.
   Jesus, Saviour, from your wounds
   the living waters flow.

3. Holy Spirit, from your pow'r
   the living waters flow.
   In your love you give me pow'r,
   pow'r so I may grow.
   Holy Spirit, from your pow'r
   the living waters flow.

4. Alleluia! From your life
   the living waters flow.
   In your love you give me joy,
   joy so I may grow.
   Alleluia! From your life
   the living waters flow.

Text: Damian Lundy (1944-1997)
Music: Gerard Markland (b.1953) arr. Andrew Moore

96 Abba, Father, send your Spirit

1. Ab - ba, Fa - ther, send your Spi - rit. Glo - ry, Je - sus Christ.

Ab - ba, Fa - ther, send your Spi - rit. Glo - ry, Je - sus Christ.

Refrain

Glo - ry, hal - le - lu - jah, glo - ry, Je - sus Christ!

Glo - ry, hal - le - lu - jah, glo - ry, Je - sus Christ! Christ!

2. I will give you living water . . .
3. If you seek me you will find me . . .
4. If you listen you will hear me . . .
5. Come, my children, I will teach you . . .
6. I'm your shepherd, I will lead you . . .
7. Peace I leave you, peace I give you . . .
8. I'm your life and resurrection . . .
9. Glory, Father, glory, Spirit . . .

Text: Virginia Vissing
Music: Virginia Vissing arr. Andrew Moore

97 Abide with me

EVENTIDE 10 10 10 10

1. A - bide with me, fast falls the e - ven - tide; the dark - ness deep - ens; Lord, with me a - bide: when o - ther help - ers fail, and com-forts flee, help of the help-less, O a - bide with me.

2. Swift to its close ebbs out life's little day;
   earth's joys grow dim, its glories pass away;
   change and decay in all around I see;
   O thou who changest not, abide with me.

3. I need thy presence ev'ry passing hour;
   what but thy grace can foil the tempter's pow'r?
   Who like thyself my guide and stay can be?
   Through cloud and sunshine, Lord, abide with me.

4. I fear no foe with thee at hand to bless;
   ills have no weight, and tears no bitterness.
   Where is death's sting? Where, grave, thy victory?
   I triumph still, if thou abide with me.

5. Hold thou thy cross before my closing eyes;
   shine through the gloom, and point me to the skies;
   heav'n's morning breaks, and earth's vain shadows flee;
   in life, in death, O Lord, abide with me.

Text: Henry Francis Lyte (1793-1847)
Music: William Henry Monk (1823-1889)

98 A child is born in Bethlehem

Unison

1. A child is born in Beth-le-hem, al-le-lu-ia, there-fore re-joice, Je-ru-sa-lem,
2. The babe who lies up-on the straw, al-le-lu-ia, will rule the world for e-ver-more
3. Up-on this joy-ful ho-ly night, al-le-lu-ia, we bless your name, O Lord of light,
4. We praise you, Ho-ly Tri-ni-ty, al-le-lu-ia, a-dor-ing you e-ter-nal-ly,

al-le-lu-ia, al-le-lu-ia. Our joy-ful hearts we raise,

Christ is born, O come a-dore him in new-found songs of praise.

Text: 14th century Latin, trans. Ruth Fox Hume
Music: Plainsong, arr. Richard Proulx

99 Across the years there echoes still

ST COLUMBA 87 87

1. A - cross the years there e - choes still the
Bap - tist's bold as - ser - tion: the call of God to
change of heart, re - pen - tance and con - ver - sion.

2. The word that John more boldly spoke
in dying, than in living,
now Christ takes up, as he proclaims
a Father all-forgiving.

3. The erring son he welcomes home
when all is spent and squandered.
He lovingly pursues the sheep
that from the flock has wandered.

4. Forgive us, Lord, all we have done
to you and one another.
So often we have gone our way,
forgetful of each other.

5. Forgetful of the cross they bear
of hunger, want, oppression –
grant, Lord, that we may make amends,
who humbly make confession.

Text: Denis E. Hurley
Music: Irish melody (Petrie Collection)

LITURGICAL

HYMNS OLD & NEW

100 Adeste fideles

ADESTE FIDELES Irregular and Refrain

1. A - de - ste fi - de - les, læ - ti tri - um - phan - tes; ve - ni - te, ve - ni - te in Beth - le - hem; na - tum vi - de - te re - gem an - ge - lo - rum:

Refrain

ve - ni - te a - do - re - mus, ve - ni - te a - do - re - mus, ve - ni - te a - do - re - mus Do - mi - num.

A higher setting will be found at No. 501

2. Deum de Deo, lumen de lumine,
   gestant puellæ viscera:
   Deum verum, genitum, non factum:

3. Cantet nunc Io! Chorus angelorum:
   cantet nunc aula cælestium;
   Gloria in excelsis Deo!

4. Ergo qui natus die hodierna,
   Jesu tibi sit gloria:
   Patris æterni Verbum caro factum!

Text and Music: John Francis Wade (1711-1786)

101 A hymn of glory let us sing!

LASST UNS ERFREUEN 88 44 88 and Alleluias

1. A hymn of glo-ry let us sing! New hymns through-out the world shall ring. Al - le - lu - ia! Al - le - lu - ia! Christ, by a road be-fore un - trod, as - cends un - to the throne of God. Al - le - lu - ia! Al - le - lu - ia! Al - le - lu - ia! Al - le - lu - ia! Al - le - lu - ia!

A lower setting will be found at No. 184

2. The holy apostolic band
   upon the Mount of Olives stand.
   Alleluia! Alleluia!
   And with his faithful foll'wers see
   their Lord ascend in majesty.
   Alleluia! Alleluia!
   Alleluia! Alleluia! Alleluia!

3. To whom the shining angels cry,
   'Why stand and gaze upon the sky?'
   Alleluia! Alleluia!
   'This is the Saviour!' Thus they say,
   'This is his glorious triumph day!'
   Alleluia! Alleluia!
   Alleluia! Alleluia! Alleluia!

4. O risen Christ, ascended Lord,
   all praise to you let earth accord:
   Alleluia! Alleluia!
   You are, while endless ages run,
   with Father and with Spirit one.
   Alleluia! Alleluia!
   Alleluia! Alleluia! Alleluia!

Text: 'Hymnum canamus gloria' by Venerable Bede (673-735) trans. 'Lutheran Book of Worship' (1978)
Music: melody from 'Geistliche Kirchengesang', Cologne (1623)
arr. Ralph Vaughan Williams (1872-1958)

102 All creation, bless the Lord

BENEDICITE 77 75 D

1. All cre-a-tion, bless the Lord. Earth and hea-ven, bless the Lord.
Spi-rits, pow-ers, bless the Lord. Praise him for e - ver.
Sun and moon, bless the Lord. Stars and pla-nets, bless the Lord.
Dews and show-ers, bless the Lord. Praise him for e - ver.

2. Winds and breezes, bless the Lord.
   Spring and autumn, bless the Lord.
   Winter, summer, bless the Lord.
   Praise him for ever.
   Fire and heat, bless the Lord.
   Frost and cold, bless the Lord.
   Ice and snow, bless the Lord.
   Praise him for ever.

3. Night and daytime, bless the Lord.
   Light and darkness, bless the Lord.
   Clouds and lightning, bless the Lord.
   Praise him for ever.
   All the earth, bless the Lord.
   Hills and mountains, bless the Lord.
   Trees and flowers, bless the Lord.
   Praise him for ever.

4. Springs and rivers, bless the Lord.
   Seas and oceans, bless the Lord.
   Whales and fishes, bless the Lord.
   Praise him for ever.
   Birds and insects, bless the Lord.
   Beasts and cattle, bless the Lord.
   Let all creatures bless the Lord.
   Praise him for ever.

5. Let God's people bless the Lord.
   Men and women, bless the Lord.
   All creation, bless the Lord.
   Praise him for ever.
   Let God's people bless the Lord.
   Men and women, bless the Lord.
   All creation, bless the Lord.
   Praise him for ever.

Text: based on the 'Canticle of Daniel', Hayward Osborne
Music: Hayward Osborne arr. Andrew Moore

103 All creatures of our God and King

LASST UNS ERFREUEN   88 44 88 and Alleluias

1. All crea-tures of our God and King, lift up your voice and with us
sing al - le - lu - ia, al - le - lu - ia! Thou
burn - ing sun with gol - den beam, thou sil - ver moon with sof - ter
gleam: O praise him, O praise him, al - le -
lu - ia, al - le - lu - ia, al - le - lu - ia!

2. Thou rushing wind that art so strong,
   ye clouds that sail in heav'n along,
   O praise him, alleluia!
   Thou rising morn, in praise rejoice,
   ye lights of evening, find a voice:

3. Thou flowing water, pure and clear,
   make music for thy Lord to hear,
   alleluia, alleluia!
   Thou fire so masterful and bright,
   that givest us both warmth and light:

4. Dear mother earth, who day by day
   unfoldest blessings on our way,
   O praise him, alleluia!
   The flow'rs and fruits that in thee grow,
   let them his glory also show.

5. All you with mercy in your heart,
   forgiving others, take your part,
   O sing ye, alleluia!
   Ye who long pain and sorrow bear,
   praise God and on him cast your care:

6. And thou, most kind and gentle death,
   waiting to hush our latest breath,
   O praise him, alleluia!
   Thou leadest home the child of God,
   and Christ our Lord the way hath trod:

7. Let all things their Creator bless,
   and worship him in humbleness,
   O praise him, alleluia!
   Praise, praise the Father, praise the Son,
   and praise the Spirit, Three in One.

A lower setting will be found at No. 184

Text: William Henry Draper (1855-1933) alt.
based on the 'Cantico di Frate Sole' of St. Francis of Assisi (1182-1226)
Music: melody from 'Geistliche Kirchengesang', Cologne (1623)
arr. Ralph Vaughan Williams (1872-1958)

104 Alleluia: All the earth

Refrain
Cantor ... Al-le-lu-ia, al-le-lu-ia. *All* ... Al-le-lu-ia, al-le-lu-ia.

Cantor ... Al-le-lu-ia, *All* ... al-le-lu-ia. *Fine*

Unison
1. All the earth, sing out to the Lord. Serve the Lord with joy in your heart; come in-to his pre-sence with song. *D.C.*

2. Come and bring your gifts to the Lord.
   Come before him, singing his praise;
   he is Lord, and he is our God.

3. God is good, his love never ends;
   he is always true to his word,
   he is faithful, age upon age.

Text: Hubert J. Richards (b.1921) based on Psalm 99
Music: Andrew Moore (b.1954)

105 Alleluia, alleluia, give thanks to the risen Lord

Al-le-lu - ia, al-le-lu - ia, give thanks to the ri-sen Lord, al-le-

lu - ia, al-le-lu - ia, give praise to his name.

1. Je - sus is Lord of all the earth.

He is the King of cre - a - tion.

2. Spread the good news o'er all the earth.
Jesus has died and is risen.

3. We have been crucified with Christ.
Now we shall live for ever.

4. God has proclaimed the just reward:
'Life for us all, alleluia!'

5. Come, let us praise the living God,
joyfully sing to our Saviour.

Text: Donald Fishel (b.1950) alt.
Music: Donald Fishel (b.1950) arr. Andrew Moore

106 Alleluia, alleluia! I will praise the Father

CONFIDO 12 4 11 5

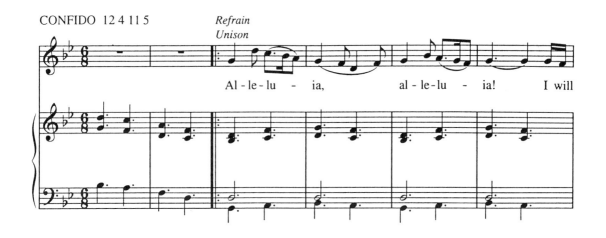

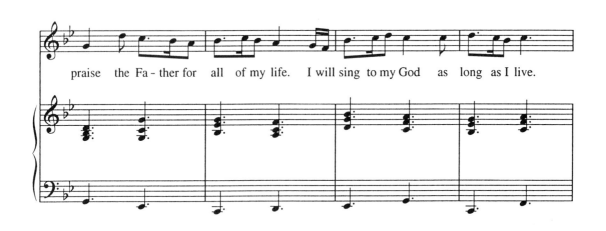

To verses

al - le - lu - ia! 1. Do not place all your trust in a wo-man or man:

they can-not save. Their schemes will all per-ish when they yield up their

breath at the end of their days.

2. But so happy are those who will trust in their God:
   they will find help.
   For God is the maker of the heavens and earth
   and of all that these hold.

3. All the searchers for justice, for freedom, for love,
   God will fulfil.
   The widow, the orphan, and the blind and the lame
   in his love are restored.

Text: Michael Cockett (b.1938) based on Psalm 145
Music: Gregory Murray (1905-1992)

LITURGICAL

HYMNS OLD & NEW

107 Alleluia: Let us sing of the Lord

Refrain

Harmony

Fine

Al - le - lu - ia! Al - le - lu - ia! Al - le - lu - ia!

Unison

1. Let us sing of the Lord, al - le - lu - ia!

D.C.

Let us give praise to his name for e - ver - more.

2. We give thanks to the Lord, for he is good;
   his loving kindness endures eternally.

3. All the works of the Lord proclaim his love;
   he is the source of contentment for his friends.

Text: Jean-Paul Lécot (b.1947) based on Psalms 110, 111, 117, 118 trans. W.R. Lawrence (1925-1997)
Music: Paul Décha

108 Alleluia: Praise God

D.C.

res - cues our life from the grave and clothes us in mer - cy and love.

2. Our God is all kindness and love,
   so patient and rich in compassion;
   not treating us as we deserve:
   not paying us back for our sins.

3. As heaven is high over earth,
   so strong is his love for his people.
   As far as the east from the west,
   so far he removes all our sins.

4. As fathers take pity on sons,
   we know God will show us compassion;
   for he knows of what we are made:
   no more than the dust of the earth.

Text: Hubert J. Richards (b.1921) based on Psalms 102 and 104
Music: Richard Lloyd (b.1933)

LITURGICAL
HYMNS OLD & NEW

109 Alleluia: Sing, my soul

2. He has honoured me in my lowliness,
   and all people to come shall call me blessèd.

3. The Almighty has shown his pow'r in me,
   and his mercy is known by all his people.

4. He has brought down the mighty and the proud,
   and exalted on high the poor and humble.

5. He has satisfied all the hungry ones,
   but has sent back the wealthy empty-handed.

6. He protected his servant, Israel,
   as he promised to Abraham, our father.

7. Praise the Father, the Spirit and the Son,
   God who was, who is now and ever shall be.

Text: Christina Wilde based on Luke 1:46-55
Music: Paul Décha
© Copyright 1988, 1999 Kevin Mayhew Ltd.

110 Alleluia, sing to Jesus

HYFRYDOL 87 87 D

1. Al - le - lu - ia, sing to Je - sus, his the
scep - tre, his the throne; al - le - lu - ia, his the
tri - umph, his the vic - to - ry a - lone:
hark, the songs of peace - ful Si - on thun - der like a
migh - ty flood: Je - sus, out of ev - 'ry

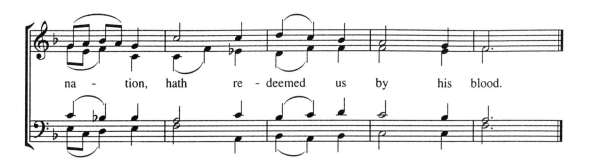

na - tion, hath re - deemed us by his blood.

2. Alleluia, not as orphans
   are we left in sorrow now;
   alleluia, he is near us,
   faith believes, nor questions how;
   though the cloud from sight received him
   when the forty days were o'er,
   shall our hearts forget his promise,
   'I am with you evermore'?

3. Alleluia, bread of angels,
   here on earth our food, our stay;
   alleluia, here the sinful
   come to you from day to day.
   Intercessor, friend of sinners,
   earth's redeemer, plead for me,
   where the songs of all the sinless
   sweep across the crystal sea.

4. Alleluia, King eternal,
   he the Lord of lords we own;
   alleluia, born of Mary,
   earth his footstool, heav'n his throne;
   he within the veil has entered
   robed in flesh, our great High Priest;
   he on earth both priest and victim
   in the Eucharistic Feast.

Text: William Chatterton Dix (1837-1898) alt. the editors.
Music: Rowland Huw Pritchard (1811-1887) arr. Ralph Vaughan Williams (1872-1958)

111 Alleluia, thank you for fathers

2. Praise for the mountains, the hills and ravines;
   praise for the rivers, the brooks and the streams;
   praise for the oceans, the sand and the sea;
   praise for the natural beauties we see!

3. Sing of the blossoms that flow'r on the trees;
   sing of the wind, and the calm and the breeze;
   sing of the autumn, and winter and spring;
   sing of the sunshine the summer will bring!

4. Thank you for giving the life that we know!
   Praise for the honesty we all must show.
   Sing against tyrants and despots and greed.
   Love be our message and peace be our creed!

Text: Mike Anderson (b.1956)
Music: Mike Anderson (b.1956) arr. Keith Stent
© Copyright 1980 Kevin Mayhew Ltd.

112 All for Jesus

ALL FOR JESUS 87 87

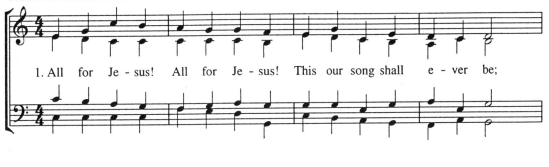

1. All for Je-sus! All for Je-sus! This our song shall e-ver be;

for we have no hope nor Sa-viour if we have not hope in thee.

2. All for Jesus! thou wilt give us
strength to serve thee hour by hour;
none can move us from thy presence
while we trust thy love and pow'r.

3. All for Jesus! at thine altar
thou dost give us sweet content;
there, dear Saviour, we receive thee
in thy holy sacrament.

4. All for Jesus! thou hast loved us,
all for Jesus! thou hast died,
all for Jesus! thou art with us,
all for Jesus, glorified!

5. All for Jesus! All for Jesus!
This the Church's song shall be,
till at last the flock is gathered
one in love, and one in thee.

Text: William John Sparrow-Simpson (1859-1952) alt.
Music: John Stainer (1840-1901)
Text © Copyright Novello & Co. Ltd. 8/9 Frith Street, London W1V 5TZ. Used by permission.

113 All glory, laud and honour

ST THEODULPH 76 76 and Refrain

All glo-ry, laud and hon - our, to thee, Re-deem-er King, to whom the lips of child - ren made sweet ho-san-nas ring.

1. Thou art the King of Is - rael, thou Da-vid's roy - al Son, who in the Lord's name com - est, the King and bless - ed one.

2. The company of angels
   are praising thee on high,
   and mortals, joined with all things
   created, make reply.

3. The people of the Hebrews
   with palms before thee went:
   our praise and prayer and anthems
   before thee we present.

4. To thee before thy passion
   they sang their hymns of praise:
   to thee now high exalted
   our melody we raise.

5. Thou didst accept their praises,
   accept the prayers we bring,
   who in all good delightest,
   thou good and gracious king.

Text: 'Gloria, laus et honor' by St Theodulph of Orleans (d.821)
trans. John Mason Neale (1818-1866)
Music: Melchior Teschner (1584-1635)

114 All glory to you, Redeemer and Lord

2. Lord Jesus Christ, to you be glory, alleluia.
You were born of the virgin, alleluia.

3. Lord Jesus Christ, to you be glory, alleluia.
You fought evil and conquered, alleluia.

4. Lord Jesus Christ, to you be glory, alleluia.
Risen Lord, we acclaim you, alleluia.

5. Lord Jesus Christ, to you be glory, alleluia.
You have ransomed God's people, alleluia.

6. Lord Jesus Christ, to you be glory, alleluia.
You have made us God's children, alleluia.

7. Lord Jesus Christ, to you be glory, alleluia.
Lead us all to your kingdom, alleluia.

Text: Damian Lundy (1944-1997)
Music: R. Jef

115 All God's people, here together

AR HYD Y NOS 84 84 88 84

1. All God's peo - ple, here to - ge - ther, wor - ship the King!

For his love will last for e - ver, wor - ship the King!

Through life's strug - gles he'll be with us, he'll be guid - ing, watch - ing o'er us.

We re - joice, sing hal - le - lu - jah, wor - ship the King!

A higher setting will be found at No. 232

2. All God's people, pray together,
   peace to the world,
   loving brother, loving sister,
   peace to the world!
   God is love and God is kindness,
   he will guide us through the darkness.
   We rejoice, sing hallelujah,
   peace to the world!

3. All God's people, love each other,
   glory to God!
   Though we die we live for ever,
   glory to God!
   We will enter life eternal,
   chosen, blessed, for ever praising.
   We rejoice, sing hallelujah,
   glory to God!

Text: Peter Watcyn-Jones (b.1944)
Music: traditional Welsh melody arr. Colin Hand
Text and this arrangement © Copyright 1978, 1999 Kevin Mayhew Ltd.

116 All hail the power of Jesus' name

MILES LANE CM

1. All hail the pow'r of Je - sus' name, let an - gels pro - strate fall; bring forth the roy - al di - a - dem and crown him, crown him, crown him, crown him Lord of all.

2. Crown him, all martyrs of your God,
who from his altar call;
praise him whose way of pain you trod,
and crown him Lord of all.

3. O prophets faithful to his word,
in matters great and small,
who made his voice of justice heard,
now crown him Lord of all.

4. All sinners, now redeemed by grace,
who heard your Saviour's call,
now robed in light before his face,
O crown him Lord of all.

5. Let every tribe and every race
who heard the freedom call,
in liberation, see Christ's face
and crown him Lord of all.

6. Let every people, every tongue
to him their heart enthral:
lift high the universal song
and crown him Lord of all.

Text: Edward Perronet (1726 -1792) adapted by Michael Forster (b.1946)
Music: William Shrubsole (1760-1806)
This version of text © Copyright 1999 Kevin Mayhew Ltd.

LITURGICAL
HYMNS OLD & NEW

117 All heaven declares

Majestically

1. All heav'n de-clares the glo-ry of the ri-sen Lord.
Who can com-pare with the beau-ty of the Lord?
For e-ver he will be the Lamb up-on the throne.
I glad-ly bow the knee and wor-ship him a-lone.

[Last time only]

2. I will proclaim
the glory of the risen Lord.
Who once was slain
to reconcile us all to God.
For ever you will be
the Lamb upon the throne.
I gladly bow the knee
and worship you alone.

Text: Tricia Richards
Music: Noel Richards

118 All I once held dear
Knowing you

1. All I once held dear, built my life u-pon, all this

world re-veres, and wars to own, all I once thought gain I have

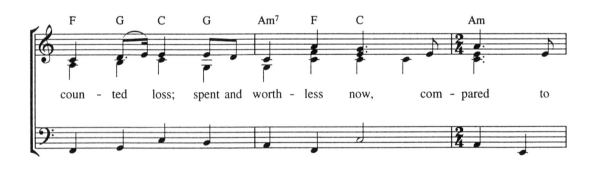

coun-ted loss; spent and worth-less now, com-pared to

this. Know-ing you, Je-sus, know-ing you, there

is no great-er thing. You're my all, you're the best, you're my

joy, my right-eous-ness, and I love you, Lord.

love you, Lord.

2. Now my heart's desire
is to know you more,
to be found in you
and known as yours.
To possess by faith
what I could not earn,
all-surpassing gift
of righteousness.

3. Oh, to know the pow'r
of your risen life,
and to know you in
your sufferings.
To become like you
in your death, my Lord,
so with you to live
and never die.

Text: Graham Kendrick (b.1950) based on Philippians 3:8-12
Music: Graham Kendrick (b.1950) arr. Keith Stent

119 All my hope on God is founded

MICHAEL 87 87 33 7

Unison

1. All my hope on God is found - ed; he doth still my trust re - new. Me through change and chance he guid - eth, on - ly good and on - ly true. God un - known, he a - lone calls my heart to be his own.

2. Human pride and earthly glory,
   sword and crown betray his trust;
   what with care and toil he buildeth,
   tow'r and temple, fall to dust.
   But God's pow'r, hour by hour,
   is my temple and my tow'r.

3. God's great goodness aye endureth,
   deep his wisdom, passing thought:
   splendour, light and life attend him,
   beauty springeth out of naught.
   Evermore, from his store,
   new-born worlds rise and adore.

4. Still from earth to God eternal
   sacrifice of praise be done,
   high above all praises praising
   for the gift of Christ his Son.
   Christ doth call one and all:
   ye who follow shall not fall.

Text: paraphrased by Robert Bridges (1844-1930) alt.
based on 'Meine Hoffnung stehet feste' by Joachim Neander (1650-1680)
Music: Herbert Howells (1892-1983)

120 All over the world

Unison

1. All o-ver the world the Spi - rit is mov-ing,
all o - ver the world, as the proph-ets said it would be.
All o-ver the world there's a migh - ty re - ve - la-tion of the
glo - ry of the Lord, as the wa - ters co-ver the sea.

2. All over this land the Spirit is moving . . .

3. All over the Church the Spirit is moving . . .

4. All over us all the Spirit is moving . . .

5. Deep down in my heart the Spirit is moving . . .

Text: Roy Turner (b.1940)
Music: Roy Turner (b.1940) arr. Andrew Moore

LITURGICAL

HYMNS OLD & NEW

121 All people that on earth do dwell

OLD HUNDREDTH LM

1. All peo - ple that on earth do dwell, sing to the Lord with cheer - ful voice; him serve with fear, his praise forth tell, come ye be - fore him and re - joice.

2. The Lord, ye know, is God indeed,
without our aid he did us make;
we are his folk, he doth us feed
and for his sheep he doth us take.

3. O enter then his gates with praise,
approach with joy his courts unto;
praise, laud and bless his name always,
for it is seemly so to do.

4. For why? the Lord our God is good:
his mercy is for ever sure;
his truth at all times firmly stood,
and shall from age to age endure.

5. To Father, Son and Holy Ghost,
the God whom heav'n and earth adore,
from us and from the angel-host
be praise and glory evermore.

Text: William Kethe (d.1594) from 'Day's Psalter' (1560) alt.
Music: from the 'Genevan Psalter' (1551), attributed to Louis Bourgeois (c.1510-c.1561)

122 All that I am

VERSION 1: KEYBOARD/GUITAR

1. All that I am, all that I do, all that I'll e-ver have, I of-fer now to you. Take and sanc-ti-fy these gifts for your hon-our, Lord. Know-ing that I love and serve you is e-nough re-ward. All that I am, all that I do, all that I'll e-ver have I of-fer now to you.

VERSION 2: ORGAN

1. All that I am, all that I do, all that I'll e-ver have I of-fer now to you. Take and sanc-ti-fy these gifts for your hon-our, Lord. Know-ing that I love and serve you is e-nough re-ward. All that I am, all that I do, all that I'll e-ver have I of-fer now to you.

2. All that I dream, all that I pray,
   all that I'll ever make I give to you today.
   Take and sanctify these gifts for your honour, Lord.
   Knowing that I love and serve you is enough reward.
   All that I am, all that I do,
   all that I'll ever have I offer now to you.

Text and Music: Sebastian Temple (1928-1997)
First version: arr. John Ballantine
Second version: arr. Andrew Moore

123 All the earth proclaim the Lord

Refrain
Unison Bb
Capo 1 A

All the earth pro-claim the Lord, sing your praise to God.

1. Serve you the Lord, heart filled with glad-ness. Come in-to his pres-ence, sing-ing for joy.

2. Know that the Lord is our creator.
   Yes, he is our Father, we are his own.

3. We are the sheep of his green pasture,
   for we are his people; he is our God.

4. Enter his gates bringing thanksgiving,
   O enter his courts while singing his praise.

5. Our Lord is good, his love enduring,
   his Word is abiding now with us all.

6. Honour and praise be to the Father,
   the Son, and the Spirit, world without end.

Text: Lucien Deiss (b.1921) based on Psalm 99
Music: Lucien Deiss (b.1921)

124 All the ends of the earth

Refrain
Unison

All the ends of the earth have seen the sal - va - tion of our God.

Fine

1. Let us sing a new song to the Lord for the won-der-ful things he has done; by his

ho - ly and pow-er-ful arm, his sal - va - tion is brought to us all.

D.C.

2. His salvation is known on the earth,
   all the nations can see he is just;
   he will never neglect to be true
   to the people he knows as his own.

3. Ev'ry part of creation has seen
   the salvation our God has bestowed.
   Let the earth shout aloud to our God,
   and the universe ring with delight.

4. O sing songs to our God with the harp,
   and with music sing praise to the Lord;
   let the horn and the trumpet give voice,
   we acknowledge the Lord who is King.

Text: Susan Sayers (b.1946) based on Psalm 97
Music: Andrew Moore (b.1954)
© Copyright 1995 Kevin Mayhew Ltd.

125 All things bright and beautiful

TUNE 1: ALL THINGS BRIGHT AND BEAUTIFUL 76 76 and Refrain

All things bright and beau - ti - ful, all crea - tures great and small,

all things wise and won - der-ful, the Lord God made them all.

1. Each lit - tle flow'r that o - pens, each lit - tle bird that sings, he

made their glow-ing col - ours, he made their ti - ny wings.

2. The purple-headed mountain,
   the river running by,
   the sunset and the morning
   that brightens up the sky.

3. The cold wind in the winter,
   the pleasant summer sun,
   the ripe fruits in the garden,
   he made them every one.

4. The tall trees in the greenwood,
   the meadows for our play,
   the rushes by the water,
   to gather ev'ry day.

5. He gave us eyes to see them,
   and lips that we might tell
   how great is God Almighty,
   who has made all things well.

TUNE 2: ROYAL OAK 76 76 and Refrain

Text: Cecil Frances Alexander (1818 - 1895)
Music: Tune 1 – William Henry Monk (1823-1889)
Tune 2 – traditional English melody arr. Adrian Vernon Fish

126 All you nations, sing out your joy

2. Lift up your hearts; sing to your God:
   tremendous his deeds on the earth!
   Vanquished your foes, struck down by power and might;
   alleluia!

3. Let all the earth kneel in his sight,
   extolling his marvellous fame;
   honour his name, in highest heaven give praise;
   alleluia!

4. Come forth and see all the great works
   that God has brought forth by his might;
   fall on your knees before his glorious throne;
   alleluia!

5. Parting the seas with might and power,
   he rescued his people from shame;
   let us give thanks for all his merciful deeds;
   alleluia!

6. His eyes keep watch on all the earth,
   his strength is forever renewed;
   and let no one rebel against his commands;
   alleluia!

7. Tested are we by God the Lord,
   as silver is tested by fire;
   burdened with pain, we fall ensnared in our sins;
   alleluia!

8. Over our heads wicked ones rode,
   we passed through the fire and the flood;
   then, Lord, you brought your people into your peace;
   alleluia!

9. Glory and thanks be to the Father;
   honour and praise to the Son;
   and to the Spirit, source of life and of love;
   alleluia!

Text: Lucien Deiss (b.1921) based on Psalm 65
Music: Lucien Deiss (b.1921)

LITURGICAL

HYMNS OLD & NEW

127 All you who seek a comfort sure

ST BERNARD CM

1. All you who seek a com-fort sure in trou-ble and distress, what-e-ver sor-row vex the mind, or guilt the soul op-press:

2. Jesus, who gave himself for you
   upon the cross to die,
   opens to you his sacred heart;
   O, to that heart draw nigh.

3. You hear how kindly he invites;
   you hear his words so blest:
   'All you that labour, come to me,
   and I will give you rest.'

4. What meeker than the Saviour's heart?
   As on the cross he lay,
   it did his murderers forgive,
   and for their pardon pray.

5. Jesus, the joy of saints on high,
   the hope of sinners here,
   attracted by those loving words
   to you I lift my prayer.

6. Wash then my wounds in that dear blood
   which forth from you does flow;
   by grace a better hope inspire,
   and risen life bestow.

Text: 'Quincunque centum quæritis' (18th century) trans. Edward Caswall (1814-1878) alt. the editors
Music: adapted from a melody in 'Tochter Sion' (1741)
This version of text © Copyright 1999 Kevin Mayhew Ltd.

128 Alma redemptoris mater

Text: Hermann the Lame (d.1054)
Music: Plainsong, accompaniment by Gregory Murray (1905-1992)
revised by Andrew Moore

129 Almighty Father, Lord most high

TALLIS'S CANON LM

1. Al - migh - ty Fa - ther, Lord most high, cre -
a - ting all, and fill - ing all, your name we praise and
mag - ni - fy, for all our needs on you we call.

A lower setting will be found at No. 282

2. We offer to you of your own,
   ourselves and all that we can bring,
   in bread and cup before you shown,
   our universal offering.

3. Were we to offer all we own,
   our wealth combined could not suffice.
   Yet all has value through your love
   and Christ's atoning sacrifice.

4. By this command in bread and cup,
   his body and his blood we plead;
   what on the cross he offered up
   is here our sacrifice indeed.

5. For all your gifts of life and grace,
   here we your servants humbly pray
   that you would look upon the face
   of your anointed Son today.

Text: Vincent Stuckey Stratton Coles (1845-1929) alt. Michael Forster (b.1946)
Music: Thomas Tallis (c.1550-1585)

130 Almighty Father, take this bread

TUNE1: ST BERNARD CM

1. Al - migh - ty Fa - ther, take this bread thy peo - ple of - fer

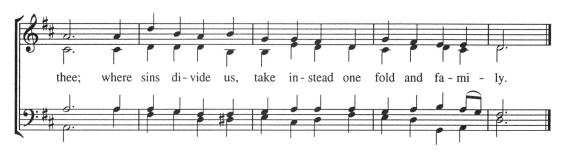

thee; where sins di - vide us, take in - stead one fold and fa - mi - ly.

2. The wine we offer soon will be
   Christ's blood, redemption's price;
   receive it, Holy Trinity,
   this holy sacrifice.

3. O God, by angels' choirs adored,
   thy name be praised on earth;
   on all may be that peace outpoured
   once promised at his birth.

TUNE 2: FARRANT CM

1. Al - migh - ty Fa - ther, take this bread thy peo - ple of - fer

thee; where sins di - vide us, take in - stead one fold and fa - mi - ly.

Text: unknown, alt.
Music: Tune 1 – adapted from a melody in 'Tochter Sion' (1741)
Tune 2 – Richard Farrant (c.1530-1585)

131 Amazing grace

AMAZING GRACE CM

1. A - maz - ing grace! How sweet the sound that saved a
wretch like me. I once was lost, but
now I'm found; was blind, but now I see.

2. 'Twas grace that taught my heart to fear,
   and grace my fears relieved.
   How precious did that grace appear
   the hour I first believed.

3. Through many dangers, toils and snares
   I have already come.
   'Tis grace that brought me safe thus far,
   and grace will lead me home.

4. The Lord has promised good to me,
   his word my hope secures;
   he will my shield and portion be
   as long as life endures.

5. When we've been there a thousand years,
   bright shining as the sun,
   we've no less days to sing God's praise
   than when we first begun.

Text: vs. 1-4: John Newton(1725-1807) alt; v.5: John Rees (1828-1900)
Music: American folk melody arr. Richard Lloyd
This arrangement © Copyright 1993 Kevin Mayhew Ltd.

132 And did those feet in ancient time
Jerusalem

VERSION 1: KEYBOARD/PIANO
JERUSALEM DLM

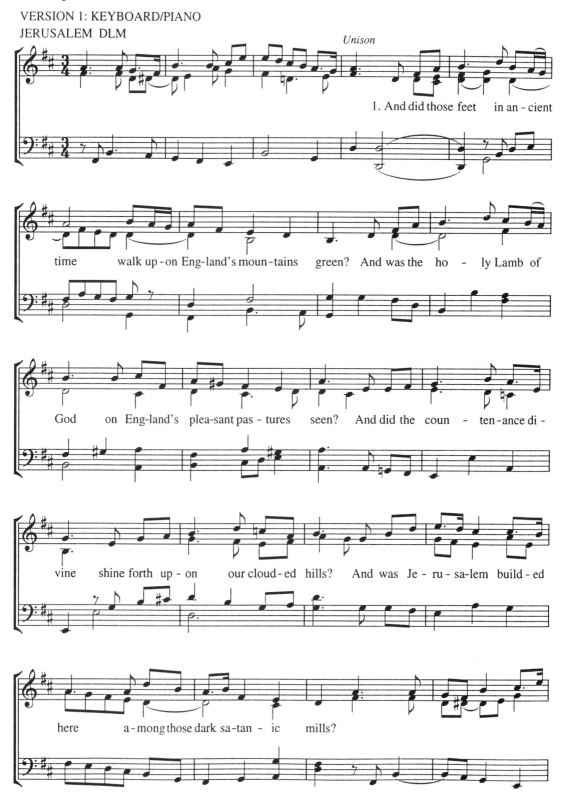

1. And did those feet in an-cient time walk up-on Eng-land's moun-tains green? And was the ho-ly Lamb of God on Eng-land's plea-sant pas-tures seen? And did the coun-ten-ance di-vine shine forth up-on our cloud-ed hills? And was Je-ru-sa-lem build-ed here a-mong those dark sa-tan-ic mills?

2. Bring me my bow of burn-ing gold! Bring me my ar-rows of de-sire! Bring me my spear! O clouds, un-fold! Bring me my cha-ri-ot of fire! I will not cease from men-tal fight, nor shall my sword sleep in my hand, till we have built Je-ru-sa-lem in Eng-land's green and plea-sant land.

VERSION 2: ORGAN

JERUSALEM DLM

Text: William Blake (1757-1827)
Music: Version 1 – Hubert Parry (1848-1918) arr. Andrew Moore; Version 2 – Hubert Parry (1848-1918)

133 A new commandment

VERSION 1: KEYBOARD/GUITAR

VERSION 2: ORGAN

2. You are my friends if you do what I command you.
   Without my help you can do nothing. *(Repeat)*

3. I am the true vine, my Father is the gard'ner.
   Abide in me: I will be with you. *(Repeat)*

4. True love is patient, not arrogant nor boastful;
   love bears all things, love is eternal. *(Repeat)*

Text: v.1 unknown based on John 13:34-35; vs. 2-4 Aniceto Nazareth based on John 15 and 1 Corinthians 13
Music: unknown arr. Andrew Moore

134 Angels we have heard in heaven

IRIS 87 87 and Refrain

2. Shepherds, why this exultation?
   Why your rapt'rous strain prolong?
   Tell us of the gladsome tidings
   which inspire your joyous song.

3. Come to Bethlehem, and see him
   o'er whose birth the angels sing:
   come, adore, devoutly kneeling,
   Christ the Lord, the new-born King.

4. See him in a manger lying
   whom the choir of angels praise!
   Mary, Joseph, come to aid us
   while our hearts in love we raise.

An easier setting of the Refrain

Text: James Chadwick (1813-1882)
Music: traditional French melody arr. Richard Runciman Terry (1865-1938),
alternative Refrain arr. Andrew Moore

135 Angels we have heard on high

IRIS 77 77 and Refrain

2. Shepherds, why this jubilee?
   Why your rapt'rous strain prolong?
   Say, what may your tidings be,
   which inspire your heavenly song.

3. Come to Bethlehem and see
   him whose birth the angels sing:
   come, adore on bended knee
   th'infant Christ, the new-born King.

4. See within a manger laid,
   Jesus, Lord of heav'n and earth!
   Mary, Joseph, lend your aid
   to celebrate our Saviour's birth.

An easier setting of the Refrain

Text: James Chadwick (1813-1882)
Music: traditional French melody arr. Richard Runciman Terry (1865-1938)
alternative Refrain arr. Andrew Moore

136 A noble flower of Judah

ES IST EIN' ROS' ENTSPRUNGEN 76 76 676

1. A noble flow'r of Judah from tender roots has sprung,
a rose from stem of Jesse, as prophets long had sung;
a blossom fair and bright, that in the midst of winter will change to dawn our night.

2. The rose of grace and beauty
of which Isaiah sings
is Mary, virgin mother,
and Christ the flow'r she brings.
By God's divine decree
she bore our loving Saviour
who died to set us free.

3. To Mary, dearest mother,
with fervent hearts we pray:
grant that your tender infant
will cast our sins away,
and guide us with his love
that we shall ever serve him
and live with him above.

Text: Vorreformatorisch (Cologne, 1599), cento paraphrased by Anthony G. Petti
Music: German carol melody, harmonies based on Michael Praetorius (1571-1621) alt.

137 Arise, come to your God

Refrain

A - rise, come to your God, sing him your songs of re - joic - ing!

1. Cry out with joy to the Lord, all the earth.
2. Know that he, the Lord, is God.
3. Go within his gates, giving thanks.
4. In - deed, how good is the Lord,
5. Give glory to the Father Al - mighty,

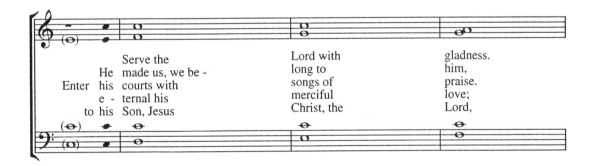

Serve the Lord with gladness.
He made us, we be - long to him,
Enter his courts with songs of praise.
e - ternal his merciful love;
to his Son, Jesus Christ, the Lord,

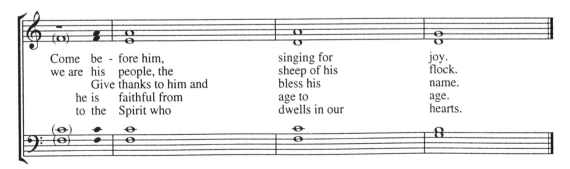

Come be - fore him, singing for joy.
we are his people, the sheep of his flock.
Give thanks to him and bless his name.
he is faithful from age to age.
to the Spirit who dwells in our hearts.

Text: Psalm 99, Grail translation
Music: Joseph Gelineau (b.1920)

LITURGICAL
HYMNS OLD & NEW

138 Arise to greet the Lord of light

REPTON 86 88 6

2. Towards his light shall kings be drawn
this majesty to see;
and in the brightness of the dawn
shall see the world in hope reborn,
in justice full and free,
in justice full and free.

3. The holy light in Judah's skies
calls sages from afar.
The hope of kings they recognise
which, in the virgin mother's eyes,
outshines the guiding star,
outshines the guiding star.

4. This majesty for long concealed
from longing human sight,
in Jesus Christ is now revealed,
and God's eternal promise sealed
in love's unending light,
in love's unending light.

Text: Michael Forster (b.1946) based on Isaiah 60:1-6
Music: Hubert Parry (1848-1918)
Text © Copyright 1993 Kevin Mayhew Ltd.

139 As bread my Lord comes to me

VERSION 1: KEYBOARD/GUITAR

2. I am far nearer to him
   than the air I breathe.
   With joy I welcome him home;
   he satisfies my heart's need.

3. The still, small voice that I hear,
   always is reminding
   my soul of love and of peace,
   that passes understanding.

VERSION 2: ALTERNATIVE HARMONISATION FOR ORGAN

1. As bread my Lord comes to me, though I am un-

wor - thy. He heals me, bo - dy and soul, and

sets my spi - rit free. *Refrain* For he is my Sa-viour and my

God: yes, he is my Sa-viour and my God.

Text and Music: Estelle White (b.1925)
Second version: arr. Andrew Moore

140 As earth that is dry

1. As earth that is dry and parched in the sun lies wait-ing for rain, my soul is a des - ert, a - rid and waste; it longs for your word, O Lord.

Refrain

Come to the wa - ters, all you who thirst, come, now, and eat my bread.

2. Though you have no money,
   come, buy my corn
   and drink my red wine.
   Why spend precious gold
   on what will not last?
   Hear me, and your soul will live.

3. As one on a journey
   strays from the road
   and falls in the dark,
   my mind is a wand'rer,
   choosing wrong paths
   and longing to find a star.

4. The Lord is your light,
   the Lord is your strength,
   turn back to him now,
   for his ways are not
   the ways you would choose,
   and his thoughts are always new.

5. As rain from the mountains
   falls on the land
   and brings forth the seed,
   the word of the Lord
   sinks deep in our hearts,
   creating the flow'r of truth.

Text: Anne Conway (b.1940) based on Isaiah 55
Music: Anne Conway (b.1940) arr. Adrian Vernon Fish

141 As I kneel before you

1. As I kneel before you, as I bow my head in prayer, take this day, make it yours and fill me with your love.

A - ve, Ma - ri - a, gra - ti - a ple - na, Do - mi - nus te - cum, be - ne - dic - ta tu.

2. All I have I give you,
   ev'ry dream and wish are yours;
   mother of Christ, mother of mine,
   present them to my Lord.

3. As I kneel before you,
   and I see your smiling face,
   ev'ry thought, ev'ry word
   is lost in your embrace.

Text: Maria Parkinson (b.1956)
Music: Maria Parkinson (b.1956) arr. Andrew Moore

142 As the deer pants for the water

2. I want you more than gold or silver,
only you can satisfy.
You alone are the real joy-giver
and the apple of my eye.

3. You're my friend and you are my brother,
even though you are a king.
I love you more than any other,
so much more than anything.

Text and Music: Martin Nystrom, based on Psalm 41:1-2

143 As we are gathered

As we are ga-thered, Je-sus is here; one with each o-ther, Je-sus is here; joined by the Spi-rit, washed in the blood, part of the bo-dy, the church of God. As we are ga-thered, Je-sus is here; one with each o-ther, Je-sus is here.

Text: John Daniels
Music: John Daniels arr. Andrew Moore

144 As with gladness men of old

DIX 77 77 77

1. As with glad-ness men of old did the guid-ing star be-hold,
as with joy they hailed its light, lead-ing on-ward, beam-ing bright;
so, most gra-cious Lord, may we e-ver-more be led to thee.

2. As with joyful steps they sped,
   to that lowly manger-bed,
   there to bend the knee before
   him whom heav'n and earth adore,
   so may we with willing feet
   ever seek thy mercy-seat.

3. As their precious gifts they laid,
   at thy manger roughly made,
   so may we with holy joy,
   pure, and free from sin's alloy,
   all our costliest treasures bring,
   Christ, to thee our heav'nly King.

4. Holy Jesu, ev'ry day
   keep us in the narrow way;
   and, when earthly things are past,
   bring our ransomed souls at last
   where they need no star to guide,
   where no clouds thy glory hide.

5. In the heav'nly country bright
   need they no created light,
   thou its light, its joy, its crown,
   thou its sun which goes not down;
   there for ever may we sing
   alleluias to our King.

Text: William Chatterton Dix (1837-1898) alt.
Music: adapted from Conrad Kocher (1786-1872) by William Henry Monk (1823-1889)

145 At the cross her station keeping

STABAT MATER 887

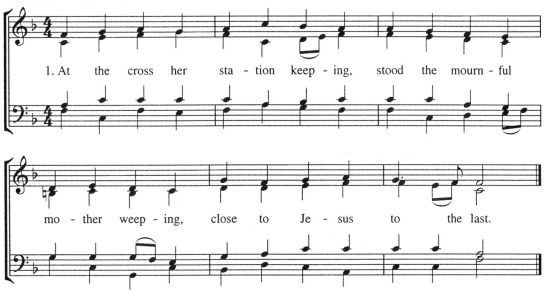

1. At the cross her sta - tion keep - ing, stood the mourn - ful

mo - ther weep - ing, close to Je - sus to the last.

2. Through her heart, his sorrow sharing,
   all his bitter anguish bearing,
   now at length the sword has passed.

3. O, how sad and sore distressed
   was that mother highly blest,
   of the sole-begotten One.

4. Christ above in torment hangs;
   she beneath beholds the pangs
   of her dying glorious Son.

5. Is there one who would not weep,
   whelmed in miseries so deep,
   Christ's dear mother to behold?

6. Can the human heart refrain
   from partaking in her pain,
   in that mother's pain untold?

7. Bruised, derided, cursed, defiled,
   she beheld her tender child,
   all with bloody scourges rent.

8. For the sins of his own nation,
   saw him hang in desolation,
   till his spirit forth he sent.

9. O thou mother! Fount of love!
   Touch my spirit from above,
   make my heart with thine accord.

10. Make me feel as thou hast felt;
    make my soul to glow and melt
    with the love of Christ my Lord.

11. Holy Mother, pierce me through,
    in my heart each wound renew
    of my Saviour crucified.

12. Let me share with thee his pain
    who for all my sins was slain,
    who for me in torments died.

13. Let me mingle tears with thee,
    mourning him who mourned for me,
    all the days that I may live.

14. By the cross with thee to stay,
    there with thee to weep and pray,
    this I ask of thee to give.

Another hymn for the Stations of the Cross will be found at No. 402

Text: 'Stabat mater', ascribed to Jacopone da Todi (d.1306) trans. Edward Caswall (1814-1878)
Music: from 'Mainz Gesangbuch' (1661)

LITURGICAL

HYMNS OLD & NEW

146 At the Lamb's high feast we sing

SALZBURG 77 77 D

1. At the Lamb's high feast we sing praise to our vic-tor-ious King,
who hath washed us in the tide flow-ing from his pier-cèd side;
praise we him, whose love di-vine gives his sa-cred blood for wine,
gives his bo-dy for the feast, Christ the vic-tim, Christ the priest.

2. Where the paschal blood is poured,
   death's dark angel sheathes his sword;
   faithful hosts triumphant go
   through the wave that drowns the foe.
   Praise we Christ, whose blood was shed,
   paschal victim, paschal bread;
   with sincerity and love
   eat we manna from above.

3. Mighty victim from above,
   conqu'ring by the pow'r of love;
   thou hast triumphed in the fight,
   thou hast brought us life and light.
   Now no more can death appal,
   now no more the grave enthral:
   thou hast opened paradise,
   and in thee thy saints shall rise.

4. Easter triumph, Easter joy,
   nothing now can this destroy;
   from sin's pow'r do thou set free
   souls new-born, O Lord, in thee.
   Hymns of glory and of praise,
   risen Lord, to thee we raise;
   holy Father, praise to thee,
   with the Spirit, ever be.

Text: 'Ad regias Agni dapes' (7th century) trans. Robert Campbell (1814-1868)
Music: Jacob Hintze (1622-1702); harmony by Johann Sebastian Bach (1685-1750)

147 At the name of Jesus

TUNE 1: EVELYNS 65 65 D

1. At the name of Je - sus ev - 'ry knee shall bow,
ev - 'ry tongue con - fess him King of glo - ry now;
'tis the Fa - ther's plea - sure we should call him Lord,
who, from the be - gin - ning, was the migh - ty Word.

2. At his voice creation
sprang at once to sight,
all the angels' faces,
all the hosts of light,
thrones and dominations,
stars upon their way,
all the heav'nly orders
in their great array.

3. Humbled for a season,
to receive a name
from the lips of sinners
unto whom he came,
faithfully he bore it,
spotless to the last,
brought it back victorious
when from death he passed.

4. Bore it up triumphant,
with its human light,
through all ranks of creatures
to the central height,
to the throne of Godhead,
to the Father's breast,
filled it with the glory
of that perfect rest.

5. In your hearts enthrone him;
there let him subdue
all that is not holy,
all that is not true;
crown him as your captain
in temptation's hour;
let his will enfold you
in its light and pow'r.

6. Truly, this Lord Jesus
shall return again,
with his Father's glory,
with his angel train;
for all wreaths of empire
meet upon his brow,
and our hearts confess him
King of glory now.

TUNE 2: CAMBERWELL 65 65 D

1. At the name of Je - sus ev - 'ry knee shall bow, ev - 'ry tongue con - fess him King of glo - ry now; 'tis the Fa - ther's plea - sure we should call him Lord, who, from the be - gin - ning, was the migh - ty Word.

verses 1-6 Word. *verse 7* now.

Text: Caroline Maria Noel (1817-1877) alt.
Music: Tune 1 - William Henry Monk (1823-1889)
Tune 2 - Michael Brierley (b.1932)

148 At your feet

SACRUM CONVIVIUM 87 87 87

1. At your feet, great God, we of-fer bread, the sign of hope we share;
all the full-ness of cre-a-tion in the feast that you pre-pare.
Christ our host, in ri - sen splen-dour, gives us food be - yond com-pare.

2. Now, in humble adoration,
   drawn by grace, we offer here
   wine that speaks of love's oblation,
   life from death and hope from fear.
   Sharing in his cup of sorrow,
   our Redeemer we revere.

3. Here, most holy God, we offer,
   with the saints in full accord,
   hearts and gifts for your acceptance,
   broken dreams to be restored.
   All creation cries for healing;
   you alone such grace afford!

Text: Michael Forster (b.1946)
Music: Alan Rees (b.1941)

149 Ave Maria, O maiden, O mother

AVE MARIA 11 10 11 10 and Refrain

1. Ave Maria, O maiden, O mother, fondly thy children are calling on thee; thine are the graces unclaimed by another, sinless and beautiful star of the sea. *Mater amabilis, ora pro nobis, pray for thy children who call upon thee, ave sanctissima, ave purissima, sinless and beautiful star of the sea.*

2. Ave Maria, the night shades are falling,
   softly, our voices arise unto thee;
   earth's lonely exiles for succour are calling,
   sinless and beautiful star of the sea.

3. Ave Maria, thy children are kneeling,
   words of endearment are murmured to thee;
   softly thy spirit upon us is stealing,
   sinless and beautiful star of the sea.

Text: 'Sister M.'
Music: Richard Runciman Terry (1865-1938)

150 Ave, Regina cælorum

Unison

A - ve, Re - gi - na cæ - lo - rum! A - ve, Do - mi - na an - ge - lo - rum!

Sal - ve rad - ix, sal - ve por - ta, ex qua mun - do lux est or - ta.

Gau - de Vir - go glo - ri - o - sa, su - per om - nes spe - ci - o - sa:

va - le, o val - de de - co - ra, et pro no - bis Chri - stum ex - o - ra.

An English version of this antiphon, 'O Queen of heaven', will be found at No. 550

Text: unknown, 12th Century
Music: Plainsong, accompaniment by Andrew Moore
Music © Copyright 1994 Kevin Mayhew Ltd.

151 Ave verum corpus

Unison

A-ve ve-rum cor-pus, na-tum ex Ma-ri-a vir-gi-ne;

ve-re pas-sum, im-mo-la-tum in cru-ce pro ho-mi-ne.

Cu-jus la-tus per-fo-ra - tum un-da flux-it et san-gui-ne;

es-to no-bis præ-gu-sta - tum mor-tis in ex-a-mi-ne.

O Je-su dul - cis! O Je-su pi - e!

O Je - su fi-li Ma-ri - æ.

Text: Traditional
Music: Plainsong arr. Andrew Moore
This arrangement © Copyright 1999 Kevin Mayhew Ltd.

152 Awake, awake and greet the new morn

REJOICE, REJOICE 98 98 87 89

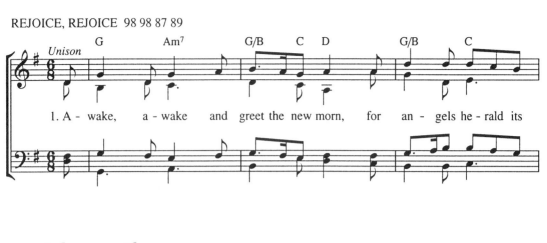

1. A - wake, a - wake and greet the new morn, for an - gels he - rald its

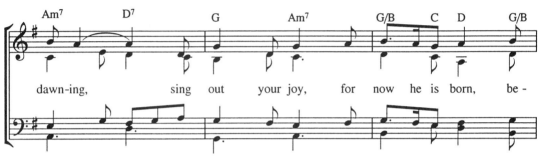

dawn-ing, sing out your joy, for now he is born, be -

hold, the child of our long - ing. Come as a ba - by

weak and poor, to bring all hearts to - ge - ther, he

o - pens wide the heav'n - ly door and lives now in - side us for

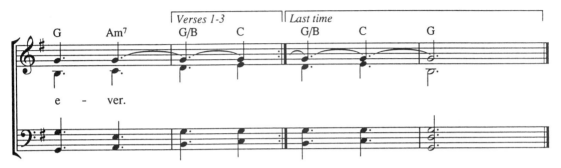

Verses 1-3 | *Last time*

e - ver.

2. To us, to all in sorrow and fear,
   Emmanuel comes a-singing,
   his humble song is quiet and near,
   yet fills the earth with its ringing;
   music to heal the broken soul
   and hymns of loving kindness,
   the thunder of his anthems roll
   to shatter all hatred and blindness.

3. In darkest night his coming shall be,
   when all the world is despairing,
   as morning light so quiet and free,
   so warm and gentle and caring.
   Then shall the mute break forth in song,
   the lame shall leap in wonder,
   the weak be raised above the strong,
   and weapons be broken asunder.

4. Rejoice, rejoice, take heart in the night,
   though dark the winter and cheerless,
   the rising sun shall crown you with light,
   be strong and loving and fearless;
   love be our song and love our prayer,
   and love our endless story,
   may God fill ev'ry day we share,
   and bring us at last into glory.

Text and Music: Marty Haugen (b.1950)

LITURGICAL

HYMNS OLD & NEW

153 Awake, awake: fling off the night

DEUS TUORUM MILITUM LM

A - wake, a - wake: fling off the night! for God has
sent his glo - rious light; and we who live in
Christ's new day must works of dark - ness put a - way.

2. Awake and rise, in Christ renewed,
   and with the Spirit's pow'r endued.
   The light of life in us must glow,
   and fruits of truth and goodness show.

3. Let in the light; all sin expose
   to Christ, whose life no darkness knows.
   Before his cross for guidance kneel;
   his light will judge and, judging, heal.

4. Awake, and rise up from the dead,
   and Christ his light on you will shed.
   Its pow'r will wrong desires destroy,
   and your whole nature fill with joy.

5. Then sing for joy, and use each day;
   give thanks for everything alway.
   Lift up your hearts; with one accord
   praise God through Jesus Christ our lord.

Text: John Raphael Peacey (1896-1971) based on Ephesians 5:6-20 alt.
Music: melody from 'Grenoble Antiphoner' (1753)

154 Awake from your slumber
City of God

1. A-wake from your slum-ber! A - rise from your sleep!
2. We are sons of the morn - ing, we are daugh-ters of day.

A new day is dawn-ing for all those who weep.
The one who has loved us has bright-ened our way.

The peo-ple in dark-ness have seen a great light.
The Lord of all kind-ness has called us to be.

The Lord of our long-ing has con-quered the night.
a light for his peo-ple to set their hearts free.

Let us build the ci-ty of God, may our tears be turned in-to dan-

- cing! For the Lord, our light and our love, has turned the

night in-to day.

3. God is light; in him there is no dark-ness.

Let us walk in his light, his chil-dren, one and

all. O com-fort my peo-ple,

make gen-tle your words. Pro-claim to my ci-ty the day of her

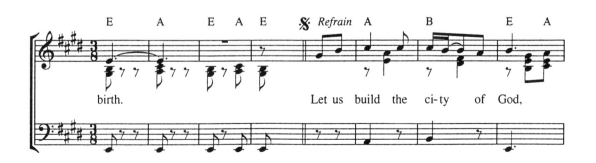

birth. Let us build the ci-ty of God,

may our tears be turned in-to dan - cing! For the Lord, our light and our love, has turned the night in-to day.

4. O ci-ty of glad-ness, now lift up your voice! Pro-claim the good ti-dings that all may re - joice!

After verse 3

Last time

Fine

D.S. al Fine

Text: Dan Schutte
Music: Dan Schutte arr. Keith Stent

155 Away in a manger

CRADLE SONG 11 11 11 11

1. A-way in a man-ger, no crib for a bed, the lit-tle Lord Je-sus laid down his sweet head. The stars in the bright sky looked down where he lay, the lit-tle Lord Je-sus, a-sleep on the hay.

An alternative version of verses 2 and 3

2. The cattle are lowing, the baby awakes,
   but little Lord Jesus no crying he makes.
   I love thee, Lord Jesus! Look down from the sky,
   and stay by my side until morning is nigh.

3. Be near me Lord Jesus; I ask thee to stay
   close by me for ever, and love me, I pray.
   Bless all the dear children in thy tender care,
   and fit us for heaven, to live with thee there.

2. The cattle are lowing, they also adore
   the little Lord Jesus who lies on the straw.
   I love you, Lord Jesus, I know you are near
   to love and protect me till morning is here.

3. Be near me, Lord Jesus; I ask you to stay
   close by me for ever, and love me, I pray.
   Bless all the dear children in your tender care,
   prepare us for heaven, to live with you there.

Original text: William James Kirkpatrick (1838-1921)
Alternative text, verses 2 and 3: Michael Forster (b.1946)
Music: William James Kirkpatrick (1838-1921) arr. John Rombaut
Alternative verses and this arrangement © Copyright 1996 Kevin Mayhew Ltd.

156 Battle is o'er, hell's armies flee

SURREXIT 888 and Alleluias.

1. Bat - tle is o'er, hell's ar - mies flee: raise we the cry of vic - to-ry with a-bound - ing joy re-sound - ing, al - le - lu - ia, al - le - lu - ia.

2. Christ who endured the shameful tree,
   o'er death triumphant welcome we,
   our adoring praise outpouring,
   alleluia, alleluia.

3. On the third morn from death rose he,
   clothed with what light in heav'n shall be,
   our unswerving faith deserving,
   alleluia, alleluia.

4. Hell's gloomy gates yield up their key,
   paradise door thrown wide we see;
   never-tiring be our choiring,
   alleluia, alleluia.

5. Lord, by the stripes men laid on thee,
   grant us to live from death set free,
   this our greeting still repeating,
   alleluia, alleluia.

Text: 'Finita iam sunt prœlia' from 'Simphonia Sirenum' (1695), trans. Ronald Arbuthnott Knox (1888-1957)
Music: Gregory Murray (1905-1992)

157 Beauty for brokenness
God of the poor

1. Beau-ty for bro-ken-ness, hope for des-pair, Lord, in the suff - 'ring, this is our prayer: bread for the chil - dren, jus - tice, joy, peace, sun - rise to sun - set your king-dom in - crease.

Refrain
God of the poor, friend of the weak, give us com - pas - sion we pray; melt our cold hearts, let tears fall like

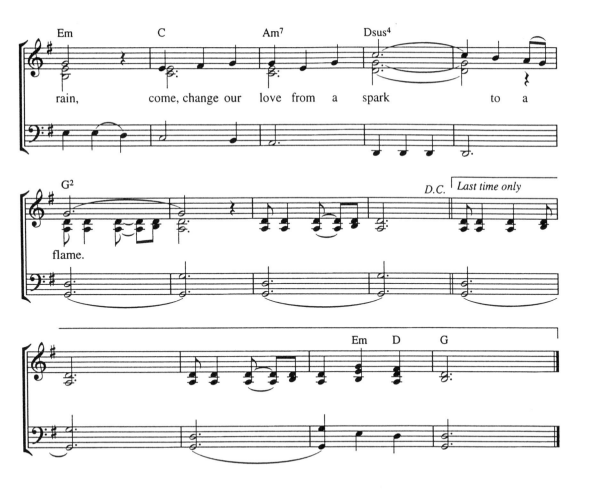

rain, come, change our love from a spark to a

flame.

D.C. | *Last time only*

2. Shelter for fragile lives,
   cures for their ills,
   work for the craftsmen,
   trade for their skills.
   Land for the dispossessed,
   rights for the weak,
   voices to plead the cause
   of those who can't speak.

3. Refuge from cruel wars,
   havens from fear,
   cities for sanctu'ry,
   freedoms to share.
   Peace to the killing fields,
   scorched earth to green,
   Christ for the bitterness,
   his cross for pain.

4. Rest for the ravaged earth,
   oceans and streams,
   plundered and poisoned,
   our future, our dreams.
   Lord, end our madness,
   carelessness, greed;
   make us content with
   the things that we need.

5. Lighten our darkness,
   breathe on this flame,
   until your justice
   burns brightly again;
   until the nations
   learn of your ways,
   seek your salvation
   and bring you their praise.

Text: Graham Kendrick (b.1950)
Music: Graham Kendrick (b.1950) arr. Keith Stent

158 Be blessed, pure of heart

2. The meek and patient will be blessed;
   they will succeed and inherit the earth.

3. All those who suffer will be blessed;
   they will be comforted in their distress.

4. All those who thirst for what is right
   will be blessed and be given their fill.

5. The merciful will all be blessed;
   they will have mercy and love shown to them.

6. The clean of heart will all be blessed;
   they will be given the vision of God.

7. Those making peace will all be blessed;
   they will be known as the children of God.

8. Those suff'ring in the cause of right
   will all be blessed in the kingdom of heav'n.

Text: W.R. Lawrence (1925-1997), from Matthew 5:3-12
Music: Alexandre Lesbordes

159 Before the light of evening fades

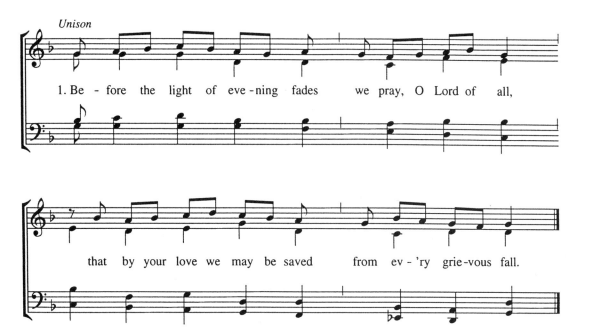

Unison

1. Be - fore the light of eve-ning fades we pray, O Lord of all,

that by your love we may be saved from ev-'ry grie-vous fall.

2. Repel the terrors of the night
   and Satan's pow'r of guile,
   impose a calm and restful sleep
   that nothing may defile.

3. Most holy Father, grant our prayer
   through Christ your only Son,
   that in your Spirit we may live
   and praise you ever one.

Text: 'Te Lucis ante terminum' (7th century) trans. Ralph Wright (b.1938)
Music: Laurence Bevenot

160 Behold, the Lamb of God

Refrain

Be - hold, the Lamb of God, the Ho - ly One!

Be - hold, the Lord who died to take our sin.

1. In your great ten - der - ness for - give my sin.

My guilt is known to you, my Lord!

2. My sin is constantly before my eyes,
   so wash me whiter than the snow.

3. Give me your joy and take away my shame,
   and fill my body with new life.

4. Create in me, O Lord, a heart renewed,
   and keep me always pure and clean.

5. Do not deprive me of your spirit, Lord,
   open my lips to sing your praise!

6. I come to offer you a sacrifice:
   the broken heart you have made new.

Text: Damian Lundy (b.1944-1997) based on Psalm 50
Music: Gerard Markland (b.1953) arr. Christopher Tambling

161 Behold, the Saviour of the nations

ST CLEMENT 98 98

1. Be - hold, the Sa - viour of the na - tions shall spring from Da - vid's roy - al line, to rule with mer - cy all the peo - ples, and judge with right - eous - ness di - vine!

A higher setting will be found at No. 563

2. He shall delight in truth and wisdom,
   with justice for the meek and poor,
   and reconcile his whole creation,
   where beasts of prey shall hunt no more.

3. Here may his word, with hope abounding,
   unite us all in peace and love,
   to live as one with all creation,
   redeemed by mercy from above.

4. Prepare the way with awe and wonder;
   salvation comes on judgement's wing,
   for God will purify his people,
   and 'Glory!' all the earth shall sing.

Text: Michael Forster (b.1946) based on Isaiah 11:1-10
Music: Clement Cotterill Scholefield (1839-1904)
Text © Copyright 1993 Kevin Mayhew Ltd.

LITURGICAL

HYMNS OLD & NEW

162 Beloved, let us love

SONG 46 11 10

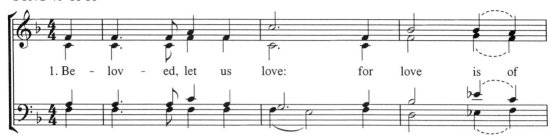

1. Be - lov - ed, let us love: for love is of

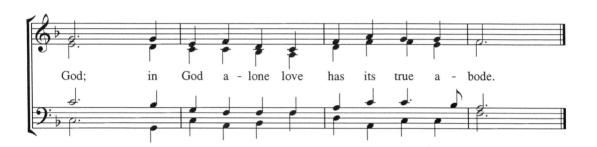

God; in God a - lone love has its true a - bode.

2. Beloved, let us love:
   for those who love,
   they only, are his children from above.

3. Beloved, let us love:
   for love is rest,
   and those who do not love cannot be blessed.

4. Beloved, let us love:
   for love is light,
   and those who do not love still live in night.

5. Beloved, let us love:
   for only thus
   shall we see God, the Lord who first loved us.

Text: Horatius Bonar (1808-1889) based on 1 John 4:7
Music: Orlando Gibbons (1583-1625)

163 Be still and know I am with you

1. Be still and know I am with you, be still, I am the Lord. I will not leave you or-phans, I leave with you my world. Be one.

2. You fear the light may be fading,
   you fear to lose your way.
   Be still, and know I am near you.
   I'll lead you to the day and the sun.

3. Be glad the day you have sorrow,
   be glad, for then you live.
   The stars shine only in darkness,
   and in your need I give my peace.

VERSION 2: ORGAN

1. Be still and know I am with you, be

still, I am the Lord. I will not

leave you or-phans, I leave with you my

world. Be one.

Text: Anne Conway (b.1940)
Music: Anne Conway (b.1940) arr. Andrew Moore

164 Be still and know that I am God

BE STILL AND KNOW 888

1. Be still and know that I am God. Be
still and know that I am God. Be
still and know that I am God.

2. I am the Lord that healeth thee.
I am the Lord that healeth thee.
I am the Lord that healeth thee.

3. In thee, O Lord, I put my trust.
In thee, O Lord, I put my trust.
In thee, O Lord, I put my trust.

Text: unknown based on Psalm 45
Music: unknown arr. Adrian Vernon Fish (b.1956)
This arrangement © Copyright 1993 Kevin Mayhew Ltd.

165 Be still, for the presence of the Lord

1. Be still, for the pre-sence of the Lord, the Ho-ly One, is here.
Come, bow be-fore him now, with re-ver-ence and fear.
In him no sin is found, we stand on ho-ly ground.
Be still, for the pre-sence of the Lord, the Ho-ly One, is here.

2. Be still, for the glory of the Lord is shining all around;
he burns with holy fire, with splendour he is crowned.
How awesome is the sight, our radiant King of light!
Be still, for the glory of the Lord is shining all around.

3. Be still, for the power of the Lord is moving in this place;
he comes to cleanse and heal, to minister his grace.
No work too hard for him, in faith receive from him.
Be still, for the power of the Lord is moving in this place.

Text and Music: David J. Evans (b.1957)

166 Be still, my soul

FINLANDIA 10 10 10 10 10 10

1. Be still, my soul: the Lord is at your side; bear patiently the cross of grief and pain; leave to your God to order and provide; in ev'ry change he faithful will remain. Be still, my soul: your best, your heav'nly friend, through thorny ways, leads to a joyful end.

2. Be still, my soul: your God will undertake
to guide the future as he has the past.
Your hope, your confidence let nothing shake,
all now mysterious shall be clear at last.
Be still, my soul: the tempests still obey
his voice, who ruled them once on Galilee.

3. Be still, my soul: the hour is hastening on
when we shall be for ever with the Lord,
when disappointment, grief and fear are gone,
sorrow forgotten, love's pure joy restored.
Be still, my soul: when change and tears are past,
all safe and blessèd we shall meet at last.

Text: Katherina von Schlegel (b.1697) trans. Jane L. Borthwick alt.
Music: Jean Sibelius (1865-1957)
Music © Copyright Breitkopf and Härtel, Walkmühlstrasse 52, D-65195 Wiesbaden, Germany.
Used by permission.

167 Bethlehem, of noblest cities

STUTTGART 87 87

1. Beth-le-hem, of nob-lest ci-ties none can once with you com-pare;

you a-lone the Lord from hea-ven did for us in-car-nate bear.

2. Fairer than the sun at morning
   was the star that told his birth,
   to the lands their God announcing,
   veiled in human form on earth.

3. Guided by its shining glory
   did the eastern kings appear;
   see them bend, their gifts to offer,
   for a greater King is here.

4. Solemn things of mystic meaning!
   incense shows God's presence here,
   gold proclaims his sovereign kingship,
   myrrh foreshadows death and tears.

5. Holy Jesus, in your brightness
   to the gentile world displayed,
   with the Father and the Spirit
   endless praise to you be paid.

Text: 'O sola magnarum urbium' by Clemens Prudentius (348-413)
trans. Edward Caswall (1814-1878) alt. Michael Forster (b.1946)
Music: German melody arr. C.F. Witt (c.1660-1716)
This version of text © Copyright 1999 Kevin Mayhew Ltd.

LITURGICAL

HYMNS OLD & NEW

168 Be thou my vision

SLANE 10 10 10 10

1. Be thou my vi - sion, O Lord of my heart,
naught be all else to me save that thou art;
thou my best thought in the day and the night,
wa - king or sleep - ing, thy pre - sence my light.

2. Be thou my wisdom, be thou my true word,
I ever with thee and thou with me, Lord;
thou my great Father, and I thy true heir;
thou in me dwelling, and I in thy care.

3. Be thou my breastplate, my sword for the fight,
be thou my armour, and be thou my might,
thou my soul's shelter, and thou my high tow'r,
raise thou me heav'nward, O Pow'r of my pow'r.

4. Riches I need not, nor all the world's praise,
thou mine inheritance through all my days;
thou, and thou only, the first in my heart,
high King of heaven, my treasure thou art!

5. High King of heaven, when battle is done,
grant heaven's joy to me, O bright heav'n's sun;
Christ of my own heart, whatever befall,
still be my vision, O Ruler of all.

Text: Irish (c.8th century) trans. Mary Byrne (1880-1931) and Eleanor Hull (1860-1935)
Music: traditional Irish melody arr. Colin Hand

169 Bind us together, Lord

there is on - ly one King.

There is on - ly one Bo - dy,

that is why we sing:

2. Fit for the glory of God,
   purchased by his precious Blood,
   born with the right to be free:
   Jesus the vict'ry has won.

3. We are the fam'ly of God,
   we are his promise divine,
   we are his chosen desire,
   we are the glorious new wine.

Text: Bob Gillman
Music: Bob Gillman arr. Andrew Moore

170 Blessed assurance

BLESSED ASSURANCE Irregular

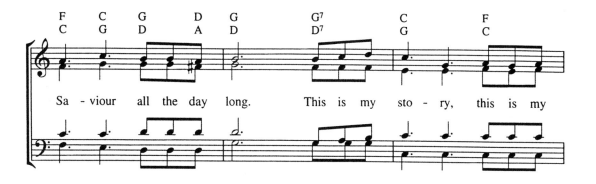

Sa - viour all the day long. This is my sto - ry, this is my

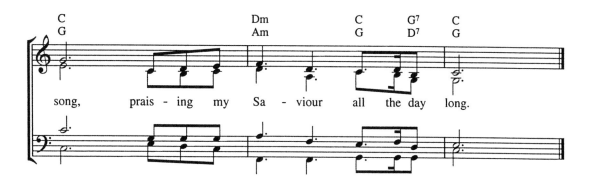

song, prais - ing my Sa - viour all the day long.

2. Perfect submission, perfect delight,
   visions of rapture burst on my sight;
   angels descending, bring from above
   echoes of mercy, whispers of love.

3. Perfect submission, all is at rest,
   I in my Saviour am happy and blest;
   watching and waiting, looking above,
   filled with his goodness, lost in his love.

Text: Frances Jane van Alstyne (Fanny J. Crosby) (1820-1915)
Music: Phoebe Palmer Knapp (1839-1908)

171 Blessed be God

2. Come, tell of all his wondrous deeds,
   come, thank him for all he has done,
   and offer your gifts to the Lord.

3. Let all creation shout for joy;
   come worship the Lord in his house,
   the Lord who made heaven and earth.

Text: Hubert J. Richards (b.1921) based on Psalm 95
Music: Richard Lloyd (b.1933)
© Copyright 1996 Kevin Mayhew Ltd.

172 Blessed be the God of Jesus Christ

OLD HUNDREDTH LM

1. Bless'd be the God of Je - sus Christ, Fa - ther of our re - deem - ing Lord: he who has bless'd us by his grace with gifts that heav'n a - lone af - fords.

2. Chosen in Christ, by God's good will,
   before the earth was set in place,
   called to be children of his love,
   and holy stand before his face:

3. We have redemption through his blood,
   pardon by his abundant grace,
   blessing eternal from above,
   by Christ made known in time and space.

4. Wisdom and insight of our God
   make known the myst'ry of his ways;
   to him all things of heav'n and earth
   shall gather on the final day.

5. In him the gospel truth is known,
   his word of wholeness is revealed.
   All who believe and trust in him
   are with the Holy Spirit sealed.

6. This is the pledge that we receive,
   sign of redemption as his own;
   then shall the heav'ns and earth unite
   to make his praise and glory known.

Text: Michael Forster (b.1946) based on Ephesians 1:3-14
Music: from the 'Genevan Psalter' (1551)
Text © Copyright 1996 Kevin Mayhew Ltd.

173 Bless the Lord, my soul

Bouncy
Refrain
Unison

Bless the Lord, my soul! Bless the Lord, my soul! Let

all that is with-in me praise his name!

Bless the Lord, my soul! Bless the Lord, my soul! Let

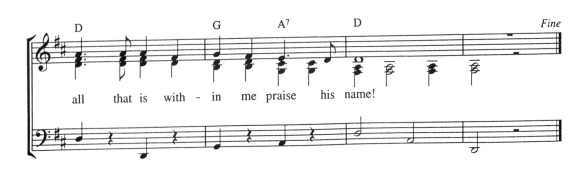

all that is with-in me praise his name!

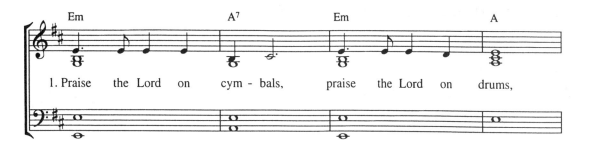

1. Praise the Lord on cym - bals, praise the Lord on drums,

praise the Lord for all that he has done.

2. Praise the Lord on trumpet,
   praise the Lord in song,
   praise him all who stand before his throne.

3. Praise him for his mercy,
   praise him for his pow'r,
   praise him for his love which conquers all.

Text: Mike Anderson (b.1956)
Music: Mike Anderson (b.1956) arr. Keith Stent

174 Blest are the pure in heart

FRANCONIA SM

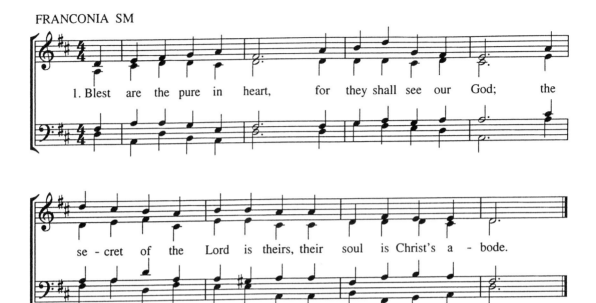

1. Blest are the pure in heart, for they shall see our God; the se-cret of the Lord is theirs, their soul is Christ's a - bode.

2. The Lord who left the heav'ns
   our life and peace to bring,
   to dwell in lowliness with us,
   our pattern and our King.

3. Still to the lowly soul
   he doth himself impart,
   and for his dwelling and his throne
   chooseth the pure in heart.

4. Lord, we thy presence seek;
   may ours this blessing be:
   give us a pure and lowly heart,
   a temple meet for thee.

Text: vs. 1, 3: John Keble (1792-1866)
vs. 2, 4: William John Hall's 'Psalms and Hymns' (1836) alt.
Music: from 'Harmonischer Liederschatz' (1738)
adapted by William Henry Havergal (1793-1870)

175 Blest are you, Lord
Blessed be God

2. Blest are you, Lord, God of all creation,
   thanks to your goodness this wine we offer:
   fruit of the earth, work of our hands,
   it will become the cup of life.

Text: Aniceto Nazareth, based on the Roman Missal
Music: Aniceto Nazareth

176 Blest are you, Lord of creation

2. Blest are you, Lord of creation,
   you provide the wine we offer,
   fruit of your earth and work of our hands.

3. Blest are you, Lord of creation,
   look with favour on our off'rings,
   pour out your Spirit over these gifts.

Text: Hubert J. Richards (b.1921) based on the prayers at the preparation of the gifts (Roman Missal)
Music: Richard Shephard (b.1949) arr. Andrew Moore
© Copyright 1996 Kevin Mayhew Ltd.

177 Blest are you, O God

ODE TO JOY 87 87 D

1. Blest are you, O God, Cre - a - tor; through your good-ness, bread we share,
by the earth con - ceived and gi - ven, made with hu - man skill and care.
Com-mon food, by grace made ho - ly, bread of life to us will be.
This will be the feast of hea - ven, blest be God e - ter - nal - ly.

2. Blest are you, O God, Creator;
   by your grace we bring you wine,
   work of human hands combining
   with the goodness of the vine;
   cup of blessing yet of sorrow,
   cup of life and love to be;
   sign of covenant eternal;
   blest be God eternally.

3. Blest are you, O God, Creator;
   Light of lights and Pow'r of pow'rs,
   yet in humble love accepting
   gifts from hands as poor as ours.
   In our gifts our lives are given,
   by your grace Christ's life to be.
   In the giving and receiving,
   blest be God eternally.

Text: Michael Forster (b.1946)
Music: Ludwig van Beethoven (1770-1827) arr. Christopher Tambling
Text and this arrangement © Copyright 1993, 1999 Kevin Mayhew Ltd.

178 Blest be the Lord

He will pro-tect me from their wick-ed hands.

Be-neath the sha-dow of his wings I will re-joice

to find a dwell-ing place se-cure.

2. I need not shrink before the terrors of the night,
   nor stand alone before the light of day.
   No harm shall come to me, no arrow strike me down,
   no evil settle in my soul.

3. Although a thousand strong have fallen at my side,
   I'll not be shaken with the Lord at hand.
   His faithful love is all the armour that I need
   to wage my battle with the foe.

Text: Dan Schutte based on Psalm 90
Music: Dan Schutte arr. Keith Stent

179 Born in the night, Mary's child

MARY'S CHILD 76 76

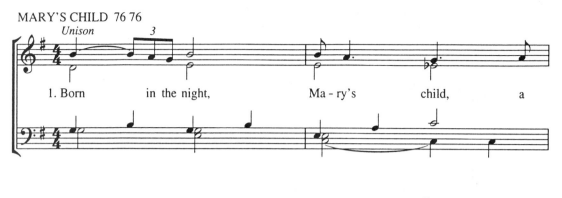

1. Born in the night, Mary's child, a

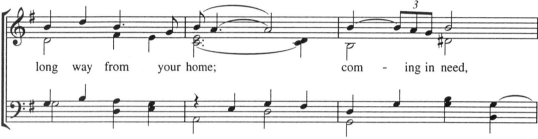

long way from your home; com - ing in need,

Ma - ry's child, born in a bor - rowed room.

2. Clear shining light,
   Mary's child,
   your face lights up our way;
   light of the world,
   Mary's child,
   dawn on our darkened day.

3. Truth of our life,
   Mary's child,
   you tell us God is good;
   prove it is true,
   Mary's child,
   go to your cross of wood.

4. Hope of the world,
   Mary's child,
   you're coming soon to reign;
   King of the earth,
   Mary's child,
   walk in our streets again.

Text and Music: Geoffrey Ainger (b.1925)

180 Bread from the earth

AMOR DEI 13 13 13

Bread from the earth, wine from the soil, A - dam made of clay:
bring to the Lord – sing to the Lord! – gifts of red and gold.
Red is the wine, roy - al and rich, gol - den gleams the wheat.

2. Fashioned from dust, what can you give, Adam, weak and poor?
   Bring to the Lord – sing to the Lord! – what he gave to you:
   spirit of flame, mastering mind, body fine and proud.

3. Cry on his name, worship your God, all who dwell on earth.
   Bring to the Lord – sing to the Lord! – heart and voice and will.
   Father and Son, Spirit most high, worship Three in One.

Text: Luke Connaughton (1917-1979)
Music: Kevin Mayhew (b.1942) arr. Andrew Moore
© Copyright McCrimmon Publishing Co. Ltd., 10-12 High Street,
Great Wakering, Southend-on-Sea, Essex SS3 0EQ. Used by arrangement.

181 Bread is blessed and broken

GRACE IN ESSENCE 65 63

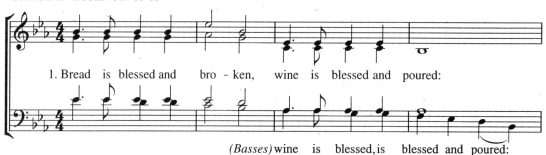

1. Bread is blessed and bro - ken, wine is blessed and poured:

(Basses) wine is blessed, is blessed and poured:

take this and re - mem - ber Christ the Lord.

2. Share the food of heaven
   earth cannot afford.
   Here is grace in essence –
   Christ the Lord.

3. Know yourself forgiven,
   find yourself restored,
   meet a friend for ever –
   Christ the Lord.

4. God has kept his promise
   sealed by sign and word:
   here, for those who want him –
   Christ the Lord.

Text and Music: John L. Bell (b.1949) and Graham Maule (b.1958)

182 Breathe on me, breath of God

CARLISLE SM

1. Breathe on me, breath of God, fill me with life a - new, that as you love, so I may love, and do what you would do.

2. Breathe on me, breath of God,
   until my heart is pure:
   until my will is one with yours
   to do and to endure.

3. Breathe on me, breath of God,
   fulfil my heart's desire,
   until this earthly part of me
   glows with your heav'nly fire.

4. Breathe on me, breath of God,
   so shall I never die,
   but live with you the perfect life
   of your eternity.

Text: Edwin Hatch (1835-1889) alt. the editors
Music: Charles Lockhart (1745-1815)

LITURGICAL

HYMNS OLD & NEW

183 Breath of God, O Holy Spirit

1. Breath of God, O Ho-ly Spi - rit, breath of God, O Ho-ly Spi - rit, breath of God, O Ho-ly Spi - rit, breathe on us now.

2. Comforter in time of sorrow,
   comforter in time of sorrow,
   comforter in time of sorrow,
   give us your peace.

3. Fount of joy and of all beauty,
   fount of joy and of all beauty,
   fount of joy and of all beauty,
   come, fill our minds.

4. Light divine and flame eternal,
   light divine and flame eternal,
   light divine and flame eternal,
   burn in us now.

5. Promise of our Saviour, Jesus,
   promise of our Saviour, Jesus,
   promise of our Saviour, Jesus,
   speak through us now.

Text and Music: Estelle White (b.1925)

184 Bring, all ye dear-bought nations

LASST UNS ERFREUEN 88 44 88 and Alleluias

1. Bring, all ye dear-bought nations, bring, your rich-est prai-ses to your King, al-le-lu – ia, al-le-lu – ia, that spot-less Lamb, who more than due, paid for his sheep, and those sheep you, al-le-lu – ia, al-le-lu – ia, al-le-lu – ia, al-le-lu – ia, al-le-lu – ia!

A higher setting will be found at No. 101

2. That guiltless Son, who bought your peace,
   and made his Father's anger cease,
   alleluia, alleluia,
   then, life and death together fought,
   each to a strange extreme were brought.

3. Life died, but soon revived again,
   and even death by it was slain,
   alleluia, alleluia.
   Say, happy Magdalen, O, say,
   what didst thou see there by the way?

4. 'I saw the tomb of my dear Lord,
   I saw himself, and him adored,
   alleluia, alleluia,
   I saw the napkin and the sheet,
   that bound his head and wrapped his feet.'

5. 'I heard the angels witness bear,
   Jesus is ris'n; he is not here,
   alleluia, alleluia;
   go, tell his foll'wers they shall see
   thine and their hope in Galilee.'

6. We, Lord, with faithful hearts and voice,
   on this thy rising day rejoice,
   alleluia, alleluia.
   O thou, whose power o'ercame the grave,
   by grace and love us sinners save.

Text: 'Victimae Paschali Laudes' attributed to Wipo of Burgundy (11th century),
trans. Walter Kirkham Blount (d.1717)
Music: melody from 'Geistliche Kirchengesang', Cologne (1623)
arr. Ralph Vaughan Williams (1872-1958)

185 Bring flowers of the rarest

1. Bring flow'rs of the rar - est, bring blos - soms the fair - est, from gar - den and wood - land and hill - side and dale; our full hearts are swell - ing, our glad voi - ces tell - ing the praise of the love - li - est flow'r of the vale. O Ma - ry, we crown thee with blos - soms to - day, Queen of the an - gels and Queen of the

May. O Ma - ry we crown thee with blos - soms to - day,
Queen of the an - gels and Queen of the May.

2. Their lady they name thee,
   their mistress proclaim thee.
   O, grant that thy children on earth be as true,
   as long as the bowers
   are radiant with flowers
   as long as the azure shall keep its bright hue.

3. Sing gaily in chorus,
   the bright angels o'er us
   re-echo the strains we begin upon earth;
   their harps are repeating
   the notes of our greeting,
   for Mary herself is the cause of our mirth.

Text: A Sister of Notre Dame
Music: A Sister of Notre Dame arr. Colin Hand

186 Brother, sister, let me serve you
The servant song

1. Brother, sister, let me serve you, let me be as
Christ to you; pray that I may have the grace to
let you be my servant, too.

2. We are pilgrims on a journey,
   fellow trav'llers on the road;
   we are here to help each other
   walk the mile and bear the load.

3. I will hold the Christlight for you
   in the night-time of your fear;
   I will hold my hand out to you,
   speak the peace you long to hear.

4. I will weep when you are weeping;
   when you laugh, I'll laugh with you.
   I will share your joy and sorrow
   till we've seen this journey through.

5. When we sing to God in heaven,
   we shall find such harmony,
   born of all we've known together
   of Christ's love and agony.

6. Brother, sister, let me serve you,
   let me be as Christ to you;
   pray that I may have the grace to
   let you be my servant, too.

Text: Richard Gillard
Music: Richard Gillard arr. Betty Pulkingham

187 By his grace

By his grace we are re- deemed, by his blood we are made clean, and we now can know him face to face. By his pow'r we have been raised, hid-den now in Christ by faith, we will praise the glo- ry of his grace.

Text: Steven Fry
Music: Steven Fry arr. Andrew Moore

LITURGICAL
HYMNS OLD & NEW

188 By the blood that flowed from thee

WESTMINSTER OLD 77 77 and Refrain

1. By the blood that flowed from thee in thy grie-vous a-go-ny;
by the trait-or's guile-ful kiss, fill-ing up thy bit-ter-ness;

Refrain

Je-sus, Sa-viour, hear our cry; thou wert suff'r-ing once as we:

now en-throned in ma-jes-ty count-less an-gels sing to thee.

2. By the cords that, round thee cast,
bound thee to the pillar fast,
by the scourge so meekly borne,
by the purple robe of scorn.

3. By the thorns that crowned thy head;
by the sceptre of a reed;
by thy foes on bended knee,
mocking at thy royalty.

4. By the people's cruel jeers;
by the holy women's tears;
by thy footsteps, faint and slow,
weighed beneath thy cross of woe.

5. By thy weeping mother's woe;
by the sword that pierced her through,
when in anguish standing by,
on the cross she saw thee die.

Text: Frederick William Faber (1814-1863)
Music: John Richardson (1816-1879)

189 By the cross

By the cross we are marked for life! We are cho-sen as God's peo-ple!

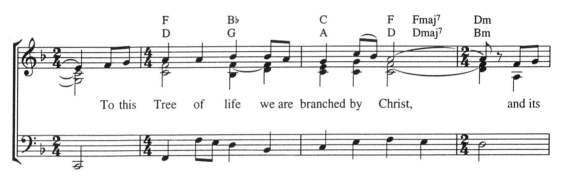

To this Tree of life we are branched by Christ, and its

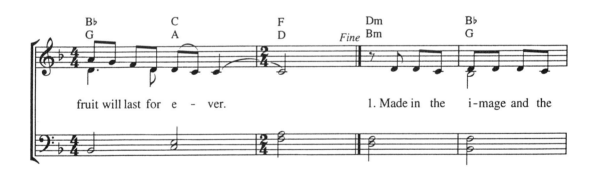

fruit will last for e - ver. 1. Made in the i-mage and the

like-ness of the one true God, we are the daugh-ters and the sons of God, our

2. Made in our image and the likeness of humanity,
   Christ came from God and taught us how to call him 'Father'!
   Then, by the Tree, did he lead us to the Garden,
   where God awaits in welcome if we're clothed in Christ.

Text and Music: Robert B. Kelly (b.1948) arr. Keith Stent

LITURGICAL

HYMNS OLD & NEW

190 By the waters of Babylon

This may be sung as a round, with entries at A *,* B *and* C

1. By the wa - ters, the wa - ters of Ba - by - lon,
we sat down and wept, and wept for thee, Zi - on;
we re - mem - ber thee, re - mem - ber thee, re - mem - ber thee, Zi - on.

2. On the willows, the willows of Babylon,
   we hung up our harps, our harps, for thee, Zion;
   how can we sing, can we sing, sing of thee, Zion?

3. There our captors, our captors from Babylon,
   tried to make us sing, to sing of thee, Zion;
   but we could not sing, we could not sing, we could not sing, Zion.

Text: based on Psalm 137
Music: Don McClean and Lee Hays arr. Adrian Vernon Fish

191 Called to be servants

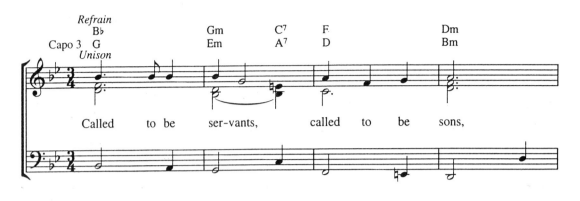

Called to be ser-vants, called to be sons,

called to be daugh-ters, we're called to be one.

Called in-to ser-vice, called to be free; you are called to be

you, and I'm called to be me.   me.

2. We are saints! Forgiveness is sure,
   not of ourselves, but the cross Christ endured.
   We're free from the law that said 'You must provide!'
   We're free to be servants; we're called, we're baptised.

3. Jesus closed the dark pit of death.
   He has breathed on us with his holy breath.
   He gives us the faith to respond to his News.
   We're free to show mercy, to love, to be bruised.

Text: James G. Johnson
Music: James G. Johnson arr. Keith Stent

192 Change my heart, O God

Change my heart, O God, make it e-ver true;

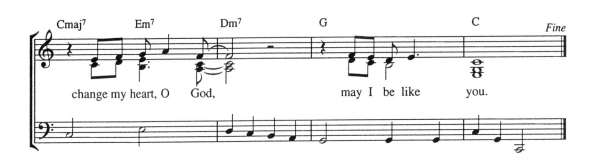

change my heart, O God, may I be like you.

You are the pot - ter, I am the clay;

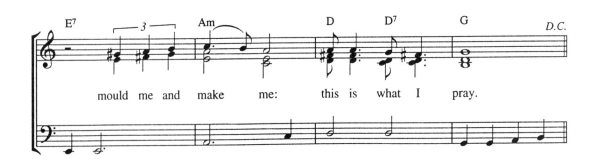

mould me and make me: this is what I pray.

Text: Eddie Espinosa based on Isaiah 64:8
Music: Eddie Espinosa arr. Keith Stent

193 Child in the manger

BUNESSAN 55 53 D

1. Child in the man - ger, in - fant of Ma - ry; out - cast and stran - ger, Lord of all; child who in - he - rits all our trans - gres - sions, all our de - me - rits on him fall.

2. Once the most holy child of salvation
gently and lowly lived below;
now as our glorious mighty Redeemer,
see him victorious o'er each foe.

3. Prophets foretold him, infant of wonder;
angels behold him on his throne;
worthy our Saviour of all their praises;
happy for ever are his own.

Text: Mary MacDonald (1817-1890) trans. Lachlan MacBean (1853-1931)
Music: traditional Gaelic melody arr. Colin Hand
Text © Copyright control. This arrangement © Copyright 1993 Kevin Mayhew Ltd.

LITURGICAL
HYMNS OLD & NEW

194 Christ be beside me

BUNESSAN 55 54 D

1. Christ be beside me, Christ be before me, Christ be behind me, King of my heart. Christ be within me, Christ be below me, Christ be above me, never to part.

2. Christ on my right hand, Christ on my left hand,
   Christ all around me, shield in the strife.
   Christ in my sleeping, Christ in my sitting,
   Christ in my rising, light of my life.

3. Christ be in all hearts thinking about me.
   Christ be in all tongues telling of me.
   Christ be the vision in eyes that see me,
   in ears that hear me, Christ ever be.

Text: adapted from 'St Patrick's Breastplate' by James Quinn (b.1919)
Music: traditional Gaelic melody arr. Colin Hand

195 Christians, lift up your hearts

SALVE FESTA DIES Irregular and Refain

Chris-tians, lift up your hearts, and make this a day of re - joic - ing;

God is our strength and song; glo - ry and praise to his name! name!

1st time only *To verses 1-6 Fine*

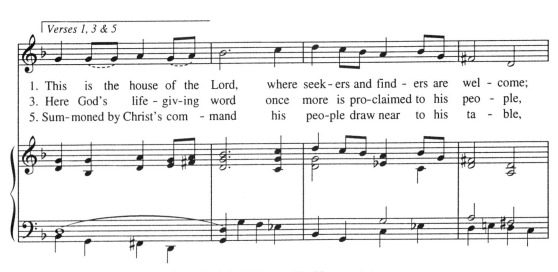

Verses 1, 3 & 5

1. This is the house of the Lord, where seek - ers and find - ers are wel - come;
3. Here God's life - giv-ing word once more is pro-claimed to his peo - ple,
5. Sum-moned by Christ's com - mand his peo-ple draw near to his ta - ble,

D.C.

en – ter its gates with your praise, fill all its courts with your song:
up – lift-ing those who are down, chal-leng-ing all with its truth:
glad – ly to greet their Lord, known in the break-ing of bread:

Verses 2, 4 & 6

2. All those bap-tised in - to Christ share the glo - ry of his re-sur-rec - tion,
4. Those who are bur-dened with sin find here the joy of for-give - ness,
6. Strong and a - lert in his grace, God's peo-ple are one in their wor - ship;

dy-ing with him un - to sin, walk-ing in new - ness of life:
lay-ing their sins be - fore Christ, par-don and peace their re - ward:
kept by his peace they de - part, rea - dy for serv - ing their Lord:

Text: John E. Bowers
Music: Ralph Vaughan Williams (1872-1958)

LITURGICAL

HYMNS OLD & NEW

196 Christ is King of earth and heaven

LAUS DEO (REDHEAD NO. 46) 87 87

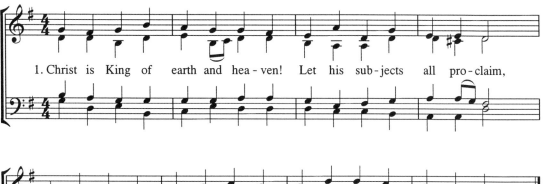

1. Christ is King of earth and hea - ven! Let his sub - jects all pro - claim,

in the splen-dour of his tem - ple, ho - nour to his ho - ly name.

A lower setting will be found at No. 340

2. Christ is King! No soul created
   can refuse to bend the knee
   to the God made man who reigneth,
   as 'twas promised, from the tree.

3. Christ is King! Let humble sorrow
   for our past neglect atone,
   for the lack of faithful service
   to the Master whom we own.

4. Christ is King! Let joy and gladness
   greet him; let his courts resound
   with the praise of faithful subjects
   to his love in honour bound.

5. Christ is King! In health and sickness,
   till we breathe our latest breath,
   till we greet in highest heaven,
   Christ the victor over death.

Text: Ivor J.E. Daniel (1883-1967)
Music: German melody adapted and arranged by Richard Redhead (1820-1901)
Text © Copyright Burns & Oates Ltd, Wellwood, North Farm Road,
Tunbridge Wells, Kent TN2 3QR. Used by permission.

197 Christ is made the sure foundation

TUNE 1: WESTMINSTER ABBEY 87 87 87

1. Christ is made the sure foun - da - tion, Christ the head and cor - ner - stone, cho - sen of the Lord, and pre - cious, bind - ing all the Church in one, ho - ly Zi - on's help for e - ver, and her con - fi - dence a - lone.

2. To this temple, where we call you,
   come, O Lord of hosts, today;
   you have promised loving kindness,
   hear your servants as we pray,
   bless your people now before you,
   turn our darkness into day.

3. Hear the cry of all your people,
   what they ask and hope to gain;
   what they gain from you, for ever
   with your chosen to retain,
   and hereafter in your glory
   evermore with you to reign.

4. Praise and honour to the Father,
   praise and honour to the Son,
   praise and honour to the Spirit,
   ever Three and ever One,
   One in might and One in glory,
   while unending ages run.

TUNE 2: REGENT SQUARE 87 87 87

1. Christ is made the sure foun-da-tion, Christ the head and cor-ner-stone,

cho-sen of the Lord, and pre-cious, bind-ing all the Church in one,

ho - ly Zi-on's help for e - ver, and her con-fi - dence a - lone.

Text: 'Urbs beata Jerusalem' (c.7th century) trans. John Mason Neale (1818-1866) alt.
Music: Tune1 – Henry Purcell (1659-1695) arr. E Hawkins (1802-1868)
Tune 2 – Henry Smart (1813-1879)

198 Christ's is the world
A touching place

DREAM ANGUS Irregular

1. Christ's is the world in which we move, Christ's are the
folk we're sum-moned to love, Christ's is the voice which
calls us to care, and Christ is the one who meets us here.

Refrain

To the lost Christ shows his face; to the un-loved he
gives his em-brace; to those who cry in pain or dis-
grace, Christ makes with his friends a touch-ing place.

2. Feel for the people we most avoid,
   strange or bereaved or never employed;
   feel for the women, and feel for the men
   who fear that their living is all in vain.

3. Feel for the parents who've lost their child,
   feel for the women whom men have defiled,
   feel for the baby for whom there's no breast,
   and feel for the weary who find no rest.

4. Feel for the lives by life confused,
   riddled with doubt, in loving abused;
   feel for the lonely heart, conscious of sin,
   which longs to be pure but fears to begin.

Text: John L. Bell (b.1949) and Graham Maule (b.1958)
Music: traditional Scottish arr. John L. Bell (b.1949) and Graham Maule (b.1958)

199 Christ the Lord is risen today

EASTER HYMN 77 77 D

1. Christ the Lord is ris'n to-day! Christ-tians, haste your vows to pay, of-fer ye your prai-ses meet at the pas-chal vic-tim's feet; for the sheep the Lamb hath bled, sin-less in the sin-ner's stead. Christ the Lord is ris'n on high; now he lives, no more to die.

2. Christ, the victim undefiled,
God and sinners reconciled
when in strange and awful strife
met together death and life;
Christians, on this happy day,
haste with joy your vows to pay.
Christ the Lord is ris'n on high;
now he lives, no more to die.

3. Say, O wond'ring Mary, say,
what thou sawest on thy way.
'I beheld, where Christ had lain,
empty tomb and angels twain,
I beheld the glory bright
of the rising Lord of light;
Christ my hope is ris'n again;
now he lives, and lives to reign.'

4. Christ, who once for sinners bled,
now the first-born from the dead,
throned in endless might and power,
lives and reigns for evermore.
Hail, eternal hope on high!
Hail, thou King of victory!
Hail, thou Prince of life adored!
Help and save us, gracious Lord.

A higher setting will be found at No. 389

Text: 'Victimae Paschali Laudes' attributed to Wipo of Burgundy (11th century)
trans. Jane Elizabeth Leeson (1809-1881) alt. Music: from 'Lyra Davidica' (1708)

200 Christ triumphant

GUITING POWER 85 85 and Refrain

2. Word incarnate, truth revealing,
   Son of Man on earth!
   Pow'r and majesty concealing
   by your humble birth:

3. Suff'ring servant, scorned, ill-treated,
   victim crucified!
   Death is through the cross defeated,
   sinners justified:

4. Priestly King, enthroned for ever
   high in heav'n above!
   Sin and death and hell shall never
   stifle hymns of love:

5. So, our hearts and voices raising
   through the ages long,
   ceaselessly upon you gazing,
   this shall be our song:

Text: Michael Saward (b.1932)
Music: John Barnard (b.1948)

201 Christus vincit

Unison

Chri-stus vin - cit, Chri-stus re - gnat, Chri-stus im - pe - rat.

Psalm tone for the verses

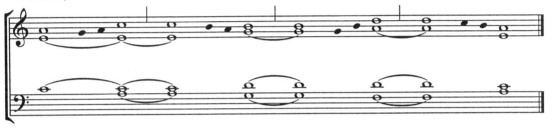

1. God has delivered us from the dominion of darkness
   and transferred us to the kingdom of his beloved Son:
   in Christ we gain our freedom,
   in him, the forgiveness of our sins.

2. Christ is the image of the unseen God,
   he is the first-born of all creation:
   in Christ, all things were created, in heaven and on earth,
   all things, visible and invisible.

3. In Christ, all things were created,
   through him and for him.
   Christ is, and was before all things,
   all things are held in unity by Christ.

4. The Church is the Body of Christ,
   he is its head:
   he is the beginning,
   the first-born from the dead.

5. In Christ all the fullness of God was pleased to dwell,
   and through Christ to reconcile all things to himself;
   to reconcile everything in heaven or on earth,
   making peace by the blood of the cross.

Text: Colossians 1:13-20 adapted by Robert B.Kelly (b.1948)
Music: Refrain – Plainsong arr. Andrew Moore
Psalm Tone – Gregory Murray (1905-1992)

202 Colours of day
Light up the fire

1. Colours of day dawn into the mind, the sun has come up, the night is behind. Go down in the city, into the street, and let's give the message to the people we meet.

Refrain
So light up the fire and let the flame burn,

o - pen the door, let Je - sus re - turn, take

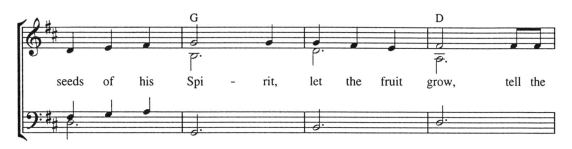

seeds of his Spi - rit, let the fruit grow, tell the

peo - ple of Je - sus, let his love show.

2. Go through the park, on into the town;
   the sun still shines on; it never goes down.
   The light of the world is risen again;
   the people of darkness are needing our friend.

3. Open your eyes, look into the sky,
   the darkness has come, the sun came to die.
   The evening draws on, the sun disappears,
   but Jesus is living, and his Spirit is near.

Text: Sue McClellan (b.1951), John Paculabo (b.1946) and Keith Ryecroft (b.1949)
Music: Sue McClellan (b.1951), John Paculabo (b.1946) and Keith Ryecroft (b.1949)
arr. Andrew Moore

203 Come and be filled

hea - ven.   This is my blood   for the life of the

world.   Come and be

2. He leads us out of the power of darkness
   and brings us safe to his kingdom of life.

3. No longer I, but now Christ lives within me.
   I live by faith in the Son of God.

4. For those in Christ there is no condemnation.
   He sets them free through the Spirit he sends.

5. Thus shall the world know you are my disciples,
   if you can love, and if you can forgive.

Text: Aniceto Nazareth based on Scripture
Music: Aniceto Nazareth arr. Andrew Moore

204 Come and be light for our eyes

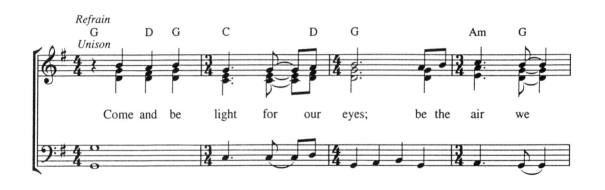

Come and be light for our eyes; be the air we

breathe, be the voice we speak! Come, be the song we

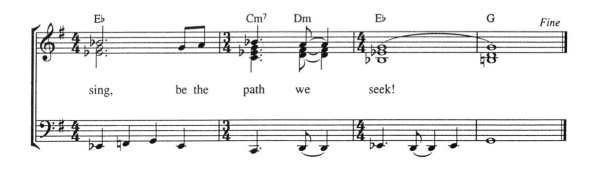

sing, be the path we seek!

1. Your life was giv - en; food for all peo - ple, bo - dy and blood, new

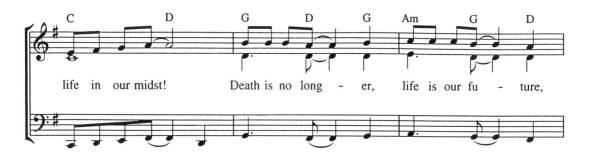

life in our midst! Death is no long - er, life is our fu - ture,

Je - sus, Mes - si - ah; name of all names!

2. We hold your presence;
   risen for ever!
   Your Name now names us people of God!
   Filled with your vision, people of mission,
   healing, forgiving;
   light for the world!

3. Lead us to justice,
   light in the darkness;
   singing, proclaiming Jesus is Lord!
   Teach us to speak, and help us to listen
   for when your truth
   and our dreams embrace!

Text: David Haas (b.1957)
Music: David Haas (b.1957) arr. Keith Stent

205 Come and go with me

Unison

1. Come and go with me to my Father's house, to my Father's house, to my Father's house. Come and go with me to my Father's house where there's joy, joy, joy.

2. It's not very far to my Father's house,
to my Father's house, to my Father's house.
It's not very far to my Father's house
where there's joy, joy, joy.

3. There is room for all in my Father's house,
in my Father's house, in my Father's house.
There is room for all in my Father's house
where there's joy, joy, joy.

4. Ev'rything is free in my Father's house,
in my Father's house, in my Father's house.
Ev'rything is free in my Father's house
where there's joy, joy, joy.

5. Jesus is the way to my Father's house,
to my Father's house, to my Father's house.
Jesus is the way to my Father's house
where there's joy, joy, joy.

6. Jesus is the light in my Father's house,
in my Father's house, in my Father's house.
Jesus is the light in my Father's house
where there's joy, joy, joy.

Other verses may be added spontaneously, such as:

We will clap our hands. . .
There is liberty. . .
We will praise the Lord. . .

Text: v.1 unknown; vs. 2 - 6 and additional verses, Damian Lundy (1944-1997)
Music: unknown arr. Adrian Vernon Fish

206 Come and praise him

Come and praise him, roy-al priest-hood. Come and
wor-ship, ho-ly na-tion. Wor-ship Je-sus, our Re-
deem-er. He is ri-sen, King of glo-ry.

Text: Andy Carter (b.1951)
Music: Andy Carter (b.1951) arr. Andrew Moore

207 Come back to me

1. Come back to me with all your heart, don't let fear keep us a-part.
(2.) wil-der-ness will lead you to your heart where I will speak.

Trees do bend, though straight and tall; so must we to o-thers' call.
In-te-gri-ty and ju-stice with ten-der-ness you shall know.

Refrain

Long have I wait-ed for your com-ing home to me and liv-ing deep-ly our new life.

2. The

2,3.

life.   *Fine*   3. You shall sleep   se - cure with peace;

faith - ful - ness   will   be your joy.   *Final Refrain*   Long have I wait-ed for your

com - ing   home to   me and   liv - ing   deep-ly   our new   life.   *Fine*

Text: Gregory Norbert based on Hosea
Music: Gregory Norbert arr. Andrew Moore

208 Come, come, come to the manger

COME TO THE MANGER Irregular

Refrain
Unison

Come, come, come to the man - ger, chil - dren, come to the chil - dren's King; sing, sing, chor - us of an - gels, star of morn - ing o'er Beth - le - hem sing.

Fine

1. He lies 'mid the beasts of the stall, who is Ma - ker and Lord of us all; the win - try wind blows

cold and drea - ry, see, he weeps, the world is wea - ry;

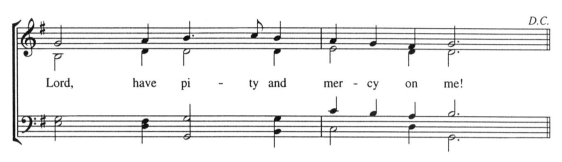

D.C.

Lord, have pi - ty and mer - cy on me!

2. He leaves all his glory behind,
   to be Saviour of all humankind,
   with grateful beasts his cradle chooses,
   thankless world his love refuses;
   Lord, have pity and mercy on me!

3. To the manger of Bethlehem come,
   to the Saviour Emmanuel's home;
   the heav'nly hosts above are singing,
   set the Christmas bells a-ringing;
   Lord, have pity and mercy on me!

Text: unknown, alt.
Music: traditional melody adapted by S. P. Waddington

209 Come down, O Love divine

DOWN AMPNEY 66 11 D

1. Come down, O Love di - vine, seek thou this soul of mine, and vi - sit it with thine own ar - dour glow - ing; O Com-for - ter, draw near, with - in my heart ap - pear, and kin - dle it, thy ho - ly flame be - stow - ing.

2. O let it freely burn,
   till earthly passions turn
   to dust and ashes in its heat consuming;
   and let thy glorious light
   shine ever on my sight,
   and clothe me round, the while my path illuming.

3. Let holy charity
   mine outward vesture be,
   and lowliness become mine inner clothing;
   true lowliness of heart,
   which takes the humbler part,
   and o'er its own shortcomings weeps with loathing.

4. And so the yearning strong,
   with which the soul will long,
   shall far outpass the pow'r of human telling;
   nor can we guess its grace,
   till we become the place
   wherein the Holy Spirit makes his dwelling.

Text: 'Discendi, amor santo' by Bianco da Siena (d.1434) trans. Richard F. Littledale (1833-1890) alt.
Music: Ralph Vaughan Williams (1872-1958)

210 Come, Holy Ghost, Creator, come

TALLIS'S ORDINAL CM

1. Come, Holy Ghost, Creator, come from thy bright heav'nly throne, come,
take possession of our souls, and make them all thine own.

2. Thou who art called the Paraclete,
   best gift of God above,
   the living spring, the living fire,
   sweet unction and true love.

3. Thou who art sev'nfold in thy grace,
   finger of God's right hand;
   his promise, teaching little ones
   to speak and understand.

4. O guide our minds with thy blest light,
   with love our hearts inflame;
   and with thy strength, which ne'er decays,
   confirm our mortal frame.

5. Far from us drive our deadly foe;
   true peace unto us bring;
   and through all perils lead us safe
   beneath thy sacred wing.

6. Through thee may we the Father know,
   through thee th'eternal Son,
   and thee the Spirit of them both,
   thrice-blessèd Three in One.

7. All glory to the Father be,
   with his co-equal Son:
   the same to thee, great Paraclete,
   while endless ages run.

Text: 'Veni, Creator Spiritus', ascribed to Rabanus Maurus (776-856) trans. unknown
Music: Thomas Tallis (c.1505-1585)

211 Come, Holy Spirit, come

DONNYBROOK DSM

1. Come, Ho-ly Spi-rit, come! In-flame our souls with love, trans-form-ing ev'ry heart and home with wis-dom from a-bove. O let us not des-pise the hum-ble path Christ trod, but choose, to shame the world-ly-wise, the fool-ish-ness of God.

2. All-knowing Spirit, prove
the poverty of pride,
by knowledge of the Father's love
in Jesus crucified.
And grant us faith to know
the glory of that sign,
and in our very lives to show
the marks of love divine.

3. Come with the gift to heal
the wounds of guilt and fear,
and to oppression's face reveal
the kingdom drawing near.
Where chaos longs to reign,
descend, O holy Dove,
and free us all to work again
the miracles of love.

4. Spirit of truth, arise;
inspire the prophet's voice:
expose to scorn the tyrant's lies,
and bid the poor rejoice.
O Spirit, clear our sight,
all prejudice remove,
and help us to discern the right,
and covet only love.

5. Give us the tongues to speak,
in ev'ry time and place,
to rich and poor, to strong and weak,
the word of love and grace.
Enable us to hear
the words that others bring,
interpreting with open ear
the special song they sing.

6. Come, Holy Spirit, dance
within our hearts today,
our earthbound spirits to entrance,
our mortal fears allay.
And teach us to desire,
all other things above,
that self-consuming holy fire,
the perfect gift of love!

Text: Michael Forster (b.1946)
Music: Colin Mawby (b.1936)

212 Come, let us raise a joyful song

Refrain

Come, let us raise a joy-ful song to the Lord, a shout of tri-umph!

Come, let us raise a joy-ful song to the Lord, and give him thanks!

verses 1-4   *Last time* Fine

1. The furth-est pla-ces on the earth are in his hands. He made them, and we sing his praise.

2. The seas and waters on the earth
   are in his hands.
   He made them, and we sing his praise.

3. The hills and valleys on the earth
   are in his hands.
   He made them, and we sing his praise.

4. All living creatures on the earth
   are in his hands.
   He made them, and we sing his praise.

5. And we his people on the earth
   are in his hands.
   He saved us, and we sing his praise.

Text: Mike Anderson (b.1956) based on Psalm 95
Music: Mike Anderson (b.1956) arr. Andrew Moore

LITURGICAL

HYMNS OLD & NEW

213 Come, Lord Jesus
Advent song

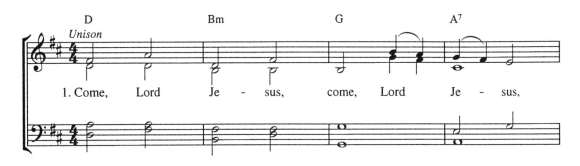

1. Come, Lord Je - sus, come, Lord Je - sus,

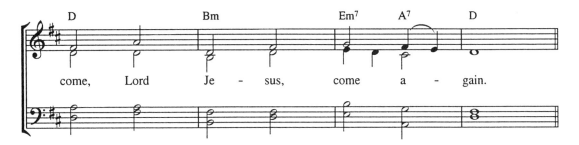

come, Lord Je - sus, come a - gain.

Refrain

Come, Lord Je - sus, come a - gain.

2. Born of Mary, *(x3)*
   come again.

3. Slain to save us, *(x3)*
   come again.

4. Raised to new life, *(x3)*
   come again.

5. At God's right hand, *(x3)*
   come again.

6. Send your Spirit, *(x3)*
   come again.

7. Come in glory, *(x3)*
   come again.

Text: Damian Lundy (1944-1997)
Music: Damian Lundy (1944-1997) arr. Andrew Moore

214 Come, Lord Jesus, come

2. Come, Lord Jesus, come.
   Come, take my eyes,
   may they shine with joy.
   Take them for your service, Lord.
   Take them for your glory, Lord.
   Come, Lord Jesus, come.
   Come, Lord Jesus, take my eyes.

3. Come, Lord Jesus, come.
   Come, take my lips,
   may they speak your truth.
   Take them for your service, Lord.
   Take them for your glory, Lord.
   Come, Lord Jesus, come.
   Come, Lord Jesus, take my lips.

4. Come, Lord Jesus, come.
   Come, take my feet,
   may they walk your path.
   Take them for your service, Lord.
   Take them for your glory, Lord.
   Come, Lord Jesus, come.
   Come, Lord Jesus, take my feet.

5. Come, Lord Jesus, come.
   Come, take my heart,
   fill it with your love.
   Take it for your service, Lord.
   Take it for your glory, Lord.
   Come, Lord Jesus, come.
   Come, Lord Jesus, take my heart.

6. Come, Lord Jesus, come.
   Come, take my life,
   take it for your own.
   Take it for your service, Lord.
   Take it for your glory, Lord.
   Come, Lord Jesus, come.
   Come, Lord Jesus, take my life.

A lower setting

Text: Kevin Mayhew (b.1942)
Music: Kevin Mayhew (b.1942) arr. Andrew Moore

215 Come, my Way, my Truth, my Life

THE CALL 77 77

1. Come, my Way, my Truth, my Life: such a

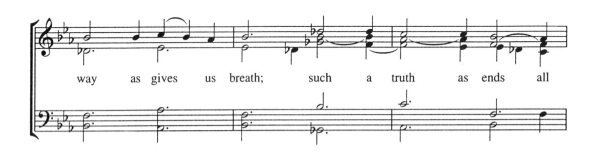

way as gives us breath; such a truth as ends all

strife; such a life as kill - eth death.

2. Come, my Light, my Feast, my Strength:
   such a light as shows a feast;
   such a feast as mends in length;
   such a strength as makes his guest.

3. Come, my Joy, my Love, my Heart:
   such a joy as none can move;
   such a love as none can part;
   such a heart as joys in love.

Text: George Herbert (1593-1633)
Music: Ralph Vaughan Williams (1872-1958), adapted by E.H. Green
Music: © Copyright 1911 Stainer & Bell Ltd, P.O. Box 110, Victoria House,
23 Gruneisen Road, Finchley, London N3 1DZ. Used by permission.

216 Come, O divine Messiah!

VENEZ, DIVIN MESSIE 78 76 and Refrain

1. Come, O divine Messiah! The world in silence waits the day when
hope shall sing its triumph, and sadness flee away.

Refrain

Sweet Saviour, haste: come, come to earth: dispel the night, and show thy face, and bid us
hail the dawn of grace. Come, O divine Messiah! The world in silence
waits the day when hope shall sing its triumph, and sadness flee away.

2. O thou, whom nations sighed for,
whom priests and prophets long foretold,
wilt break the captive fetters,
redeem the long-lost fold.

3. Shalt come in peace and meekness,
and lowly will thy cradle be:
all clothed in human weakness
shall we thy Godhead see.

Text: Sister Mary of St. Philip
Music: French traditional carol, arr. Andrew Moore
This arrangement © Copyright 1999 Kevin Mayhew Ltd.

217 Come, O God of all the earth
Sing out, earth and skies

1. Come, O God of all the earth: Come to us, O right-eous one; come, and bring our love to birth: in the glo-ry of your Son.

Sing out, earth and skies! Sing of the God who loves you! Raise your joy-ful cries! Dance to the life a-round you!

2. Come, O God of wind and flame:
   fill the earth with righteousness;
   teach us all to sing your name:
   may our lives your love confess.

3. Come, O God of flashing light:
   twinkling star and burning sun;
   God of day and God of night:
   in your light we all are one.

4. Come, O God of snow and rain:
   shower down upon the earth;
   come, O God of joy and pain:
   God of sorrow, God of mirth.

5. Come, O justice, come, O peace:
   come and shape our hearts anew;
   come and make oppression cease:
   bring us all to life to you.

Text: Marty Haugen (b.1950)
Music: Marty Haugen (b.1950) arr. Andrew Moore

218 Come, O long-expected Jesus

CROSS OF JESUS 87 87

1. Come, O long-ex-pec-ted Je-sus, born to set your peo-ple free;
from our fears and sins re-lease us; free us from cap - ti-vi-ty.

2. Israel's strength and consolation,
you the hope of all the earth,
dear desire of ev'ry nation,
come, and save us by your birth!

3. Born your people to deliver;
born a child and yet a King!
Born to reign in us for ever,
now your gracious kingdom bring.

4. By your own eternal Spirit
rule in all our hearts alone;
by your all-sufficient merit
raise us to your glorious throne.

Text: Charles Wesley (1701-1788) based on Haggai 2:7, alt. the editors.
Music: John Stainer (1840-1901)

219 Come on and celebrate

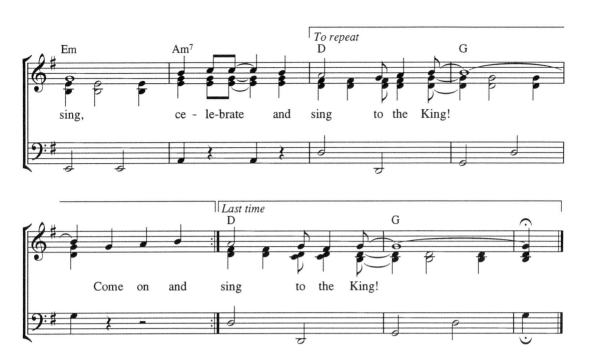

To repeat

sing, ce-le-brate and sing to the King!

Last time

Come on and sing to the King!

Words and Music: Patricia Morgan and Dave Bankhead

LITURGICAL

HYMNS OLD & NEW

220 Come, praise the Lord

LOBE DEN HERREN 14 14 4 7 8

1. Come, praise the Lord, the al - migh - ty, the King of all na - tions! Tell forth his fame, O ye peo - ples, with loud ac - cla - ma - tions! His love is sure; faith - ful his word shall en - dure, stead - fast through all ge - ne - ra - tions!

2. Praise to the Father most gracious,
   the Lord of creation!
   Praise to his Son, the Redeemer,
   who wrought our salvation!
   O heav'nly Dove,
   praise to thee, fruit of their love,
   giver of all consolation!

Text: Psalm 116 versified by James Quinn (b.1919)
Music: melody from 'Praxis Pietatis Melica' (1668)

221 Come, prepare the way
Song of the Advent Prophets

Come, pre - pare the way of the Lord!

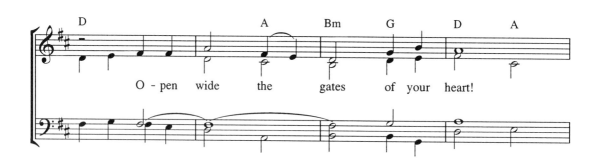

O - pen wide the gates of your heart!

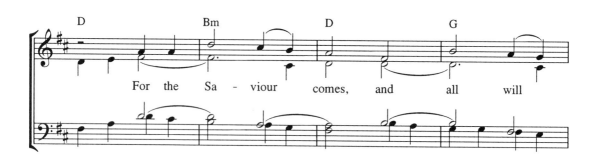

For the Sa - viour comes, and all will

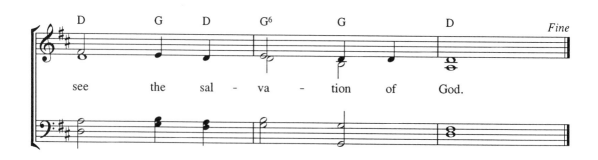

see the sal - va - tion of God.

1. Cast off the rags that speak of sad - ness! God means to crown you with his glad - ness! Wear his in - te - gri - ty with pride, God him-self casts sor - row a - side!

2. Tell the faint-hearted, tell the fearful,
   no need to worry, God will save you!
   God comes, salvation in his hand,
   leads you to the new Promised Land!

3. See them laid low, the hills and mountains.
   Valleys are filled, becoming great plains.
   We are no longer left to roam,
   God himself will shepherd us home.

4. Those who were blind now see God's glory,
   those who were deaf now hear God's story.
   Those who were hungry eat their fill,
   those once lame now cannot keep still!

5. Fresh water irrigates the dry land,
   flowers now grow in what was dead sand.
   Earth now lies ready for the grain,
   earth is ripe for planting the vine!

Text: Joseph Gelineau (b.1920) and Robert B. Kelly (b.1948) based on Isaiah 35 and 40 and Baruch 5
Music: Joseph Gelineau (b.1920)

LITURGICAL

HYMNS OLD & NEW

222 Come to me

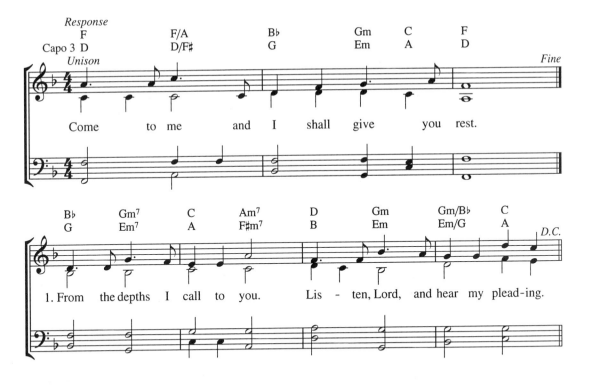

Come to me and I shall give you rest.

1. From the depths I call to you. Lis - ten, Lord, and hear my plead-ing.

2. Love and mercy flow from you,
   Lord of life and kind Redeemer.

3. In the dark I hope for you,
   you are light of new day dawning.

4. Weak and frail we come to you,
   God of love and new beginning.

Text: Noel Donnelly (b.1932) based on Psalm 129
Music: Noel Donnelly (b.1932)

223 Come to me, all who labour

Come to me, all who la-bour and are hea-vy bur - dened, and I shall give you rest. Take up my yoke and learn from me, for I am meek and hum - ble of heart. And you'll find rest for your souls. Yes, my yoke is ea - sy and my

Text: Gregory Norbert based on Psalm 22 and Matthew 11:8-30
Music: Gregory Norbert arr. Andrew Moore

224 Come to me, come, my people
Be humble of heart

1. Come to me, come, my people; learn from me, be humble of heart.

2. I your Lord, I your master;
   learn from me, be humble of heart.

3. Follow me to my Father;
   learn from me, be humble of heart.

4. In my death, in my rising;
   learn from me, be humble of heart.

5. Be transformed by my Spirit;
   learn from me, be humble of heart.

6. Glory be to my Father;
   learn from me, be humble of heart.

Alternative accompaniment

Text: Gerard Markland (b.1953)
Music: Gerard Markland (b.1953) arr. Keith Stent

225 Come to the table of the Lord

Refrain
Unison

Come to the ta - ble of the Lord, sin-ners by faith and grace re-stored;

taste here what earth can - not af-ford, al-le-lu - ia!

1. How I re-joiced when Je - sus said, 'Come to my ta - ble,

share my bread, where souls and bod - ies both are fed.'

2. 'This is my body, giv'n to be
   broken for you eternally:
   do this when you remember me.'

3. This is my lifeblood, flowing free,
   shed for the world eternally:
   do this when you remember me.'

Text: Michael Forster (b.1946)
Music: Refrain – G.P. da Palestrina (c.1525-1594)
Verses – Jean Paul Lécot (b.1947)
Text © Copyright 1999 Kevin Mayhew Ltd.
Music (verse) © Copyright Jean-Paul Lécot, 'Espélugues', 1 Ave Mgr. Théas, 65100 Lourdes, France. Used by permission.

226 Come, ye thankful people, come

SAINT GEORGE'S WINDSOR 77 77 D

1. Come, ye thank-ful peo-ple, come, raise the song of har-vest-home! All is safe-ly ga-thered in, ere the win-ter storms be-gin; God, our ma-ker, doth pro-vide for our wants to be sup-plied; come to God's own tem-ple, come; raise the song of har-vest-home!

2. We ourselves are God's own field,
fruit unto his praise to yield;
wheat and tares together sown,
unto joy or sorrow grown;
first the blade and then the ear,
then the full corn shall appear:
grant, O harvest Lord, that we
wholesome grain and pure may be.

3. For the Lord our God shall come,
and shall take his harvest home,
from his field shall purge away
all that doth offend, that day;
give his angels charge at last
in the fire the tares to cast,
but the fruitful ears to store
in his garner evermore.

4. Then, thou Church triumphant, come,
raise the song of harvest-home;
all be safely gathered in,
free from sorrow, free from sin,
there for ever purified
in God's garner to abide:
come, ten thousand angels, come,
raise the glorious harvest-home!

Text: Henry Alford (1810-1871) alt.
Music: George Job Elvey (1816-1893)

227 Comfort, comfort my people

Refrain

'Comfort, comfort my people,' says the Lord, your God. 'Cry out loud to Jerusalem, God has pardoned you!' 1. Ev-'ry valley shall be filled, ev-'ry mount and hill made low.

2. In the desert make a path
   for the Lord Emmanuel.

3. For the glory of the Lord
   soon shall be revealed to me.

Text: Anthony D'Souza (b.1950) based on Isaiah 40
Music: Anthony D'Souza (b.1950) arr. Aniceto Nazareth
© Copyright 1984 Kevin Mayhew Ltd.

LITURGICAL

HYMNS OLD & NEW

228 Creator of the day

GLORIA CHRISTI 88 88 and Refrain

1. Cre - a - tor of the day and night, who turned the dark - ness in - to light and changed us to pro - claim the Word, whom we have touched and seen and heard. The glo - ry that you gave the Son, he gives to us, to make us one.

2. Your kingdom in a mystery,
   began with twelve in Galilee,
   through whom the Son would teach and cure;
   whose fruit would ripen and endure.

3. At Pentecost, with wind and flame,
   you sent the Spirit in his name,
   to make the Church a present Christ;
   anointed Prophet, King and Priest.

4. And when your purpose is complete,
   the Son of Man will take his seat;
   and Christ will be identified
   with these, the least, for whom he died.

Text: Michael Hodgetts (b.1936)
Music: Seóirse Bodley

229 Crown him with many crowns

TUNE 1: CORONA DSM

1. Crown him with ma-ny crowns, the Lamb up-on his throne; hark, how the heav'n-ly an-them drowns all mu-sic but its own: a-wake, my soul, and sing of him who died for thee, and hail him as thy match-less King through all e-ter-ni-ty.

2. Crown him the Virgin's Son,
   the God incarnate born,
   whose arm those crimson trophies won
   which now his brow adorn;
   fruit of the mystic Rose,
   as of that Rose the Stem,
   the Root, whence mercy ever flows,
   the Babe of Bethlehem.

3. Crown him the Lord of love;
   behold his hands and side,
   rich wounds, yet visible above,
   in beauty glorified:
   no angel in the sky
   can fully bear that sight,
   but downward bends each burning eye
   at mysteries so bright.

4. Crown him the Lord of peace,
   whose pow'r a sceptre sways
   from pole to pole, that wars may cease,
   absorbed in prayer and praise:
   his reign shall know no end,
   and round his piercèd feet
   fair flow'rs of paradise extend
   their fragrance ever sweet.

5. Crown him the Lord of years,
   the Potentate of time,
   Creator of the rolling spheres,
   ineffably sublime.
   All hail, Redeemer, hail!
   for thou hast died for me;
   thy praise shall never, never fail
   throughout eternity.

TUNE 2: DIADEMATA DSM

1. Crown him with ma-ny crowns, the Lamb up-on his throne, hark, how the heav'n-ly an-them drowns all mu-sic but its own: a-wake, my soul, and sing of him who died for thee, and hail him as thy match-less King through all e-ter-ni-ty.

A higher setting will be found at No. 292

Text: Matthew Bridges (1800-1894)
Music: Tune 1 – Richard Runciman Terry (1865-1938)
Tune 2 – George Job Elvey (1816-1893)

230 Daily, daily, sing to Mary

TUNE 1: DAILY, DAILY 87 87 D

1. Dai-ly, dai-ly, sing to Ma-ry, sing, my soul, her prai-ses due; all her
feasts, her ac-tions wor-ship, with her heart's de-vo-tion true. Lost in
wond-'ring con-tem-pla-tion be her ma-jes-ty con-fessed: call her
mo-ther, call her vir-gin, hap-py mo-ther, vir-gin blest.

2. She is mighty to deliver;
   call her, trust her lovingly.
   When the tempest rages round thee,
   she will calm the troubled sea.
   Gifts of heaven she has given,
   noble lady, to our race:
   she, the queen, who decks her subjects,
   with the light of God's own grace.

3. Sing, my tongue, the virgin's trophies,
   who for us her Maker bore;
   for the curse of old inflicted,
   peace and blessings to restore.
   Sing in songs of praise unending,
   sing the world's majestic queen;
   weary not, nor faint in telling
   all the gifts she gives to men.

4. All my senses, heart, affections,
   strive to sound her glory forth;
   spread abroad, the sweet memorials,
   of the virgin's priceless worth.
   Where the voice of music thrilling,
   where the tongues of eloquence,
   that can utter hymns beseeming
   all her matchless excellence?

5. All our joys do flow from Mary,
   all then join her praise to sing;
   trembling, sing the virgin mother,
   mother of our Lord and King,
   while we sing her awful glory,
   far above our fancy's reach,
   let our hearts be quick to offer
   love the heart alone can teach.

TUNE 2: LAUDES MARIAE   87 87 D

1. Dai - ly, dai - ly, sing to Ma - ry, sing, my soul, her prai - ses due;
all her feasts, her ac - tions wor - ship, with her heart's de - vo - tion true.
Lost in wond-'ring con - tem-pla - tion be her ma - jes - ty con-fessed:
call her mo-ther, call her vir - gin, hap - py mo-ther, vir - gin blest.

See over for Tune 3: Omni die dic Mariae

TUNE 3: OMNI DIE DIC MARIAE 87 87 D

1. Dai - ly, dai - ly, sing to Ma - ry, sing, my soul, her prai - ses due;

all her feasts, her ac - tions wor - ship, with her heart's de - vo - tion true.

Lost in wond-'ring con - tem - pla - tion be her ma - jes - ty con - fessed:

call her mo - ther, call her vir - gin, hap - py mo - ther, vir - gin blest.

2. She is mighty to deliver;
   call her, trust her lovingly.
   When the tempest rages round thee,
   she will calm the troubled sea.
   Gifts of heaven she has given,
   noble lady, to our race:
   she, the queen, who decks her subjects,
   with the light of God's own grace.

3. Sing, my tongue, the virgin's trophies,
   who for us her Maker bore;
   for the curse of old inflicted,
   peace and blessings to restore.
   Sing in songs of praise unending,
   sing the glorious queen of earth;
   weary not, nor faint in telling
   of the hope she brings to birth.

4. All my senses, heart, affections,
   strive to sound her glory forth;
   spread abroad, the sweet memorials,
   of the virgin's priceless worth.
   Where the voice of music thrilling,
   where the tongues of eloquence,
   that can utter hymns beseeming
   all her matchless excellence?

5. All our joys do flow from Mary,
   all then join her praise to sing;
   trembling, sing the virgin mother,
   mother of our Lord and King,
   while we sing her awful glory,
   far above our fancy's reach,
   let our hearts be quick to offer
   love the heart alone can teach.

Text: 'Omni die dic Mariae', ascribed to St. Bernard of Cluny (12th century)
trans. Henry Bittleston (1818 - 1886)
Music: Tune 1 – from the 'Paderborn Gesangbuch' (1765)
Tune 2 – Henri Friedrich Hémy (1818-1888)
Tune 3 – German melody

231 Dance in your Spirit

1. Je - sus, you showed us the way to live, and your Spi-rit sets us free, free now to sing, free to dance and shout, 'Glo - ry, glo - ry' to your name.

2. Jesus, you opened your arms for us,
   but we nailed them to a cross;
   but you are risen and now we live,
   free from, free from ev'ry fear.

3. Your Spirit brings peace and gentleness,
   kindness, self-control and love,
   patience and goodness and faith and joy,
   Spirit, Spirit fill us now.

Text and Music: Mike Anderson (b.1956)

232 Day is done, but love unfailing

AR HYD Y NOS 84 84 88 84

1. Day is done, but love un-fail-ing dwells e - ver here;
sha - dows fall, but hope pre-vail - ing calms ev - 'ry fear.
Lov-ing Fa - ther, none for-sak - ing, take our hearts, of love's own mak-ing,
watch our sleep - ing, guard our wak - ing, be al - ways near!

A lower setting will be found at No. 233 (opposite)

2. Dark descends, but light unending
shines through our night;
you are with us, ever lending
new strength to sight;
one in love, your truth confessing,
one in hope of heaven's blessing,
may we see, in love's possessing,
love's endless light!

3. Eyes will close, but you, unsleeping,
watch by our side;
death may come; in love's safe keeping
still we abide.
God of love, all evil quelling,
sin forgiving, fear dispelling,
stay with us, our hearts indwelling,
this eventide!

Text: James Quinn (b.1919)
Music: traditional Welsh melody arr. Colin Hand

233 Day of wrath and day of wonder

AR HYD Y NOS 84 84 88 84

1. Day of wrath and day of won - der, whence hope has fled!

See the bo - dy torn a - sun - der, blood free - ly shed.

Stripped of ma - jes - ty we saw him, hu - man sight re - coiled be - fore him,

yet it was our sor - rows tore him; for us he bled.

A higher setting will be found at No. 232 (opposite)

2. Day of hope and day of glory,
   though unperceived!
   See redemption's dreadful story,
   long, long conceived.
   Evil pow'rs, in downfall lying,
   knowing death itself is dying,
   hear the voice triumphant crying,
   'All is achieved!'

3. Day of majesty and splendour,
   here ends the race!
   Christ, our Priest, our soul's defender,
   us will embrace.
   He who walked this earth before us,
   tried and tempted, yet victorious,
   calls us to the kingdom glorious,
   O perfect grace!

Text: Michael Forster (b.1946)
Music: traditional Welsh melody arr. Colin Hand
Text and this arrangement © Copyright 1993 Kevin Mayhew Ltd.

234 Dear Lord and Father of mankind

REPTON 86 88 6

1. Dear Lord and Father of mankind, forgive our foolish ways! Reclothe us in our rightful mind, in purer lives thy service find, in deeper rev-'rence praise, in deeper rev-'rence praise.

2. In simple trust like theirs who heard,
   beside the Syrian sea,
   the gracious calling of the Lord,
   let us, like them, without a word,
   rise up and follow thee,
   rise up and follow thee.

3. O Sabbath rest by Galilee!
   O calm of hills above,
   where Jesus knelt to share with thee
   the silence of eternity,
   interpreted by love!
   Interpreted by love!

4. Drop thy still dews of quietness,
   till all our strivings cease;
   take from our souls the strain and stress,
   and let our ordered lives confess
   the beauty of thy peace,
   the beauty of thy peace.

5. Breathe through the heats of our desire
   thy coolness and thy balm;
   let sense be dumb, let flesh retire;
   speak through the earthquake, wind and fire,
   O still small voice of calm!
   O still small voice of calm!

Text: John Greenleaf Whittier (1807-1892)
Music: Charles Hubert Hastings Parry (1848-1918)

235 Deep calls to deep

DEEP CALLS TO DEEP 4 10 4 10 and Refrain

1. Deep calls to deep, and my soul finds no rest-ing place but him.
He is my God, the yearn-ings of my heart his touch can still. And each rare
mo - ment that I've felt his pres - ence, I shall re -
1,2. mem - ber and for-ev - er cher - ish.
3. cher - ish.

2. Deep calls to deep,
   and at his feast I am a welcome guest.
   He gives me food,
   the hunger of my soul is laid to rest.

3. Deep calls to deep,
   for he created me to be his own.
   He understands,
   the joy and pain of life he too has known.

Text and Music: Estelle White (b.1925)
© Copyright 1978 Kevin Mayhew Ltd.

236 Deep peace of the running wave to you

Deep peace of the run-ning wave to you,
deep peace of the flow-ing air to you,
deep peace of the qui-et earth to you,
deep peace of the shi-ning stars to you,
deep peace of the Son of peace to you.

Text: Fiona MacLeod (1855-1905)
Music: Robert B. Kelly (b.1948) arr. Andrew Moore

237 Deep within my heart

1. Deep with-in my heart I know Je - sus loves me, deep with-in my heart I know he loves me. Guilt and shame are con-quered in his name, and I'm a-live now. Deep with-in my heart I know he loves me.

2. Deep within my heart I know I'm forgiven,
   deep within my heart I know that I'm free.
   Free from sin, a new life to begin, and I'm alive now.
   Deep within my heart I know that I'm free.

3. Deep within my heart Jesus' love is healing,
   deep within my heart he is healing me.
   Tears like rain are flooding out the pain, and I'm alive now.
   Deep within my heart he is healing me.

Text: Mike Anderson (b. 1956)
Music: Mike Anderson (b.1956) arr. Keith Stent

238 Ding dong, merrily on high

BRANSLE DE L'OFFICIAL 77 77 and Refrain

1. Ding dong, mer-ri-ly on high! In heav'n the bells are ring - ing;

ding dong, ve-ri-ly the sky is riv'n with an-gels sing - ing.

Glo - - - -

- - ri - a, ho - san - na in ex - cel - sis!

An easier setting of the Refrain
Refrain
Unison

Glo - - - -

- - ri - a, ho - san - na in ex - cel - sis!

2. E'en so here below, below,
   let steeple bells be swungen,
   and io, io, io,
   by priest and people sungen.

3. Pray you, dutifully prime
   your matin chime, ye ringers;
   may you beautifully rhyme
   your evetime song, ye singers.

Text: George Ratcliffe Woodward (1848-1934)
Music: traditional French melody arr. Charles Wood (1866-1926)
Alternative Refrain arr. Colin Hand

239 Dona nobis pacem

This may be sung as a round, the voices entering as indicated

Translation: Give us peace

Text: Traditional

Music: Unknown arr. Keith Stent

240 Do not be afraid

Refrain

Do not be a-fraid, for I have re-deemed you.

I have called you by your name; you are

mine.

1. When you walk through the wa-ters, I'll be
with you. You will ne-ver sink be-neath the waves.

2. When the fire is burning all around you,
   you will never be consumed by the flames.

3. When the fear of loneliness is looming,
   then remember I am at your side.

4. When you dwell in the exile of the stranger,
   remember you are precious in my eyes.

5. You are mine, O my child, I am your Father,
   and I love you with a perfect love.

Text: Gerard Markland (b.1953) based on Isaiah 43:1-4
Music: Gerard Markland arr. Andrew Moore
© Copyright 1978 Kevin Mayhew Ltd.

241 Dying you destroyed our death
Song of farewell

Dy-ing you de-stroyed our death; ris-ing you re-stored our life.

Lord Je-sus, Lord Je-sus, come in glo-ry!

1. May Christ who died for you lead you in-to his king-dom;

2. May Christ, the Good Shep-herd, lead you home to-day,

* 2. May Christ, the Good Shep-herd, take you on his shoul-ders

3. May the an-gels lead you in-to Pa-ra-dise; may the mar-tyrs come to wel-come you and

4. May the choirs of an-gels come to meet you, may the choirs of an-gels come to meet you where

* 4. May the choirs of an-gels come to meet you, may the choirs of an-gels come to meet you;

*Alternative children's verses

(1) may Christ who died for you lead you this day in-to Par-a-dise.

(2) and give you a place with-in his flock.

(*2) and bring you home, bring you home to-day.

(3) take you to the Ho-ly Ci-ty, the new and e-ter-nal Je-ru-sa-lem.

(4) Laz-a-rus is poor no long-er, may you have e-ter-nal life in Christ.

(*4) and with all God's chil-dren may you have e-ter-nal life in Christ.

Text: Michael Marchal
Music: Michael Joncas (b.1951) arr. Keith Stent

242 Enter in the wilderness

Refrain

Enter in the wilderness, the Lord is coming, in the desert make the highway straight. Ev'ry valley shall be lifted up before him, ev'ry mountain levelled at his feet.

1. God comes, run out to meet him; God comes, hurry to greet him; God comes, try to be ready, for the King is on his way. So,

2. Christ comes, now we will heed him;
Christ comes, all of us need him;
Christ comes, hope of the nations,
Son of justice, Prince of Peace. So,

3. Look up, bonds cut asunder;
look up, waiting in wonder;
look up, soon you will see him,
Christ the Lord is on his way. So,

Text: Willard F. Jabusch (b.1930)
Music: Hasidic melody arr. Andrew Moore

243 Eternal Father, strong to save

MELITA 88 88 88

1. E - ter - nal Fa - ther, strong to save, whose arm doth bind the rest - less wave, who
bidd'st the migh - ty o - cean deep its own ap - poin - ted lim - its keep: O
hear us when we cry to thee for those in per - il on the sea.

2. O Saviour, whose almighty word
   the winds and waves submissive heard,
   who walkedst on the foaming deep,
   and calm, amid its rage, didst sleep:
   O hear us when we cry to thee
   for those in peril on the sea.

3. O sacred Spirit, who didst brood
   upon the waters dark and rude,
   and bid their angry tumult cease,
   and give, for wild confusion, peace:
   O hear us when we cry to thee
   for those in peril on the sea.

4. O Trinity of love and pow'r,
   our brethren shield in danger's hour.
   From rock and tempest, fire and foe,
   protect them whereso'er they go,
   and ever let there rise to thee
   glad hymns of praise from land and sea.

Text: William Whiting (1825-1878) alt.
Music: John Bacchus Dykes (1823-1876)

244 Faithful Cross

BLAENWERN 87 87 D

1. Faith-ful Cross, sus-tain your bur-den, do not splin-ter, do not crack, though the load of all our sor-rows hangs, a dead-weight on your back; up-right on the hill of sad-ness in the gale of ev-il's pow'r, hold him strong-ly, hold him gent-ly at his co-ve-nan-ted hour.

2. Nameless in the forest mounting,
shoot and sapling, branch and tree,
felled, dismembered, planed and jointed
for this day's dark mystery.
Gibbet, infamous, ennobled
by this death and by this birth,
hold your cross-grained branches open
harbour for a shipwrecked earth.

3. When, the noontide darkness ending,
he whom you have borne is dead,
in his mother's arms laid gently
you are left untenanted:
sharp against the soul's horizon
still uphold us, shining tree,
emblem of the Saviour's passion
standard of his victory.

Text: Kevin Nichols (b.1929) based on 'Crux fidelis'
Music: William Penfro Rowlands (1860-1937)

245 Faith in God

Refrain

Faith in God can move the moun-tains, trust in him can calm the sea.

He's my for-tress, he's my strong-hold, he's the rock who res-cues me.

1. Lord, you are my ref - uge, ne - ver let me be a-shamed.

In your jus-tice res - cue me, turn to me and hear my prayer.

The guitar and keyboard parts should not be played together

2. You are my salvation,
   from oppression set me free.
   Ever since my childhood,
   you have been my only hope.

3. Bitter troubles burden me,
   but you fill me with new life.
   From the grave you raise me up,
   so my tongue will sing your praise.

Text: Aniceto Nazareth, based on Psalm 61
Music: Aniceto Nazareth
© Copyright 1984 Kevin Mayhew Ltd.

246 Faith of our fathers

SAWSTON LM and Refrain

1. Faith of our fa - thers, liv - ing still in spite of dun-geon, fire and sword; O, how our hearts beat high with joy when - e'er we hear that glo-rious word! Faith of our fa - thers! Ho - ly Faith! We will be true to thee till death, we will be true to thee till death.

2. Our fathers, chained in prisons dark,
were still in heart and conscience free;
how sweet would be their children's fate,
if they, like them, could die for thee!

3. Faith of our fathers, Mary's prayers
shall win our country back to thee;
and through the truth that comes from God
this land shall then indeed be free.

4. Faith of our fathers, we will love
both friend and foe in all our strife,
and preach thee too, as love knows how,
by kindly words and virtuous life.

Text: Frederick William Faber (1814-1863)
Music: traditional melody from 'Crown of Jesus' hymnal (1864)

247 Father and life-giver

PRINCETHORPE 65 65 D

1. Father and life-giver, grace of Christ impart;
he, the Word incarnate, food for mind and heart.
Children of the promise, homage now we pay;
sacrificial banquet cheers the desert way.

A higher setting will be found at No. 392

2. Wine and bread the symbols, love and life convey,
offered by your people, work and joy portray.
All we own consigning, nothing is retained;
tokens of our service, gifts and song contain.

3. Transformation wondrous, water into wine;
mingled in the Godhead we are made divine.
Birth into his body brought us life anew,
total consecration, fruit from grafting true.

4. Christ, the head, and members living now as one,
offered to the Father by his holy Son;
and our adoration purified we find,
through the Holy Spirit breathing in mankind.

Text: A. J. Newman
Music: William Pitts (1829-1903)

248 Father God, gentle Father God

2. My heart, my innermost being
   was made by you.
   My body, secretly formed in the womb,
   was always with you.

3. What place, what heavens could
   hide me away from you?
   Were I to fly to the ends of the sea,
   your hand would guide me.

4. Your works, your knowledge, your love
   are beyond my mind.
   My Lord, I thank you for these
   and the wonder of my being.

5. O Lord, come search me, come find
   what is in my heart;
   that I may never stray far
   from your path of life eternal.

Text: Gerard Markland (b.1953) based on Psalm 138
Music: Gerard Markland (b.1953)

LITURGICAL

HYMNS OLD & NEW

249 Father God, I wonder
I will sing your praises

Father God, I wonder how I managed to exist without the knowledge of your parenthood and your loving care. But now I am your child, I am adopted in your family and I can never be alone, 'cause, Father God, you're there beside me.

I will sing your praises, I will sing your praises, I will sing your praises, for evermore. for evermore.

Text and Music: Ian Smale
© Copyright 1984 Kingsway's Thankyou Music, P.O. Box 75, Eastbourne,
East Sussex BN23 6NW, UK. Used by permission.

250 Father, in my life I see
Trinity Song

Effective when men's voices sing one line, and women's the other

2. Jesus, in my life I see
   you are God who walks with me.
   You hold my life in your hands;
   close beside you I will stand.
   I give all my life to you:
   help me, Jesus, to be true.

3. Spirit, in my life I see
   you are God who walks with me.
   You hold my life in your hands;
   close beside you I will stand.
   I give all my life to you:
   help me, Spirit, to be true.

Text: Frank Andersen
Music: Frank Andersen arr. Keith Stent

251 Father, I place into your hands

Gently

Capo 1 E

Unison

1. Fa-ther, I place in - to your hands the things I can - not do.

Fa-ther, I place in - to your hands the things that I've been

through. Fa-ther, I place in - to your hands the way that I should

go, for I know I al - ways can trust you.

2. Father, I place into your hands
my friends and family.
Father, I place into your hands
the things that trouble me.
Father, I place into your hands
the person I would be,
for I know I always can trust you.

3. Father, we love to see your face,
we love to hear your voice.
Father, we love to sing your praise
and in your name rejoice.
Father, we love to walk with you
and in your presence rest,
for we know we always can trust you.

4. Father, I want to be with you
and do the things you do.
Father, I want to speak the words
that you are speaking too.
Father, I want to love the ones
that you will draw to you,
for I know that I am one with you.

Text and Music: Jenny Hewer (b.1945)

252 Father, we adore you

This may be sung in unison as a round, with entries at A, B and C

1. Fa - ther, we a - dore you, lay our lives be -

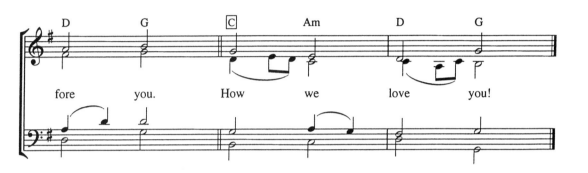

fore you. How we love you!

2. Jesus, we adore you,
   lay our lives before you.
   How we love you!

3. Spirit, we adore you,
   lay our lives before you.
   How we love you!

Text: Terrye Coelho (b.1952)
Music: Terrye Coelho (b.1952) arr. Colin Hand
© Copyright 1972 Maranatha! Music. Administered by CopyCare, P.O. Box 77, Hailsham,
East Sussex BN27 3EF, UK. Used by permission.

253 Father, we come to you

Strong, steady rhythm

bound us in love and peace: God in the midst of us, ho-ly, un-seen.

All
Bles-sed is he who comes, pierc-ing our night of sin. O-pen your

hearts to him. Great is his name. Bread of life shared with us,

Cantor

bo-dy of Christ the Lord, bro-ken and died for us: life for the world.

poco rall.

Text and Music: James Walsh

255 Fight the good fight

DUKE STREET LM

1. Fight the good fight with all thy might; Christ is thy strength, and Christ thy right; lay hold on life, and it shall be thy joy and crown e - ter - nal - ly.

2. Run the straight race through God's good grace,
   lift up thine eyes and seek his face;
   life with its way before us lies;
   Christ is the path, and Christ the prize.

3. Cast care aside, lean on thy guide;
   his boundless mercy will provide;
   trust, and thy trusting soul shall prove
   Christ is its life, and Christ its love.

4. Faint not nor fear, his arms are near;
   he changeth not, and thou art dear;
   only believe, and thou shalt see
   that Christ is all in all to thee.

Text: John Samuel Bewley Monsell (1811-1875) alt.
Music: melody attributed to John Hatton (d.1793)

256 Fill my house

1. Fill my house un-to the full - est, eat my bread and drink my wine. The love I bear is held from no one. All I own and all I

do   I   give   to   you.

2. Take my time unto the fullest,
   find in me the trust you seek,
   and take my hands to you outreaching.

3. Christ our Lord with love enormous
   from the cross his lesson taught:
   'Show love to all, as I have loved you.'

4. Join with me as one in Christ-love,
   may our hearts all beat as one,
   and may we give ourselves completely.

Text: Peter Kearney
Music: Peter Kearney arr. Keith Stent

257 Fill your hearts with joy and gladness

ODE TO JOY 87 87 D

1. Fill your hearts with joy and glad-ness, sing and praise your God and mine!
Great the Lord in love and wis-dom, might and ma-jes-ty di-vine!
He who framed the star-ry hea-vens knows and names them as they shine.
Fill your hearts with joy and glad-ness, sing and praise your God and mine!

2. Praise the Lord, his people, praise him!
Wounded souls his comfort know.
Those who fear him find his mercies,
peace for pain and joy for woe;
humble hearts are high exalted,
human pride and pow'r laid low.
Praise the Lord, his people, praise him!
Wounded souls his comfort know.

3. Praise the Lord for times and seasons,
cloud and sunshine, wind and rain;
spring to melt the snows of winter
till the waters flow again;
grass upon the mountain pastures,
golden valleys thick with grain.
Praise the Lord for times and seasons,
cloud and sunshine, wind and rain.

4. Fill your hearts with joy and gladness,
peace and plenty crown your days!
Love his laws, declare his judgements,
walk in all his words and ways;
he the Lord and we his children,
praise the Lord, all people, praise!
Fill your hearts with joy and gladness,
peace and plenty crown your days!

Text: Timothy Dudley-Smith (b.1926)
Music: Ludwig van Beethoven (1770-1827) arr. Christopher Tambling

258 Firmly I believe

OMNI DIE 87 87

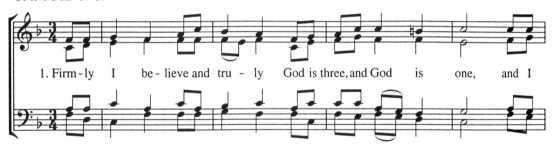

1. Firm-ly I be-lieve and tru-ly God is three, and God is one, and I

next ac-know-ledge du-ly man-hood ta-ken by the Son.

2. And I trust and hope most fully
   in the Saviour crucified;
   and each thought and deed unruly
   do to death, as he has died.

3. Simply to his grace and wholly
   light and life and strength belong;
   and I love supremely, solely,
   him the holy, him the strong.

4. And I hold in veneration,
   for the love of him alone,
   Holy Church, as his creation,
   and her teachings, as his own.

5. Adoration aye be given,
   with and through th'angelic host,
   to the God of earth and heaven,
   Father, Son and Holy Ghost.

Text: John Henry Newman (1801-1890) alt.
Music: from 'Corners Gesangbuch' (1631) arr. W.S. Rockstro (1823-1895)

259 Follow me

Son of Man has no place to lie down, I
do not of-fer com-fort, I do not of-fer wealth, but in
me will all hap-pi ness be found. Fol-low

2. If you would follow me,
   you must leave old ways behind.
   You must take my cross and
   follow on my path.
   You may be far from loved ones,
   you may be far from home,
   but my Father will welcome you at last.

3. Although I go away
   you will never be alone,
   for the Spirit will be
   there to comfort you.
   Though all of you may scatter,
   each follow his own path,
   still the Spirit of love will lead you home.

Text: Michael Cockett (b.1938)
Music: Sister Madeleine arr. Donald Thomson

260 For all the saints

SINE NOMINE 10 10 10 4

Unison

1. For all the saints who from their la-bours rest, who
2. Thou wast their rock, their fort-ress and their might;
3. O may thy sol - diers, faith-ful, true and bold,

thee by faith be - fore the world con - fessed, thy
thou, Lord, their cap - tain in the well-fought fight;
fight as the saints who no - bly fought of old, and

name, O Je - sus, be for e - ver blest.
thou in the dark - ness drear their one true light. Al -
win, with them, the vic-tor's crown of gold.

- le - lu - ia, al - le - lu - ia!

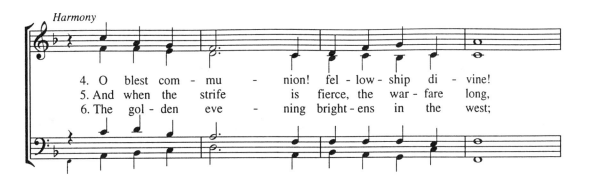

Harmony

4. O blest com - mu - nion! fel - low - ship di - vine!
5. And when the strife is fierce, the war - fare long,
6. The gol - den eve - ning bright - ens in the west;

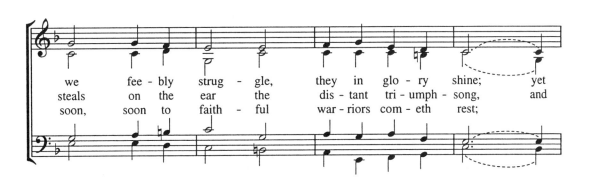

we fee - bly strug - gle, they in glo - ry shine; yet
steals on the ear the dis - tant tri - umph - song, and
soon, soon to faith - ful war - riors com - eth rest;

all are one in thee, for all are thine.
hearts are brave a - gain, and arms are strong. Al -
sweet is the calm of pa - ra - dise the blest.

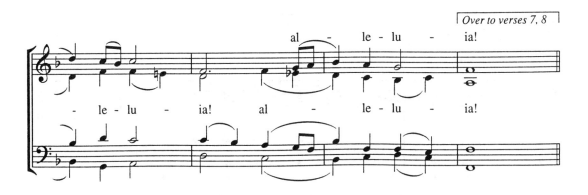

Over to verses 7, 8

al - le - lu - ia!
- le - lu - ia! al - le - lu - ia!

Text: William Walsham How (1823-1897)
Music: Ralph Vaughan Williams (1872-1958)

261 For the fruits of his creation

EAST ACKLAM 84 84 888 4

1. For the fruits of his cre - a - tion, thanks be to God;
for his gifts to ev - 'ry na - tion, thanks be to God;
for the plough-ing, sow - ing, reap-ing, si - lent growth while we are sleep-ing,
fu - ture needs in earth's safe-keep-ing, thanks be to God.

2. In the just reward of labour,
   God's will is done;
   in the help we give our neighbour,
   God's will is done;
   in our world-wide task of caring
   for the hungry and despairing,
   in the harvests we are sharing,
   God's will is done.

3. For the harvests of his Spirit,
   thanks be to God;
   for the good we all inherit,
   thanks be to God;
   for the wonders that astound us,
   for the truths that still confound us,
   most of all, that love has found us,
   thanks be to God.

Text: Fred Pratt Green (b.1903)
Music: Francis Jackson (b.1917)

262 For the healing of the nations

PICARDY 87 87 87

1. For the heal-ing of the na - tions, Lord, we pray with one ac - cord; for a just and e - qual shar - ing of the things that earth af - fords. To a life of love in act - ion help us rise and pledge our word.

2. Lead us, Father, into freedom,
from despair your world release;
that, redeemed from war and hatred,
all may come and go in peace.
Show us how through care and goodness
fear will die and hope increase.

3. All that kills abundant living,
let it from the earth be banned;
pride of status, race or schooling
dogmas that obscure your plan.
In our common quest for justice
may we hallow life's brief span.

4. You, creator-God, have written
your great name on humankind;
for our growing in your likeness
bring the life of Christ to mind;
that by our response and service
earth its destiny may find.

*Another arrangement of this tune
will be found at No. 418*

Text: Fred Kaan (b. 1929)
Music: traditional French melody arr. Richard Lloyd

263 Forth in the peace of Christ we go

SONG 34 (ANGELS' SONG) LM

1. Forth in the peace of Christ we go; Christ to the
world with joy we bring; Christ in our minds, Christ on our
lips, Christ in our hearts, the world's true King.

2. King of our hearts, Christ makes us kings;
   kingship with him his servants gain;
   with Christ, the Servant-Lord of all,
   Christ's world we serve to share Christ's reign.

3. Priests of the world, Christ sends us forth
   this world of time to consecrate,
   our world of sin by grace to heal,
   Christ's world in Christ to re-create.

4. Prophets of Christ, we hear his word:
   he claims our minds, to search his ways,
   he claims our lips, to speak his truth,
   he claims our hearts, to sing his praise.

5. We are his Church, he makes us one:
   here is one hearth for all to find,
   here is one flock, one Shepherd-King,
   here is one faith, one heart, one mind.

Text: James Quinn (b.1919)
Music: Orlando Gibbons (1583-1625)
Text © Copyright 1969 Geoffrey Chapman, an imprint of Cassell plc,
Wellington House, 125 Strand, London WC2R 0BB. Used by permission.

264 Forty days and forty nights

AUS DER TIEFE (HEINLEIN) 77 77

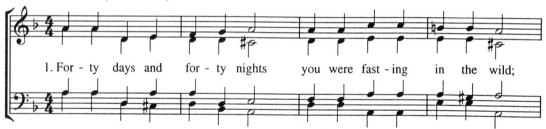

1. For - ty days and for - ty nights you were fast - ing in the wild;
for - ty days and for - ty nights, temp - ted still, yet un - be - guiled.

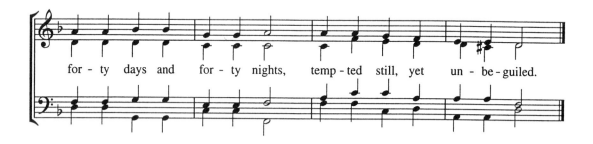

2. Sunbeams scorching all the day,
   chilly dew-drops nightly shed,
   prowling beasts about your way,
   stones your pillow, earth your bed.

3. Let us your endurance share,
   and from earthly greed abstain,
   with you vigilant in prayer,
   with you strong to suffer pain.

4. Then if evil on us press,
   flesh or spirit to assail,
   Victor in the wilderness,
   help us not to swerve or fail.

5. So shall peace divine be ours;
   holy gladness, pure and true:
   come to us, angelic powers,
   such as ministered to you.

6. Keep, O keep us, Saviour dear,
   ever constant by your side,
   that with you we may appear
   at th' eternal Eastertide.

Text: George Hunt Smyttan (1822-1870) adapted by Michael Forster (b.1946)
Music: melody from 'Nürnbergisches Gesangbuch' (1676)
This version of text © Copyright 1999 Kevin Mayhew Ltd.

265 For you my soul is thirsting

Refrain
Unison

For you my soul is thirst-ing, O Lord, for you my soul is thirst-ing, O Lord, for you my soul is thirst-ing.

Fine

1. You are my God, it is you that I seek. I am thirst-ing for you; just as a land that is wea-ry and parched, longs my bo-dy for you.

D.C.

2. Day after day I will watch in your house.
   You are glory and pow'r;
   better than life is your love for your child,
   I shall sing to your praise.

3. All my life long I will bless you, my God,
   lift my hands in your name;
   richly my soul will be feasted with love,
   I shall praise you with joy.

4. I will remember you, Lord, when I sleep.
   I will watch through the night;
   you are my help and with you I am safe
   in the shade of your wing.

Text: Susan Sayers (b.1946) based on Psalm 62
Music: Andrew Moore (b.1954)

266 Freedom for my people

2. Through the desert they were led to liberty;
   with the manna they were fed so they could be free.
   And I gave my law to them for liberty,
   so that they might live in peace and in unity.

3. Oh, when will my people know how to be free?
   All my prophets tried to show: the people would not see.
   So I gave my only Son, precious to me;
   on the cross he hung in pain for your liberty.

4. Jesus rose on Easter Day to liberty.
   He will never go away - he will set you free!
   Never will he die again! He is with me,
   and we have begun our reign with his victory!

(after vs.4 and 5) *Gloria! Alleluia!*
   Gloria! Alleluia!
   Sing of his victory! Alleluia!
   Gloria! Alleluia!
   Gloria! Alleluia!
   Set all my people free!

5. I'm your God and you are mine: now you are free!
   Eat my bread and drink my wine! Come and follow me!
   You will know my Spirit's love and you will see
   power coming from above to set all people free!

Text: Damian Lundy (1944-1997)
Music: Traditional South American melody arr. Keith Stent

267 From heaven you came
The Servant King

Worshipfully

1. From heav'n you came, help-less babe, en-tered our world, your glo - ry veiled; not to be served but to serve, and give your life that we might live. This is our God, the Ser-vant

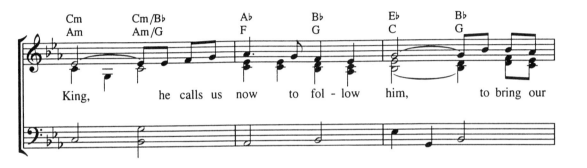

King, he calls us now to fol - low him, to bring our

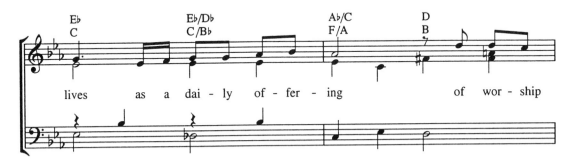

lives as a dai - ly of - fer - ing of wor - ship

to the Ser - vant King. King.

2. There in the garden of tears,
   my heavy load he chose to bear;
   his heart with sorrow was torn.
   'Yet not my will but yours,' he said.

3. Come see his hands and his feet,
   the scars that speak of sacrifice,
   hands that flung stars into space,
   to cruel nails surrendered.

4. So let us learn how to serve,
   and in our lives enthrone him;
   each other's needs to prefer,
   for it is Christ we're serving.

Text and Music: Graham Kendrick (b.1950)

268 From many grains

SONG 1 10 10 10 10 10 10 10

1. From many grains, once scattered far and wide, each one alone, to grow as best it may, now safely gathered in and unified, one single loaf we offer here today. So may your Church, in ev'ry time and place, be in this meal united by your grace.

2. From many grapes, once living on the vine,
now crushed and broken under human feet,
we offer here this single cup of wine:
the sign of love, unbroken and complete.
So may we stand among the crucified,
and live the risen life of him who died.

3. From many places gathered, we are here,
each with a gift that we alone can bring.
O Spirit of the living God, draw near,
make whole by grace our broken offering.
O crush the pride that bids us stand alone;
let flow the love that makes our spirits one.

Text: Michael Forster (b.1946) based on the Didaché
Music: Orlando Gibbons (1583-1625)

269 From the depths we cry to thee

CULBACH 77 77

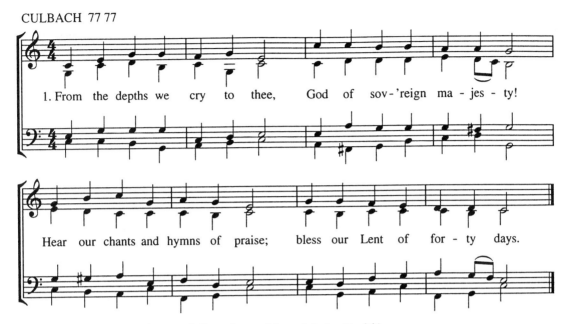

1. From the depths we cry to thee, God of sov-'reign ma-jes-ty!
Hear our chants and hymns of praise; bless our Lent of for-ty days.

This may also be sung to the tune of 'Forty days and forty nights' at No. 264

2. Though our consciences proclaim
   our transgressions and our shame,
   cleanse us, Lord, we humbly plead,
   from our sins of thought and deed.

3. Lord, accept our Lenten fast
   and forgive our sinful past,
   that we may partake with thee
   in the Easter mystery.

Text: Sister M. Teresine based on Psalm 129
Music: Johann Scheffler 'Heilige Seelenlust' (1657)

270 From the sun's rising

1. From the sun's rising un-to the sun's set-ting, Je-sus, our Lord, shall be great in the earth; and all earth's king-doms shall be his do-min-ion, all of cre-a-tion shall sing of his worth.

Refrain
Let ev'-ry heart, ev'-ry voice, ev'-ry tongue join with spi - rits a-blaze; one in his love, we will cir-cle the world with the

song of his praise. O let all his peo - ple re -

joice, and let all the earth hear his voice.

2. To evr'y tongue, tribe and nation he sends us,
   to make disciples, to teach and baptise.
   For all authority to him is given;
   now, as his witnesses, we shall arise.

3. Come, let us join with the Church from all nations,
   cross ev'ry border, throw wide ev'ry door;
   workers with him as he gathers his harvest,
   till earth's far corners our Saviour adore.

Text: Graham Kendrick (b.1950)
Music: Graham Kendrick (b.1950) arr. Keith Stent

271 From the very depths of darkness

TUNE 1: CAMERON'S 15 15 15 7 and Refrain

Unison

1. From the ve - ry depths of dark - ness springs a bright and liv - ing light; out of

false - hood and de - ceit a grea - ter truth is brought to sight; in the

halls of death, de - fi - ant, life is dan - cing with de - light! The

Refrain

Lord is ri - sen in - deed! Christ is ri - sen! Hal - le -

lu - jah! Christ is ri - sen! Hal - le - lu - jah!

Christ is ri-sen! Hal-le-lu - jah! The Lord is ri-sen in-deed!

See overleaf for another tune

2. Jesus meets us at the dawning
   of the resurrection day;
   speaks our name with love, and gently
   says that here we may not stay:
   'Do not cling to me, but go to all
   the fearful ones and say,
   "The Lord is risen indeed!" '

3. So proclaim it in the high-rise,
   in the hostel let it ring;
   make it known in Cardboard City,
   let the homeless rise and sing:
   'He is Lord of life abundant,
   and he changes everything;
   the Lord is risen indeed!'

4. In the heartlands of oppression,
   sound the cry of liberty;
   where the poor are crucified,
   behold the Lord of Calvary;
   from the fear of death and dying,
   Christ has set his people free;
   the Lord is risen indeed!

5. To the tyrant, tell the gospel
   of a love he's never known
   in his guarded palace tomb,
   condemned to live and die alone:
   'Take the risk of love and freedom;
   Christ has rolled away the stone!
   The Lord is risen indeed!'

6. When our spirits are entombed
   in mortal prejudice and pride;
   when the gates of hell itself
   are firmly bolted from inside;
   at the bidding of his Spirit,
   we may fling them open wide;
   The Lord is risen indeed!

Text: Michael Forster (b.1946)
Music: Christopher Tambling (b.1964)

TUNE 2: BATTLE HYMN 77 87 87 6 and Refrain

1. From the ve - ry depths of dark - ness springs a bright and liv - ing light; out of false - hood and de - ceit a great - er truth is brought to sight; in the halls of death, de - fi - ant, life is danc - ing with de - light! The Lord is ri - sen in - deed! Christ is ri - sen! Hal - le - lu - jah! Christ is ri - sen! Hal - le-

lu - jah! Christ is ri - sen! Hal - le - lu - jah! The

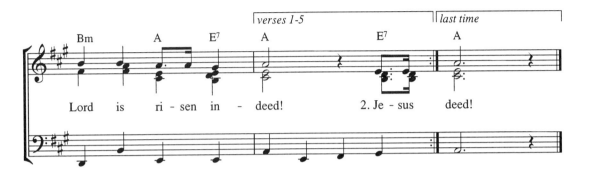

Lord is ri - sen in - deed! 2. Je - sus deed!

2. Jesus meets us at the dawning
   of the resurrection day;
   speaks our name with love, and gently
   says that here we may not stay:
   'Do not cling to me, but go to all
   the fearful ones and say,
   "The Lord is risen indeed!" '

3. So proclaim it in the high-rise,
   in the hostel let it ring;
   make it known in Cardboard City,
   let the homeless rise and sing:
   'He is Lord of life abundant,
   and he changes everything;
   the Lord is risen indeed!'

4. In the heartlands of oppression,
   sound the cry of liberty:
   where the poor are crucified,
   behold the Lord of Calvary;
   from the fear of death and dying,
   Christ has set his people free;
   the Lord is risen indeed!

5. To the tyrant, tell the gospel
   of a love he's never known
   in his guarded palace tomb,
   condemned to live and die alone:
   'Take the risk of love and freedom;
   Christ has rolled away the stone!
   The Lord is risen indeed!'

6. When our spirits are entombed
   in mortal prejudice and pride;
   when the gates of hell itself
   are firmly bolted from inside;
   at the bidding of his Spirit,
   we may fling them open wide;
   The Lord is risen indeed!

Text: Michael Forster (b.1946)
Music: traditional American arr. Christopher Tambling (b. 1964)

272 Gather around, for the table is spread

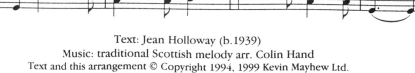

1. Gather around, for the table is spread, welcome the food and rest!
Wide is our circle, with Christ at the head, he is the honoured guest.
Learn of his love, grow in his grace, pray for the peace he gives;
here at this meal, here in this place, know that his Spirit lives!
Once he was known in the breaking of bread, shared with a chosen few;
multitudes gathered and by him were fed, so will he feed us too.

Text: Jean Holloway (b.1939)
Music: traditional Scottish melody arr. Colin Hand
Text and this arrangement © Copyright 1994, 1999 Kevin Mayhew Ltd.

273 Gifts of bread and wine

1. Gifts of bread and wine, gifts we've offered, fruits of labour, fruits of love, taken, offered, sanctified, blessed and broken; words of one who died; 'Take my body, take my saving blood.' Gifts of bread and wine: Christ our Lord.

2. Christ our Saviour, living presence here,
   as he promised while on earth:
   'I am with you for all time,
   I am with you in this bread and wine.'

3. To the Father, with the Spirit,
   one in union with the Son,
   for God's people, joined in prayer,
   faith is strengthened by the food we share.

Text: Christine McCann (b.1951)
Music: Christine McCann (b.1951) arr. Andrew Moore

LITURGICAL

HYMNS OLD & NEW

274 Give me joy in my heart
Sing hosanna

1. Give me joy in my heart, keep me prais-ing, give me joy in my heart, I pray. Give me joy in my heart, keep me prais-ing, keep me prais-ing till the end of day. Sing ho-san-na! Sing ho-san-na! Sing ho-san-na to the King of kings! Sing ho-san-na! Sing ho-san-na! Sing ho-san-na to the King!

2. Give me peace in my heart, keep me resting,
   give me peace in my heart, I pray.
   Give me peace in my heart, keep me resting,
   keep me resting till the end of day.

3. Give me love in my heart, keep me serving,
   give me love in my heart, I pray.
   Give me love in my heart, keep me serving,
   keep me serving till the end of day.

4. Give me oil in my lamp, keep me burning,
   give me oil in my lamp, I pray.
   Give me oil in my lamp, keep me burning,
   keep me burning till the end of day.

Text: traditional
Music traditional arr. Colin Hand
This arrangement © Copyright 1994 Kevin Mayhew Ltd.

275 Give thanks to God

1. Give thanks to God, for he is good, his love will never end. To our eternal Saviour let songs of praise ascend. Let all his people say with joy, 'His love will never end.'

Refrain
Sing alleluia! Praise the Lord! Alleluia!

Sing al - le - lu - ia! Praise the Lord!

2. The Lord has triumphed gloriously,
   his hand has raised me high.
   Now I shall tell his wonders,
   and never shall I die.
   Let all his people sing with joy,
   'His hand has raised me high.'

3. The stone the builders cast aside
   is now the cornerstone,
   a work by which God's glory
   and faithfulness are shown.
   Let all his people sing with joy,
   'He is our cornerstone.'

Text: Michael Forster (b.1946) based on Psalm 117
Music: Christopher Tambling (b.1964)

276 Give thanks with a grateful heart

Text and Music: Henry Smith

LITURGICAL

HYMNS OLD & NEW

277 Glorify the Lord

Refrain
Unison

Glo-ri-fy the Lord, glo - ri-fy the Lord, glo - ri-fy the Lord with me!

1. I sought the Lord and he ans-wered me, from all my ter-rors he has set me free. Come

join with me and bless his ho - ly name.

2. Look at the Lord, do not be ashamed,
   he will deliver those who call his name.
   The poor have called, the Lord has heard their plea.

3. O taste and see that the Lord is good.
   Happy are those who put their trust in him.
   So fear the Lord and you will know no want.

Text: Peter Gonsalves based on Psalm 33
Music: Peter Gonsalves arr. Christopher Tambling
© Copyright 1984 Kevin Mayhew Ltd.

278 Glorious God, King of creation

Lord of hearts, Christ the King.

Lord of love, Ho - ly Spi - rit, to

whom we hom - age bring.

2. Glorious God, magnificent, holy,
   we love you, adore you,
   and come to you in pray'r.
   Glorious God, mighty, eternal,
   we sing your praise ev'rywhere.

Text and Music: Sebastian Temple (1928-1997)

279 Glory and praise to our God

ev - 'ry heart that sings.

2. In his wisdom he strengthens us,
   like gold that's tested in fire.
   Though the power of sin prevails,
   our God is there to save.

3. Ev'ry moment of ev'ry day
   our God is waiting to save,
   always ready to seek the lost,
   to answer those who pray.

4. God has wa-tered our bar - ren land and sent his mer - ci - ful

rain. Now the riv - ers of life run full for

a - ny - one to drink.

Text: Dan Schutte based on Psalm 64, 65
Music: Dan Schutte arr. Christopher Tambling

280 Glory be to Jesus

CASWALL 65 65

1. Glo - ry be to Je - sus who, in bit - ter pains,

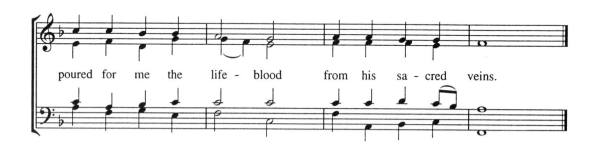

poured for me the life - blood from his sa - cred veins.

2. Grace and life eternal
   in that blood I find:
   blest be his compassion,
   infinitely kind.

3. Blest, through endless ages,
   be the precious stream
   which, from endless torment,
   did the world redeem.

4. There the fainting spirit
   drinks of life her fill;
   there, as in a fountain,
   laves herself at will.

5. Abel's blood for vengeance
   pleaded to the skies,
   but the blood of Jesus
   for our pardon cries.

6. Oft as it is sprinkled
   on our guilty hearts
   Satan in confusion
   terror-struck departs.

7. Oft as earth exulting
   wafts its praise on high
   angel hosts rejoicing,
   make their glad reply.

8. Lift, then, all your voices,
   swell the mighty flood;
   louder still and louder,
   praise the precious blood.

Text: 'Viva, viva, Gesù' (18th century) trans. Edward Caswall (1814-1878) alt.
Music: Friedrich Filitz (1804-1876)

281 Glory to thee, Lord God

CORONA DSM

1. Glo - ry to thee, Lord God! In faith and hope we sing. Through
this com - ple - ted sa - cri - fice our love and praise we bring. We
give thee for our sins a price be - yond all worth, which
none could e - ver fit - ly pay but this thy Son on earth.

2. Here is the Lord of all,
to thee in glory slain;
of worthless givers, worthy gift,
a victim without stain.
Through him we give thee thanks,
with him we bend the knee,
in him be all our life, who is
our one true way to thee.

3. So may this sacrifice
we offer here this day,
be joined with our poor lives in all
we think and do and say.
By living true to grace,
for thee and thee alone,
our sorrows, labours, and our joys
will be his very own.

Text: John Greally
Music: Richard Runciman Terry (1865-1938)

282 Glory to thee, my God, this night

TALLIS'S CANON LM

1. Glo - ry to thee, my God, this night for all the bless - ings of the light; keep me, O keep me, King of kings, be - neath thine own al - migh - ty wings.

A higher setting will be found at No. 129

2. Forgive me, Lord, for thy dear Son,
the ill that I this day have done,
that with the world, myself and thee,
I, ere I sleep, at peace may be.

3. Teach me to live, that I may dread
the grave as little as my bed;
teach me to die, that so I may
rise glorious at the aweful day.

4. O may my soul on thee repose,
and with sweet sleep mine eyelids close;
sleep that may me more vig'rous make
to serve my God when I awake.

5. Praise God, from whom all blessings flow;
praise him, all creatures here below;
praise him above, ye heav'nly host;
praise Father, Son and Holy Ghost.

Text: Thomas Ken (1637-1710)
Music: Thomas Tallis (c.1505-1585)

283 God be in my head

GOD BE IN MY HEAD Irregular

Text: 'Book of Hours' (1514)
Music: Henry Walford Davies (1869-1941)

LITURGICAL
HYMNS OLD & NEW

284 God everlasting, wonderful and holy

CHRISTE SANCTORUM 11 11 11 5

1. God everlasting, wonderful and holy, Father most gracious, we who stand before thee here at thine altar, as thy Son has taught us, come to adore thee.

A lower setting will be found at No. 615

2. Countless the mercies thou has lavished on us,
   source of all blessing to all creatures living;
   to thee we render, for thy love o'erflowing,
   humble thanksgiving.

3. Now in remembrance of our great Redeemer,
   dying on Calv'ry, rising and ascending,
   through him we offer what he ever offers,
   sinners befriending.

4. Strength to the living, rest to the departed,
   grant, Holy Father, through this pure oblation:
   may the life-giving bread for ever bring us
   health and salvation.

Text: Harold Riley
Music: from the 'Paris Antiphoner' (1681)

285 God fills me with joy

God fills me with joy, al-le-lu - ia. His ho-ly pre - sence is my robe, al-le-lu - ia. *Fine* 1. My soul, now glo - ri - fy the Lord who is my Sa - viour. Re - joice, for who am I, that God has shown me fa - vour. God

2. The world shall call me blest
   and ponder on my story.
   In me is manifest
   God's greatness and his glory.

3. For those who are his friends,
   and keep his laws as holy,
   his mercy never ends,
   and he exalts the lowly.

4. But by his pow'r the great,
   the proud, the self-conceited,
   the kings who sit in state,
   are humbled and defeated.

5. He feeds the starving poor,
   he guards his holy nation,
   fulfilling what he swore
   long since in revelation.

6. Then glorify with me
   the Lord who is my Saviour:
   one holy Trinity
   for ever and for ever.

Text: Jean-Paul Lécot (b.1947) based on Luke 1:46-55 trans. Michael Hodgetts (b.1936)
Music: Paul Décha

286 God forgave my sin
Freely, freely

1. God for-gave my sin in Je - sus' name. I've been born a - gain in Je - sus' name. And in Je - sus' name I come to you to share his love as he told me to. He said: 'Free - ly, free - ly you have re-ceived; free - ly, free - ly give. Go in my name, and be-cause you be-lieve, o - thers will know that I live.'

2. All pow'r is giv'n in Jesus' name,
in earth and heav'n in Jesus' name.
And in Jesus' name I come to you
to share his pow'r as he told me to.

3. God gives us life in Jesus' name,
he lives in us in Jesus' name.
And in Jesus' name I come to you
to share his peace as he told me to.

Text: Carol Owens
Music: Carol Owens arr. Andrew Moore

287 Godhead here in hiding

ADORO TE 11 11 11 11

1. God-head here in hid - ing, whom I do a-dore,
masked by these bare sha - dows, shape and no-thing more, see, Lord, at thy ser - vice
low lies here a heart lost, all lost in won - der at the God thou art.

Another translation of this hymn will be found at No. 396

2. Seeing, touching, tasting are in thee deceived;
how, says trusty hearing, that shall be believed?
What God's Son hath told me, take for truth I do;
truth himself speaks truly, or there's nothing true.

3. On the cross thy Godhead made no sign to men;
here thy very manhood steals from human ken;
both are my confession, both are my belief;
and I pray the prayer of the dying thief.

4. I am not like Thomas, wounds I cannot see,
but can plainly call thee Lord and God as he;
this faith each day deeper be my holding of,
daily make me harder hope and dearer love.

5. O thou our reminder of Christ crucified,
living Bread, the life of us for whom he died,
lend this life to me then; feed and feast my mind,
there be thou the sweetness man was meant to find.

6. Jesu, whom I look at shrouded here below,
I beseech thee send me what I long for so,
some day to gaze on thee face to face in light
and be blest for ever with thy glory's sight.

Text: ascribed to St. Thomas Aquinas (1227-1274)
trans. Gerard Manley Hopkins (1844-1889) alt.
Music: Plainsong, accompaniment by Gregory Murray (1905-1992)
This arrangement © Copyright 1976 Kevin Mayhew Ltd.

LITURGICAL

HYMNS OLD & NEW

288 God in the planning
Bridegroom and bride

SLANE 10 10 10 10

1. God, in the plan-ning and pur-pose of life, hal-lowed the
un-ion of hus-band and wife: this we em-bo-dy where love is displayed, rings are pre-sen-ted and pro-mi-ses made.

2. Jesus was found, at a similar feast,
   taking the roles of both water and priest,
   turning the worldly towards the divine,
   tears into the laughter and water to wine.

3. Therefore we pray that his Spirit preside
   over the wedding of bridegroom and bride,
   fulfilling all that they've hoped will come true,
   lighting with love all they dream of and do.

4. Praise then the Maker, the Spirit, the Son,
   source of the love through which two are made one.
   God's is the glory, the goodness and grace
   seen in this marriage and known in this place.

Text: John L. Bell (b.1949) and Graham Maule (b. 1958)
Music: traditional Irish melody arr. Colin Hand

289 God is love

1. God is love, and the one who lives in love lives in God, and God lives in

him. God is love, and the one who lives in love lives in

God, and God lives in her. And we have come to know and have be-

lieved the love which God has for us.

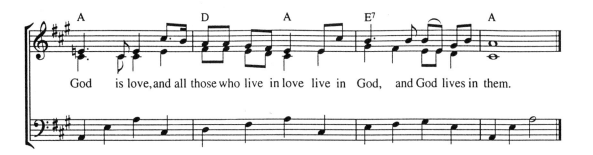

God   is love, and all those who live in love live in God,   and God lives in them.

2. God is hope, and the one who lives in hope
lives in God, and God lives in him.
God is hope, and the one who lives in hope
lives in God, and God lives in her.
And we have come to know and have believed
the love which God has for us.
God is hope, and all those who live in hope
live in God, and God lives in them.

3. God is peace, and the one who lives in peace
lives in God, and God lives in him.
God is peace, and the one who lives in peace
lives in God, and God lives in her.
And we have come to know and have believed
the love which God has for us.
God is peace, and all those who live in peace
live in God, and God lives in them.

4. God is joy, and the one who lives in joy
lives in God, and God lives in him.
God is joy, and the one who lives in joy
lives in God, and God lives in her.
And we have come to know and have believed
the love which God has for us.
God is joy, and all those who live in joy
live in God, and God lives in them.

Text: traditional
Music: traditional arr. Christopher Tambling

290 God is love: his the care

VERSION 1: PERSONENT HODIE (THEODORIC) 666 66 and Refrain

1. God is love: his the care,
tend-ing each, ev-'ry-where. God is love, all is there!
Je - sus came to show him, that we all might know him!

Refrain

Sing a-loud, loud, loud! Sing a-loud, loud, loud!
God is good! God is truth! God is beau - ty! Praise him!

VERSION 2: PERSONENT HODIE (THEODORIC) 666 66 and Refrain

1. God is love: his the care,
tend-ing each, ev-'ry-where.
God is love, all is there!
Je-sus came to show him,
that we all might know him!

Refrain

Sing-a-loud, loud, loud!
Sing-a-loud, loud, loud!
God is good!
God is truth! God is beau-ty!
Praise him! Praise him!

2. None can see God above;
we can share life and love;
thus may we Godward move,
seek him in creation,
holding ev'ry nation.

3. Jesus lived on the earth,
hope and life brought to birth
and affirmed human worth,
for he came to save us
by the truth he gave us.

4. To our Lord praise we sing,
light and life, friend and King,
coming down, love to bring,
pattern for our duty,
showing God in beauty.

Text: Percy Dearmer (1867-1936) alt.
Music: from 'Piae Cantones' (1582) – Version 1: arr. Gustav Holst (1874-1934)
Version 2: arr. Andrew Moore

291 God is my great desire

LEONI 66 84 D

1. God is my great de-sire, his face I seek the first; to him my heart and soul a-spire, for him I thirst. As one in de-sert lands, whose ve-ry flesh is flame, in burn-ing love I lift my hands and bless his name.

2. God is my true delight,
   my richest feast his praise,
   through silent watches of the night,
   through all my days.
   To him my spirit clings,
   on him my soul is cast;
   beneath the shadow of his wings
   he holds me fast.

3. God is my strong defence
   in ev'ry evil hour;
   in him I face with confidence
   the tempter's pow'r.
   I trust his mercy sure,
   with truth and triumph crowned:
   my hope and joy for evermore
   in him are found.

Text: Timothy Dudley-Smith (b.1926) based on Psalm 62
Music: transcribed from the 'Yigdal' by Meyer Lyon (c.1751-1797)

292 God of eternal light

DIADEMATA DSM

1. God of e-ter-nal light, your pro-mis-es we claim; as A-bram's heirs, we re-cog-nise the hon-our of your name. Our sa-cri-fice ac-cept, our lives of faith in-spire, and ev-'ry fear-ful heart trans-form with pu-ri-fy-ing fire.

A lower setting will be found at No. 229

2. High on the mountain side
your glory was revealed,
and yet, that great mysterious light
a deeper truth concealed!
What fearful shadows still
those sights and sounds portray:
a dreadful kind of majesty
that words cannot convey!

3. Christ, from the heav'ns descend,
eternal life make known,
and all our mortal bodies change
to copies of your own.
Your great and glorious light
creation then shall see,
when truth and peace are all around,
and justice flowing free!

Text: Michael Forster (b.1946)
Music: George Job Elvey (1816-1893)
Text © Copyright 1993 Kevin Mayhew Ltd.

293 God of mercy and compassion

AU SANG QU'UN DIEU 87 87 D

1. God of mer - cy and com-pas - sion, look with pi - ty u-pon me; Fa- ther, let me call thee Fa - ther, 'tis thy child re - turns to thee.

Refrain

Je - sus, Lord, I ask for mer - cy, know-ing it is not in vain: all my sins I now de -test them, help me not to sin a - gain.

2. Only by thy grace and mercy
   may I hope for heav'n above,
   where the Saints rejoice for ever
   in a sea of boundless love.

3. See our Saviour, bleeding, dying
   on the cross of Calvary;
   to that cross my sins have nailed him,
   yet he bleeds and dies for me.

Text: Edmund Vaughan (1827-1908) alt.
Music: French melody adapted by Giovanni Battista Pergolesi (1710-1736)

294 God of the covenant

LOBE DEN HERREN 14 14 4 7 8

1. God of the co-ve-nant, yours is the Word of sal-va-tion, mov-ing the heart to re-pen-tance and true a-do-ra-tion. Blood is the seal, pow'r-ful to cleanse and to heal, sprink-led on all your cre-a-tion.

2. God of the covenant, known in the breaking and pouring,
   body and blood of the Saviour, creation restoring:
   here we prepare,
   Christ, in your passion to share,
   humbly your presence adoring.

3. God of the covenant, yours is the Word of salvation
   bearing the terrible cost of the world's liberation.
   Freedom at last!
   Christ through the curtain has passed.
   God is at one with creation!

Text: Michael Forster (b.1946)
Music: melody from 'Praxis Pietatis Melica' (1668)

295 God of the Passover

LOBE DEN HERREN 14 14 4 7 8

1. God of the Pass-o-ver, Au-thor and Lord of sal-va-tion, glad-ly we ga-ther to bring you our hearts' a-dor-a-tion; ran-somed and free, called and com-mis-sioned to be signs of your love for cre-a-tion.

2. Here we remember that evening of wonder enthralling,
myst'ry of passion divine, and betrayal appalling.
Breaking the bread,
'This is my body,' he said,
'do this, my passion recalling.'

3. God of the Eucharist, humbly we gather before you
and, at your table, for pardon and grace we implore you.
Under the cross,
counting as profit our loss,
safe in its shade, we adore you.

Text: Michael Forster (b.1946)
Music: melody from 'Praxis Pietatis Melica' (1668)

296 God rest you merry, gentlemen

GOD REST YOU MERRY 86 86 86 and Refrain

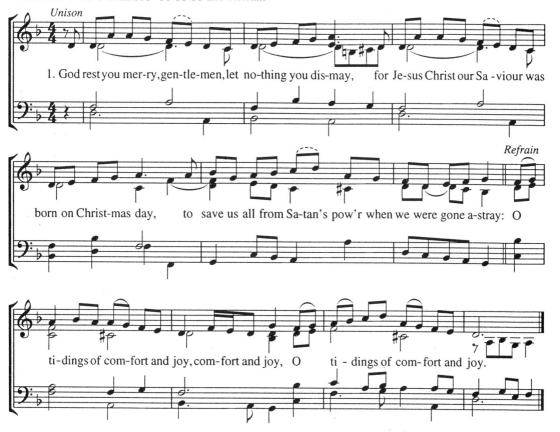

1. God rest you mer-ry, gen-tle-men, let no-thing you dis-may, for Je-sus Christ our Sa-viour was born on Christ-mas day, to save us all from Sa-tan's pow'r when we were gone a-stray: O ti-dings of com-fort and joy, com-fort and joy, O ti-dings of com-fort and joy.

2. In Bethlehem, in Jewry,
   this blessèd babe was born,
   and laid within a manger,
   upon this blessèd morn;
   the which his mother Mary
   did nothing take in scorn.

3. From God, our heav'nly Father,
   a blessèd angel came,
   and unto certain shepherds
   brought tidings of the same,
   how that in Bethlehem was born
   the Son of God by name.

4. 'Fear not,' then said the angel,
   'let nothing you affright,
   this day is born a Saviour,
   of virtue, pow'r and might;
   by him the world is overcome
   and Satan put to flight.'

5. The shepherds at those tidings
   rejoicèd much in mind,
   and left their flocks a-feeding,
   in tempest, storm and wind,
   and went to Bethlehem straightway
   this blessèd babe to find.

6. But when to Bethlehem they came,
   whereat this infant lay,
   they found him in a manger,
   where oxen feed on hay;
   his mother Mary kneeling,
   unto the Lord did pray.

7. Now to the Lord sing praises,
   all you within this place,
   and with true love and fellowship
   each other now embrace;
   this holy tide of Christmas
   all others doth deface.

Text: traditional English alt.
Music: traditional English melody arr. Adrian Vernon Fish
This arrangement © Copyright 1994 Kevin Mayhew Ltd.

297 God's Spirit is in my heart
Go, tell everyone

Tempo rubato

1. God's Spi-rit is in my heart. He has called me and set me a-part. This is what I have to do, what I have to do. He sent me to give the Good News to the poor, tell pris-'ners that they are pris-'ners no more, tell blind peo-ple that they can see, and set the

down-trod-den free, and go tell ev-'ry-one the news that the king-dom of God has come, and go tell ev-'ry-one the news that God's king-dom has come. 3/4. Don't

2. Just as the Father sent me,
   so I'm sending you out to be
   my witnesses throughout the world,
   the whole of the world.

3. Don't carry a load in your pack,
   you don't need two shirts on your back.
   A workman can earn his own keep,
   can earn his own keep.

4. Don't worry what you have to say,
   don't worry because on that day
   God's Spirit will speak in your heart,
   will speak in your heart.

Text: Alan Dale and Hubert J. Richards (b.1921)
Music: Hubert J. Richards (b.1921) arr. Keith Stent

298 Going home

1. Go - ing home, mov - ing on, through God's o - pen door;
hush, my soul, have no fear, Christ has gone be - fore.
Part - ing hurts, love pro - tests, pain is not de - nied;
yet, in Christ, life and hope span the great di - vide.
Go - ing home, mov - ing on, through God's o - pen door;

C   G   Am   Dm   Csus[4] C

hush, my soul, have no fear, Christ has gone be - fore,

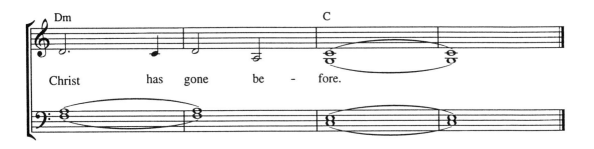

Dm   C

Christ has gone be - fore.

2. No more guilt, no more fear,
   all the past is healed:
   broken dreams now restored,
   perfect grace revealed.
   Christ has died, Christ is ris'n,
   Christ will come again:
   death destroyed, life restored,
   love alone shall reign.
   Going home, moving on,
   through God's open door;
   hush, my soul, have no fear,
   Christ has gone before,
   Christ has gone before.

Text: Michael Forster (b.1946)
Music: adapted from Dvořák's 'New World Symphony' arr. Christopher Tambling

299 Go in peace

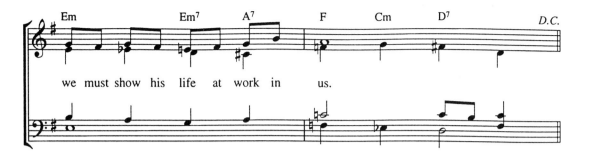

we must show his life at work in us.

2. Though our outer nature may seem wasted,
   daily is the inner self renewed.
   For the love of Jesus Christ controls us,
   since we know that one man died for all.

Text and Music: Aniceto Nazareth

300 Good Christians all, rejoice

IN DULCI JUBILO Irregular

1. Good Christ - ians all, re - joice with
heart and soul and voice! Give ye heed to
what we say: News! News! Je - sus Christ is born to - day;
ox and ass be - fore him bow, and he is in the man - ger now:
Christ is born to - day, Christ is born to - day!

2. Good Christians all, rejoice
   with heart and soul and voice!
   Now ye hear of endless bliss:
   Joy! Joy! Jesus Christ was born for this.
   He hath opened heaven's door,
   and we are blest for evermore:
   Christ was born for this,
   Christ was born for this.

3. Good Christians all, rejoice
   with heart and soul and voice!
   Now ye need not fear the grave:
   Peace! Peace! Jesus Christ was born to save:
   calls you one, and calls you all,
   to gain his everlasting hall:
   Christ was born to save,
   Christ was born to save.

Text: John Mason Neale (1818-1866) alt.
Music: 14th century German carol melody arr. John Stainer (1840-1901)

301 Good King Wenceslas

TEMPUS ADEST FLORIDUM 76 76 D

1. Good King Wen-ces-las looked out on the feast of Ste-phen, when the snow lay round a-bout, deep, and crisp, and e-ven; bright-ly shone the moon that night, though the frost was cru-el, when a poor man came in sight, gath-'ring win-ter fu - el.

2. 'Hither, page, and stand by me,
if thou know'st it, telling,
yonder peasant, who is he,
where and what his dwelling?'
'Sire, he lives a good league hence,
underneath the mountain,
right against the forest fence,
by Saint Agnes' fountain.'

3. 'Bring me flesh, and bring me wine,
bring me pine logs hither:
thou and I will see him dine,
when we bring them thither.'
Page and monarch, forth they went,
forth they went together;
through the rude wind's wild lament,
and the bitter weather.

4. 'Sire, the night is darker now,
and the wind blows stronger;
fails my heart, I know not how;
I can go no longer.'
'Mark my footsteps good, my page;
tread thou in them boldly:
thou shalt find the winter's rage
freeze thy blood less coldly.'

5. In his master's steps he trod,
where the snow lay dinted;
heat was in the very sod
which the Saint had printed.
Therefore, Christians all, be sure,
wealth or rank possessing,
ye who now will bless the poor,
shall yourselves find blessing.

Text: John Mason Neale (1818-1866) alt.
Music: from 'Piae Cantiones' (1582) arr. John Stainer (1840-1901)

302 Go, tell it on the mountain

Refrain
Unison

Go,   tell it on the moun - tain,   o-ver the hills and   ev - 'ry-where,

Fine

go,   tell it on the moun - tain that Je - sus Christ is   born.

1. While shep-herds kept their watch-ing   o'er wand-'ring flocks by   night,   be -

D.C.

hold, from out of   hea - ven,   there shone a   ho - ly   light.

2. And lo, when they had seen it,
   they all bowed down and prayed;
   they travelled on together
   to where the babe was laid.

3. When I was a seeker,
   I sought both night and day:
   I asked my Lord to help me
   and he showed me the way.

4. He made me a watchman
   upon the city wall,
   and, if I am a Christian,
   I am the least of all.

Text: traditional
Music: traditional arr. Adrian Vernon Fish
This arrangement © Copyright 1994 Kevin Mayhew Ltd.

303 Go, the Mass is ended

1. Go, the Mass is end-ed, chil-dren of the Lord.
Take his Word to o-thers as you've heard it spo-ken to you.
Go, the Mass is end-ed, go and tell the world the
Lord is good, the Lord is kind, and he loves ev-'ry-one.

2. Go, the Mass is ended,
   take his love to all.
   Gladden all who meet you,
   fill their hearts with hope and courage.
   Go, the Mass is ended,
   fill the world with love,
   and give to all what you've received
   – the peace and joy of Christ.

3. Go, the Mass is ended,
   strengthened in the Lord,
   lighten ev'ry burden,
   spread the joy of Christ around you.
   Go, the Mass is ended,
   take his peace to all.
   This day is yours to change the world
   – to make God known and loved.

Text: Marie Lydia Pereira (b.1920)
Music: Marie Lydia Pereira (b.1920) arr. Adrian Vernon Fish
© Copyright 1976 Kevin Mayhew Ltd.

304 Grant to us, O Lord

Refrain
Unison

Grant to us, O Lord, a heart re - newed;

re - cre - ate in us your own Spi - rit, Lord!

Fine

1. Be - hold, the days are com - ing, says the Lord our God,

when I will make a new co - ve - nant with the house of Is - ra - el.

D.C.

2. Deep with - in their be - ing I will im - plant my law; I will write it in their hearts.

D.C.

D.C.

3. I will be their God, and they shall be my peo-ple.

4. And for all their faults I will grant for-give-ness;

D.C.

ne - ver - more will I re - mem - ber their sins.

Text: Lucien Deiss (b.1921) adapted from Ezekiel 36:26 and Jeremiah 31: 31-34
Music: Lucien Deiss (b.1921)

305 Grant us your peace

Grant *us your peace, Lord, shel-ter us from harm, Lord, grant us your peace, Lord, shield us with your love.

Just as a {fa-ther / mo-ther} cares for {his / her} chil-dren grant us your peace, Lord, shield us with your love.

or 'them'; 'her'; 'him' as appropriate

2. Grant us your strength, Lord,
shelter us from harm, Lord,
grant us your strength, Lord,
shield us with your love.
From dusk till daybreak,
each waking moment,
grant us your strength, Lord,
shield us with your love.

Text: Francesca Leftley (b.1955)
Music: traditional Israeli melody arr. Andrew Moore
Text and this arrangement © Copyright 1976, 1999 Kevin Mayhew Ltd.

306 Great indeed are your works, O Lord

2. You are the path which we tread,
   you will lead us onward.
   From ev'ry corner of earth
   all the nations gather.

3. You lead them all by the hand
   to the heav'nly kingdom.
   Then, at the end of all times,
   you will come in glory.

Text: Aniceto Nazareth based on the Psalms
Music: Aniceto Nazareth arr. Donald Thomson

LITURGICAL

HYMNS OLD & NEW

307 Guide me, O thou great Redeemer

CWM RHONDDA 87 87 47

1. Guide me, O thou great Re - deem - er, pil - grim through this bar - ren land; I am weak, but thou art migh - ty, hold me with thy pow'r - ful hand: Bread of Hea - ven, Bread of Hea - ven, feed me till I want no more, (want no more,) feed me till I want no more. (want no more,)

A lower setting will be found at No. 338

2. Open now the crystal fountain,
whence the healing stream doth flow;
let the fire and cloudy pillar
lead me all my journey through;
strong deliv'rer, strong deliv'rer,
be thou still my strength and shield,
be thou still my strength and shield.

3. When I tread the verge of Jordan,
bid my anxious fears subside;
death of death, and hell's destruction,
land me safe on Canaan's side;
songs of praises, songs of praises,
I will ever give to thee,
I will ever give to thee.

Text: William Williams (1717-1791) trans. Peter Williams (1727-1796) and others
Music: John Hughes (1873-1932)
Music © Copyright control

308 Hail, glorious Saint Patrick

SAINT PATRICK 11 11 11 11 and Refrain

1. Hail, glo-rious Saint Pat-rick, dear saint of our isle, on
us thy poor chil-dren be-stow a sweet smile; and now thou art
high in the man-sions a-bove, on E-rin's green val-leys look
down in thy love. On E-rin's green val-leys, on E-rin's green

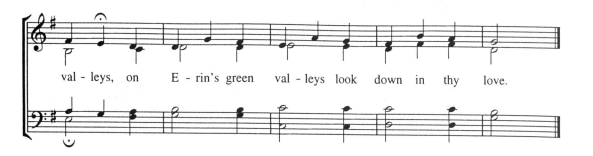

val - leys, on E - rin's green val - leys look down in thy love.

2. Hail, glorious Saint Patrick, thy words were once strong
   against Satan's wiles and an infidel throng;
   not less is thy might where in heaven thou art;
   O, come to our aid, in our battle take part.

3. In the war against sin, in the fight for the faith,
   dear saint, may thy children resist unto death;
   may their strength be in meekness, in penance, in prayer,
   their banner the Cross which they glory to bear.

4. Thy people, now exiles on many a shore,
   shall love and revere thee till time be no more;
   and the fire thou hast kindled shall ever burn bright,
   its warmth undiminished, undying its light.

5. Ever bless and defend the sweet land of our birth,
   where the shamrock still blooms as when thou wert on earth,
   and our hearts shall yet burn, wheresoever we roam,
   for God and Saint Patrick, and our native home.

Text: Sister Agnes
Music: traditional melody arr. John Rombaut

309 Hail, Queen of heaven

STELLA 88 88 88

1. Hail, Queen of heav'n, the o - cean star,

guide of the wand – 'rer here be - low; thrown on life's

surge, we claim thy care; save us from pe - ril

and from woe. Mo - ther of Christ, star of the

sea,   pray   for   the   wand - 'rer,   pray   for   me.

2. O gentle, chaste and spotless maid,
    we sinners make our prayers through thee;
    remind thy Son that he has paid
    the price of our iniquity.
    Virgin most pure, star of the sea,
    pray for the sinner, pray for me.

3. Sojourners in this vale of tears,
    to thee, blest advocate, we cry;
    pity our sorrows, calm our fears,
    and soothe with hope our misery.
    Refuge in grief, star of the sea,
    pray for the mourner, pray for me.

4. And while to him who reigns above,
    in Godhead One, in persons Three,
    the source of life, of grace, of love,
    homage we pay on bended knee,
    do thou, bright Queen, star of the sea,
    pray for thy children, pray for me.

Text: John Lingard (1771-1851)
Music: traditional melody arr. Henri Friedrich Hémy (1818-1888)

LITURGICAL

HYMNS OLD & NEW

310 Hail, Redeemer, King divine

KING DIVINE 77 77 and Refrain

1. Hail, Re-deem-er, King di-vine! Priest and Lamb, the throne is thine,
King, whose reign shall ne - ver cease, Prince of e - ver - last -ing peace.

Refrain

An - gels, saints and na - tions sing: 'Praised be Je - sus Christ, our King,
Lord of life, earth, sky and sea, King of love on Cal - va - ry.'

2. King whose name creation thrills,
rule our minds, our hearts, our wills,
till in peace each nation rings
with thy praises, King of kings.

3. King most holy, King of truth,
guide the lowly, guide the youth;
Christ thou King of glory bright,
be to us eternal light.

4. Shepherd-King, o'er mountains steep,
homeward bring the wand'ring sheep,
shelter in one royal fold
states and kingdoms, new and old.

Text: Patrick Brennan (1877-1952)
Music: Charles Rigby (1901-1962)

311 Hail the day that sees him rise

LLANFAIR 77 77 and Alleluias

1. Hail the day that sees him rise, al - le - lu - ia!
to his throne a - bove the skies; al - le - lu - ia!
Christ the Lamb, for sin - ners giv'n, al - le - lu - ia!
en - ters now the high - est heav'n! al - le - lu - ia!

Unison

Org.

2. There for him high triumph waits;
   lift your heads, eternal gates!
   He hath conquered death and sin;
   take the King of Glory in!

3. Circled round with angel-pow'rs,
   their triumphant Lord and ours;
   wide unfold the radiant scene,
   take the King of Glory in!

4. Lo, the heav'n its Lord receives,
   yet he loves the earth he leaves;
   though returning to his throne,
   calls the human race his own.

5. See, he lifts his hands above;
   see, he shows the prints of love;
   hark, his gracious lips bestow
   blessings on his Church below.

6. Still for us he intercedes,
   his prevailing death he pleads;
   near himself prepares our place,
   he the first-fruits of our race.

7. Lord, though parted from our sight,
   far above the starry height,
   grant our hearts may thither rise,
   seeking thee above the skies.

8. Ever upward let us move,
   wafted on the wings of love;
   looking when our Lord shall come,
   longing, sighing after home.

Text: Charles Wesley (1707-1788), Thomas Cotterill (1779-1823) and others, alt.
Music: Robert Williams (1781-1821)

312 Hail the risen Lord, ascending

PRAISE MY SOUL 87 87 87

1. Hail the risen Lord, ascending
to his holy Father's side,
angels lost in awe and wonder
now acclaim the Lord who died.
Alleluia, alleluia,
Christ triumphant, glorified!

2. He who once, from royal splendour,
came to share our state of blame,
now ascends in clouds of glory
to the heights from which he came.
Alleluia, alleluia,
Christ for evermore the same!

3. He will grant his praying servants,
from the riches of his power,
grace to live as risen people
in this present watching hour.
Alleluia, alleluia,
God on us his blessings shower.

4. Now he bids us tell his story,
where the lost and fearful roam:
he will come again triumphant,
and will lead his people home.
Alleluia, alleluia,
Maranatha! Come, Lord, come!

An extended setting will be found at No. 576

Text: Michael Forster (b.1946)
Music: John Goss (1800-1880)
Text © Copyright 1993 Kevin Mayhew Ltd.

313 Hail, thou star of ocean

LAUDES 65 65 D

1. Hail, thou star of o - cean, por - tal of the sky,
e - ver vir - gin mo - ther of the Lord most high.

Verse 4: end here

O, by Ga - briel's 'A - ve', ut - tered long a - go,
E - va's name re - vers - ing, 'stab - lish peace be - low.

D.C.

2. Break the captive's fetters, light on blindness pour,
   all our ills expelling, ev'ry bliss implore.
   Show thyself a mother; offer him our sighs,
   who for us incarnate did not thee despise.

3. Virgin of all virgins, to thy shelter take us;
   gentlest of the gentle, chaste and gentle make us.
   Still, as on we journey, help our weak endeavour;
   till with thee and Jesus we rejoice for ever.

4. Through the highest heaven, to th'almighty Three,
   Father, Son and Spirit, One same glory be.

Text: 'Ave, maris stella' (9th century) trans. Edward Caswall (1814-1878)
Music: John Richardson (1816-1879)

LITURGICAL

HYMNS OLD & NEW

314 Hail to the Lord's anointed

CRÜGER 76 76 D

1. Hail to the Lord's a-noint-ed, great Da-vid's great-er son! Hail, in the time ap-point-ed, his reign on earth be-gun! He comes to break op-pres-sion, to set the cap-tive free; to take a-way trans-gres-sion, and rule in e-qui-ty.

2. He comes with succour speedy
to those who suffer wrong;
to help the poor and needy,
and bid the weak be strong;
to give them songs for sighing,
their darkness turn to light,
whose souls, condemned and dying,
were precious in his sight.

3. He shall come down like showers
upon the fruitful earth,
and love, joy, hope, like flowers,
spring in his path to birth:
before him on the mountains
shall peace the herald go;
and righteousness in fountains
from hill to valley flow.

4. Kings shall fall down before him,
and gold and incense bring;
all nations shall adore him,
his praise all people sing;
to him shall prayer unceasing
and daily vows ascend;
his kingdom still increasing,
a kingdom without end.

5. O'er ev'ry foe victorious,
he on his throne shall rest,
from age to age more glorious,
all-blessing and all-blest;
the tide of time shall never
his covenant remove;
his name shall stand for ever;
that name to us is love.

Text: paraphrase of Psalm 71 by James Montgomery (1771-1854)
Music: from a melody in Johann Crüger's 'Gesangbuch' adapted by William Henry Monk (1823-1889)

315 Hail, true Body

TUNE 1: PLAINSONG Irregular

1. Hail, true Body, born of Mary, by a wondrous virgin birth.

You who on the cross were offered to redeem us all on earth.

2. You whose side became a fountain pouring forth your precious blood,

give us now, and at our dying, your own self to be our food.

O kindest Jesu, O gracious Jesu,

O Je - su, bles - sed Ma - ry's Son.

TUNE 2: STANDISH Irregular

1. Hail, true Bo - dy, born of Ma - ry, by a won-drous vir - gin -
2. You whose side be - came a foun - tain pour-ing forth your pre - cious

birth. You who on the Cross were of - fered to re -
blood, give us now, and at our dy - ing, your own

After verse 2

deem us all on earth;
self to be our food. O kind - est Je - su, O gra-cious

Je - su, O Je - su, bles - sed Ma - ry's Son.

The original Latin text of this hymn, Ave Verum, will be found at No. 151

Text: Latin 14th century trans. H.N. Oxenham (1852-1941) alt.
Music: Tune 1 – Plainsong arr. Alan Rees (b.1941)
Tune 2 – J. Dykes Bower (1905-1981)

LITURGICAL

HYMNS OLD & NEW

316 Hark! a herald voice is calling

MERTON 87 87

1. Hark! a her-ald voice is call-ing: 'Christ is nigh!' it seems to say;
'Cast a-way the dreams of dark-ness, O ye chil-dren of the day!'

2. Startled at the solemn warning,
   let the earth-bound soul arise;
   Christ, her sun, all sloth dispelling,
   shines upon the morning skies.

3. Lo, the Lamb, so long expected,
   comes with pardon down from heav'n;
   let us haste, with tears of sorrow,
   one and all to be forgiv'n.

4. So when next he comes with glory,
   wrapping all the earth in fear,
   may he then, as our defender,
   on the clouds of heav'n appear.

5. Honour, glory, virtue, merit,
   to the Father and the Son,
   with the co-eternal Spirit,
   while unending ages run.

Text: 'Vox clara ecce intonat' (6th century) trans. Edward Caswall (1814-1878)
Music: William Henry Monk (1823-1889)

317 Hark, the herald-angels sing

MENDELSSOHN 77 77 D and Refrain

1. Hark, the he - rald - an - gels sing glo - ry to the new-born King; peace on earth and mer-cy mild, God and sin - ners re - con - ciled: joy-ful, all ye na - tions rise, join the tri - umph of the skies, with th'an - ge - lic host pro - claim, 'Christ is born in Beth - le - hem.'

Refrain .... *Unison*

Hark, the her-ald-an-gels sing glo-ry to the new-born King.

Ped.

2. Christ, by highest heav'n adored,
   Christ, the everlasting Lord,
   late in time behold him come,
   offspring of a virgin's womb!
   Veiled in flesh the Godhead see,
   hail, th'incarnate Deity!
   Pleased as man with us to dwell,
   Jesus, our Emmanuel.

3. Hail, the heav'n-born Prince of Peace!
   Hail, the Sun of Righteousness!
   Light and life to all he brings,
   ris'n with healing in his wings;
   mild he lays his glory by,
   born that we no more may die,
   born to raise us from the earth,
   born to give us second birth.

Text: Charles Wesley (1707-1788), George Whitefield (1714-1770),
Martin Madan (1726-1790) and others, alt.
Music: adapted from Felix Mendelssohn (1809-1847)
by William Hayman Cummings (1831-1915)

318 Have mercy on us, O Lord

Have mer-cy on us, O Lord, for we have sinned. Have mer-cy on us, O

Lord, for we have sinned. 1. O God, in your kind-ness, have mer-cy on me, and

in your com-pas-sion blot out my of-fence. O wash me, O wash me from

all of my guilt, un - til you have cleansed me from sin.

2. For all my offences I know very well.
   I cannot escape from the sight of my sin.
   Against you, O Lord, only you, have I sinned,
   and done what is wrong in your eyes.

3. A pure heart create in your servant, O Lord;
   a steadfast and trustworthy spirit in me.
   O cast me not out from your presence, I pray,
   and take not your spirit from me.

4. Restore to me, Lord, all the joy of your help;
   sustain me with fervour, sustain me with zeal.
   Then open my lips, and my mouth shall declare
   the praise of my Lord and my God.

Text: Susan Sayers (b.1946) based on Psalm 50
Music: Alan Ridout (1934-1996)
© Copyright 1989 Kevin Mayhew Ltd.

319 Healer of our every ill

Refrain
Unison

Heal - er of our ev - 'ry ill, light of each to - mor - row, give us peace be - yond our fear, and hope be - yond our sor - row

1,2,3. row

Last time row. *Fine*

1. You who know our fears and sad-ness, grace us with your peace and glad-ness.

Spi-rit of all com - fort: fill our hearts. *D.C.*

2. In the pain and joy beholding,
   how your grace is still unfolding.
   Give us all your vision: God of love.

3. Give us strength to love each other,
   ev'ry sister, ev'ry brother.
   Spirit of all kindness: be our guide.

4. You who know each thought and feeling,
   teach us all your way of healing.
   Spirit of compassion: fill each heart.

Text: Marty Haugen (b.1950)
Music: Marty Haugen (b.1950) arr. Keith Stent

LITURGICAL

HYMNS OLD & NEW

320 Healer of the sick

1. Heal-er of the sick, Lord Je-sus, Son of God; Lord, how we long for you: walk here a-mong us. Bind up our bro-ken lives, com-fort our, bro-ken hearts, ban-ish our hid-den fears. Lord, come with power, bring new light to the blind, bring peace to troub-led minds, hold us now in your arms, set us free now.

2. Bearer of our pain,
   Lord Jesus, Lamb of God;
   Lord, how we cry to you:
   walk here among us.

3. Calmer of our fears,
   Lord Jesus, Prince of Peace;
   Lord, how we yearn for you:
   walk here among us.

4. Saviour of the world,
   Lord Jesus, mighty God;
   Lord, how we sing to you:
   walk here among us.

Text: Francesca Leftley (b.1955)
Music: Francesca Leftley (b.1955) arr. Keith Stent

321 Hear my cry

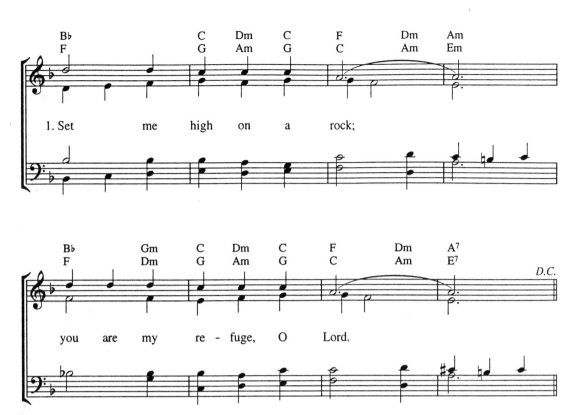

2. Let me stay in your tent;
   safe in the shade of your wings.

3. I will echo your praise;
   pay my vows day after day.

Text: Anthony D'Souza (b.1950) based on Psalm 60
Music: Anthony D'Souza (b.1950) arr. Christopher Tambling

322 Hear our cry

is thirs - ty, come now and drink the wa - ters

(All) Who - e - ver is thirs - ty, come now and drink the wa - ters

(Cantor)
of life;

Last time

(All) of life. 'Je - sus, come!' 'Je - sus, come!'

(Cantor)
Hear our cry, O hear our cry: Hear our cry, O hear our cry: Come!'

3. The streets of teeming cities
cry out for healing rivers –

4. Refresh them with your presence,
give grace for deep repentance –

5. Tear back the shroud of shadows
that covers all the peoples –

6. Revealing your salvation
in ev'ry tribe and nation –

Text and Music: Graham Kendrick (b.1950)

323 Heaven is open wide

DIADEMATA DSM

1. Hea-ven is o-pen wide, and Christ in glo-ry stands, with all au-tho-ri-ty en-dowed and set at God's right hand. A-bove the world of noise ex-tends his reign of peace, and all the blood of mar-tyrs calls our an-gry ways to cease.

A lower setting will be found at No. 229

2. Heaven is open wide,
   and perfect love we see
   in God's eternal self revealed:
   the blessèd Trinity.
   Christ for the Church has prayed,
   that we may all be one,
   and share the triune grace whereby
   creation was begun.

3. Heaven is open wide,
   and Christ in glory stands:
   the Source and End, the First and Last,
   with justice in his hands.
   Let all the thirsty come
   where life is flowing free,
   and Christ, in splendour yet unknown,
   our morning star will be.

Text: Michael Forster (b.1946)
Music: George Job Elvey (1816-1893)
Text © Copyright 1993 Kevin Mayhew Ltd.

324 He brings us into his banqueting table
His banner over me is love

2. The one way to peace is the power of the cross,
   his banner over me is love;

3. He builds his Church on a firm foundation,
   his banner over me is love;

4. In him we find a new creation,
   his banner over me is love;

5. He lifts us up to heavenly places,
   his banner over me is love;

Text: traditional
Music: unknown arr. Christopher Tambling

325 He is Lord

2. He is King, he is King.
   He is risen from the dead and he is King.
   Ev'ry knee shall bow, ev'ry tongue confess
   that Jesus Christ is King.

3. He is love, he is love.
   He is risen from the dead and he is love.
   Ev'ry knee shall bow, ev'ry tongue confess
   that Jesus Christ is love.

Text: unknown
Music: unknown arr. Adrian Vernon Fish
This arrangement © Copyright 1994 Kevin Mayhew Ltd.

326 He is risen, tell the story

WZLOBIE LEZY 87 87 88 7

1. He is ri-sen, tell the sto-ry to the na-tions of the night; from their sin and from their blind-ness, let them walk in Eas-ter light. Now be-gins a new cre-a-tion, now has come our true sal-va-tion, Je-sus Christ, the Son of God!

2. Mary goes to tell the others
of the wonders she has seen;
John and Peter come a-running
– what can all this truly mean?
O Rabboni, Master holy,
to appear to one so lowly!
Jesus Christ, the Son of God!

3. He has cut down death and evil,
he has conquered all despair;
he has lifted from our shoulders
all the weight of anxious care.
Risen Brother, now before you,
we will worship and adore you,
Jesus Christ, the Son of God!

4. Now get busy, bring the message,
so that all may come to know
there is hope for saint and sinner,
for our God has loved us so.
Ev'ry church bell is a-ringing,
ev'ry Christian now is singing,
Jesus Christ, the Son of God!

Text: Willard F. Jabusch (b.1930)
Music: traditional Polish melody arr. Andrew Moore

327 Here in this place
Gather us in

1. Here in this place, new light is stream-ing, now is the dark - ness van - ished a - way; see in this space, our fears and our dream-ings, brought here to you in the light of this day.

Gath - er us in, the lost and for - sak - en, gath - er us in, the blind and the lame; call to us now, and we shall a - wak - en,

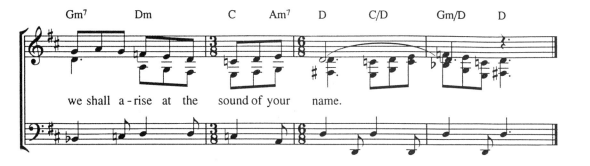

we shall a-rise at the sound of your name.

2. We are the young, our lives are a myst'ry,
   we are the old who yearn for your face;
   we have been sung throughout all of hist'ry,
   called to be light to the whole human race.
   Gather us in, the rich and the haughty,
   gather us in, the proud and the strong;
   give us a heart so meek and so lowly,
   give us the courage to enter the song.

3. Here we will take the wine and the water,
   here we will take the bread of new birth;
   here you shall call your sons and your daughters,
   call us anew to be salt for the earth.
   Give us to drink the wine of compassion,
   give us to eat the bread that is you;
   nourish us well, and teach us to fashion
   lives that are holy and hearts that are true.

4. Not in the dark of buildings confining,
   not in some heaven, light years away,
   but here in this place the new light is shining,
   now is the kingdom, now is the day.
   Gather us in and hold us for ever,
   gather us in and make us your own;
   gather us in, all peoples together,
   fire of love in our flesh and our bone.

Text and Music: Marty Haugen (b.1950)

328 Here is bread

1. Here is bread, here is wine, Christ is with us, he is with us.
Break the bread, taste the wine, Christ is with us here.

Refrain
In this bread there is heal-ing, in this cup is life for e - ver.
In this mo - ment, by the Spi - rit, Christ is with us here.

2. Here is grace, here is peace,
Christ is with us, he is with us;
know his grace, find his peace,
feast on Jesus here.

3. Here we are, joined in one,
Christ is with us, he is with us;
we'll proclaim, till he comes,
Jesus crucified.

Text: Graham Kendrick (b.1950)
Music: Graham Kendrick (b.1950) arr. Keith Stent
© Copyright 1991 Make Way Music, P.O. Box 263, Croydon, Surrey CR9 5AP, UK.
International copyright secured. All rights reserved. Used by permission.

329 Here's a child for you, O Lord

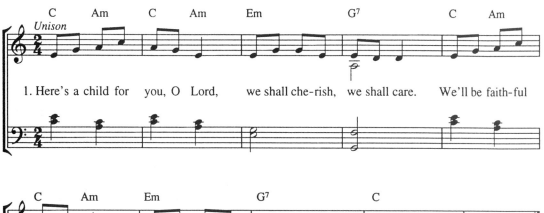

1. Here's a child for you, O Lord, we shall che-rish, we shall care. We'll be faith-ful

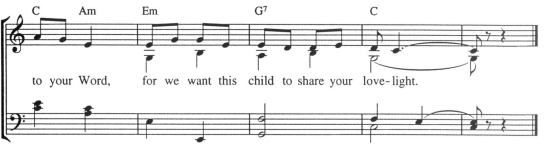

to your Word, for we want this child to share your love-light.

2. May he *(she)* hold his *(her)* head up high,
   graceful, joyful, strong of limb.
   May his *(her)* eyes be clear and bright,
   seeing beauty in all things
   that you've made.

3. We were young ourselves, O Lord,
   we were eager, we were fresh
   like the op'ning buds of spring,
   and we wanted happiness
   in your way.

4. Then, at times, we went astray,
   we were foolish, we were weak,
   and the innocence we had
   vanished like the trace of feet
   when snow melts.

5. But we come, O Lord and King,
   at your bidding, and we pray
   that the precious gift we bring
   will grow stronger every day
   in your love.

6. By the water poured out here
   and your promise, we believe,
   he *(she)* will master ev'ry fear,
   and at last will come to see
   your Godhead.

Text: Estelle White (b.1925)
Music: Estelle White (b.1925) arr. Andrew Moore
© Copyright 1976 Kevin Mayhew Ltd.

330 He's got the whole world in his hand

1. He's got the whole world in his hand. He's got the whole world in his hand. He's got the whole world in his hand. He's got the whole world in his hand.

2. He's got you and me, brother, in his hand. *(3)*
He's got the whole world in his hand.

3. He's got you and me, sister, in his hand. *(3)*
He's got the whole world in his hand.

4. He's got the little tiny baby in his hand. *(3)*
He's got the whole world in his hand.

5. He's got ev'rybody here in his hand. *(3)*
He's got the whole world in his hand.

Text: traditional
Music: traditional arr. Christopher Tambling
This arrangement © Copyright 1994 Kevin Mayhew Ltd.

331 He who would valiant be

MONKS GATE 65 65 66 65

1. He who would val-iant be 'gainst all dis-as-ter,
let him in con-stan-cy fol-low the Mas-ter.
There's no dis-cour-age-ment shall make him once relent his first a-vowed in-tent to be a pil-grim.

2. Who so beset him round
with dismal stories,
do but themselves confound –
his strength the more is.
No foes shall stay his might,
though he with giants fight:
he will make good his right
to be a pilgrim.

3. Since, Lord, thou dost defend
us with thy Spirit,
we know we at the end
shall life inherit.
Then fancies flee away!
I'll fear not what men say,
I'll labour night and day
to be a pilgrim.

Text: Percy Dearmer (1867-1936) after John Bunyan (1628-1688)
Music: traditional English melody collected and arranged by
Ralph Vaughan Williams (1872-1958)

332 Holy God, of righteous glory

BLAENWERN 87 87 D

1. Ho - ly God, of right - eous glo - ry, see your peo - ple ga - thered
here, in a so - lemn con - gre - ga - tion, your for - giv - ing
word to hear. God of love and slow to an - ger,
gra - cious, long - ing to re - store, hear your priests and
peo - ple call - ing, give us grace to sin no more.

2. We confess the pride we suffer,
needs which none can satisfy;
how we love the praise of mortals,
swift to flow'r and quick to die.
Let us find rewards eternal
as we quietly seek your face,
and our open, public living
witness only to your grace.

3. Free us from our self-bound living,
better witnesses to be,
to the world by grace appealing,
telling forth the mystery:
how creation's pure Redeemer
walked among us undefiled,
by his deathless love proclaiming,
God with us is reconciled.

Text: Michael Forster (b.1946) Music: William Penfro Rowlands (1860-1937)
Text © Copyright 1993 Kevin Mayhew Ltd.
Music © Copyright control

333 Holy God, we praise thy name

GROSSER GOTT 78 78 77

1. Ho-ly God, we praise thy name; Lord of all, we bow be-fore thee. All on earth thy scep-tre own, all in heav'n a-bove a-dore thee. In-fin-ite thy vast do-main, e-ver-last-ing is thy reign.

2. Hark, the loud celestial hymn,
angel choirs above are raising;
cherubim and seraphim,
in unceasing chorus praising,
fill the heavens with sweet accord,
holy, holy, holy Lord.

3. Holy Father, Holy Son,
Holy Spirit, three we name thee,
while in essence only one
undivided God we claim thee;
and adoring bend the knee,
while we own the mystery.

4. Spare thy people, Lord, we pray,
by a thousand snares surrounded;
keep us without sin today;
never let us be confounded.
Lo, I put my trust in thee,
never, Lord, abandon me.

Text: adaptation of a hymn by Ambrose (d.397) ascribed to Ignaz Franz (1719-1790)
trans. Clarence Walworth (1820-1900)
Music: from 'Katholisches Gesangbuch' (c.1774)

334 Holy God, your pilgrim people

AR HYD Y NOS 84 84 88 84

1. Ho - ly God, your pil - grim peo - ple by you were fed, through the vast and dread - ful de - sert guid - ed and led; wa - ter from the rock - face pour - ing, hope to ev - 'ry heart re - stor - ing, sets the fail - ing spi - rit soar - ing, life from the dead!

A higher setting will be found at No. 232

2. Living bread for mortals broken,
gift from above,
live in us the life eternal,
perfect in love.
Come, the word of wholeness bringing,
where our fearful souls are clinging;
and of life abundant singing,
all fear remove.

3. One the bread and one the chalice,
one work of grace;
one the Church of Christ, united
in his embrace.
One the gospel of salvation,
for the wholeness of creation;
Christ is poured in ev'ry nation,
and ev'ry race.

Text: Michael Forster (b.1946)
Music: traditional Welsh melody arr. Colin Hand

335 Holy, holy, holy

Unison

1. Ho-ly, ho-ly, ho-ly, ho-ly. Ho-ly, ho-ly, ho-ly Lord God al-migh-ty; and we lift our hearts be-fore you as a to-ken of our love, ho-ly, ho-ly, ho-ly, ho-ly, ho-ly.

Verses 1-4 | *Last time* 2. Gra-cious lu-jah.

2. Gracious Father, gracious Father,
   we are glad to be your children, gracious Father;
   and we lift our heads before you as a token of our love,
   gracious Father, gracious Father.

3. Risen Jesus, risen Jesus,
   we are glad you have redeemed us, risen Jesus;
   and we lift our hands before you as a token of our love,
   risen Jesus, risen Jesus.

4. Holy Spirit, Holy Spirit,
   come and fill our hearts anew, Holy Spirit;
   and we lift our voice before you as a token of our love,
   Holy Spirit, Holy Spirit.

5. Hallelujah, hallelujah,
   hallelujah, hallelujah, hallelujah;
   and we lift our hearts before you as a token of our love,
   hallelujah, hallelujah.

Text: Jimmy Owens
Music: Jimmy Owens arr. Christopher Tambling

336 Holy, holy, holy is the Lord

ho - ly, ho - ly, ho - ly is the Lord.

2. Jesus, Jesus, Jesus is the Lord,
Jesus is the Lord God almighty.
Jesus, Jesus, Jesus is the Lord,
Jesus is the Lord God almighty:
who was, and is, and is to come;
Jesus, Jesus, Jesus is the Lord.

3. Worthy, worthy, worthy is the Lord,
worthy is the Lord God almighty.
Worthy, worthy, worthy is the Lord,
worthy is the Lord God almighty:
who was, and is, and is to come;
worthy, worthy, worthy is the Lord.

4. Glory, glory, glory to the Lord,
glory to the Lord God almighty.
Glory, glory, glory to the Lord,
glory to the Lord God almighty:
who was, and is, and is to come;
glory, glory, glory to the Lord.

For liturgical version (Sanctus) see hymn No. 65

Text: unknown
Music: unknown arr. Colin Hand

337 Holy, holy, holy! Lord God almighty

NICAEA 11 12 12 10

1. Ho-ly, ho-ly, ho-ly! Lord God al-migh-ty!
Ear-ly in the morn-ing our song shall rise to thee;
ho-ly, ho-ly, ho-ly! Mer-ci-ful and migh-ty!
God in three per-sons, bles-sed Tri-ni-ty!

* 2. Holy, holy, holy! All the saints adore thee,
    casting down their golden crowns around the glassy sea;
    cherubim and seraphim falling down before thee,
    which wert, and art, and evermore shall be.

3. Holy, holy, holy! Though the darkness hide thee,
    though the eye made blind by sin thy glory may not see,
    only thou art holy, there is none beside thee,
    perfect in pow'r, in love, and purity.

4. Holy, holy, holy! Lord God almighty!
    All thy works shall praise thy name, in earth, and sky and sea;
    holy, holy, holy! Merciful and mighty!
    God in three persons, blessèd Trinity!

* *May be omitted*

Text: Reginald Heber (1783-1826)
Music: John Bacchus Dykes (1823-1876)

338 Holy Jesus, in our likeness born

CWM RHONDDA 87 87 47

1. Ho-ly Je-sus, in our like-ness born, a hu-man home to share, you who knew a fa-ther's kind-ness and a lov-ing mo-ther's care, by your e-ver-pre-sent mer-cy, may we catch this vi-sion fair, (vi-sion fair,) may we catch this vi-sion fair!

(vi-sion fair,)

A higher setting will be found at No. 307

2. Look with kindness and compassion
on each mortal family.
Give us joy in one another,
touching here eternity!
Saviour, hold your many people
in the sweetest harmony,
in the sweetest harmony.

3. May we live for one another,
growing through life's ev'ry stage,
with protection for the youngest
and respect for greater age;
all a common value sharing,
what a holy heritage,
what a holy heritage!

Text: Michael Forster (b.1946)
Music: John Hughes (1873-1932)

339 Holy Mary, you were chosen

O SANCTISSIMA Irregular

1. Holy Mary, you were chosen by the Father, the God of life, joyfully responding, you became a mother. Pray now for us, and show a mother's love.

2. Holy Mary, you were chosen,
   called to carry the Son of God.
   Gratefully responding,
   you became his mother.
   Pray now for us, and show a mother's love.

3. Holy Mary, you were chosen,
   so the Spirit could work in you.
   Faithfully responding,
   you became God's mother.
   Pray now for us, and show a mother's love.

4. Holy Mary, you were chosen
   all God's children are blessed in you.
   Joyfully responding,
   you became our mother.
   Pray now for us, and show a mother's love.

Text: Damian Lundy (1944-1997)
Music: traditional Sicilian melody arr. John Ballantine

340 Holy Spirit, come, confirm us

LAUS DEO (REDHEAD NO. 46) 87 87

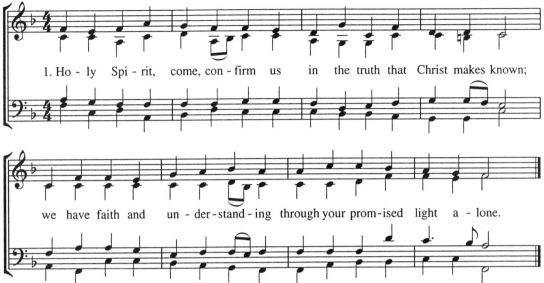

1. Ho - ly Spi - rit, come, con - firm us in the truth that Christ makes known;
we have faith and un - der - stand - ing through your prom - ised light a - lone.

A higher setting will be found at No. 196

2. Holy Spirit, come, console us,
   come as Advocate to plead;
   loving Spirit from the Father,
   grant in Christ the help we need.

3. Holy Spirit, come renew us,
   come yourself to make us live;
   holy through your loving presence,
   holy through the gifts you give.

4. Holy Spirit, come, possess us,
   you the love of Three in One,
   Holy Spirit of the Father,
   Holy Spirit of the Son.

Text: Brian Foley (b.1919)
Music: German melody adapted by Richard Redhead (1820-1901)

341 Holy Spirit, Lord of light

VENI SANCTE SPIRITUS 777 D

1. Ho-ly Spi-rit, Lord of light, from the clear ce-les-tial height, thy pure beam-ing ra-diance give; come, thou Fa-ther of the poor, come with trea-sures which en-dure; come, thou light of all that live!

2. Thou, of all consolers best,
   thou, the soul's delightsome guest,
   dost refreshing peace bestow:
   thou in toil art comfort sweet;
   pleasant coolness in the heat;
   solace in the midst of woe.

3. Light immortal, light divine,
   visit thou these hearts of thine,
   and our inmost being fill:
   if thou take thy grace away,
   nothing pure in us will stay;
   all his good is turned to ill.

4. Heal our wounds, our strength renew;
   on our dryness pour thy dew;
   wash the stains of guilt away;
   bend the stubborn heart and will;
   melt the frozen, warm the chill;
   guide the steps that go astray.

5. Thou, on those who evermore
   thee confess and thee adore,
   in thy sev'nfold gifts descend:
   give them comfort when they die;
   give them life with thee on high;
   give them joys that never end.

Text: ascribed to Stephen Langton (d.1228) trans. Edward Caswall (1814-1878) alt.
Music: Samuel Webbe (1740-1816)

342 Holy Spirit of fire

Ho-ly Spi-rit of fire, flame e-ver-last-ing, so bright and clear,
speak this day in our hearts. Light-en our dark-ness and purge us of fear,
Ho-ly Spi-rit of fire.

Refrain
The wind can blow or be still, or wa-ter be parched by the sun. A fire can die in-to dust: but here the e-ter-nal Spi-rit of God tells us a new world's be-gun.

2. Holy Spirit of love,
strong are the faithful who trust your pow'r.
Love who conquers our will,
teach us the words of the gospel of peace,
Holy Spirit of love.

3. Holy Spirit of God,
flame everlasting so bright and clear,
speak this day in our hearts.
Lighten our darkness and purge us of fear,
Holy Spirit of God.

Text: John Glynn (b.1948)
Music: John Glynn (b.1948) arr. Andrew Moore

343 Holy virgin, by God's decree
New Lourdes Hymn

1. Holy virgin, by God's decree, you were called eternally; that he could give his Son to our race. Mary, we praise you, hail, full of grace.

Refrain

Ave, ave, ave, Maria.

2. By your faith and loving accord,
   as the handmaid of the Lord,
   you undertook God's plan to embrace.
   Mary, we thank you, hail, full of grace.

3. Joy to God you gave and expressed,
   of all women none more blessed,
   when in our flesh your Son took his place.
   Mary, we love you, hail, full of grace.

4. Refuge for your children so weak,
   sure protection all can seek.
   Problems of life you help us to face.
   Mary, we trust you, hail, full of grace.

5. To our needy world of today
   love and beauty you portray,
   showing the path to Christ we must trace.
   Mary, our mother, hail, full of grace.

Text: Jean-Paul Lécot (b.1947) trans. W.R. Lawrence (1925-1997), alt.
Music: Paul Dècha

344 Hosanna, hosanna

2. Glory, glory, glory to the King of kings!
Glory, glory, glory to the King of kings!

Text and Music: Carl Tuttle
© Copyright 1985 Mercy/Vineyard Publishing/Music Services. Administered by CopyCare,
P.O. Box 77, Hailsham, East Sussex BN27 3EF, UK. Used by permission.

LITURGICAL

HYMNS OLD & NEW

345 How great is our God

How great is our God,
how great is his name!
How great is our God,
for e-ver the same!
same!

1. He rolled back the wa-ters
of the migh-ty Red Sea,
and he said: 'I'll ne-ver leave you.
Put your trust in me.'

2. He sent his Son, Jesus,
   to set us all free,
   and he said: 'I'll never leave you.
   Put your trust in me.'

3. He gave us his Spirit,
   and now we can see.
   And he said: 'I'll never leave you.
   Put your trust in me.'

Text: unknown
Music: unknown arr. Donald Thomson
This arrangement © Copyright 1999 Kevin Mayhew Ltd.

346 How lovely on the mountains
Our God reigns

1. How love-ly on the moun-tains are the
feet of him who brings good news, good
news, an-nounc-ing peace, pro-claim-ing news of
hap - pi-ness: our God reigns, our God
reigns. *Refrain* Our God reigns, our God reigns

our God reigns,   our God reigns.

2. You watchmen, lift your voices
   joyfully as one,
   shout for your King, your King!
   See eye to eye,
   the Lord restoring Zion:
   our God reigns, our God reigns.

3. Wasteplaces of Jerusalem,
   break forth with joy!
   We are redeemed, redeemed.
   The Lord has saved
   and comforted his people:
   our God reigns, our God reigns.

4. Ends of the earth, see
   the salvation of our God!
   Jesus is Lord, is Lord!
   Before the nations,
   he has bared his holy arm:
   our God reigns, our God reigns.

Text: v.1 Leonard E. Smith Jnr. (b.1942) based on Isaiah 52,53; vs. 2-4 unknown
Music: Leonard E. Smith Jnr. (b.1942) arr. Keith Stent

347 How shall they hear the word of God

VERBUM DEI 86 86 88

Unison

1. How shall they hear the word of God unless the truth is told? How shall the sin - ful be set free, the sor - row - ful con - soled? To all who speak the truth to - day im - part your Spi - rit, Lord, we pray.

2. How shall they call to God for help
   unless they have believed?
   How shall the poor be given hope,
   the prisoner reprieved?
   To those who help the blind to see
   give light and love and clarity.

3. How shall the gospel be proclaimed
   that sinners may repent?
   How shall the world find peace at last
   if heralds are not sent?
   So send us, Lord, for we rejoice
   to speak of Christ with life and voice.

Text: Michael Perry (b.1942)
Music: Andrew Moore (b.1954)

348 I am the bread of life (Konstant)

2. I am the spring of life.
   You who hope in me will never be thirsty.
   I will raise you up, I will raise you up,
   I will raise you up to eternal life.
   I am the spring of life.

3. I am the way of life.
   You who follow me will never be lonely.
   I will raise you up, I will raise you up,
   I will raise you up to eternal life.
   I am the way of life.

4. I am the truth of life.
   You who look for me will never seek blindly.
   I will raise you up, I will raise you up,
   I will raise you up to eternal life.
   I am the truth of life.

5. I am the life of life.
   You who die with me will never die vainly.
   I will raise you up, I will raise you up,
   I will raise you up to eternal life.
   I am the life of life.

Text: David Konstant (b.1930)
Music: Kevin Mayhew (b.1942) arr. Andrew Moore
© Copyright 1976 Kevin Mayhew Ltd.

349 I am the bread of life (Toolan)

1. I am the bread of life. You who come to me shall not hunger; and who believe in me shall not thirst.
2. The bread that I will give is my flesh for the life of the world, and if you eat of this bread,
3. Unless you eat of the flesh of the Son of Man, and drink of his blood, and
4. I am the resurrection, I am the life. If you believe in me,
5. Yes, Lord, I believe that you are the Christ, the Son of God,

Text and Music: Suzanne Toolan (b.1927)

350 I am the Light
Come, follow me

1. I am the Light, bring-ing you out of dark-ness, so come, take my light to the world. I am the Bread you must feed to the hun-gry, the Wine that must fill ev-'ry heart. Fox-es have holes, birds have their nests,

but the Son of Man has no place to rest.

Refrain

Come, fol-low me; be the light of the na - tions. Leave your

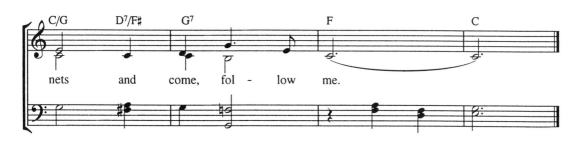

nets and come, fol - low me.

2. I am the Life
   that must change ev'ry life
   and the Way that must alter your ways.
   I am the Truth and my word is the cross
   you must take if you want to be free.
   Foxes have holes, birds have their nests,
   but the Son of Man has no place to rest.

3. I am the Sower,
   come, work in my vineyard, my field.
   Tend my vines, sow the grain.
   And should it fall to the ground,
   it can only spring up
   with new life, hundredfold.
   Foxes have holes, birds have their nests,
   but the Son of Man has no place to rest.

4. I am the Shepherd,
   come into the sheepfold
   to help feed my lambs, feed my sheep.
   Bring back the straying,
   and bind up their wounds, and rejoice
   when you've found what was lost.
   Foxes have holes, birds have their nests,
   but the Son of Man has no place to rest.

Text: Aniceto Nazareth based on the Gospel of John
Music: Aniceto Nazareth

351 I cannot tell

LONDONDERRY AIR 11 10 11 10 11 10 11 12

Unison

1. I can-not tell how he whom an-gels wor - ship should stoop to

love the peo -ples of the earth, or why as

shep - herd he should seek the wand - 'rer with his mys -

te - rious pro-mise of new birth. But this I know, that he was born of

Ma - ry, when Beth-l'em's man - ger was his on - ly

home, and that he lived at Na - za - reth and

la - boured, and so the Sa-viour, Sa-viour of the world, is come.

2. I cannot tell how silently he suffered,
   as with his peace he graced this place of tears,
   or how his heart upon the cross was broken,
   the crown of pain to three and thirty years.
   But this I know, he heals the broken-hearted,
   and stays our sin, and calms our lurking fear,
   and lifts the burden from the heavy laden,
   for yet the Saviour, Saviour of the world, is here.

3. I cannot tell how he will win the nations,
   how he will claim his earthly heritage,
   how satisfy the needs and aspirations
   of east and west, of sinner and of sage.
   But this I know, all flesh shall see his glory,
   and he shall reap the harvest he has sown,
   and some glad day his sun shall shine in splendour
   when he the Saviour, Saviour of the world, is known.

4. I cannot tell how all the lands shall worship,
   when, at his bidding, ev'ry storm is stilled,
   or who can say how great the jubilation
   when ev'ry heart with perfect love is filled.
   But this I know, the skies will thrill with rapture,
   and myriad, myriad human voices sing,
   and earth to heav'n and heav'n to earth, will answer:
   'At last the Saviour, Saviour of the world, is King!'

Text: William Young Fullerton (1857-1932) alt.
Music: traditional Irish melody arr. Noel Rawsthorne

LITURGICAL

HYMNS OLD & NEW

352 I come like a beggar

2. I come like a prisoner to set you free,
   I come like a prisoner to set you free.

3. The need of another is the gift that I bring,
   the need of another is the gift that I bring.

4. I come like a beggar, what you do for my sake
   is the wine that I offer you, the bread that I break.

Text: Sydney Carter (b.1915)
Music: Sydney Carter (b.1915) arr. Andrew Moore

353 I danced in the morning
Lord of the dance

1. I danced in the mor-ning when the world was be-gun, and I danced in the moon and the stars and the sun, and I came down from hea-ven and I danced on the earth, at Beth-le-hem I had my birth.

Refrain

Dance, then, wher-e-ver you may be, I am the Lord of the

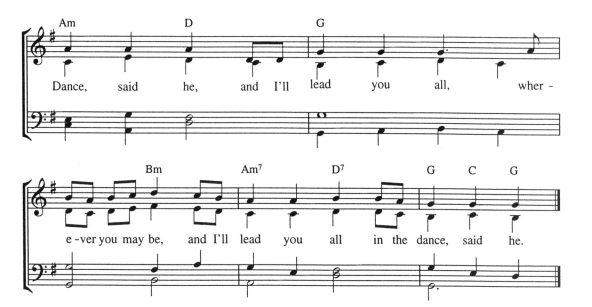

Dance, said he, and I'll lead you all, wher-
e-ver you may be, and I'll lead you all in the dance, said he.

2. I danced for the scribe and the Pharisee,
   but they would not dance and they wouldn't follow me.
   I danced for the fishermen, for James and John –
   they came with me and the dance went on.

3. I danced on the Sabbath and I cured the lame;
   the holy people, they said it was a shame.
   They whipped and they stripped and they hung me on high,
   and they left me there on a cross to die.

4. I danced on a Friday when the sky turned black –
   it's hard to dance with the devil on your back.
   They buried my body, and they thought I'd gone,
   but I am the dance, and I still go on.

5. They cut me down and I leapt up high;
   I am the life that'll never, never die;
   I'll live in you if you'll live in me –
   I am the Lord of the Dance, said he.

Text: Sydney Carter (b.1915)
Music: traditional American melody adapted by Sydney Carter (b.1915) arr. Noel Rawsthorne

354 If God is for us

Eb C   Bb G   F D

1. I know that no-thing in this world

Eb C   Bb G   C A   D.S.

can e-ver take us from his love.

2. Nothing can take us from his love,
   poured out in Jesus, the Lord.

3. And nothing present or to come
   can ever take us from his love.

4. I know that neither death nor life
   can ever take us from his love.

Text: John Foley based on Romans 8:31-39
Music: John Foley arr. Donald Thomson

LITURGICAL

HYMNS OLD & NEW

355 If I am lacking love

2. Love is patient, love is kindly,
   never jealous, never proud;
   not conceited, nor ill-mannered,
   never selfish, never rude.

3. Love is gracious and forgiving,
   taking no delight in sin;
   love rejoices in the truth,
   will not lose heart, will not give in.

4. I know love is everlasting;
   other gifts will pass away.
   Only faith and hope and love
   will never die, will ever stay.

5. God is bountiful in giving;
   all his gifts are my desire,
   but I set my heart on love.
   May his love set my heart on fire!

Text: Damian Lundy (1944-1997) based on 1 Corinthians 13
Music: South American melody arr. Andrew Moore
Text and this arrangement © Copyright 1982, 1998 Kevin Mayhew Ltd.

356 I give you love
Reproaches

FINLANDIA 10 10 10 10 10 10

1. I give you love, and how do you re-pay?
When you were slaves I strove to set you free; I led you
out from un-der Pha-raoh's yoke, but you led out your
Christ to Cal-va-ry. *Refrain* My peo-ple, tell me, what is my offence? What have I done to harm you? Ans-wer me!

2. For forty years I was your constant guide,
   I fed you with my manna from on high.
   I led you out to live in hope and peace,
   but you led out my only Son to die.

3. With cloud and fire I marked the desert way,
   I heard your cries of rage and calmed your fear.
   I opened up the sea and led you through,
   but you have opened Christ with nail and spear.

4. When in distress you cried to me for food,
   I sent you quails in answer to your call,
   and saving water from the desert rock,
   but to my Son you offered bitter gall.

5. I gave you joy when you were in despair,
   with songs of hope, I set your hearts on fire;
   crowned you with grace, the people of my choice,
   but you have crowned my Christ with thorny briar.

6. When you were weak, exploited and oppressed,
   I heard your cry and listened to your plea.
   I raised you up to honour and renown,
   but you have raised me on a shameful tree.

Text: Michael Forster (b.1946) based on the Good Friday Reproaches
Music: Jean Sibelius (1865-1957)

357 I have loved you with an everlasting love

2. Seek the face of the Lord and long for him:
   he will bring you his joy and his hope.

3. Seek the face of the Lord and long for him:
   he will bring you his care and his love.

Text: Michael Joncas (b.1951)
Music: Michael Joncas (b.1951) arr. Keith Stent

358 I'll sing a hymn to Mary

TURRIS DAVIDICA 76 76 D

1. I'll sing a hymn to Ma - ry, the mo - ther of my God, the
vir - gin of all vir - gins, of Da - vid's roy - al blood. O
teach me, ho - ly Ma - ry, a lov - ing song to frame, when
wick - ed ones blas-pheme thee, to love and bless thy name.

2. O noble Tower of David,
   of gold and ivory,
   the Ark of God's own promise,
   the gate of heav'n to me,
   to live and not to love thee,
   would fill my soul with shame;
   when wicked ones blaspheme thee,
   I'll love and bless thy name.

3. The saints are high in glory,
   with golden crowns so bright;
   but brighter far is Mary,
   upon her throne of light.
   O that which God did give thee,
   let mortal ne'er disclaim;
   when wicked ones blaspheme thee,
   I'll love and bless thy name.

4. But in the crown of Mary,
   there lies a wondrous gem,
   as queen of all the angels,
   which Mary shares with them:
   no sin hath e'er defiled thee,
   so doth our faith proclaim;
   when wicked ones blaspheme thee,
   I'll love and bless thy name.

Text: John Wyse (1825-1898) alt.
Music: Henri Friedrich Hémy (1818-1888)

359 I'll turn my steps to the altar of God

2. Lead me on with your power and strength,
   then my courage will never be spent.

3. Fill my heart with your truth and your light
   as I enter with joy in your sight.

4. Holy praises of God will I sing;
   I will trust and will hope in my King.

5. Glory be to the Father, the Son
   and the Spirit, while endless years run.

Text: Aniceto Nazareth based on Psalm 42
Music: Aniceto Nazareth

360 Immaculate Mary
Lourdes Hymn

LOURDES 65 65 and Refrain

1. Im - mac - u - late Ma - ry! Our hearts are on fire; that ti - tle so wond - rous fills all our de - sire. *Refrain* A - ve, a - ve, a - ve Ma - ri - a! A - ve, a - ve, a - ve Ma - ri - a!

2. We pray for God's glory,
may his kingdom come!
We pray for his vicar,
our father, and Rome.

3. We pray for our mother
the Church upon earth,
and bless, sweetest lady,
the land of our birth.

4. For poor, sick, afflicted
thy mercy we crave;
and comfort the dying,
thou light of the grave.

5. In grief and temptation,
in joy or in pain,
we'll ask thee, our mother,
nor seek thee in vain.

6. In death's solemn moment,
our mother, be nigh;
as children of Mary,
O teach us to die.

7. And crown thy sweet mercy
with this special grace,
and worship in heaven
God's ravishing face.

8. To God be all glory
and worship for aye;
to God's virgin mother
an endless Ave.

Text: unknown
Music: traditional French melody arr. John Ballantine
This arrangement © Copyright 1978 Kevin Mayhew Ltd.

LITURGICAL

HYMNS OLD & NEW

361 Immortal, invisible, God only wise

SAINT DENIO 11 11 11 11

1. Immortal, invisible, God only wise, in light inaccessible hid from our eyes, most blessed, most glorious, the Ancient of Days, almighty, victorious, thy great name we praise.

2. Unresting, unhasting, and silent as light,
nor wanting, nor wasting, thou rulest in might;
thy justice like mountains high soaring above
thy clouds which are fountains of goodness and love.

3. To all life thou givest, to both great and small;
in all life thou livest, the true life of all;
we blossom and flourish as leaves on the tree,
and wither and perish; but naught changeth thee.

4. Great Father of glory, pure Father of light,
thine angels adore thee, all veiling their sight;
all laud we would render, O help us to see
'tis only the splendour of light hideth thee.

Text: Walter Chalmers Smith (1824-1908) based on 1 Timothy 1:17
Music: adapted from a traditional Welsh hymn melody in John Roberts' 'Caniadu y Cyssegr' (1839)

362 In bread we bring you, Lord

1. In bread we bring you, Lord, our bo-dies' la-bour.
In wine we of-fer you our spi-rits' grief.
We do not ask you, Lord, who is my neigh-bour,
but stand u-ni-ted now, one in be-lief.
O we have glad-ly heard your Word, your ho-ly Word,

and now in ans - wer, Lord, our gifts we bring.

Our self - ish hearts make true, our fail - ing faith re-new,

our lives be - long to you, our Lord and King.

2. The bread we offer you is blessed and broken,
   and it becomes for us our spirits' food.
   Over the cup we bring your Word is spoken;
   make it your gift to us, your healing blood.
   Take all that daily toil plants in our hearts' poor soil,
   take all we start and spoil, each hopeful dream,
   the chances we have missed, the graces we resist,
   Lord, in thy Eucharist, take and redeem.

Text: Kevin Nichols (b.1929)
Music: Kevin Nichols (b.1929) arr. Andrew Moore

363 In company with Christians past

TALLIS' CANON LM

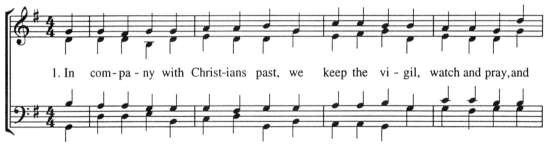

1. In com-pa-ny with Christ-ians past, we keep the vi - gil, watch and pray, and

with the temp-ted Christ, re - ject the su - per - fi - cial, ea - sy way.

A lower setting will be found at No. 282

2. We will not turn our stones to bread,
   or from the temple's heights be hurled;
   nor look for cheap success within
   the ways and values of the world.

3. Forgive us, Lord, the times we fail
   to keep that promise day by day,
   and give us grace to follow you
   on faith's more costly, rocky way.

4. Then lead us on to find once more
   the glory veiled but never lost:
   the image of our God in us,
   restored by grace at such a cost!

5. O perfectly related God,
   eternal Father, Spirit, Son,
   renew us in the Covenant
   that makes your many people one.

6. Then move us on from fast to feast.
   where life and wholeness are restored,
   and you, in triune majesty
   are honoured, worshipped and adored.

Text: Michael Forster (b.1946) based on St Gregory the Great (540-604)
Music: Thomas Tallis (c.1505-1585)

364 Infant holy, infant lowly

WZLOBIE LEZY 87 87 88 77

1. Infant holy, infant lowly, for his bed a cattle stall; oxen lowing, little knowing Christ the babe is Lord of all. Swift are winging angels singing, nowells ringing, tidings bringing, Christ the babe is Lord of all, Christ the babe is Lord of all.

2. Flocks were sleeping, shepherds keeping
   vigil till the morning new;
   saw the glory, heard the story,
   tidings of a gospel true.
   Thus rejoicing, free from sorrow,
   praises voicing, greet the morrow,
   Christ the babe was born for you,
   Christ the babe was born for you.

Text: trans. from the Polish by Edith Margaret Gellibrand Reed (1885-1933)
Music: traditional Polish melody arr. Colin Hand

365 In the bleak mid-winter

CRANHAM Irregular

1. In the bleak mid-winter frosty wind made
2. Our God, heav'n cannot hold him nor earth sus-
3. Enough for him, whom cherubim worship night and
4. Angels and archangels may have gathered
5. What can I give him, poor as I

moan, earth stood hard as iron, water like a
tain; heav'n and earth shall flee away when he comes to
day, a breast-ful of milk, and a manger-ful of
there, cherubim and seraphim thronged the
am? If I were a shepherd I would bring a

stone; snow had fallen, snow on snow, snow on
reign. In the bleak mid-winter a stable-place suf-
hay: enough for him, whom angels fall down be-
air; but only his mother in her maiden
lamb; if I were a wise man I would do my

snow, in the bleak mid-winter, long ago.
ficed the Lord God almighty, Jesus Christ.
fore, the ox and ass and camel which adore.
bliss worshipped the beloved with a kiss.
part, yet what I can I give him: give my heart.

Text: Christina Georgina Rossetti (1830-1894)
Music: Gustav Holst (1874-1934)

366 In the love of God and neighbour

1. In the love of God and neigh-bour we are ga-thered at his ta-ble: gifts of bread and wine will be-come a sign of the love our Fa-ther gave us, through the Son who came to save us, by the Spi-rit blest. praise.

2. So we offer our tomorrows,
   all our present joys and sorrows,
   ev'ry heart and will, talent, gift and skill.
   For the riches we've been given
   to the Trinity of heaven
   we give thanks and praise.

Text and Music: Estelle White (b.1925)
© Copyright 1978 Kevin Mayhew Ltd.

367 In the tomb so cold
Christ is risen!

1. In the tomb so cold they laid him, death its vic-tim claimed.

Pow'rs of hell, they could not hold him; back to life he came!

Refrain

(Men) Christ is ri-sen! (Women) Christ is ri-sen! (Men) Death has been con-quered.

(Women) Death has been con-quered. (Men) Christ is ri-sen! (Women) Christ is ri-sen!

(All)
He shall reign for e - ver.

2. Hell had spent its fury on him,
   left him crucified.
   Yet, by blood, he boldly conquered,
   sin and death defied.

3. Now the fear of death is broken,
   love has won the crown.
   Pris'ners of the darkness listen,
   walls are tumbling down.

4. Raised from death to heav'n ascending,
   love's exalted King.
   Let his song of joy, unending,
   through the nations ring!

Text: Graham Kendrick (b.1950)
Music: Graham Kendrick (b.1950) arr. Andrew Moore

368 Into one we all are gathered

CARITAS 13 8 5 9 8 and Refrain

Unison

1. In-to one we all are ga-thered through the love of Christ. Let us then re-joice with glad-ness. In him we find love. Let us fear and love the li-ving God, and love and che-rish hu-man-kind.

Refrain

Where cha-ri-ty and love are, there is God.

2. Therefore, when we are together
in the love of Christ,
let our minds know no division,
strife or bitterness;
may the Christ our God be in our midst.
Through Christ our Lord all love is found.

3. May we see your face in glory,
Christ our loving God.
With the blessèd saints of heaven
give us lasting joy.
We will then possess true happiness,
and love for all eternity.

Text: Michael Cockett (b.1938) adapted from 'Ubi Caritas'
Music: Eric Welch

369 In you, my God

1. In you, my God, may my soul find its peace;
you are my ref-uge, my rock and my strength,
calm-ing my fears with the touch of your love.
Here in your pre-sence my trou-bles will cease.

2. In you, my God, may my soul find its joy;
you are the radiance, the song of my heart,
drying my tears with the warmth of your love.
Here in your presence my troubles will cease.

3. In you, my God, may my soul find its rest;
you are the meaning, the purpose of life,
drawing me near to the fire of your love,
safe in your presence my yearning will cease.

Text: Francesca Leftley (b.1955)
Music: Francesca Leftley (b.1955) arr. Andrew Moore

370 In your coming and going

HILLSDOWN 11 11 8 9 and Refrain

In your com-ing and go-ing God is with you, He will keep you in safe-ty night and day.

1. You raise your eyes and you look at the moun-tains; you cry a-loud to the hills, 'Come and help me!' Now, see our God is on his way; he will stay be-side you night and day.

2. His arm outstretched to protect you in danger,
   he never sleeps all the time he is watching.
   He is the maker of the skies,
   but he knows your name, he hears your cries.

3. His loving care shelters you like a shadow,
   to keep you safe from the evil around you.
   He shields you from the burning sun,
   and the moon at night will do no harm.

Text: Damian Lundy (1944-1997) based on Psalm 120
Music: Andrew Moore (b.1954)
© Copyright 1978, 1999 Kevin Mayhew Ltd.

371 I received the living God

Refrain
Unison

I re-ceived the liv-ing God, and my heart is full of joy. I received the liv-ing God, and my heart is full of joy. *Fine*

1. He has said: I am the Bread, knead-ed long to give you life; you who
will par-take of me need not e-ver fear to die. *D.C.*

2. He has said: I am the Way,
   and my Father longs for you;
   so I come to bring you home
   to be one with him anew.

3. He has said: I am the Truth;
   if you follow close to me
   you will know me in your heart,
   and my word shall make you free.

4. He has said: I am the Life
   far from whom no thing can grow,
   but receive this living bread,
   and my Spirit you shall know.

Text: from the Gospel of John
Music: Unknown arr. Andrew Moore
This arrangement © Copyright 1999 Kevin Mayhew Ltd.

372 I saw streams of water flowing

Refrain
Unison

I saw streams of wa-ter flow-ing from the tem-ple's right side, heal-ing pow'r and life be-stow-ing from the one who had died: Al-le-lu-ia, al-le-lu-ia, from our Sav-iour glo-ri-fied.

1st time only *To verses* *Last time* *Fine*

1. In - to day from deep - est night, out of dark - ness in - to light, Christ our Sav - iour comes once more, o - pens up sal - va-tion's door!

D.C.

2. He has healed us with his blood,
   led us safe through Jordan's flood,
   on the further bank we stand,
   gazing on the promised land!

3. He has raised us from the grave,
   from the Red Sea's mighty wave;
   dead to sin we rise with Christ,
   paschal Lamb now sacrificed.

Text and Music: Stephen Dean

373 I saw the holy city

Refrain
Unison

I saw the ho-ly ci - ty, from the o-pened heav'n des - cend - ing.
God's gift of new Je - ru - sa-lem on earth, and pre-pared as a bride to meet her
hus - band, a - dorned for her great day. 1. Now the home of God is
made up-on the earth, he will dwell a-mong his peo - ple and be with them.

Fine

D.C.

2. He will wipe away the tears from every eye,
   and no more will death be known, that is his promise.

3. No more mourning, no more pain, and no more tears,
   for the former things have passed away for ever.

4. Praise the Father, Son and Spirit, Three in One,
   God who was, and who is now, and ever shall be.

Text: Michael Forster (b.1946) based on Revelation 21
Music: Alexandre Lesbordes

374 I sing a song to you, Lord

Refrain

I sing a song to you, Lord, a song of love and praise.

All glo-ry be to you, Lord, through e-ver-last-ing days.

1. Ho-ly, ho-ly, ho-ly, migh-ty Lord and God.
He who was and is now, and who is to come.

2. Worthy is the slain Lamb,
   honour him and praise.
   We rejoice with gladness,
   sing our love today.

3. He has used his power,
   has begun his reign.
   So rejoice, you heavens,
   and proclaim his name.

4. Shine your light on us, Lord,
   let us know your way.
   Be our guide for ever,
   make us yours today.

Text: Richard Beaumont (b.1974)
Music: Richard Beaumont (b.1974) arr. Andrew Moore

LiTURGiCAL
HYMNS OLD & NEW

375 It came upon the midnight clear

NOEL DCM

1. It came up-on the mid-night clear, that glo-rious song of old, from an-gels bend-ing near the earth to touch their harps of gold: 'Peace on the earth, good-will to all, from heav'ns all-gra-cious King!' The world in so-lemn still-ness lay to hear the an-gels sing.

2. Still through the cloven skies they come,
with peaceful wings unfurled;
and still their heav'nly music floats
o'er all the weary world:
above its sad and lowly plains
they bend on hov'ring wing;
and ever o'er its Babel-sounds
the blessèd angels sing.

3. Yet with the woes of sin and strife
the world has suffered long;
beneath the angel-strain have rolled
two thousand years of wrong;
and warring humankind hears not
the love-song which they bring:
O hush the noise of mortal strife,
and hear the angels sing!

4. And ye, beneath life's crushing load,
whose forms are bending low,
who toil along the climbing way
with painful steps and slow:
look now! for glad and golden hours
come swiftly on the wing;
O rest beside the weary road,
and hear the angels sing.

5. For lo, the days are hast'ning on,
by prophets seen of old,
when with the ever-circling years
comes round the age of gold;
when peace shall over all the earth
its ancient splendours fling,
and all the world give back the song
which now the angels sing.

Text: Edmund Hamilton Sears (1810-1876) alt.
Music: traditional English melody arr. Arthur Seymour Sullivan (1842-1900)

376 I, the Lord of sea and sky
Here I am, Lord

HERE I AM 77 74 D and Refrain

1. I, the Lord of sea and sky, I have heard my peo-ple cry.
All who dwell in dark and sin my hand will save.
I who made the stars of night, I will make their dark-ness bright.
Who will bear my light to them? Whom shall I send?

2. I, the Lord of snow and rain,
   I have borne my people's pain.
   I have wept for love of them.
   They turn away.
   I will break their hearts of stone,
   give them hearts for love alone.
   I will speak my word to them.
   Whom shall I send?

3. I, the Lord of wind and flame,
   I will tend the poor and lame.
   I will set a feast for them.
   My hand will save.
   Finest bread I will provide
   till their hearts be satisfied.
   I will give my life to them.
   Whom shall I send?

Text and Music: Dan Schutte

377 I, the Servant-Lord

Response

I, the Ser-vant-Lord, serve you; serve one an-oth-er.

Fine

Love and ser-vice are the signs you are my dis-ci-ples.

1. Je-sus rose from ta-ble, put a tow'l a-round him,

D.C.

poured some wa-ter in a dish, knelt be-fore his friends.

2. In the manner of a slave
Jesus washed their feet.
One by one he came to them,
all who were at supper.

3. With the tow'l he wiped their feet –
Judas too – and Peter.
'Do you understand,' he said,
'this is my example.'

4. 'Happiness will come to you
   if you serve each other.
   I, the Lord, have washed your feet;
   be each other's servant.'

5. 'Trust in God and trust in me;
   let no heart be troubled.
   I'll prepare a place for you,
   I will come back for you.'

6. Thomas said, 'What do you mean?
   Which way are you going?'
   'Through the darkness follow me;
   I go to the Father.'

7. 'Way and truth and life am I.
   Learn my way as servant.
   Love each other as I do;
   serve me in each other.'

8. 'Let us see the Father, Lord.'
   Philip asked of Jesus.
   'He is in me,' Jesus said,
   'I am in the Father.'

9. 'I in you and you in me,
   we are one together.
   Father, may we all be one,
   serving one another.'

10. 'If you love me, keep my word.
    Thus my Father loves you.
    We shall make our home in you.
    You shall live for ever.'

11. 'I have said these things to you
    while I still am with you.
    In my name the Spirit comes,
    sent soon from my Father.'

12. 'My own peace I give to you,
    not of this world's giving.
    Fear must not constrain your heart.
    My own peace I leave you.'

Text: Noel Donnelly (b.1932) based on John 13 and 14
Music: Noel Donnelly (b.1932)

378 I watch the sunrise
Close to you

2. I watch the sunlight shine through the clouds,
   warming the earth below.
   And at the mid-day, life seems to say:
   'I feel your brightness near me.'
   For you are always . . .

3. I watch the sunset fading away,
   lighting the clouds with sleep.
   And as the evening closes its eyes,
   I feel your presence near me.
   For you are always . . .

4. I watch the moonlight guarding the night,
   waiting till morning comes.
   The air is silent, earth is at rest
   – only your peace is near me.
   Yes you are always . . .

Text: John Glynn (b.1948)
Music: Colin Murphy arr. Christopher Tambling

379 I will be with you

I will be with you wher - e - ver you go. Go now through - out the world! I will be with you in all that you say. Go now and

spread my word! 1. Come,

walk with me on stor - my

wa - ters. Why fear? Reach out, and

I'll be there.

2. And you, my friend, will you now leave me,
   or do you know me as your Lord?

3. Your life will be transformed with power
   by living truly in my name.

4. And if you say: 'Yes, Lord, I love you,'
   then feed my lambs and feed my sheep.

Text: Gerard Markland (b.1953)
Music: Gerard Markland (b.1953) arr. Christopher Tambling

LITURGICAL
HYMNS OLD & NEW

380 I will bless the Lord

2. When I was in pain,
   when I lived in fear,
   I was calling out to him.
   He rescued me from death,
   he wiped my tears away,
   I will sing your praise, O Lord.

3. Trust him with your life,
   trust him with today,
   come and praise the Lord with me;
   O come and know his love,
   O taste and understand,
   let us sing your praise, O Lord.

Text: Susan Sayers (b.1946) based on Psalm 33
Music: Andrew Moore (b.1954)

381 I will enter his gates
He has made me glad

I will en - ter his gates with thanks-giv-ing in my heart, I will
en - ter his courts with praise, I will say this is the day that the
Lord has made, I will re - joice for he has made me
glad. He has made me glad, he has made me glad, I
will re - joice for he has made me glad.

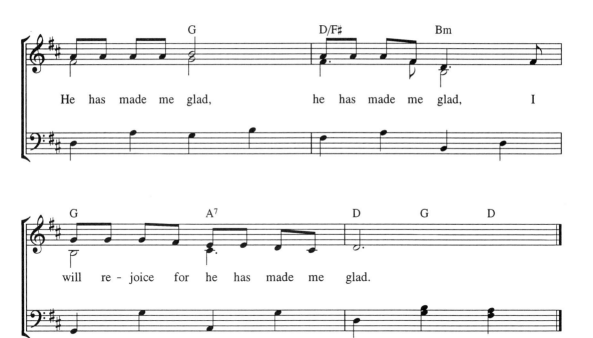

He has made me glad, he has made me glad, I

will re - joice for he has made me glad.

Words and Music: Leona von Brethorst

382 I will never forget you

1. I will ne - ver for - get you, my peo - ple;

I have carved you on the palm of my hand.

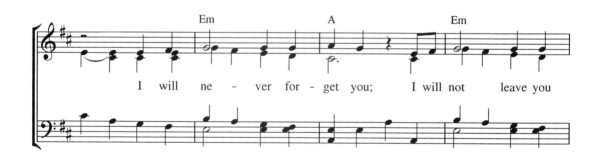

I will ne - ver for - get you; I will not leave you

or - phaned. I will ne - ver for - get my own.

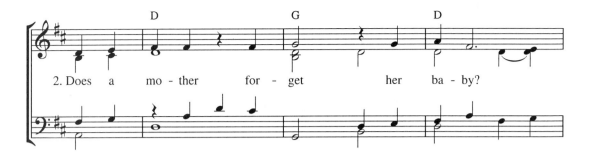

2. Does a mo - ther for - get her ba - by?

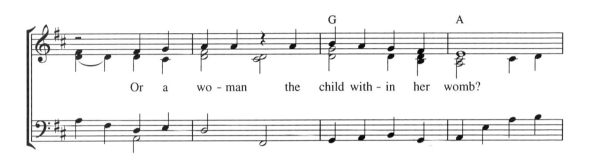

Or a wo - man the child with - in her womb?

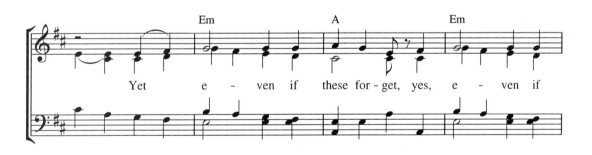

Yet e - ven if these for - get, yes, e - ven if

these for - get, I will ne - ver for - get my own.

Text: Carey Landry based on Isaiah 49:15-16
Music: Carey Landry arr. Christopher Tambling

383 I will seek your face, O Lord

1. Lord, how awe-some is your pre - sence.

Who can stand in your light?

Those who by your grace and mer - cy

are made ho - ly in your sight.

D.C. al Fine

2. I will dwell in your presence
all the days of my life;
there to gaze upon your glory,
and to worship only you.

Text and Music: Noel and Tricia Richards

384 I will sing a song

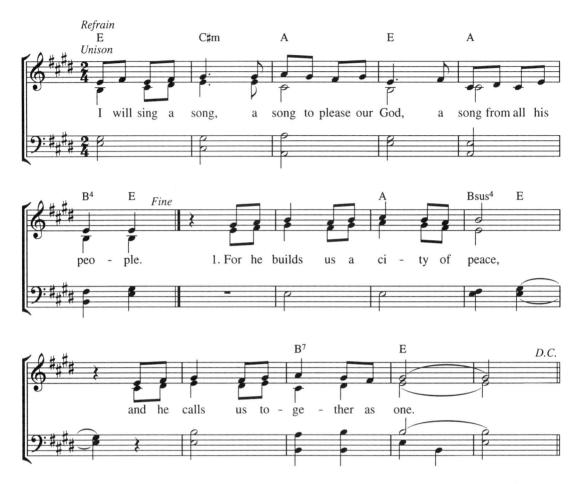

I will sing a song, a song to please our God, a song from all his peo - ple.

1. For he builds us a ci - ty of peace, and he calls us to - ge - ther as one.

2. We were scattered, but he called us home;
   broken-hearted but now we are whole.

3. We are healed – he has bound up our wounds,
   he who calls all the stars by their names.

4. He is God of the world that he made,
   he is God of the poor that he helps.

5. How he covers the heavens with clouds!
   How he clothes mountain valleys with green!

6. He sends food to young ravens in need.
   he will come if you wait for his love.

7. To the Father and Son sing a song,
   to the Spirit who fills us with life.

Text: Damian Lundy (1944-1997) based on Psalm 146
Music: Joseph Gelineau (b.1920)

385 I will sing, I will sing

1. I will sing, I will sing a song un-to the Lord. I will
Refrain: Al - le - lu, al - le - lu - ia, glo - ry to the Lord. Al - le -

sing, I will sing a song un-to the Lord. I will sing, I will sing a song
lu, al - le - lu - ia, glo - ry to the Lord. Al- le - lu, al - le - lu - ia, glo-

un - to the Lord. Al - le - lu - ia, glo - ry to the Lord.
- ry to the Lord. Al- le - lu - ia, glo - ry to the Lord.

2. We will come, we will come as one before the Lord. *(x3)*
   Alleluia, glory to the Lord.

3. If the Son, if the Son shall make you free, *(x3)*
   you shall be free indeed.

4. They that sow in tears shall reap in joy. *(x3)*
   Alleluia, glory to the Lord.

5. Ev'ry knee shall bow and ev'ry tongue confess *(x3)*
   that Jesus Christ is Lord.

6. In his name, in his name we have the victory. *(x3)*
   Alleluia, glory to the Lord.

Text: Max Dyer (b.1951)
Music: Max Dyer (b.1951) arr. Christopher Tambling

386 I will walk in the presence of God

2. Your servant, Lord, is ever trusting.
   My bonds you have loosened with care.
   I offer thanks and sacrifice,
   I will walk in the presence of God.

3. My vows to God I keep with gladness,
   I dwell in the house of my Lord.
   My promises I will fulfil.
   I will walk in the presence of God.

Text: Noel Donnelly (b.1931) based on Psalm 115
Music: Noel Donnelly (b.1931)

387 Jerusalem the golden

EWING 76 76 D

1. Je - ru - sa - lem the gold - en, with milk and hon - ey blest, be - neath thy con - tem - pla - tion sink heart and voice op - pressed. I know not, ah, I know not what joys a-wait us there, what ra - dian - cy of glo - ry, what bliss be - yond com-pare.

2. They stand, those halls of Zion,
all jubilant with song,
and bright with many angels,
and all the martyr throng;
the prince is ever with them,
the daylight is serene;
the pastures of the blessèd
are decked in glorious sheen.

3. There is the throne of David;
and there, from care released,
the shout of them that triumph,
the song of them that feast;
and they, who with their leader
have fully run the race,
are robed in white for ever
before their Saviour's face.

4. O sweet and blessèd country,
the home of God's elect!
O sweet and blessèd country
that eager hearts expect!
Jesus, in mercy, bring us
to that dear land of rest;
who art, with God the Father
and Spirit, ever blest.

Text: from 'De Contemptu Mundi' by St Bernard of Cluny (12th century)
trans. John Mason Neale (1818-1866) alt.
Music: Alexander Ewing (1830-1895)

388 Jesus calls us

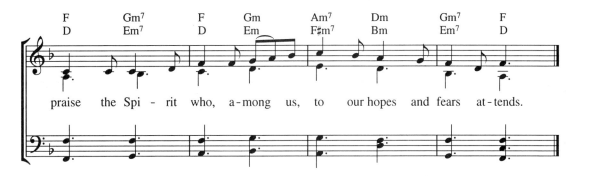

praise the Spi - rit who, a-mong us, to our hopes and fears at-tends.

2. Jesus call us to confess him
   Word of life and Lord of All,
   sharer of our flesh and frailness
   saving all who fail or fall.
   Tell his holy human story;
   tell his tales that all may hear;
   tell the world that Christ in glory
   came to earth to meet us here.

3. Jesus calls us to each other:
   found in him are no divides.
   Race and class and sex and language –
   such are barriers he derides.
   Join the hand of friend and stranger;
   join the hands of age and youth;
   join the faithful and the doubter
   in their common search for truth.

4. Jesus calls us to his table,
   rooted firm in time and space,
   where the Church in earth and heaven
   finds a common meeting place.
   Share the bread and wine, his body;
   share the love of which we sing;
   share the feast for saints and sinners
   hosted by our Lord and King.

Text: John L. Bell (b.1949) and Graham Maule (b.1958)
Music: Gaelic air, adapted and arr. John L. Bell (b.1949) and Graham Maule (b.1958)

389 Jesus Christ is risen today

EASTER HYMN 77 77 and Alleluias

1. Je - sus Christ is ris'n to - day, al - le - lu - ia!
our tri - um - phant ho - ly day, al - le - lu - ia!
who did once, u - pon the cross, al - le - lu - ia!
suf - fer to re - deem our loss, al - le - lu - ia!

A lower setting will be found at No. 199

2. Hymns of praise then let us sing, alleluia!
unto Christ, our heav'nly King, alleluia!
who endured the cross and grave, alleluia!
sinners to redeem and save, alleluia!

3. But the pains that he endured, alleluia!
our salvation have procured; alleluia!
now above the sky he's King, alleluia!
where the angels ever sing, alleluia!

Text: v.1 'Surrexit hodie' (14th century), anonymous translation, as in 'Lyra Davidica' (1708);
vs. 2-3 from J. Arnold's 'Compleat Psalmodist' (1749)
Music: melody from 'Lyra Davidica' (1708), harmony by William Henry Monk (1823-1889)

390 Jesus Christ is waiting

NOEL NOUVELET 11 11 10 11

1. Je - sus Christ is wait - ing, wait - ing in the streets:
no one is his neigh - bour, all a - lone he eats.
Lis - ten, Lord Je - sus, I am lone - ly too;
make me, friend or stran - ger, fit to wait on you.

2. Jesus Christ is raging,
   raging in the streets
   where injustice spirals
   and all hope retreats.
   Listen, Lord Jesus,
   I am angry too;
   in the kingdom's causes
   let me rage with you.

3. Jesus Christ is healing,
   healing in the streets
   curing those who suffer,
   touching those he greets.
   Listen, Lord Jesus,
   I have pity too;
   let my care be active,
   healing just like you.

4. Jesus Christ is dancing,
   dancing in the streets,
   where each sign of hatred
   his strong love defeats.
   Listen, Lord Jesus,
   I feel triumph too;
   on suspicion's graveyard,
   let me dance with you.

5. Jesus Christ is calling,
   calling in the streets,
   'Come and walk faith's tightrope,
   I will guide your feet.'
   Listen, Lord Jesus,
   let my fears be few;
   walk one step before me,
   I will follow you.

Text: John L. Bell (b.1949) and Graham Maule (b.1958)
Music: traditional French melody arr. John Rombaut

391 Jesus, ever-flowing fountain
Come to me

COME TO ME 87 87 and Refrain

Je-sus, e-ver-flow-ing foun-tain, give us wa - ter from your well.

In the gra-cious gift you of - fer there is joy no tongue can tell.

1. Come to me, all pil-grims thir - sty, drink the wa - ter I will give.

If you knew what gift I of - fer, you would come to me and live.

2. Come to me, all trav'lers weary,
   come that I may give you rest.
   Drink the cup of life I offer;
   at this table be my guest.

3. Come to me, believers burdened,
   find refreshment in this place.
   If you knew the gift I offer,
   you would turn and seek my face.

4. Come to me, repentant sinners;
   leave behind your guilt and shame.
   If you knew divine compassion,
   you would turn and call my name.

5. Come to me distressed and needy;
   I would be your trusted friend.
   If you seek the gift I offer,
   come, your open hands extend.

6. Come to me abandoned, orphaned;
   lonely ways no longer roam.
   If you knew the gift I offer,
   you would make in me your home.

Text: Delores Dufner
Music: Rosalie Bonighton (b.1946)

392 Jesus, gentlest Saviour

PRINCETHORPE 65 65 D

1. Je - sus, gent - lest Sa - viour, God of might and power,
thou thy - self art dwell - ing in us at this hour.
Na - ture can - not hold thee, heav'n is all too strait
for thine end - less glo - ry, and thy roy - al state.

A lower setting will be found at No. 247

2. Yet the hearts of children,
   hold what worlds cannot,
   and the God of wonders
   loves the lowly spot.
   Jesus, gentlest Saviour,
   thou art in us now,
   fill us full of goodness,
   till our hearts o'erflow.

3. Pray the prayer within us
   that to heav'n shall rise;
   sing the song that angels
   sing above the skies;
   multiply our graces,
   chiefly love and fear;
   and, dear Lord, the chiefest,
   grace to persevere.

Text: Frederick William Faber (1814-1863)
Music: William Pitts (1829-1903)

LITURGICAL

HYMNS OLD & NEW

393 Jesus is God

ELLACOMBE 76 76 D

1. Je - sus is God! The so - lid earth, the o - cean broad and bright, the
count - less stars, the gol - den dust, that strew the skies at night, the
wheel - ing storm, the dread - ful fire, the pleas - ant whole - some air, the
sum - mer's sun, the win - ter's frost, his own cre - a - tions were.

2. Jesus is God! The glorious bands
   of golden angels sing
   songs of adoring praise to him,
   their Maker and their King.
   He was true God in Bethlehem's crib,
   on Calv'ry's cross, true God,
   he who in heav'n eternal reigned,
   in time on earth abode.

3. Jesus is God! Let sorrow come,
   and pain and ev'ry ill;
   all are worthwhile, for all are meant
   his glory to fulfil;
   worthwhile a thousand years of life
   to speak one little word,
   if by our Credo we might own
   the Godhead of our Lord.

Text: Frederick William Faber (1814-1863)
Music: from the 'Württemberg Gesangbuch' (1784)

394 Jesus is Lord! Creation's voice proclaims it

JESUS IS LORD 11 12 11 12 and Refrain

1. Jesus is Lord! Creation's voice proclaims it,
for by his pow'r each tree and flow'r was planned and made.
Jesus is Lord! The universe declares it;
sun, moon and stars in heaven cry: Jesus is Lord!

Refrain
Jesus is Lord! Jesus is Lord!

Praise him with al - le - lu - ias, for Je - sus is Lord!

2. Jesus is Lord! Yet from his throne eternal
   in flesh he came to die in pain on Calv'ry's tree.
   Jesus is Lord! From him all life proceeding,
   yet gave his life as ransom thus setting us free.

3. Jesus is Lord! O'er sin the mighty conqu'ror,
   from death he rose and all his foes shall own his name.
   Jesus is Lord! God sends his Holy Spirit
   to show by works of power that Jesus is Lord.

Text and Music: David J. Mansell

LITURGICAL

HYMNS OLD & NEW

395 Jesus is Lord! In love he came

MALVERN 88 88 8

1. Je - sus is Lord! In love he came to glo - ri -
fy the Fa - ther's name. To die, to rise, and
in that hour re - lease the Spi - rit's heal - ing
power. Al - le - lu - ia! Al - le - lu - ia!

2. Jesus is Lord! He'll come again,
   in empty hearts take up his reign;
   where living springs of water flow
   in desert land, new orchards grow.

3. Jesus is Lord! Be still for he
   will come with healing, quietly.
   Deep in your heart, you'll hear his voice,
   and in that stillness you'll rejoice.

4. Jesus is Lord! Be glad and know
   he is the way by which we go
   into our Father's home to share
   the joyful welcome waiting there.

5. Jesus is Lord! His victory
   the deaf will hear, the blind will see,
   and from their graves the dead will rise,
   with saints and angels crowd the skies.

Text: Damian Lundy (1944-1997)
Music: Edward Elgar (1857-1934) adapted by Alan Ridout (1934-1996)

396 Jesus, Lord of glory

ADORO TE 11 11 11 11

1. Jesus, Lord of glory, clothed in heaven's light,
here I bow before you, hidden from my sight.
Lord to whom my body, mind and heart belong,
mind and heart here falter, Love so deep, so strong.

Another translation of this hymn will be found at No. 287

2. Here distrust, my spirit, eye and tongue and hand,
   trust faith's ear and listen, hear and understand.
   Hear the voice of Wisdom, speaking now to you;
   when God's Word has spoken, what can be more true?

3. Once you hid your glory, Jesus crucified,
   now you hide your body, Jesus glorified.
   When you come in judgement, plain for all to see,
   God and man in splendour, Lord, remember me.

4. Once you showed to Thomas wounded hands and side.
   Here I kneel adoring, faith alone my guide.
   Help me grow in faith, Lord, grow in hope and love,
   living by your Spirit, gift of God above.

5. Here I see your dying, Jesus, victim-priest,
   here I know your rising, host and guest and feast.
   Let me taste your goodness, manna from the skies,
   feed me, heal me, save me, food of Paradise.

6. Heart of Jesus, broken, pierced and open wide,
   wash me in the water flowing from your side.
   Jesus' blood so precious that one drop could free
   all the world from evil, come and ransom me.

7. How I long to see you, Jesus, face to face,
   how the heart is thirsting, living spring of grace.
   Show me soon your glory, be my great reward,
   be my joy for ever, Jesus, gracious Lord.

Text: 'Adoro te devote' ascribed to St Thomas Aquinas (1227-1274) trans. James Quinn (b.1919)
Music: Plainsong arr. Gregory Murray (1905-1992)

397 Jesus, my Lord, my God, my all

CORPUS CHRISTI LM and Refrain

1. Jesus, my Lord, my God, my all, how can I love thee as I ought? And how revere this wondrous gift so far surpassing hope or thought?

Refrain

Sweet Sacrament, we thee adore; O make us love thee more and more.

2. Had I but Mary's sinless heart
to love thee with, my dearest King,
O, with what bursts of fervent praise
thy goodness, Jesus, would I sing!

3. Ah, see, within a creature's hand
the vast Creator deigns to be,
reposing, infant-like, as though
on Joseph's arm, or Mary's knee.

4. Thy body, soul and Godhead, all;
O mystery of love divine!
I cannot compass all I have,
for all thou hast and art are mine.

5. Sound, sound, his praises higher still,
and come, ye angels, to our aid;
'tis God, 'tis God, the very God
whose pow'r both us and angels made.

Text: Frederick William Faber (1814-1863)
Music: from 'Crown of Jesus' hymn book (1894)

398 Jesus, Name above all names

Text: Naida Hearn (b.1944)
Music: Naida Hearn (b.1944) arr. Roland Fudge

399 Jesus rose on Easter Day

RESONET IN LAUDIBUS 777 11

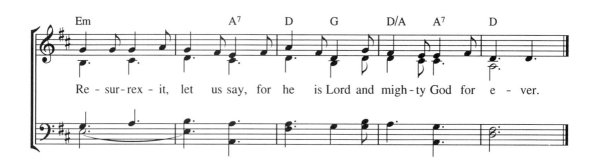

2. He has conquered death and sin.
   All God's people now begin
   singing praises unto him,
   for he is Lord and mighty God for ever.

3. 'Alleluia' is our cry,
   for he lives, no more to die.
   Glory be to God on high,
   for he is Lord and mighty God for ever.

4. Alleluia! May we know
   all the joy which long ago
   set the Easter sky aglow,
   for he is Lord and mighty God for ever.

5. Alleluia! Let us be
   filled with love, our hearts set free
   as we praise his victory,
   for he is Lord and mighty God for ever.

Text: Damian Lundy (1944-1997)
Music: German carol melody (16th century) arr. Andrew Moore

400 Jesu, the very thought of thee

TOZER CM

1. Je - su, the ve - ry thought of thee with

sweet - ness fills my breast; but sweet - er far thy

face to see, and in thy pres - ence rest.

2. No voice can sing, no heart can frame,
   nor can the mind recall,
   a sweeter sound than thy blest name,
   O Saviour of us all.

3. O hope of ev'ry contrite heart,
   O joy of all the meek,
   to those who fall, how kind thou art,
   how good to those who seek!

4. But what to those who find? Ah, this
   no tongue nor pen can show;
   the love of Jesus, what it is
   none but his lovers know.

5. Jesu, our only joy be thou,
   as thou our prize wilt be,
   Jesu, be thou our glory now,
   and through eternity.

Text: 11th century trans. Edward Caswall (1814-1878) alt.
Music: A. Edmunds Tozer (1857-1910)

401 Jesus, the Word, has lived among us

WHENCE IS THAT GOODLY FRAGRANCE? 98 98 98

1. Je-sus, the Word, has lived a-mong us, shar-ing his full - ness, truth and grace, God's on-ly Son, the Fa-ther's loved one re-veals him to the hu - man race. Je-sus, the Word, has lived a - mong us shar-ing his full - ness, truth and grace.

2. He was with God from the beginning
   and through him all things came to be.
   He lightens darkness, conquers evil,
   gives life for living, glad and free.
   He was with God from the beginning
   and through him all things came to be.

3. Sing praise to God who sent Christ Jesus
   to be his sign of endless love;
   sent him to live his life among us,
   lifting our hearts to things above.
   Sing praise to God who sent Christ Jesus
   to be his sign of endless love!

Text: Keith D. Pearson based on John 1 and 3
Music: French carol melody arr. Andrew Moore
Text © 1996 Keith D. Pearson. Used by permission. This arrangement © Copyright 1999 Kevin Mayhew Ltd.

402 Jesus, who condemns you?
The Stations of the Cross

HOLY CROSS 65 65

1. Je - sus, who con - demns you? Who cries 'Cru - ci - fy'?
Priest or po - li - ti - cian? Je - sus, is it I?

2. Heavy, oh too heavy,
   weighs a world of hate;
   Christ, be our Redeemer,
   Jesus, bear the weight.

3. Perfect in obedience
   to your Father's call,
   Christ, creation's glory,
   shares creation's fall.

4. Where the humble suffer,
   and the proud deride,
   Mary, blessed Mother,
   calls us to your side.

5. Christ, our only Saviour,
   you must bear the loss;
   yet give us compassion,
   let us bear the cross.

6. Christ, where now you suffer,
   in each painful place,
   let each act of kindness
   still reveal your face.

7. Mortal flesh exhausted,
   tortured sinews fail,
   yet the spirit triumphs,
   and the will prevails.

8. Still the faithful women
   stand beside the way,
   weeping for the victims
   of the present day.

9. Bowed beneath the burden
   of creation's pain,
   Saviour, be beside us
   when we fall again.

10. Church of God, resplendent
    in the robes of pow'r,
    be the Saviour's body,
    share his triumph hour!

11. All the pow'rs of evil
    join to strike the nail;
    patience and compassion
    silently prevail.

12. Lonely and forsaken,
    in this dying breath,
    love alone can bear him
    through the veil of death.

13. Arms that cradled Jesus,
    both at death and birth,
    cradle all who suffer
    in the pains of earth.

14. Christ, who came with nothing
    from your Mother's womb,
    rest in destitution,
    in a borrowed tomb.

15. Broken but triumphant,
    birthing gain from loss,
    let us share your glory,
    let us share your cross.

Text: Michael Forster (b.1946)
Music: Andrew Moore (b.1954)
© Copyright 1997 Kevin Mayhew Ltd.

403 Join in the dance

Join in the dance of the earth's ju-bi-la - tion!
This is the feast of the love of God.
Shout from the heights to the ends of cre-a - tion:
Je - sus the Sa - viour is ris - en from the grave!
grave! 1. Wake, O

2. All creation, like a mother,
   labours to give birth.
   Soon the pain will be forgotten,
   joy for all the earth!

3. Now our shame becomes our glory
   on this holy tree.
   Now the reign of death is ended;
   now we are set free!

4. None on earth, no prince or power,
   neither death nor life,
   nothing now can ever part us
   from the love of Christ.

5. Love's triumphant day of vict'ry
   heaven opens wide.
   On the tree of hope and glory
   death itself has died!

6. Christ for ever, Lord of ages,
   love beyond our dreams:
   Christ our hope of heaven's glory,
   all that yet will be!

Text: Dan Schutte
Music: Dan Schutte arr. Keith Stent

404 Joy to the world

ANTIOCH CM

1. Joy to the world! The Lord is come; let earth receive her King; let ev-'ry heart prepare him room, and heav'n and na-ture sing, and heav'n and na-ture sing, and heav'n, and heav'n and na-ture sing.

2. Joy to the earth! The Saviour reigns;
   let us our songs employ;
   while fields and floods, rocks, hills and plains
   repeat the sounding joy,
   repeat the sounding joy,
   repeat, repeat the sounding joy.

3. He rules the world with truth and grace,
   and makes the nations prove
   the glories of his righteousness,
   and wonders of his love,
   and wonders of his love,
   and wonders, and wonders of his love.

Text: Isaac Watts (1674-1748) based on Psalm 97 alt.
Music: George Frideric Handel (1685-1759)

405 Jubilate Deo

2. To the Lord offer thanks and give praise to his name;
   sing aloud new songs to proclaim his mighty power.

3. For the Word of the Lord is both faithful and sure;
   all the things he does show his justice, truth and love.

4. All creation is filled with the love of the Lord;
   everything that is was created through the Word.

5. May the People of God in all ages be bless'd;
   day by day his grace is outpoured upon us all.

6. May our hearts never waver, but trust in the Lord;
   he, the living God, is both merciful and good.

7. May your love, Lord, be with us in all that we do;
   all our hope and longing we humbly place in you.

Text: Jean-Paul Lécot (b.1947) based on Psalm 32 trans. W. R. Lawrence alt.
Music: Jean-Paul Lécot (b.1947)
© Copyright 1988 Kevin Mayhew Ltd.

406 Jubilate, everybody

JUBILATE DEO 88 87 88 86

Text and Music: Fred Dunn (1907-1979)

407 Keep in mind

Refrain
Unison

Keep in mind that Je-sus Christ has died for us and is ri-sen from the dead. He is our sav-ing Lord, he is joy for all a - ges.

Fine

D.C.

1. If we die with the Lord, we shall live with the Lord.
2. If we en-dure with the Lord, we shall reign with the Lord.

D.C.

3. In him hope of glo - ry, in him all our love.
4. In him our re-demp - tion, in him all our grace.
5. In him our sal-va - tion, in him all our peace.

Text: Lucien Deiss (b.1921) based on 2 Timothy 2:8-11
Music: Lucien Deiss (b.1921)

408 King of glory, King of peace

GWALCHMAI 74 74 D

1. King of glo - ry, King of peace, I will love thee;
and, that love may ne - ver cease, I will move thee.
Thou hast gran - ted my ap - peal, thou hast heard me;
thou didst note my ar - dent zeal, thou hast spared me.

2. Wherefore with my utmost art,
   I will sing thee,
   and the cream of all my heart
   I will bring thee.
   Though my sins against me cried,
   thou didst clear me,
   and alone, when they replied,
   thou didst hear me.

3. Sev'n whole days, not one in sev'n,
   I will praise thee;
   in my heart, though not in heav'n,
   I can raise thee.
   Small it is, in this poor sort
   to enrol thee:
   e'en eternity's too short
   to extol thee.

Text: George Herbert (1593-1633)
Music: John David Jones (1827-1870)

409 King of kings and Lord of lords

May be sung as a 2-part round, the second voices beginning when the first voices reach B

King of kings and Lord of lords, glo-ry, hal-le-lu-jah.

King of kings and Lord of lords, glo-ry, hal-le-lu-jah.

Je - sus, Prince of Peace, glo-ry, hal-le-lu-jah.

Optional ending

Je - sus, Prince of Peace, glo-ry, hal-le-lu-jah.

Text and Music: Naomi Batya and Sophie Conty

410 Lamb of God, Holy One

Text and Music: Chris Bowater

LITURGICAL

HYMNS OLD & NEW

411 Lauda, Jerusalem

Response

D · · · G A⁷ D · Em A⁷ D · A

Lau - da, Je-ru-sa-lem, Do - mi-num. Lau - da De-um tu-um Zi - on.

F♯ · Bm A · D · A⁷ D G · D A⁷ D · *Fine*

Ho - san - na! Ho - san - na! Ho - san - na fi-li-o Da - vid!

D · · G · D

1. O praise the Lord, Je - ru - sa - lem!
2. He has strengthened the bars of your gates,
3. He has established peace on your borders,
4. He sends out his word to the earth
5. He showers down snow white as wool,
6. He hurls down hail - stones like crumbs.
7. He sends forth his word and it melts them:
8. He makes his word known to Jacob,
9. He has not dealt thus with o - ther nations;

G · A⁷ · D · *D.C.*

1. O Zion, sing praise to your God!
2. he has blessed the child - ren with - in you.
3. he feeds you with fin - est wheat.
4. and swiftly runs his com - mand.
5. he scatters hoar - frost like ashes.
6. The waters are fro - zen at his touch.
7. at the breath of his mouth the wa - ters flow.
8. to Israel his laws and de - crees.
9. he has not taught them his de - crees.

Text: Psalm 147, Grail translation
Music: Response – Th. Deckers; Verses – Alexandre Lesbordes

412 Laudato sii, O mi Signore

in the wind, air and fire and flow - ing wa - ter.

2. For our sister, mother earth,
   she who feeds us and sustains us;
   for her fruits, her grass, her flowers,
   for the mountains and the oceans.

3. Praise for those who spread forgiveness,
   those who share your peace with others,
   bearing trials and sickness bravely!
   Even sister death won't harm them.

4. For our life is but a song,
   and the reason for our singing
   is to praise you for the music;
   join the dance of your creation.

5. Praise to you, Father most holy,
   praise and thanks to you, Lord Jesus,
   praise to you, most Holy Spirit,
   life and joy of all creation!

The Italian phrase 'Laudate sii, O mi Signore'
translates as 'Praise be to you, O my Lord'.

Text: Damian Lundy (1944-1997) from St Francis of Assisi (1182-1226)
Music: unknown Italian origin arr. Christopher Tambling

413 Lay your hands gently upon us

You were sent to give sight to the blind.

You de - sire to heal all our ill - ness.

Lay your hands, gent - ly lay your hands.

2. Lord, we come to you through one another,
   Lord, we come to you in all our need.
   Lord, we come to you seeking wholeness.
   Lay your hands, gently lay your hands.

Text: Carey Landry
Music: Carey Landry arr. Christopher Tambling

LITURGICAL
HYMNS OLD & NEW

414 Leader, now on earth no longer

SWAVESEY 87 87 and Refrain

1. Lead - er, now on earth no lon-ger, sol-dier of th'e-ter-nal King, vic - tor in the fight for hea - ven, we thy lov - ing prai - ses sing.

Refrain

Great Saint George, our pat - ron, help us, in the con - flict be thou nigh; help us in that dai - ly bat - tle, where each one must win or die.

2. Praise him who in deadly battle
   never shrank from foeman's sword,
   proof against all earthly weapon,
   gave his life for Christ the Lord.

3. Who, when earthly war was over,
   fought, but not for earth's renown;
   fought, and won a nobler glory,
   won the martyr's purple crown.

4. Help us when temptation presses,
   we have still our crown to win;
   help us when our soul is weary
   fighting with the pow'rs of sin.

5. Clothe us in thy shining armour,
   place thy good sword in our hand;
   teach us how to wield it, fighting
   onward t'wards the heav'nly land.

6. Onward till, our striving over,
   on life's battlefield we fall,
   resting then, but ever ready,
   waiting for the angel's call.

Text: Joseph W. Reeks (1849-1900)
Music: J. Crookall (1821-1887)

415 Lead, kindly light

TUNE 1: SANDON 10 4 10 4 10 10

1. Lead, kind-ly light, a-mid th'en-cir-cling gloom, lead thou me on; the night is dark, and I am far from home; lead thou me on. Keep thou my feet; I do not ask to see the dis-tant scene; one step e-nough for me.

2. I was not ever thus, nor prayed that thou
  shouldst lead me on;
 I loved to choose and see my path; but now
  lead thou me on.
 I loved the garish day, and, spite of fears,
 pride ruled my will: remember not past years.

3. So long thy pow'r hath blest me, sure it still
  will lead me on,
 o'er moor and fen, o'er crag and torrent, till
  the night is gone;
 and with the morn those angel faces smile,
 which I have loved long since, and lost awhile.

TUNE 2: LUX BENIGNA 10 4 10 4 10 10

1. Lead, kind - ly light, a - mid th'en - cir - cling gloom,
lead thou me on; the night is dark, and I am far from
home; lead thou me on. Keep thou my
feet; I do not ask to see
the dis - tant scene; one step e - nough for me.

Text: John Henry Newman (1801-1890)
Music: Tune 1 – Charles Henry Purday (1799-1885)
Tune 2 – John Bacchus Dykes (1823-1876)

416 Lead us, heavenly Father, lead us

MANNHEIM 87 87 87

1. Lead us, heav'n-ly Fa-ther, lead us o'er the world's tem - pes-tuous sea;
guard us, guide us, keep us, feed us, for we have no help but thee;
yet pos - ses - sing ev - 'ry bless - ing if our God our Fa - ther be.

2. Saviour, breathe forgiveness o'er us,
   all our weakness thou dost know,
   thou didst tread this earth before us,
   thou didst feel its keenest woe;
   lone and dreary, faint and weary,
   through the desert thou didst go.

3. Spirit of our God, descending,
   fill our hearts with heav'nly joy,
   love with ev'ry passion blending,
   pleasure that can never cloy;
   thus provided, pardoned, guided,
   nothing can our peace destroy.

Text: James Edmeston (1791-1867)
Music: Friedrich Filitz (1804-1876)

417 Leave your country and your people

Refrain
Unison

Leave your coun-try and your peo - ple, leave your fam'- ly and your friends.

Trav - el to the land I'll show you; God will bless the ones he sends.

1. Go, like A - bra-ham be-fore you, when he heard the Fa-ther's call,

walk - ing forth in faith and trust - ing; God is mas-ter of us all.

2. Sometimes God's word is demanding,
   leave security you know,
   breaking ties and bonds that hold you,
   when the voice of God says, 'Go'.

3. Take the path into the desert;
   barren seems the rock and sand.
   God will lead you through the desert
   when you follow his command.

4. Go with courage up the mountain,
   climb the narrow, rocky ledge,
   leave behind all things that hinder,
   go with only God as pledge.

Text: Willard Jabusch (b.1930)
Music: Willard Jabusch (b.1930) arr. Andrew Moore

418 Let all mortal flesh keep silence

PICARDY 87 87 87

1. Let all mor-tal flesh keep sil - ence and with fear and trem - bling stand; pon-der no-thing earh - ly - mind - ed, for with bless-ing in his hand Christ our God on earth des - cend - eth, our full hom -age to de - mand.

2. King of kings, yet born of Mary,
   as of old on earth he stood,
   Lord of lords, in human vesture,
   in the body and the blood.
   He will give to all the faithful
   his own self for heav'nly food.

3. Rank on rank the host of heaven
   spreads its vanguard on the way,
   as the Light of light descendeth
   from the realms of endless day,
   that the pow'rs of hell may vanish
   as the darkness clears away.

4. At his feet the six-winged seraph;
   cherubim, with sleepless eye,
   veil their faces to the Presence,
   as with ceaseless voice they cry,
   alleluia, alleluia,
   alleluia, Lord most high.

Text: Liturgy of St James trans. G. Moultrie (1829-1885)
Music: traditional French melody arr. Christopher Tambling
This arrangement © Copyright 1993 Kevin Mayhew Ltd.

419 Let all that is within me

2. Let all that is within me cry: mighty. *(x2)*
   Mighty, mighty, mighty is the Lamb that was slain.

3. Let all that is within me cry: worthy. *(x2)*
   Worthy, worthy, worthy is the Lamb that was slain.

4. Let all that is within me cry: blessèd. *(x2)*
   Blessèd, blessèd, blessèd is the Lamb that was slain.

5. Let all that is within me cry: Jesus. *(x2)*
   Jesus, Jesus, Jesus is the Lamb that was slain.

Text: unknown
Music: unknown arr. Andrew Moore
This arrangement © Copyright 1999 Kevin Mayhew Ltd.

LITURGICAL

HYMNS OLD & NEW

420 Let all the world in every corner sing

LUCKINGTON 10 4 66 66 10 4

1. Let all the world in ev-'ry cor-ner sing, my God and King! The heav'ns are not too high, his praise may thi-ther fly; the earth is not too low, his prai-ses there may grow. Let all the world in ev-'ry cor-ner sing, my God and King!

2. Let all the world in ev'ry corner sing,
   my God and King!
   The Church with psalms must shout,
   no door can keep them out;
   but, above all, the heart
   must bear the longest part.
   Let all the world in ev'ry corner sing,
   my God and King!

Text: George Herbert (1593-1633)
Music: Basil Harwood (1859-1949)

421 Let love be real

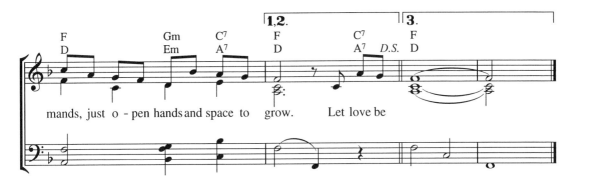

mands, just o - pen hands and space to grow. Let love be

2. Let love be real, not grasping or confining,
   that strange embrace that holds yet sets us free;
   that helps us face the risk of truly living,
   and makes us brave to be what we might be.
   Give me your strength when all my words are weakness;
   give me your love in spite of all you know.

3. Let love be real, with no manipulation,
   no secret wish to harness or control;
   let us accept each other's incompleteness,
   and share the joy of learning to be whole.
   Give me your hope through dreams and disappointments;
   give me your trust when all my failings show.

Text: Michael Forster (b.1946)
Music: Christopher Tambling (b.1964) arr. Keith Stent

422 Let our praise to you be as incense

Let our praise to you be as in-cense, let us

bless your ho-ly name; let our praise to

you be as in-cense, as your glo-ry we pro-

claim. May our voi-ces join with the an-gels

Text: Bryan Spinks based on Psalm 140
Music: Malcolm Archer (b.1952) arr. Andrew Moore

423 Let the heavens declare

1. All the sins we've e-ver sinned died u-pon the cross with him, but we know he lives a-gain: the vic-t'ry is won, the vic-t'ry is won, the vic-t'ry is won, the vic-t'ry is won.

2. Hanging on the cross for me
   Jesus died in agony.
   Blood and tears he shed for me,
   that I might have life. *(x4)*

3. In the kingdom he revealed
   broken hearts can all be healed,
   through the covenant he sealed
   with his holy blood. *(x4)*

Text and Music: Mike Anderson (b.1956)

424 Let the hungry come to me

ADORO TE Plainsong

1. Let the hun-gry come to me, let the poor be fed. Let the thir-sty come and drink, share my wine and bread. Though you have no mon - ey, come to me and eat. Drink the cup I of - fer, feed on fin-est wheat!

2. I myself am living bread;
   feed on me and live.
   In this cup, my blood for you;
   drink the wine I give.
   All who eat my body,
   all who drink my blood
   shall have joy for ever,
   share the life of God.

3. Here among you shall I dwell,
   making all things new.
   You shall be my very own,
   I, your God with you.
   Blest are you invited
   to my wedding feast.
   You shall live for ever,
   all your joys increased.

4. Nourished by the Word of God,
   now we eat the bread.
   With the gift of God's own life,
   hungry hearts are fed.
   Manna in the desert,
   in our darkest night!
   Food for pilgrim people,
   pledge of glory bright!

5. Many grains become one loaf,
   many grapes, the wine.
   So shall we one body be,
   who together dine.
   As the bread is broken,
   as the wine is shared:
   so must we be given,
   caring as Christ cared.

6. Risen Saviour, walk with us,
   lead us by the hand.
   Heal our blinded eyes and hearts,
   help us understand.
   Lord, make known your presence
   at this table blest.
   Stay with us for ever,
   God, our host and guest!

Text: Delores Dufner
Music: Plainsong arr. Gregory Murray (1905-1992)

425 Let there be love

Let there be love shared a-mong us, let there be love in our eyes. May now your love sweep this na-tion; cause us, O Lord, to a-rise. Give us a fresh un-der-stand-ing, bro-ther-ly love that is real. Let there be love shared a-mong us, let there be love.

Text: Dave Bilbrough
Music: Dave Bilbrough arr. Donald Thomson

426 Let the world in concert sing

This song should be unaccompanied

Let the world in con-cert sing prai-ses to our glo-rious King.*

Let the world in con-cert sing prai-ses to our glo-rious King.

Refrain

Al - le-lu - ia, al - le-lu - ia to our King!

Al - le-lu - ia, al - le-lu - ia to our King!

2. Of his pow'r and glory tell;
   all his work he does right well:

3. Come, behold what he has done,
   deeds of wonder, every one:

4. O you fearful ones, draw near;
   praise our God who holds you dear:

5. Let us now in concert sing
   praises to our glorious King: *

* For Eastertide 'risen King' may be substituted

Text: traditional Zulu trans. Helen Taylor, adapted by Tom Colvin
Music: 'Charu chose ngoni' traditional Zulu dance tune

427 Let us sing your glory

Steadily

1. Let us sing your glory, Lord, al-le-lu - ia,
let us praise your name a - dored, al-le-lu - ia.
Joy and beau - ty come from you, al-le-lu - ia,
and each hour your love shines through, al-le-lu - ia. Al-le-
lu - ia, al-le-lu - ia, al-le-lu, al-le-lu - ia.

2. Leaf that quivers on the tree, alleluia,
flowers that we delight to see, alleluia.
Planets as they reel in space, alleluia,
tell us of your pow'r and grace, alleluia.

3. All creation sings your praise, alleluia,
young and old their voices raise, alleluia.
Children as they laugh and sing, alleluia,
to your goodness homage bring, alleluia.

Text and Music: Marie Lydia Pereira arr. Keith Stent

LITURGICAL

HYMNS OLD & NEW

428 Let us, with a gladsome mind

MONKLAND 77 77

1. Let us, with a glad - some mind, praise the Lord, for he is kind;

Refrain

for his mer - cies ay en - dure, e - ver faith - ful, e - ver sure.

2. Let us blaze his name abroad,
   for of gods he is the God;

3. He, with all-commanding might,
   filled the new-made world with light;

4. He the golden-tressèd sun
   caused all day his course to run;

5. And the moon to shine at night,
   'mid her starry sisters bright;

6. All things living he doth feed,
   his full hand supplies their need;

7. Let us, with a gladsome mind,
   praise the Lord, for he is kind;

Text: John Milton (1608-1674) based on Psalm 135
Music: from 'Hymn Tunes of the United Brethren' (1824)
adapt. by John Bernard Wilkes (1785-1869)

429 Lift high the Cross

CRUCIFER 10 10 and Refrain

Refrain
Unison

Lift high the Cross, the love of Christ pro - claim till

all the world a - dore his sa - cred name!

Harmony

1. Come, Christ - ians, fol - low where our Sa - viour trod, o'er

death vic - tor - ious, Christ the Son of God.

2. Led on their way by this triumphant sign,
   the hosts of God in joyful praise combine:

3. Each new disciple of the Crucified
   is called to bear the seal of him who died:

4. Saved by the Cross whereon their Lord was slain,
   now Adam's children their lost home regain:

5. From north and south, from east and west they raise
   in growing harmony their song of praise:

6. O Lord, once lifted on the glorious tree,
   as thou hast promised, draw us unto thee:

7. Let ev'ry race and ev'ry language tell
   of him who saves from fear of death and hell:

8. From farthest regions, let them homage bring,
   and on his Cross adore their Saviour King:

9. Set up thy throne, that earth's despair may cease
   beneath the shadow of its healing peace:

10. For thy blest Cross which doth for all atone,
    creation's praises rise before thy throne:

11. So let the world proclaim with one accord
    the praises of our ever-living Lord.

Text: George William Kitchin (1827-1912) and Michael Robert Newbolt (1874-1956) alt.
Music: Sydney Hugo Nicholson (1875-1947)

430 Lift up your hearts

Refrain

Unison

Lift up your hearts to the Lord in praise of his mer - cy!

Sing out your joy to the Lord: his love is en - dur - ing.

1. Shout with joy to the Lord, all the earth! Praise the glo - ry of his name!

Say to God 'How won-drous your works, how glo-rious your name!'

2. Let the earth worship, singing your praise.
Praise the glory of your name!
Come and see the deeds of the Lord;
come, worship his name!

3. At his touch the dry land did appear;
paths were opened in the sea.
Let the earth rejoice in his might,
the might of his love.

4. Listen now, all you servants of God,
as I tell of his great works.
Blessed be the Lord of my life!
His love shall endure!

431 Like a sea without a shore
Maranatha

1. Like a sea with-out a shore, love di-vine is bound-less.

Time is now and e-ver-more, and his love sur-rounds us.

Refrain

Ma - ra - na - tha! Ma - ra - na - tha!

Ma - ra - na - tha! Come, Lord Je - sus, come!

2. So that we could all be free,
   he appeared among us.
   Blest are those who have not seen,
   yet believe his promise.

3. All our visions, all our dreams,
   are but ghostly shadows
   of the radiant clarity
   waiting at life's close.

4. Death, where is your victory?
   Death, where is your sting?
   Closer than air we breathe
   is our risen King.

'Maranatha' is an Aramaic expression meaning 'Lord, come!'
See 1 Corinthians 16:22

Text and Music: Estelle White (b.1925)

432 Like as the deer

Slow and reflective

Response

Like as the deer that yearns for flow-ing wa - ters, so longs my soul for God, the liv-ing God.

Fine

1. My soul is thirst-ing for God, the God of my life; when can I en-ter and see the face of God?

D.C.

2. These things will I re-mem-ber as I pour out my soul: how I would lead the re-joic-ing crowd in-to the house of God.

D.C.

Text: Psalm 41, Grail translation
Music: Abbaye de Notre Dame de Tamié arr. Charles Watson

433 Like the deer that yearns

BRIXTON CM

2. Gladly I would lead your people,
   rejoicing to your house.
   Trust in God, my soul, and praise him,
   and he will dry your tears.

3. Grief and pain, like roaring torrents,
   had swept my soul away.
   But his mercy is my rescue,
   I will praise him all my days.

4. Weeping, I have heard them taunt me:
   'What help is in your God?'
   Rock of strength, do not forget me,
   in you alone I trust.

5. To the Father praise and honour,
   all glory to the Son,
   honour to the Holy Spirit:
   let God be glorified.

Text: Luke Connaughton (1917-1979) and Kevin Mayhew (b.1942) based on Psalm 41
Music: Kevin Mayhew (b.1942)
© Copyright 1976 Kevin Mayhew Ltd.

434 Like the murmur of the dove's song

BRIDEGROOM 87 87 6

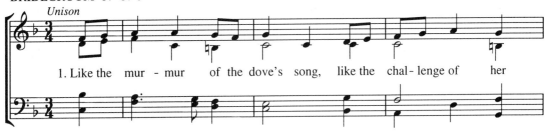

Unison

1. Like the mur - mur of the dove's song, like the chal - lenge of her

flight, like the vig - our of the wind's rush, like the new flame's ea - ger

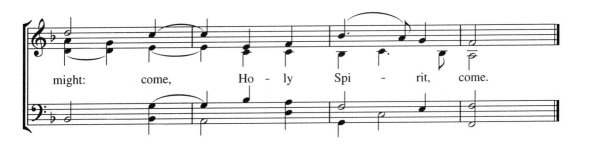

might: come, Ho - ly Spi - rit, come.

2. To the members of Christ's body,
   to the branches of the Vine,
   to the Church in faith assembled,
   to her midst as gift and sign:
   come, Holy Spirit, come.

3. With the healing of division,
   with the ceaseless voice of prayer,
   with the pow'r to love and witness,
   with the peace beyond compare:
   come, Holy Spirit, come.

Text: Carl P. Daw Jr.
Music: Peter Cutts

435 Listen, let your heart keep seeking

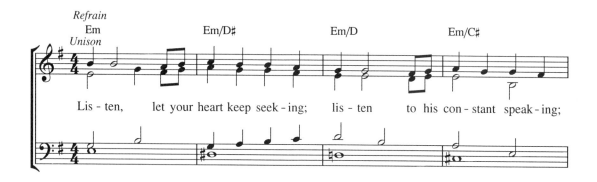

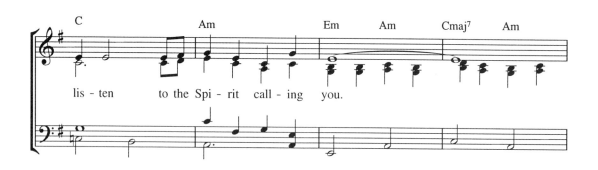

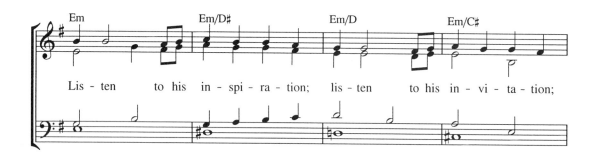

1. He's in the sound of the thun-der, in the whis-per of the breeze.

He's in the might of the whirl-wind, in the roar-ing of the seas.

2. He's in the laughter of children,
   in the patter of the rain.
   Hear him in cries of the suff'ring,
   in their moaning and their pain.

3. He's in the noise of the city,
   in the singing of the birds.
   And in the night-time the stillness
   helps you listen to his word.

Text: Aniceto Nazareth
Music: Aniceto Nazareth arr. Andrew Moore

436 Listen to me, Yahweh

2. Lord, in your goodness, please forgive me;
   listen to me, hear my plea.

3. Lord, you are merciful and faithful;
   turn to me now in my need.

4. Lord, give me strength, I am your servant;
   show me that you really care.

Text: Mike Anderson (b.1956) based on Psalm 85
Music: Mike Anderson (b.1956)

LITURGICAL

HYMNS OLD & NEW

437 Listen to my voice
A healing song

1. Lis-ten to my voice, and then turn back to me:
I will heal your heart, and I will set you free.
Oh, my dear-est child, how much you mean to me:
let me fill your life and love you ten-der-ly.

2. Rest within my arms and let your fears depart,
feel my peace and joy bind up your broken heart.
I will wipe your tears and make you whole again:
come to me, my child, and turn away from sin.

3. Take my hand, and now we will begin once more,
I will walk beside you as I did before.
I have never left you, though your eyes were dim:
walk with me in light, and turn away from sin.

Text: Francesca Leftley (b.1955)
Music: Francesca Leftley (b.1955) arr. Keith Stent
© Copyright 1999 Kevin Mayhew Ltd.

438 Lo, he comes with clouds descending

HELMSLEY 87 87 47

1. Lo, he comes with clouds des - cend - ing, once for mor - tal sin - ners slain; thou - sand thou - sand saints at - tend - ing swell the tri - umph of his train. Al - le -

lu - ia! Al - le - lu - ia! Al - le -

lu - ia! Christ ap - pears on earth to reign.

2. Ev'ry eye shall now behold him
   robed in dreadful majesty;
   we who set at naught and sold him,
   pierced and nailed him to the tree,
   deeply grieving, deeply grieving, deeply grieving,
   shall the true Messiah see.

3. Those dear tokens of his passion
   still his dazzling body bears,
   cause of endless exultation
   to his ransomed worshippers:
   with what rapture, with what rapture, with what rapture
   gaze we on those glorious scars!

4. Yea, amen, let all adore thee,
   high on thine eternal throne;
   Saviour, take the pow'r and glory,
   claim the kingdom for thine own.
   Alleluia! Alleluia! Alleluia!
   Thou shalt reign, and thou alone.

Text: Charles Wesley (1707-1788), John Cennick (1718-1755)
and Martin Madan (1726-1790) alt.
Music: from John Wesley's 'Select Hymns with Tunes Annext' (1765)

439 Longing for light
Christ be our light

Church gath-ered to - day.

2. Longing for peace, our world is troubled.
   Longing for hope, many despair.
   Your word alone has power to save us.
   Make us your living voice.

3. Longing for food, many are hungry.
   Longing for water, still many thirst.
   Make us your bread, broken for others,
   shared until all are fed.

4. Longing for shelter, many are homeless.
   Longing for warmth, many are cold.
   Make us your building, sheltering others,
   walls made of living stone.

5. Many the gifts, many the people,
   many the hearts that yearn to belong.
   Let us be servants to one another,
   making your kingdom come.

Text and Music: Bernadette Farrell

440 Look around you
Kyrie eleison

1. Look a-round you, can you see?
Times are trou-bled, peo-ple grieve.
See the vio-lence, feel the hard-ness;
all my peo - ple, weep with me.

Refrain
Ky - ri - e, e - lei - son. Chris - te, e-

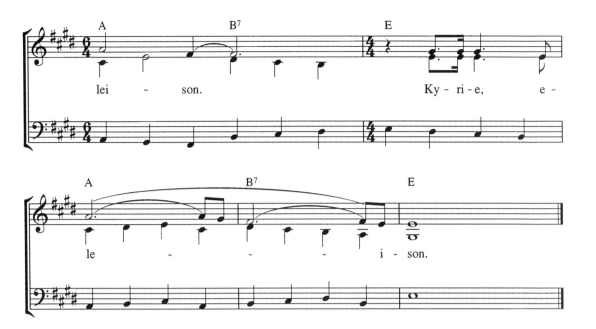

lei - son. Ky - ri - e, e -

le - - - i - son.

2. Walk among them, I'll go with you.
   Reach out to them with my hands.
   Suffer with me, and together
   we will serve them, help them stand.

3. Forgive us, Father; hear our prayer.
   We'll walk with you anywhere,
   through your suff'ring, with forgiveness,
   take your life into the world.

Text: Jodi Page Clark (b.1941)
Music: Jodi Page Clark (b.1941) arr. Christopher Tambling

LITURGICAL

HYMNS OLD & NEW

441 Look at the sky

1. Look at the sky! The stars pro-claim my glo - ry. I am the Lord, the auth-or of your sto - ry. Sing and make mu - sic, share my ce - le - bra - tion! Spread the good news! Bring joy to ev-'ry na - tion. I am your God, your Fa - ther and your joy. You are my own, my chil-dren and my joy!

2. See I am near you, in my own creation!
   May ev'ry moment bring you my salvation!
   The moon is your sister and the sun your brother!
   Living and fruitful is the earth, your mother.

3. Listen to all my Word is still revealing!
   Filled with my Spirit, you will know my healing,
   for I am near you – in your heart I'm living.
   You'll recognise me, loving and forgiving.

4. Know I am with you, I am all around you.
   All my attention and my love surround you.
   You are my children: Jesus is your brother.
   Find me in him, and him in one another.

Text: Damian Lundy (1944-1997)
Music: Traditional Italian melody arr. Andrew Moore
Text and this arrangement © Copyright 1982, 1999 Kevin Mayhew Ltd.

442 Look down, O mother Mary

VAUGHAN 76 76 D and Refrain

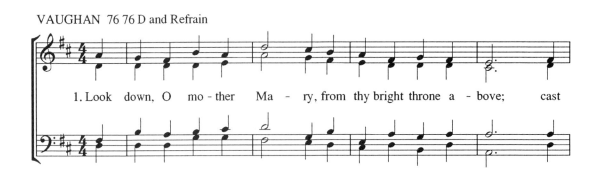

1. Look down, O mo-ther Ma - ry, from thy bright throne a - bove; cast

down u - pon thy chil - dren one on - ly glance of love; and

if a heart so ten - der with pi - ty flows not o'er, then

turn a - way, O mo - ther, and look on us no more.

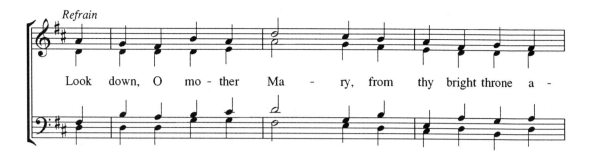

Refrain

Look down, O mo-ther Ma - ry, from thy bright throne a -

bove, cast down u-pon thy chil - dren one on - ly glance of love.

2. See how, ungrateful sinners,
   we stand before thy Son;
   his loving heart upbraids us
   the evil we have done,
   but if thou wilt appease him,
   speak for us but one word;
   for thus thou canst obtain us,
   the pardon of our Lord.

3. O Mary, dearest mother,
   if thou wouldst have us live,
   say that we are thy children,
   and Jesus will forgive.
   Our sins make us unworthy
   that title still to bear,
   but thou art still our mother;
   then show a mother's care.

4. Unfold to us thy mantle,
   there stay we without fear;
   what evil can befall us
   if, mother, thou art near?
   O kindest, dearest mother,
   thy sinful children save;
   look down on us with pity,
   who thy protection crave.

Text: 'Dal tuo celeste' by St Alphonsus (1696-1787) trans. Edmund Vaughan (1827-1908)
Music: John Richardson (1816-1879)

443 Lord, accept the gifts we offer

ST THOMAS 87 87 87

1. Lord, ac-cept the gifts we of-fer at this Eu-cha-ris-tic feast, bread and wine to be trans-formed now through the ac-tion of thy priest. Take us too, Lord, and trans-form us, be thy grace in us in-creased.

A lower setting will be found at No. 509

2. May our souls be pure and spotless
   as the host of wheat so fine;
   may all stain of sin be crushed out,
   like the grape that forms the wine,
   as we, too, become partakers,
   in the sacrifice divine.

3. Take our gifts, almighty Father,
   living God, eternal, true,
   which we give through Christ our Saviour,
   pleading here for us anew.
   Grant salvation to all present,
   and our faith and love renew.

Text: Sister M. Teresine
Music: Samuel Webbe (1740-1816)

444 Lord, enthroned in heavenly splendour

REGENT SQUARE 87 87 87

1. Lord, en-throned in heav'n - ly splen-dour, glo-rious first-born from the dead,
you a - lone our strong de-fen-der lift-ing up your peo-ple's head:
al - le-lu- ia, al - le-lu - ia, Je - sus, true and liv - ing bread!

2. Prince of life, for us now living,
   by your body souls are healed;
   Prince of peace, your pardon giving,
   by your blood our peace is sealed:
   Alleluia, alleluia,
   Word of God in flesh revealed.

3. Paschal Lamb! your off'ring finished,
   once for all, when you were slain;
   in its fulness undiminished
   shall for evermore remain:
   Alleluia, alleluia,
   cleansing souls from ev'ry stain.

4. Great High Priest of our profession,
   through the veil you entered in,
   by your mighty intercession
   grace and mercy there to win:
   Alleluia, alleluia,
   only sacrifice for sin.

5. Life-imparting heav'nly Manna,
   stricken rock, with streaming side;
   heav'n and earth, with loud hosanna,
   worship you, the Lamb who died:
   Alleluia, alleluia,
   ris'n, ascended, glorified!

Text: George Hugh Bourne (1840-1925)
Music: Henry Smart (1813-1879)

LITURGICAL

HYMNS OLD & NEW

445 Lord, for tomorrow and its needs

LORD FOR TOMORROW (PROVIDENCE) 84 84

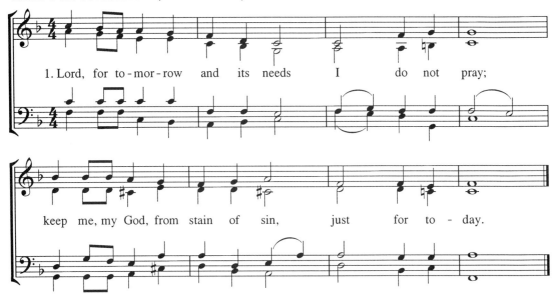

1. Lord, for to-mor-row and its needs I do not pray;
keep me, my God, from stain of sin, just for to - day.

2. Let me both diligently work
and duly pray;
let me be kind in word and deed,
just for today.

3. Let me no wrong or idle word
unthinking say;
set thou a seal upon my lips,
just for today.

4. And if today my tide of life
should ebb away,
give me thy sacraments divine,
sweet Lord, today.

5. So, for tomorrow and its needs
I do not pray;
but keep me, guide me, love me, Lord,
just for today.

Text: Sister M. Xavier
Music: Richard Runciman Terry (1865-1938)
Music © Copyright Burns & Oates Ltd, Wellwood, North Farm Road,
Tunbridge Wells, Kent TN2 3QR. Used by permission.

446 Lord, have mercy

EZECHIEL 88 88 98 11 7

Refrain

Lord, have mer - cy. Lord, have mer - cy. Lord, have

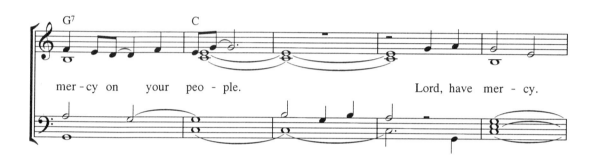

mer - cy on your peo - ple. Lord, have mer - cy.

Lord, have mer - cy. Lord, have mer - cy on your

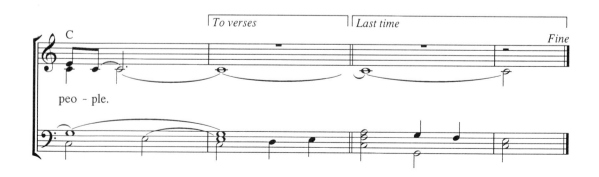

peo - ple.

1. Give me the heart of stone with - in you,
and I'll give you a heart of flesh. Clean wa - ter
I will use to cleanse all your wounds. My Spi - rit
I give to you.

2. You'll find me near the broken-hearted:
those crushed in spirit I will save.
So turn to me, for my pardon is great;
my word will heal all your wounds.

Text: Gerard Markland based on Ezekiel
Music: Gerard Markland arr. Adrian Vernon Fish

447 Lord Jesus Christ
Living Lord

LIVING LORD 9 8 88 83

1. Lord Je-sus Christ, you have come to us,

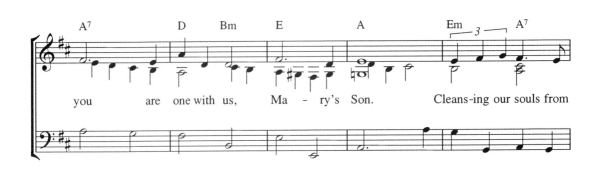

you are one with us, Ma - ry's Son. Cleans-ing our souls from

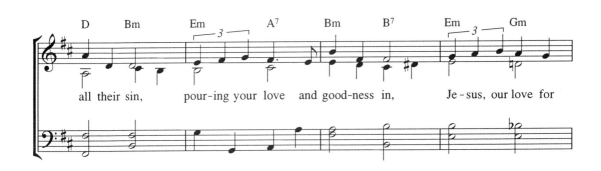

all their sin, pour-ing your love and good-ness in, Je-sus, our love for

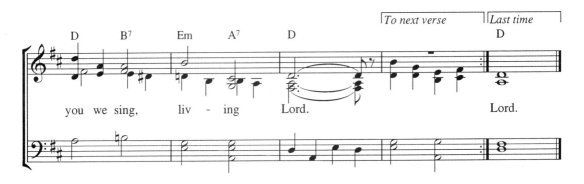

To next verse / *Last time*

you we sing, liv - ing Lord. Lord.

2. Lord Jesus Christ,
   now and ev'ry day
   teach us how to pray,
   Son of God.
   You have commanded us to do
   this in remembrance, Lord, of you.
   Into our lives your pow'r breaks through,
   living Lord.

3. Lord Jesus Christ,
   you have come to us,
   born as one of us,
   Mary's Son.
   Led out to die on Calvary,
   risen from death to set us free,
   living Lord Jesus, help us see
   you are Lord.

4. Lord Jesus Christ,
   I would come to you,
   live my life for you,
   Son of God.
   All your commands I know are true,
   your many gifts will make me new,
   into my life your pow'r breaks through,
   living Lord.

Text and Music: Patrick Appleford (b.1925)

448 Lord Jesus, think on me

SOUTHWELL (DAMON) SM

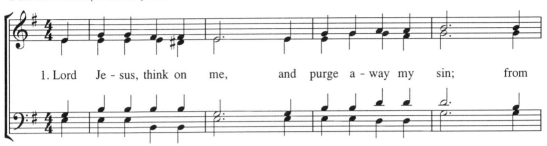

1. Lord Je - sus, think on me, and purge a - way my sin; from

earth - born pas - sions set me free, and make me pure with - in.

2. Lord Jesus, think on me,
   with care and woe opprest;
   let me thy loving servant be,
   and taste thy promised rest.

3. Lord Jesus, think on me
   amid the battle's strife;
   in all my pain and misery
   be thou my health and life.

4. Lord Jesus, think on me,
   nor let me go astray;
   through darkness and perplexity
   point thou the heav'nly way.

5. Lord Jesus, think on me,
   when flows the tempest high:
   when on doth rush the enemy,
   O Saviour, be thou nigh.

6. Lord Jesus, think on me,
   that, when the flood is past,
   I may th'eternal brightness see,
   and share thy joy at last.

Text: 'Mnōeo Christe' by Bishop Synesius (375-430) trans. Allen William Chatfield (1808-1896)
Music: from 'The Psalms in English Metre' (1570) adapted by William Damon (1540-1591)

449 Lord, make me a means of your peace

1. Lord, make me a means of your peace. Where there's ha - tred grown, let me sow your love. Where there's in - j'ry, Lord, let for- give-ness be my sword. Lord, make me a means of your peace.

2. Lord, make me a means of your peace.
   Where there's doubt and fear,
   let me sow your faith.
   In this world's despair,
   give me hope in you to share.
   Lord, make me a means of your peace.

3. Lord, make me a means of your peace.
   When there's sadness here,
   let me sow your joy.
   When the darkness nears,
   may your light dispel our fears.
   Lord, make me a means of your peace.

4. Lord, grant me to seek and to share:
   less to be consoled
   than to help console,
   less be understood
   than to understand your good.
   Lord, make me a means of your peace.

5. Lord, grant me to seek and to share:
   to receive love less
   than to give love free,
   just to give in thee,
   just receiving from your tree.
   Lord, make me a means of your peace.

6. Lord, grant me to seek and to share:
   to forgive in thee,
   you've forgiven me;
   for to die in thee
   is eternal life to me.
   Lord, make me a means of your peace.

Text: John B. Foley based on the Prayer of St Francis
Music: John B. Foley arr. Keith Stent

450 Lord of all hopefulness

SLANE 10 11 11 12

1. Lord of all hope-ful-ness, Lord of all joy, whose trust, e-ver child-like, no cares could des-troy, be there at our wak-ing, and give us, we pray, your bliss in our hearts, Lord, at the break of the day.

2. Lord of all eagerness,
Lord of all faith,
whose strong hands were skilled
at the plane and the lathe,
be there at our labours,
and give us, we pray,
your strength in our hearts, Lord,
at the noon of the day.

3. Lord of all kindliness,
Lord of all grace,
your hands swift to welcome,
your arms to embrace,
be there at our homing,
and give us, we pray,
your love in our hearts, Lord,
at the eve of the day.

4. Lord of all gentleness,
Lord of all calm,
whose voice is contentment,
whose presence is balm,
be there at our sleeping,
and give us, we pray,
your peace in our hearts, Lord,
at the end of the day.

Text: Jan Struther (1901-1953)
Music: traditional Irish melody arr. Colin Hand
Text © Copyright Oxford University Press, Great Clarendon Street, Oxford OX2 6DP.
Used by permission from 'Enlarged Songs of Praise.'
This arrangement © Copyright 1993 Kevin Mayhew Ltd.

451 Lord of life

Unison

1. Lord of life, you give us all our days:
let your life fill ours with hope and praise.
May our learn-ing, seek-ing, yearn-ing, lead us
on to share your ris-en life.

2. 'Come to me, and I will give you rest.'
Help us see your Way is richly blest;
guide our questing, working, resting,
till we hear you calling 'follow me'.

3. Lord, we come, encouraged by your grace,
Lord, we come, and things fall into place;
pilgrims ever, we endeavour,
Lord, to follow as you bring us home.

4. Lord, may we bring all our strength and skill:
help us be prepared to do your will.
Turn our living into giving
love and service as you set us free.

5. Glory be to God for all his love;
here may we with saints below, above,
go rejoicing, ever voicing
praise for such a welcome 'Come to me'.

Text: Patrick Appleford (b.1925)
Music: Patrick Appleford (b.1925) arr. Frances M. Kelly
© Copyright 1984 Kevin Mayhew Ltd.

LITURGICAL

HYMNS OLD & NEW

452 Lord our God

LAMBOURN 87 87

Unison

1. Lord our God, O Lord our Father, Lord of

love and Lord of fear, now we ga - ther round your

al - tar and we know your Word is near.

2. All our lives lie open to you,
   Lord of age, and Lord of youth,
   as we bring our sins and falsehoods
   to the judgement of your truth.

3. Lord of times and Lord of seasons,
   Lord of calmness, Lord of stress,
   heart that sees our secret terrors,
   Lord of strength and gentleness.

4. Lord of storms and Lord of sunsets,
   Lord of darkness, Lord of light,
   cast the shadow of your blessing
   on us gathered in your sight.

5. Lord of foes and Lord of friendships,
   Lord of laughter, Lord of tears,
   Lord of toil and Lord of Sabbath,
   Master of the hurrying years.

6. Lord of hope and Lord of hunger,
   Lord of atoms, Lord of space,
   take this world we bring before you
   to the haven of your grace.

Text: Kevin Nichols (b.1929)
Music: Andrew Moore (b.1954)

453 Lord, the light of your love
Shine, Jesus, shine

SHINE, JESUS, SHINE 9 9 10 10 6

1. Lord, the light of your love is shin - ing,
in the midst of the dark - ness, shin - ing; Je - sus, Light of the
World, shine up-on us, set us free by the truth you now bring us.
Shine on me, shine on me.

Refrain

Shine, Je-sus, shine, fill this land with the Fa-ther's glo-ry;
Flow, ri-ver, flow, flood the na-tions with grace and mer-cy;

blaze, Spi-rit, blaze, set our hearts on fire.
send forth your word, Lord, and

let there be light.

2. Lord, I come to your awesome presence,
   from the shadows into your radiance;
   by the blood I may enter your brightness,
   search me, try me, consume all my darkness.
   Shine on me, shine on me.

3. As we gaze on your kingly brightness,
   so our faces display your likeness,
   ever changing from glory to glory;
   mirrored here may our lives tell your story.
   Shine on me, shine on me.

   (Refrain twice to end)

Words and Music: Graham Kendrick (b.1950)

454 Lord, thy word abideth

RAVENSHAW 66 66

1. Lord, thy word a - bi - deth, and our foot-steps guid - eth;

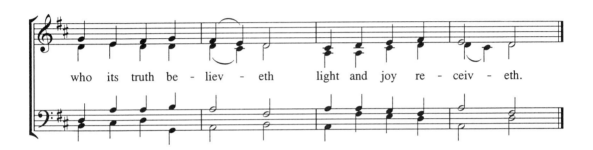

who its truth be - liev - eth light and joy re - ceiv - eth.

2. When our foes are near us,
   then thy word doth cheer us,
   word of consolation,
   message of salvation.

3. When the storms are o'er us,
   and dark clouds before us,
   then its light directeth,
   and our way protecteth.

4. Who can tell the pleasure,
   who recount the treasure,
   by thy word imparted
   to the simple-hearted?

5. Word of mercy, giving
   succour to the living;
   word of life, supplying
   comfort to the dying.

6. O that we, discerning
   its most holy learning,
   Lord, may love and fear thee,
   evermore be near thee.

Text: Henry Williams Baker (1821-1877)
Music: melody from M. Weisse's 'Neu Gesangbüchlein' (1531)
adapted by William Henry Monk (1823-1889)

455 Lord, unite all nations

2. Fill us with love, give us your peace,
   let grace abound and charity increase.
   From East to West may all be one in love:
   Lord, unite all nations in your love.

3. Teach us your love, teach us your peace,
   that joy may grow and happiness increase.
   Help us to work to make all nations one;
   Lord, unite all nations in your love.

Text: Marie Lydia Pereira (b.1920)
Music: Marie Lydia Pereira (b.1920) arr. Keith Stent
© Copyright 1999 Kevin Mayhew Ltd.

456 Lord, we come to ask your healing

AR HYD Y NOS 84 84 88 84

1. Lord, we come to ask your heal-ing, teach us of love;
all un-spo-ken shame re-veal-ing, teach us of love.
Take our self-ish thoughts and ac-tions, pet-ty feuds, di-vi-sive fac-tions,
hear us now to you ap-peal-ing, teach us of love.

A higher setting will be found at No. 232

2. Soothe away our pain and sorrow,
   hold us in love;
   grace we cannot buy or borrow,
   hold us in love.
   Though we see but dark and danger,
   though we spurn both friend and stranger,
   though we often dread tomorrow,
   hold us in love.

3. When the bread is raised and broken,
   fill us with love;
   words of consecration spoken,
   fill us with love.
   As our grateful prayers continue,
   make the faith that we have in you
   more than just an empty token,
   fill us with love.

4. Help us live for one another,
   bind us in love;
   stranger, neighbour, father, mother –
   bind us in love.
   All are equal at your table,
   through your Spirit make us able
   to embrace as sister, brother,
   bind us in love.

Text: Jean Holloway (b.1939)
Music: traditional Welsh melody arr. Colin Hand
Text and this arrangement © Copyright 1995 Kevin Mayhew Ltd.

457 Lord, when I wake I turn to you

MELCOMBE LM

1. Lord, when I wake I turn to you, your-
self my day's first thought and prayer, your strength to help, your
peace to bless, your will to guide me ev - 'ry - where!

2. I live with many in our world
   – their worldly eyes too blind to see –
   who never think what is your will,
   or why you brought our world to be!

3. Your thought for me, your loving care,
   those favours I could never earn,
   call for my thanks in praise and prayer,
   call me to love you in return!

4. There is no blessing, Lord, from you
   for those who make their will their way,
   no praise for those who do not praise,
   no peace for those who do not pray!

5. Make then my life a life of love,
   keep me from sin in all I do,
   your way to be my only way,
   your will my will for love of you!

Text: Brian Foley (b.1919) based on Psalm 5
Music: Samuel Webbe (1740-1816)

LiTURGiCAL
HYMNS OLD & NEW

458 Lord, who throughout these forty days

ST FLAVIAN CM

1. Lord, who through-out these for-ty days for us didst fast and pray, teach us with thee to mourn our sins, and at thy side to stay.

2. As thou with Satan didst contend
and didst the vict'ry win,
O give us strength in thee to fight,
in thee to conquer sin.

3. As thirst and hunger thou didst bear,
so teach us, gracious Lord,
to die to self, and daily live
by thy most holy word.

4. And through these days of penitence,
and through thy Passiontide,
yea, evermore, in life and death,
Lord Christ, with us abide.

Text: Claudia Frances Hernaman (1838-1898)
Music: from 'Day's Psalter' (1563)

459 Lord, you give the great commission

ABBOT'S LEIGH 87 87 D

1. Lord, you give the great com-mis-sion: 'Heal the sick and preach the word.' Lest the Church ne-glect its mis-sion, and the Gos-pel go un-heard, help us wit-ness to your pur-pose with re-newed in-teg-ri-ty; with the Spi-rit's gifts em-

pow'r us for the work of mi - nis - try.

2. Lord, you call us to your service:
   'In my name baptise and teach,'
   that the world may trust your promise,
   life abundant meant for each,
   give us all new fervour,
   draw us closer in community;
   with the Spirit's gifts empow'r us
   for the work of ministry.

3. Lord, you make the common holy:
   'This my body, this my blood.'
   Let us all, for earth's true glory,
   daily lift life heavenward,
   asking that the world around us
   share your children's liberty;
   with the Spirit's gifts empow'r us
   for the work of ministry.

4. Lord, you show us love's true measure;
   'Father what they do, forgive.'
   Yet we hoard as private treasure
   all that you so freely give.
   May your care and mercy lead us
   to a just society;
   with the Spirit's gifts empow'r us
   for the work of ministry.

5. Lord, you bless with words assuring:
   'I am with you to the end.'
   Faith and hope and love restoring,
   may we serve as you intend,
   and, amid the cares that claim us,
   hold in mind eternity;
   with the Spirit's gifts empow'r us
   for the work of ministry.

Text: Jeffrey Rowthorn (b.1934)
Music: Cyril Vincent Taylor (1907-1991)

LITURGICAL

HYMNS OLD & NEW

460 Love came down at Christmas

LOVE CAME DOWN 67 67

1. Love came down at Christ - mas, Love all love - ly, Love di - vine;
Love was born at Christ - mas, star and an - gels gave the sign.

2. Worship we the Godhead,
   Love incarnate, Love divine;
   worship we our Jesus:
   but wherewith for sacred sign?

3. Love shall be our token,
   love be yours and love be mine,
   love to God and all men,
   love for plea and gift and sign.

Text: Christina Georgina Rossetti (1830-1894)
Music: Malcolm Archer (b.1952)
Music © Copyright 1991 Kevin Mayhew Ltd.

461 Love divine, all loves excelling

TUNE 1: LOVE DIVINE 87 87

1. Love di - vine, all loves ex - cel - ling, joy of heav'n, to earth come down, fix in us thy hum - ble dwell - ing, all thy faith - ful mer - cies crown.

2. Jesu, thou art all compassion,
   pure unbounded love thou art;
   visit us with thy salvation,
   enter ev'ry trembling heart.

3. Breathe, O breathe thy loving Spirit
   into ev'ry troubled breast;
   let us all in thee inherit,
   let us find thy promised rest.

4. Take away the love of sinning,
   Alpha and Omega be;
   end of faith, as its beginning,
   set our hearts at liberty.

5. Come, almighty to deliver,
   let us all thy grace receive;
   suddenly return, and never,
   never more thy temples leave.

6. Thee we would be always blessing,
   serve thee as thy hosts above;
   pray, and praise thee without ceasing,
   glory in thy perfect love.

7. Finish then thy new creation,
   pure and spotless let us be;
   let us see thy great salvation
   perfectly restored in thee.

8. Changed from glory into glory,
   till in heav'n we take our place,
   till we cast our crowns before thee,
   lost in wonder, love, and praise.

TUNE 2: BLAENWERN 87 87 D

1. Love di-vine, all loves ex-cel-ling, joy of heav'n, to earth come
down, fix in us thy hum-ble dwell-ing, all thy
faith-ful mer-cies crown. Je-su, thou art all com-
pas-sion, pure un-bound-ed love thou art; vi-sit
us with thy sal-va-tion, en-ter ev-'ry trem-bling heart.

Text: Charles Wesley (1707-1788) alt.
Music: Tune 1: – John Stainer (1840-1901)
Tune 2: – William Penfro Rowlands (1860-1937)

LITURGICAL

HYMNS OLD & NEW

462 Love is his word

CRESSWELL 88 97 and Refrain

1. Love is his word, love is his way, feast-ing with all, fast-ing a-lone, liv-ing and dy-ing, ri-sing a-gain, love, on-ly love, is his way.

Refrain

Rich-er than gold is the love of my Lord: bet-ter than splen-dour and wealth.

2. Love is his way, love is his mark,
sharing his last Passover feast,
Christ at the table, host to the twelve,
love, only love, is his mark.

3. Love is his mark, love is his sign,
bread for our strength, wine for our joy,
'This is my body, this is my blood.'
Love, only love, is his sign.

4. Love is his sign, love is his news,
'Do this,' he said, 'lest you forget
all my deep sorrow, all my dear blood.'
Love, only love, is his name.

5. Love is his news, love is his name,
we are his own, chosen and called,
family, brethren, cousins and kin.
Love, only love, is his name.

6. Love is his name, love is his law,
hear his command, all who are his,
'Love one another, I have loved you.'
Love, only love, is his law.

7. Love is his law, love is his word:
love of the Lord, Father and Word,
love of the Spirit, God ever one,
love, only love, is his word.

Text: Luke Connaughton (1917-1979) alt.
Music: Anthony Milner (b.1925)

463 Love is patient

2. If my faith is strong,
   then I might make the mountains move,
   feed the hungry people,
   but what does all that prove?
   I can give up all things –
   possessions come and go –
   but unless there's love
   it doesn't count, I know.

3. Love goes on for evermore
   but prophecies will pass;
   tongues will cease their wagging,
   and knowledge will not last;
   for we know so little,
   the future's very dim,
   but with faith and hope,
   our love leads us to him.

Text: Sister Patrick Ignatius, based on 1 Corinthians 13
Music: Adapted from a Spiritual by Sister Patrick Ignatius, arr. Andrew Moore

464 Love is the only law

1. Love is the on - ly law for God and hu - man - kind,
love your God with all your heart, your strength and soul and mind.
Love your neigh - bour as your - self, of ev' - ry creed and race,
turn the wa - ter of end - less laws in - to the wine of grace.

Refrain
Love is God's on - ly law, love is God's on - ly law;

love   is God's wis - dom,   love   is God's strength,   love   of such height,   such

depth,   such   length,   love   is   God's on - ly   law.

2. Give to the poor a voice
   and help the blind to see,
   feed the hungry, heal the sick
   and set the captive free.
   All that God requires of you
   will then fall into place,
   turn the water of endless laws
   into the wine of grace.

3. Let love like fountains flow
   and justice like a stream,
   faith become reality
   and hope your constant theme.
   Then shall freedom, joy and peace
   with righteousness embrace,
   turn the water of endless laws
   into the wine of grace.

Text: Michael Forster (b.1946)
Music: Andrew Moore (b.1954) arr. Keith Stent

465 Lovely in your littleness
Jesus is our joy

Semplice, con gioia (♩ = 80)

1. Love - ly in your lit-tle-ness, long - ing for our low-li-ness,
long - ing for our low-li-ness, search - ing for our meek - ness:
Je - sus is our joy, Je - sus is our joy.

Last time

Je - sus is our joy, Je - sus is our joy.

2. Peace within our powerlessness,
hope within our helplessness,
hope within our helplessness,
love within our loneliness:
Jesus is our joy, Jesus is our joy.

3. Held in Mary's tenderness,
tiny hands are raised to bless,
tiny hands are raised to bless,
touching us with God's caress:
Jesus is our joy, Jesus is our joy.

4. Joy, then, in God's graciousness,
peace comes with gentleness,
peace comes with gentleness,
filling hearts with gladness:
Jesus is our joy, Jesus is our joy.

Text: Pamela Hayes
Music: Margaret Rizza (b.1929)

466 Loving shepherd of thy sheep

LÜBECK · 77 77

1. Lov-ing shep-herd of thy sheep, keep me, Lord, in safe-ty keep; noth-ing can thy pow'r with-stand, none can pluck me from thy hand.

2. Loving shepherd, thou didst give
   thine own life that I might live;
   may I love thee day by day,
   gladly thy sweet will obey.

3. Loving shepherd, ever near,
   teach me still thy voice to hear;
   suffer not my steps to stray
   from the straight and narrow way.

4. Where thou leadest may I go,
   walking in thy steps below;
   then, before thy Father's throne,
   Jesu, claim me for thine own.

Text: Jane Elizabeth Leeson (1809-1881)
Music: from Freylinghausen's 'Gesangbuch' (1704)

467 Lumen Christi

Refrain
Unison

Lu - men Chris - ti, al - le - lu - ia! A - men!

Fine

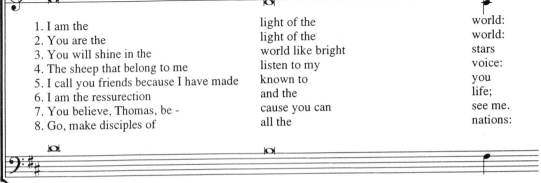

1. I am the
2. You are the
3. You will shine in the
4. The sheep that belong to me
5. I call you friends because I have made
6. I am the ressurection
7. You believe, Thomas, be -
8. Go, make disciples of

light of the
light of the
world like bright
listen to my
known to
and the
cause you can
all the

world:
world:
stars
voice:
you
life;
see me.
nations:

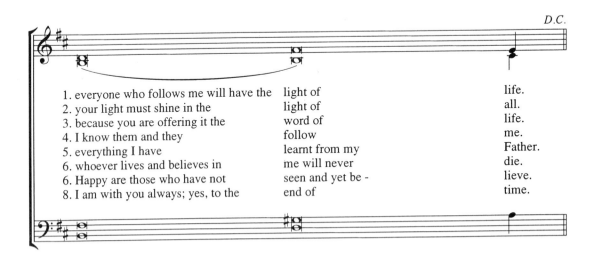

D.C.

1. everyone who follows me will have the
2. your light must shine in the
3. because you are offering it the
4. I know them and they
5. everything I have
6. whoever lives and believes in
6. Happy are those who have not
8. I am with you always; yes, to the

light of
light of
word of
follow
learnt from my
me will never
seen and yet be -
end of

life.
all.
life.
me.
Father.
die.
lieve.
time.

Text: from the Gospel of John
Music: Jean-Paul Lécot (b.1947)
© Copyright 1988 Kevin Mayhew Ltd.

468 Maiden, yet a mother

NOEL NOUVELET 11 11 11 11

1. Mai-den, yet a mo - ther, daugh-ter of thy Son,
high be-yond all o - ther, low-li - er is none;
thou the con-sum-ma - tion planned by God's de - cree,
when our lost cre - a - tion nob-ler rose in thee!

2. Thus his place preparèd,
   he who all things made
   'mid his creatures tarried,
   in thy bosom laid;
   there his love he nourished,
   warmth that gave increase
   to the root whence flourished
   our eternal peace.

3. Lady, lest our vision,
   striving heav'nward, fail,
   still let thy petition
   with thy Son prevail,
   unto whom all merit,
   pow'r and majesty
   with the Holy Spirit
   and the Father be.

Text: Dante Alighieri (1265-1321) trans. Ronald Arbuthnott Knox (1888-1957)
Music: traditional French melody arr. Christopher Tambling

469 Majesty, worship his majesty

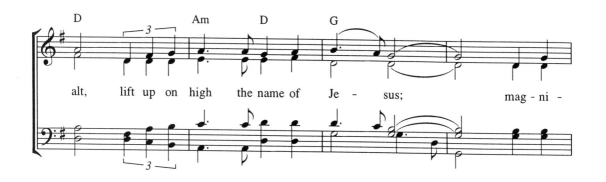

alt, lift up on high the name of Je - sus; mag - ni -

fy, come glo - ri - fy Christ Je - sus the King.

Ma - jes - ty, wor - ship his ma - jes - ty, Je - sus who

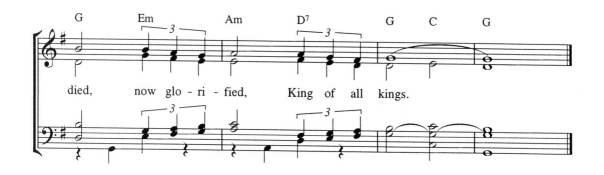

died, now glo - ri - fied, King of all kings.

Text and Music: Jack W. Hayford (b.1934)

470 Make me a channel of your peace

Text: Sebastian Temple (1928-1997) based on the Prayer of St Francis
Music: Sebastian Temple (1928-1997) arr. Andrew Moore

471 Make way, make way

1. Make way, make way, for Christ the King in splen - dour ar - rives; fling wide the gates and wel - come him in - to your lives. Make way, *make way,* make way, *make way,* for the King of kings; *for the King of kings;* make way, *make way,* make way, *make way,* and let his king - dom in!

2. He comes the broken hearts to heal,
   the pris'ners to free;
   the deaf shall hear, the lame shall dance,
   the blind shall see.

3. And those who mourn with heavy hearts,
   who weep and sigh,
   with laughter, joy and royal crown
   he'll beautify.

4. We call you now to worship him
   as Lord of all,
   to have no gods before him,
   their thrones must fall.

Text and Music: Graham Kendrick (b.1950)

472 Mary had a baby

2. What did she name him, yes, Lord? *(x3)*
   The people came to Bethlehem to see her son.

3. Mary named him Jesus, yes, Lord. *(x3)*
   The people came to Bethlehem to see her son.

4. Where was he born, yes, Lord? *(x3)*
   The people came to Bethlehem to see her son.

5. Born in a stable, yes, Lord. *(x3)*
   The people came to Bethlehem to see her son.

6. Where did she lay him, yes, Lord? *(x3)*
   The people came to Bethlehem to see her son.

7. Laid him in a manger, yes, Lord. *(x3)*
   The people came to Bethlehem to see her son.

Text: West Indian Spiritual alt.
Music: West Indian Spiritual arr. Keith Stent

473 Mary immaculate

LIEBSTER IMMANUEL 11 10 11 10

1. Ma-ry im-ma-cu-late, star of the morn-ing, cho-sen be-fore the cre-a-tion be-gan, cho-sen to bring, for thy bri-dal a-dorn-ing, woe to the ser-pent and res-cue to man.

2. Here, in an orbit of shadow and sadness
veiling thy splendour, thy course thou hast run;
now thou art throned in all glory and gladness,
crowned by the hand of thy Saviour and Son.

3. Sinners, we worship thy sinless perfection,
fallen and weak, for thy pity we plead;
grant us the shield of thy sov'reign protection,
measure thine aid by the depth of our need.

4. Frail is our nature and strict our probation,
watchful the foe that would lure us to wrong,
succour our souls in the hour of temptation,
Mary immaculate, tender and strong.

5. See how the wiles of the serpent assail us,
see how we waver and flinch in the fight;
let thine immaculate merit avail us,
make of our weakness a proof of thy might.

6. Bend from thy throne at the voice of our crying;
bend to this earth which thy footsteps have trod;
stretch out thine arms to us living and dying,
Mary immaculate, mother of God.

Text: F. W. Weatherell
Music: melody adapted from 'Himmels-Lust', Jena (1679);
harmony, slightly adjusted, from a cantata by Johann Sebastian Bach (1685-1750)

474 May you see the face of God

LUX PERPETUA 12 12 and Refrain

1. May you see the face of God, your lov-ing Fa-ther.

May you live in joy with him whose hands once made you. May the

light of God now shine on you for e-ver.

2. May you rest in Christ the Shepherd-King who feeds you.
   May his peace be yours where sorrow may not enter.

3. May the flame of love, the Holy Spirit, warm you.
   May he welcome you to perfect love in heaven.

Text and Music: Gregory Murray (1905-1992)
© Copyright 1999 Kevin Mayhew Ltd.

475 Meekness and majesty
This is your God

THIS IS YOUR GOD 66 65 D and Refrain

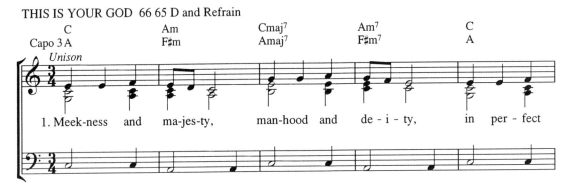

1. Meek-ness and ma-jes-ty, man-hood and de-i-ty, in per-fect

har-mo-ny, the Man who is God. Lord of e - ter-ni-ty

dwells in hu - ma-ni-ty, kneels in hu - mi-li-ty and wash-es our

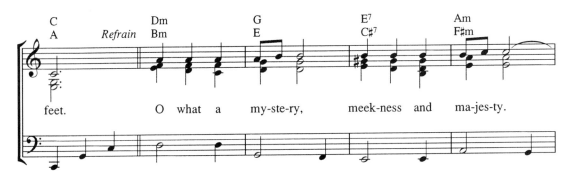

feet. O what a my-ste-ry, meek-ness and ma-jes-ty.

2. Father's pure radiance,
   perfect in innocence,
   yet learns obedience
   to death on a cross.
   Suff'ring to give us life,
   conqu'ring through sacrifice,
   and as they crucify
   prays: 'Father forgive.'

3. Wisdom unsearchable,
   God the invisible,
   love indestructible
   in frailty appears.
   Lord of infinity,
   stooping so tenderly,
   lifts our humanity
   to the heights of his throne.

Text and Music: Graham Kendrick (b.1950)

LITURGICAL

HYMNS OLD & NEW

476 Morning has broken

BUNESSAN 55 54 D

1. Morn-ing has bro-ken like the first morn - ing, black-bird has spo-ken like the first bird. Praise for the sing - ing! Praise for the morn - ing! Praise for them, spring - ing fresh from the Word!

2. Sweet the rain's new fall,
   sunlit from heaven,
   like the first dew-fall
   on the first grass.
   Praise for the sweetness
   of the wet garden,
   sprung in completeness
   where his feet pass.

3. Mine is the sunlight!
   Mine is the morning
   born of the one light
   Eden saw play!
   Praise with elation,
   praise ev'ry morning,
   God's re-creation
   of the new day!

Text: Eleanor Farjeon (1881-1965)
Music: traditional Gaelic melody arr. Colin Hand (b.1929)

477 Moses, I know you're the man

1. 'Mo-ses, I know you're the man,' the Lord said. 'You're going to work out my plan,' the Lord said. 'Lead all the Is-rae-lites out of sla-ve-ry, and I shall make them a wan-der-ing race called the peo-ple of God.' So ev-'ry day we're on our way, for we're a tra-vel-ling, wan-der-ing

race called the peo-ple of God.

2. 'Don't get too set in your ways,'
   the Lord said.
   'Each step is only a phase,'
   the Lord said.
   'I'll go before you and I shall be a sign
   to guide my travelling, wandering race.
   You're the people of God.'

3. 'No matter what you may do,'
   the Lord said,
   'I shall be faithful and true,'
   the Lord said.
   'My love will strengthen you as you go along,
   for you're my travelling, wandering race.
   You're the people of God.'

4. 'Look at the birds in the air,'
   the Lord said.
   'They fly unhampered by care,'
   the Lord said.
   'You will move easier if you're trav'lling light,
   for you're a wandering, vagabond race.
   You're the people of God.'

5. 'Foxes have places to go,'
   the Lord said,
   'but I've no home here below,'
   the Lord said.
   'So if you want to be with me all your days,
   keep up the moving and travelling on.
   You're the people of God.'

Text: Estelle White (b.1925)
Music: Estelle White (b.1925) arr. Christopher Tambling

478 Mother of God's living Word

ORIENTIS PARTIBUS 77 77

1. Mo - ther of God's liv - ing Word, glo - ri - fy - ing Christ your Lord; full of joy, God's peo - ple sing, grate - ful for your mo - ther - ing.

2. Virgin soil, untouched by sin,
   for God's seed to flourish in;
   watered by the Spirit's dew,
   in your womb the Saviour grew.

3. Sharing his humility,
   Bethlehem and Calvary,
   with him in his bitter pain,
   now as queen with him you reign.

4. We are God's new chosen race,
   new-born children of his grace,
   citizens of heaven who
   imitate and honour you.

5. We, God's people on our way,
   travelling by night and day,
   moving to our promised land,
   walk beside you hand in hand.

6. Christ, your Son, is always near,
   so we journey without fear,
   singing as we walk along:
   Christ our joy, and Christ our song!

7. Sing aloud to Christ with joy,
   who was once a little boy.
   Sing aloud to Mary, sing,
   grateful for her mothering.

Text: Damian Lundy (1944-1997)
Music: 'L'Office de la Circoncision' attributed to Pierre de Corbeil (d.1222)
Text © Copyright 1978 Kevin Mayhew Ltd.

479 My God, accept my heart this day

BELMONT CM

1. My God, ac - cept my heart this day, and make it whol - ly thine, that I from thee no more may stray, no more from thee de - cline.

2. Before the cross of him who died,
   behold, I prostrate fall;
   let ev'ry sin be crucified,
   and Christ be all in all.

3. Anoint me with thy heav'nly grace,
   and seal me for thine own,
   that I may see thy glorious face,
   and worship at thy throne.

4. Let ev'ry thought and work and word
   to thee be ever giv'n,
   then life shall be thy service, Lord,
   and death the gate of heav'n.

5. All glory to the Father be,
   all glory to the Son,
   all glory, Holy Ghost, to thee,
   while endless ages run.

Text: Matthew Bridges (1800-1894)
Music: adapted from William Gardiner's 'Sacred Melodies' (1812)

480 My God, and is thy table spread

ROCKINGHAM LM

1. My God, and is thy ta - ble spread, and does thy cup with love o'er - flow? Thi - ther be all thy chil - dren led, and let them all thy sweet - ness know.

A higher setting will be found at No. 731

2. Hail, sacred feast, which Jesus makes!
   Rich banquet of his flesh and blood!
   Thrice happy all, who here partake
   that sacred stream, that heav'nly food.

3. What wondrous love! What perfect grace,
   for Jesus, our exalted host,
   invites us to this special place
   who offer least and need the most.

4. O let thy table honoured be,
   and furnished well with joyful guests:
   and may each soul salvation see,
   that here its sacred pledges tastes.

Text: Philip Doddridge (1702-1751) alt., v. 3: Michael Forster (b.1946)
Music: from A. Williams' 'Second supplement to Psalmody in Miniature' (c.1780)
adapted by Edward Miller (1735-1807)
This version of text © Copyright 1996 Kevin Mayhew Ltd.

481 My God, how wonderful you are

WESTMINSTER CM

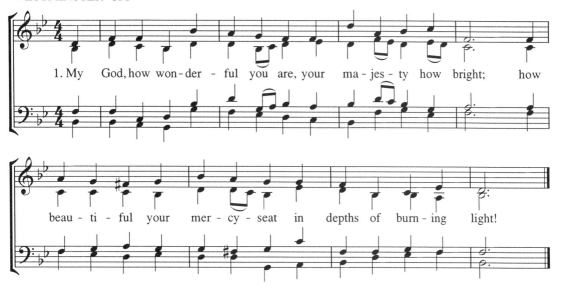

1. My God, how won-der - ful you are, your ma - jes - ty how bright; how

beau - ti - ful your mer - cy - seat in depths of burn - ing light!

2. Creator from eternal years
   and everlasting Lord,
   by holy angels day and night
   unceasingly adored!

3. How wonderful, how beautiful
   the sight of you must be –
   your endless wisdom, boundless power,
   and awesome purity!

4. O how I fear you, living God,
   with deepest, tenderest fears,
   and worship you with trembling hope
   and penitential tears!

5. But I may love you too, O Lord,
   though you are all-divine,
   for you have stooped to ask of me
   this feeble love of mine.

6. Father of Jesus, love's reward,
   great King upon your throne,
   what joy to see you as you are
   and know as I am known!

Text: Frederick William Faber (1814-1863) alt.
Music: James Turle (1802-1882)

482 My God, my God, why have you forsaken me?

Refrain
Unison

My God, my God, why have you for-sa-ken me?

1. Peo - ple who see me are scorn - ful, sneer - ing at me, and tos - sing their heads, 'His trust was in God, let God save him, come to the aid of his own spe - cial friend!'

2. Dogs have surrounded me, howling;
   criminal gangs approach and attack.
   My hands and my feet they are tearing,
   all of my bones can be easily seen.

3. They have divided my clothing,
   gambling with straws or dice for my robe.
   Please, God, do not leave me forsaken,
   hasten to help me, O God of my strength.

4. I will proclaim to my people;
   your name, O Lord, they worship and praise.
   All children of Jacob, give glory,
   children of Israel, come worship your God.

Text: Susan Sayers (b.1946) based on Psalm 21
Music: Andrew Moore (b.1954)
© Copyright 1995 Kevin Mayhew Ltd.

483 My God said to me, 'Follow!'

My God said to me, 'Fol-low!' My God said to me, 'Come!'
My God called out my name. Here I am! Here I am to
do your will! 1. To fol-low the Lord is to
be set free; to fol-low the Lord is to know his way.

2. To live with the Lord is to live in love;
to live with the Lord is to live in peace.

Text: Louis Welker
Music: Louis Welker arr. Keith Stent
© Copyright 1982 Kevin Mayhew Ltd.

484 My heart will sing to you
Great love

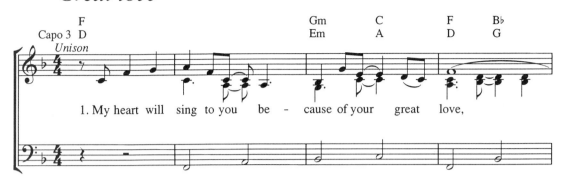

1. My heart will sing to you be - cause of your great love,

a love so rich, so pure, a love be -yond com - pare;

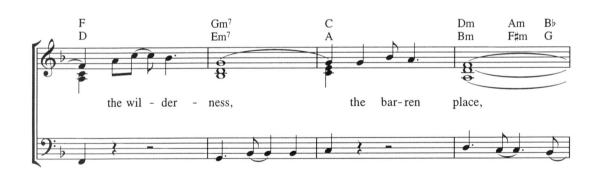

the wil - der - ness, the bar - ren place,

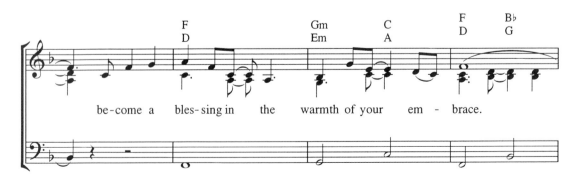

be-come a bles-sing in the warmth of your em - brace.

2. When earthly wisdom dims the light of knowing you,
   or if my search for understanding clouds your way,
   to you I fly, my hiding-place,
   where revelation is beholding face to face.

Text and Music: Robin Mark arr. Keith Stent

LITURGICAL

HYMNS OLD & NEW

485 My people, what have I done to you?

My peo - ple, what have I done to you? How have I
hurt you? An-swer me. 1. I led you out of
E - gypt, I set you free, I set you free.
I led you through the des - ert,
and yet you turn a - way from me.

2. I fed you in the desert,
   I led you through the raging sea.
   I gave you saving water,
   and yet you found a cross for me.

3. I gave you a royal sceptre;
   you offered me a crown of thorns.
   I raised you as a nation;
   you mocked and treated me with scorn.

Text: Francesca Leftley (b.1955) based on the Good Friday Reproaches
Music: Francesca Leftley (b.1955) arr. Andrew Moore
© 1984 Kevin Mayhew Ltd.

486 My shepherd is the Lord

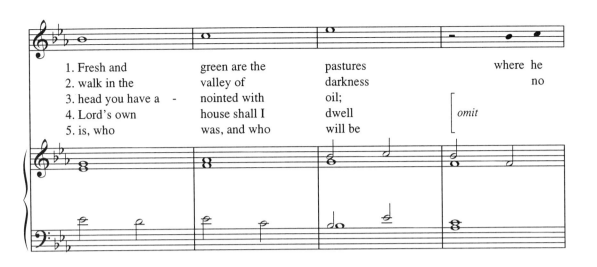

1. Fresh and green are the pastures where he
2. walk in the valley of darkness no
3. head you have a - nointed with oil;
4. Lord's own house shall I dwell [omit
5. is, who was, and who will be

1. gives me re - pose. Near restful waters he
2. evil would I fear. You are there with your crook and your

1. leads me, to re - vive my droop - ing spi - rit.
2. staff; with these you give me com - fort.
3. my cup is o - ver - flow - ing.
4. for e - ver and e - ver.
5. for e - ver and e - ver.

Text: Psalm 22, Grail translation
Music: Psalm and Response 1 – Joseph Gelineau (b.1920)
Response 2 – Gregory Murray (1905-1992)

LiTURGiCAL
HYMNS OLD & NEW

487 My song is love unknown

LOVE UNKNOWN 66 66 44 44

1. My song is love un - known, my Sa -viour's love to me, love
to the love - less shown, that they might love - ly be. O
who am I, that for my sake, my Lord should take frail flesh and die?

2. He came from his blest throne,
   salvation to bestow;
   but sin made blind, and none
   the longed-for Christ would know.
   But O, my friend, my friend indeed,
   who at my need his life did spend!

3. Sometimes they strew his way,
   and his sweet praises sing;
   resounding all the day
   hosannas to their King;
   then 'Crucify'! is all their breath,
   and for his death they thirst and cry.

4. Why, what hath my Lord done?
   What makes this rage and spite?
   He made the lame to run,
   he gave the blind their sight.
   Sweet injuries! Yet they at these
   themselves displease, and 'gainst him rise.

5. They rise, and needs will have
   my dear Lord made away;
   a murderer they save,
   the Prince of Life they slay.
   Yet cheerful he to suff'ring goes,
   that he his foes from thence might free.

6. Here might I stay and sing,
   no story so divine;
   never was love, dear King,
   never was grief like thine.
   This is my friend in whose sweet praise
   I all my days could gladly spend.

Text: Samuel Crossman (c.1624-1684) alt.
Music: John Ireland (1879-1962)

488 My soul doth magnify the Lord

spi - rit hath re - joiced in God my Sa - viour, for

he that is migh - ty hath done great things, and

ho - ly is his name.

2. From age to age he shows his love,
   and his mercy is for ever to his servants,
   for he stretches out his arm, casts down the mighty,
   and raises up the meek.

3. He fills the hungry with good food.
   When the rich demand their share, their hands are empty.
   He has kept all his promises to Israel:
   his mercy is made known.

4. To God the Father we sing praise,
   and to Jesus, whom he sent to be our Saviour!
   To the Spirit of God be all glory,
   for holy is his name!

Text: v.1 unknown based on Luke 1:46-55; vs.2-4 Damian Lundy (1944-1997)
Music: unknown arr. Andrew Moore

489 My soul is filled with joy

2. I am lowly as a child,
   but I know from this day forward
   that my name will be remembered
   and the world will call me blessèd.

3. I proclaim the pow'r of God!
   He does marvels for his servants;
   though he scatters the proud-hearted
   and destroys the might of princes.

4. To the hungry he gives food,
   sends the rich away empty.
   In his mercy he is mindful
   of the people he has chosen.

5. In his love he now fulfills
   what he promised to our fathers.
   I will praise the Lord, my Saviour.
   Everlasting is his mercy.

Text: unknown based on Luke 1:46-55
Music: Scottish Folk melody arr. Christopher Tambling

490 My soul is longing for your peace

My soul is long-ing for your peace, near to you, my God.

1. Lord, you know that my heart is not proud and my eyes are not lift-ed from the earth.

2. Lofty thoughts have never filled my mind,
   far beyond my sight all ambitious deeds.

3. In your peace I have maintained my soul,
   I have kept my heart in your quiet peace.

4. As a child rests on a mother's knee,
   so I place my soul in your loving care.

5. Israel, put all your hope in God,
   place your trust in him, now and evermore.

Text: Lucien Deiss (b.1921) based on Psalm 130
Music: Lucien Deiss (b.1921)

491 My soul proclaims you, mighty God

AMAZING GRACE CM

1. My soul proclaims you, mighty God. My spirit sings your praise. You look on me, you lift me up, and gladness fills my days.

2. All nations now will share my joy;
   your gifts you have outpoured.
   Your little one you have made great;
   I magnify my God.

3. For those who love your holy name,
   your mercy will not die.
   Your strong right arm puts down the proud
   and lifts the lowly high.

4. You fill the hungry with good things,
   the rich you send away.
   The promise made to Abraham
   is filled to endless day.

5. Magnificat, magnificat,
   magnificat, praise God!
   Praise God, praise God, praise God, praise God,
   magnificat, praise God!

Text: Anne Carter (1944-1993) based on Luke 1:46-55
Music: American folk melody arr. Richard Lloyd

492 New daytime dawning

1. New day-time dawn - ing, break-ing like the spring.
New voi - ces sing - ing, and new songs to sing!
Christ has come back, al - le - lu - ia! He is ri - sen,
like the spring - time! Say, what does he bring?

2. Death in the tree tops!
Jesus cried with pain,
hanging in the branches. Now he lives again!
For the tree of death has flowered,
life has filled the furthest branches!
Sunlight follows rain.

3. The man of sorrows,
sleeping in his tomb,
the man of sorrows, he is coming home.
He is coming like the springtime.
Suddenly you'll hear him talking,
you will see him come.

4. Say, are you hungry?
Come and eat today!
Come to the table, nothing to pay!
Take your place, the meal is waiting.
Come and share the birthday party,
and the holiday.

5. Look where the garden
door is open wide!
Come to the garden, there's no need to hide.
God has broken down the fences
and he stands with arms wide open.
Come along inside!

Text: Damian Lundy (1944-1997) based on a French poem
Music: traditional Polish melody arr. Colin Hand
Text and this arrangement © Copyright 1978, 1994 Kevin Mayhew Ltd.

493 New praises be given

ST DENIO 11 11 11 11

1. New prai-ses be giv-en to Christ new-ly crowned, who back to his hea-ven a new way hath found; God's bles-sed-ness shar-ing be-fore us he goes, what man-sions pre-par-ing, what end-less re-pose!

2. His glory still praising on thrice holy ground,
th'apostles stood gazing, his mother around;
with hearts that beat faster, with eyes full of love,
they watched while their master ascended above.

3. 'No star can disclose him,' the bright angels said;
'eternity knows him, your conquering head;
those high habitations, he leaves not again,
till, judging all nations, on earth he shall reign.'

4. Thus spoke they and straightway, where legions defend
heav'n's glittering gateway, their Lord they attend,
and cry, looking thither, 'Your portals let down
for him who rides hither in peace and renown.'

5. They asked, who keep sentry in that blessèd town,
'Who thus claimeth entry, a king of renown?'
'The Lord of all valiance,' that herald replied,
'who Satan's battalions laid low in their pride.'

6. Grant, Lord, that our longing may follow thee there,
on earth who are thronging thy temples with prayer;
and unto thee gather, Redeemer, thine own,
where thou with thy Father dost sit on the throne.

Text: 'Hymnum canamus gloria' by the Venerable Bede (673-735)
trans. Ronald Arbuthnott Knox (1888-1957)
Music: Welsh melody from John Roberts' 'Caniadau y Cyssegr' (1839)
Text © Copyright Burns and Oates Ltd, Wellwood, North Farm Road,
Tunbridge Wells, Kent TN2 3QR. Used by permission.

494 Nothing shall separate us

Refrain
Unison

No - thing shall se - pa - rate us from the love of God.

No - thing shall se - pa - rate us from the love of God. God.

1. God did not spare his on - ly Son, gave him to save us all.

Sin's price was met by Je - sus' death and hea ven's mer - cy falls.

2. Up from the grave Jesus was raised
to sit at God's right hand;
pleading our cause in heaven's courts,
forgiven we can stand.

3. Now by God's grace we have embraced
a life set free from sin;
we shall deny all that destroys
our union with him.

Text and Music: Noel and Tricia Richards

495 Now as the evening shadows fall

TUNE 1: TE LUCIS LM

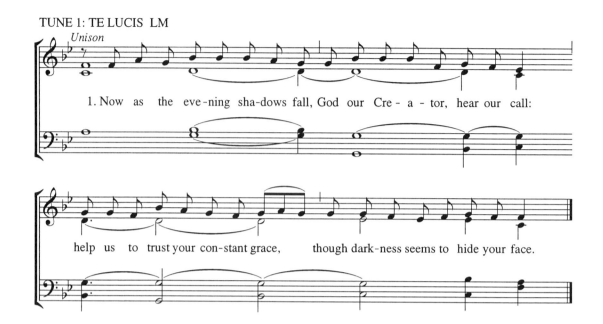

1. Now as the eve-ning sha-dows fall, God our Cre-a-tor, hear our call: help us to trust your con-stant grace, though dark-ness seems to hide your face.

2. Help us to find, in sleep's release,
bodily rest and inner peace;
so may the darkness of the night
refresh our eyes for morning light.

3. Father almighty, holy Son,
Spirit eternal, three in One,
grant us the faith that sets us free
to praise you for eternity.

TUNE 2: BLACKHEATH LM

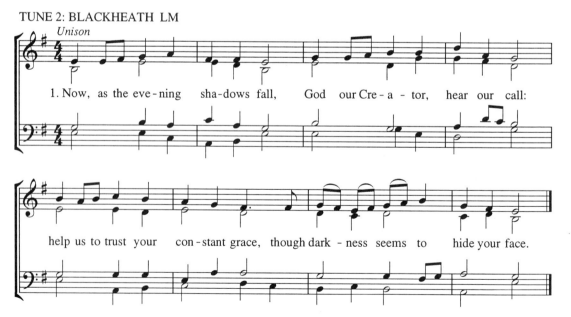

1. Now, as the eve-ning sha-dows fall, God our Cre-a-tor, hear our call: help us to trust your con-stant grace, though dark-ness seems to hide your face.

Text: Michael Forster (b.1946) based on 'Te lucis ante terminum'
Music: Tune 1 – Plainsong arr. Andrew Moore
Tune 2 – Anthony Milner (b.1928)

496 Now I know what love is

2. Darkness will not hide your love,
   shining like a star.

3. What could ever quench your love,
   love that changes hearts.

Text: Mike Anderson (b.1956)
Music: Mike Anderson (b.1956) arr. Keith Stent
© Copyright 1999 Kevin Mayhew Ltd.

497 Now thank we all our God

NUN DANKET 67 67 66 66

1. Now thank we all our God, with hearts and hands and voi - ces, who won - drous things hath done, in whom his world re - joic - es; who from our mo - ther's arms hath blessed us on our way with count-less gifts of love, and still is ours to - day.

A lower setting will be found at No. 586

2. O may this bounteous God
   through all our life be near us,
   with ever joyful hearts
   and blessèd peace to cheer us;
   and keep us in his grace,
   and guide us when perplexed,
   and free us from all ills
   in this world and the next.

3. All praise and thanks to God
   the Father now be given,
   the Son and him who reigns
   with them in highest heaven,
   the one eternal God,
   whom earth and heav'n adore;
   for thus it was, is now,
   and shall be evermore.

Text: 'Nun danket alle Gott' by Martin Rinkart (1586-1649) trans. Catherine Winkworth (1827-1878)
Music: melody by Johann Crüger (1598-1662); harmony by William Henry Monk (1823-1889)

498 Now the green blade riseth

NOEL NOUVELET 11 11 10 11

2. In the grave they laid him, Love by hatred slain,
thinking that never he would wake again,
laid in the earth like grain that sleeps unseen:
Love is come again, like wheat that springeth green.

3. Forth he came at Easter, like the risen grain,
he that for three days in the grave had lain;
quick from the dead, my risen Lord is seen:
Love is come again, like wheat that springeth green.

4. When our hearts are wintry, grieving or in pain,
thy touch can call us back to life again;
fields of our hearts, that dead and bare have been:
Love is come again, like wheat that springeth green.

Text: John Macleod Campbell Crum (1872-1958) alt.
Music: traditional French melody arr. Christopher Tambling

499 Now with the fast-departing light

GROSSER GOTT LM

1. Now with the fast - de - part - ing light, ma - ker of all, we ask of thee, of thy great mer - cy, through the night our guar - dian and de - fence to be.

2. Far off let idle visions fly,
no phantom of the night molest;
curb thou our raging enemy,
that we in chaste repose may rest.

3. Father of mercies, hear our cry,
hear us, O sole-begotten Son
who, with the Holy Ghost most high,
reignest while endless ages run.

Text: 'Te lucis ante terminum' trans. Edward Caswall (1814-1878)
Music: from 'Katholisches Gesangbuch' (c.1774)

500 O bread of heaven

ST CATHERINE (TYNEMOUTH) 88 88 88

1. O bread of heav'n be-neath this veil thou dost my ve - ry God con - ceal; my Je - sus, dear - est trea - sure, hail; I love thee and a - dor - ing kneel; each lov-ing soul by thee is fed with thine own self in form of bread.

2. O food of life, thou who dost give
   the pledge of immortality;
   I live; no, 'tis not I that live;
   God gives me life, God lives in me:
   he feeds my soul, he guides my ways,
   and ev'ry grief with joy repays.

3. O bond of love, that dost unite
   the servant to his living Lord;
   could I dare live, and not requite
   such love – then death were meet reward:
   I cannot live unless to prove
   some love for such unmeasured love.

4. Beloved Lord in heav'n above,
   there, Jesus, thou awaitest me;
   to gaze on thee with changeless love,
   yes, thus I hope, thus shall it be:
   for how can he deny me heav'n
   who here on earth himself hath given?

Text: St Alphonsus (1696-1787) trans. Edmund Vaughan (1827-1908)
Music: Henri Friedrich Hémy (1818-1888)

501 O come, all ye faithful

ADESTE FIDELES Irregular and Refrain

1. O come, all ye faith - ful, joy-ful and tri - um - phant, O come ye, O come ye to Beth - le - hem; come and be - hold him, born the king of an - gels:

Refrain

O come, let us a - dore him, O come, let us a - dore him, O come, let us a - dore him, Christ the Lord.

A lower setting will be found at No. 100

2. God of God,
   Light of Light,
   lo, he abhors not the Virgin's womb;
   very God, begotten not created:

3. Sing, choirs of angels,
   sing in exultation,
   sing, all ye citizens of heav'n above;
   glory to God in the highest:

4. Yea, Lord, we greet thee,
   born this happy morning,
   Jesu, to thee be glory giv'n;
   Word of the Father, now in flesh appearing:

Text: original Latin attributed to John Francis Wade (1711-1786)
trans. Frederick Oakeley (1802-1880)
Music: attributed to John Francis Wade (1711-1786)

502 O come and mourn with me awhile

OLD HALL GREEN 888 and Refrain

1. O come and mourn with me a - while; see,
Ma - ry calls us to her side; O
come and let us mourn with her; Je - sus our
love, Je - sus our love, is cru - ci - fied.

2. Have we no tears to shed for him
while soldiers scoff and people sneer?
Ah, look how patiently he hangs!

3. How fast his feet and hands are nailed,
his blessèd tongue with thirst is tied;
his failing eyes are blind with blood;

4. Sev'n times he spoke, sev'n words of love,
and all three hours his silence cried
for mercy on poor human souls.

5. O break, O break, hard heart of mine:
thy weak self-love and guilty pride
his Pilate and his Judas were:

6. A broken heart, a fount of tears,
ask, and they will not be denied;
a broken heart, love's cradle is;

7. O love of God! O mortal sin!
In this dread act your strength is tried;
and victory remains with love;

Text: Frederick William Faber (1814-1863) alt. the Editors
Music: J. Crookall (1821-1887)

LITURGICAL

HYMNS OLD & NEW

503 O come, O come, Emmanuel

VENI EMMANUEL LM and Refrain

1. O come, O come, Emmanuel, and ransom captive
Israel, that mourns in lonely exile here, until the Son of God appear. Rejoice, rejoice! Emmanuel shall come to thee, O Israel.

2. O come, thou rod of Jesse, free
thine own from Satan's tyranny;
from depths of hell thy people save,
and give them vic'try o'er the grave.

3. O come, thou dayspring, come and cheer
our spirits by thine advent here;
disperse the gloomy clouds of night,
and death's dark shadows put to flight.

4. O come, thou key of David, come
and open wide our heav'nly home;
make safe the way that leads on high,
and close the path to misery.

5. O come, O come, thou Lord of might,
who to thy tribes on Sinai's height
in ancient times didst give the Law,
in cloud and majesty and awe.

Text: from the 'Great O Antiphons' (12th-13th century) trans. John Mason Neale (1818-1866)
Music: adapted by Thomas Helmore (1811-1890) from a French Missal, arr. Andrew Moore

504 O, come to the water

FELSHAM 86 96 and Refrain

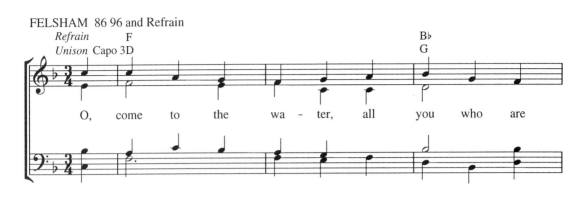

O, come to the wa - ter, all you who are

thir - sty, and drink, drink deep - ly.

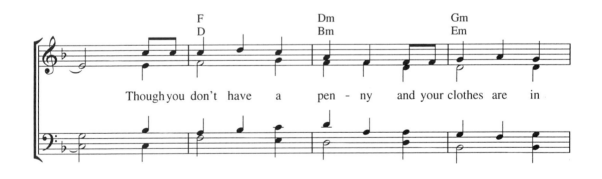

Though you don't have a pen - ny and your clothes are in

rags, you'll be wel - come to drink all you can.

2. Now, listen well and you will find
   food that will feed your soul.
   Just come to me to receive your share,
   food that will feed your soul.

3. I promise you good things to come;
   you are my chosen ones.
   I name you witnesses to my world;
   you are my chosen ones.

Text: Kevin Mayhew (b.1942) based on Isaiah 55:1-4
Music: Kevin Mayhew (b.1942) arr. Colin Hand

505 O comfort my people

COMFORT 11 11 11 11

1. O com-fort my peo-ple and calm all their
fear, and tell them the time of sal-va-tion draws near. O
tell them I come to re-move all their shame. Then
they will for-e-ver give praise to my name.

2. Proclaim to the cities
of Judah my word;
that 'gentle yet strong is
the hand of the Lord.
I rescue the captives,
my people defend,
and bring them to justice
and joy without end.'

3. 'All mountains and hills
shall become as a plain,
for vanished are mourning
and hunger and pain.
And never again shall
these war against you.
Behold, I come quickly
to make all things new.'

Text: Chrysogonus Waddell based on Isaiah 40
Music: Irish traditional melody arr. Richard Lloyd

506 O food of travellers

EISENACH LM

1. O food of trav-'llers, an-gels' bread, man-na where-with the blest are fed, come nigh, and with thy sweet-ness fill the hun-gry hearts that seek thee still.

2. O fount of love, O well unpriced,
   outpouring from the heart of Christ,
   give us to drink of very thee,
   and all we pray shall answered be.

3. O Jesus Christ, we pray to thee
   that this thy presence which we see,
   though now in form of bread concealed,
   to us may be in heav'n revealed.

Text: 'O esca viatorum' from 'Maintzisch Gesangbuch' (1661) trans. Walter H. Shewring and others
Music: melody by Johann Hermann Schein (1586-1630)
harmonised by Johann Sebastian Bach (1685-1750)

507 O fountain of life

O foun-tain of life and in - fi - nite grace, un - al-tered by time, un -

Guitar tacet

hin-dered by space. Im - mor - tal well-spring of ho - li-ness and peace; e -

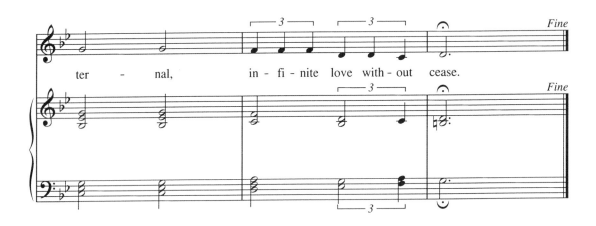

ter - nal, in - fi - nite love with - out cease.

2. Lord, lead me out and guide me in.
   Protect me both from fear and sin.
   Enfold me in your constant love,
   with grace abundant from above.

3. Be there to guide me when I speak.
   To strengthen when my love is weak:
   be there to calm my final breath,
   and light the way to life through death.

Text: Michael Forster (b.1946)
Music: Margaret Rizza (b.1929)

508 Of the Father's love begotten

CORDE NATUS (DIVINUM MYSTERIUM) 87 87 87 7

1. Of the Fa - ther's love be - got - ten, ere the worlds be - gan to be, he is Al - pha and O - me - ga, he the source, the end - ing he, of the things that are, and have been, and that fu - ture years shall

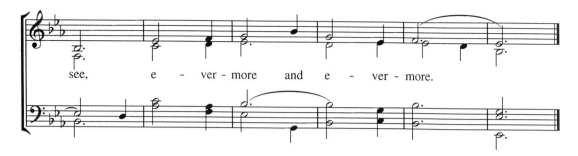

see,   e - ver - more   and   e - ver - more.

2. At his word they were created;
   he commanded; it was done:
   heav'n and earth and depths of ocean
   in their threefold order one;
   all that grows beneath the shining
   of the light of moon and sun,
   evermore and evermore.

3. O that birth for ever blessèd,
   when the Virgin, full of grace,
   by the Holy Ghost conceiving,
   bore the Saviour of our race,
   and the babe, the world's Redeemer,
   first revealed his sacred face,
   evermore and evermore.

4. O ye heights of heav'n, adore him;
   angel hosts, his praises sing;
   pow'rs, dominions, bow before him,
   and extol our God and King:
   let no tongue on earth be silent,
   ev'ry voice in concert ring,
   evermore and evermore.

5. This is he whom seers and sages
   sang of old with one accord;
   whom the writings of the prophets
   promised in their faithful word;
   now he shines, the long-expected:
   let our songs declare his worth,
   evermore and evermore.

6. Christ, to thee, with God the Father,
   and, O Holy Ghost, to thee,
   hymn and chant and high thanksgiving,
   and unwearied praises be;
   honour, glory, and dominion,
   and eternal victory,
   evermore and evermore.

Text: 'Corde natus ex parentis' by Aurelius Clemens Prudentius (348-413)
trans. John Mason Neale (1818-1866) alt.
Music: Plainsong melody (13th century) adapted by Theodoricus Petrus in 'Piae Cantiones' (1582)

LITURGICAL

HYMNS OLD & NEW

509 Of the glorious body telling

ST THOMAS 87 87 87

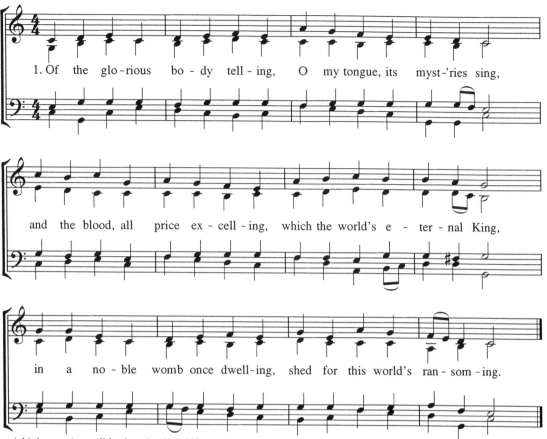

1. Of the glo-rious bo-dy tell-ing, O my tongue, its myst-'ries sing,
and the blood, all price ex-cell-ing, which the world's e-ter-nal King,
in a no-ble womb once dwell-ing, shed for this world's ran-som-ing.

A higher setting will be found at No. 443

2. Giv'n for us, for us descending,
of a virgin to proceed,
he with us in converse blending,
scattered he the gospel seed,
till his sojourn drew to ending,
which he closed in wondrous deed.

3. At the last great supper lying,
circled by his brethren's band,
meekly with the law complying,
first he finished its command.
Then, immortal food supplying,
gave himself with his own hand.

4. Word made flesh, by word is making
very bread his flesh to be;
we, in wine, Christ's blood partaking,
and if senses fail to see,
faith alone the true heart waking,
to behold the mystery.

5. Therefore, we before him bending,
this great sacrament revere;
types and shadows have their ending,
for the newer rite is here;
faith, our outward sense befriending,
makes the inward vision clear.

6. Glory let us give, and blessing,
to the Father and the Son,
honour, might and praise addressing,
while eternal ages run;
ever too his love confessing,
who from both, with both is one.

Text: St Thomas Aquinas (1227-1274) trans. John Mason Neale (1818-1866) alt.
Music: Samuel Webbe (1740-1816)

510 O God beyond all praising

THAXTED 13 13 13 13 13 13

Unison

1. O God be-yond all prais - ing, we wor-ship you to - day, and sing the love a - maz - ing that songs can-not re - pay; for we can on - ly won - der at ev - 'ry gift you send, at bless-ings with - out num - ber and mer - cies with - out end: we lift our hearts be - fore you and wait up - on your

511 O Godhead hid

AQUINAS 11 11 11 11

1. O God-head hid, de-vout-ly I a-dore thee, who tru-ly art with-in the forms be-fore me; to thee my heart I bow with bend-ed knee, as fail-ing quite in con-tem-plat-ing thee.

2. Sight, touch and taste in thee are each deceived,
the ear alone most safely is believed:
I believe all the Son of God has spoken;
than Truth's own word there is no truer token.

3. God only on the cross lay hid from view;
but here lies hid at once the manhood too;
and I, in both professing my belief,
make the same prayer as the repentant thief.

4. Thy wounds, as Thomas saw, I do not see;
yet thee confess my Lord and God to be;
make me believe thee ever more and more,
in thee my hope, in thee my love to store.

5. O thou memorial of our Lord's own dying!
O bread that living art and vivifying!
Make ever thou my soul on thee to live;
ever a taste of heav'nly sweetness give.

6. O loving Pelican! O Jesus, Lord!
Unclean I am, but cleanse me in thy blood,
of which a single drop, for sinners spilt,
is ransom for a world's entire guilt.

7. Jesus, whom for the present veiled I see,
what I so thirst for, O, vouchsafe to me:
that I may see thy countenance unfolding,
and may be blest thy glory in beholding.

Text: 'Adoro te devote,' ascribed to St Thomas Aquinas (1227-1274) trans. Edward Caswall (1814-1878)
Music: Richard Runciman Terry (1865-1938)

512 O God of earth and altar

TUNE 1: KING'S LYNN 76 76 D

1. O God of earth and al - tar, bow down and hear our
cry, our earth - ly ru - lers fal - ter, our peo - ple drift and
die; the walls of gold en - tomb us, the swords of scorn di -
vide, take not thy thun - der from us, but take a - way our pride.

2. From all that terror teaches,
from lies of tongue and pen,
from all the easy speeches
that comfort cruel men,
from sale and profanation
of honour and the sword,
from sleep and from damnation,
deliver us, good Lord!

3. Tie in a living tether
the prince and priest and thrall,
bind all our lives together,
smite us and save us all;
in ire and exultation
aflame with faith and free,
lift up a living nation,
a single sword to thee.

TUNE 2: WILLSBRIDGE 76 76 D

1. O God of earth and al - tar, bow down and hear our

cry, our earth - ly ru - lers fal - ter, our peo - ple drift and

die; the walls of gold en - tomb us, the swords of scorn di -

vide, take not thy thun - der from us, but take a - way our pride.

Text: Gilbert Keith Chesterton (1874-1936)
Music: Tune 1– traditional English melody collected and arr. Ralph Vaughan Williams (1872-1958)
Tune 2– Robert Lucas de Pearsall (1795-1856)

513 O God of grace, we thank you

AURELIA 76 76 D

1. O God of grace, we thank you for that most bles-sed tree, from
which the Sa - viour fa - shioned sal - va - tion full and free. Your
sto - ry of re - demp - tion is proud - ly carved in wood, since
in the Ark you res - cued a rem - nant from the flood.

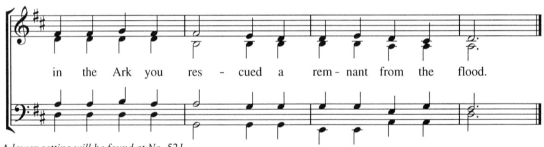

A lower setting will be found at No. 521

Text © Copyright 1996 Kevin Mayhew Ltd.

2. The bush that lit the desert –
   'though burned, yet not consumed –
   became the seed of promise
   from which salvation bloomed.
   The light of life eternal
   still shines with hope and joy,
   from him whom hell's inferno
   could burn but not destroy.

3. The staff which Moses carried,
   as shepherd of your choice,
   is lifted high to rally
   the sheep who know your voice.
   From farthest bounds, you call us,
   as people of the cross,
   to find eternal value
   in your most bitter loss.

4. Christ is the vine eternal,
   producing wholesome fruit;
   the rod that brings salvation,
   the branch from Jesse's root.
   In crib and crucifixion,
   in boats upon the sea,
   the Saviour's earthly journey
   is shadowed by the tree.

5. This tree of life gives knowledge
   of love that conquers all,
   the fruits of goodness ripen,
   and evil's strongholds fall.
   It sprang from this creation
   of which we all are made,
   and where, by sign and symbol,
   your purpose is displayed.

6. The log which, in the desert,
   made bitter water sweet,
   transforms the foulest hatred,
   and renders hope complete;
   for in its awesome presence
   all earthly glory pales:
   the Carpenter is reigning,
   enthroned on wood and nails.

Text: Michael Forster (b.1946)
Music: Samuel Sebastian Wesley (1810-1876)

514 O God, our help in ages past

ST ANNE CM

1. O God, our help in a-ges past, our hope for years to come, our shel-ter from the stor-my blast, and our e-ter-nal home.

2. Beneath the shadow of thy throne,
   thy saints have dwelt secure;
   sufficient is thine arm alone,
   and our defence is sure.

3. Before the hills in order stood,
   or earth received her frame,
   from everlasting thou art God,
   to endless years the same.

4. A thousand ages in thy sight
   are like an evening gone;
   short as the watch that ends the night
   before the rising sun.

5. Time, like an ever-rolling stream,
   will bear us all away;
   we fade and vanish, as a dream
   dies at the op'ning day.

6. O God, our help in ages past,
   our hope for years to come,
   be thou our guard while troubles last,
   and our eternal home.

Text: Isaac Watts (1674-1748) alt.
Music: William Croft (1678-1727)

515 O God, please listen
In the shadow of your wings

1. O God, please lis-ten to my cry, and give me ans-wer.
I am a-fraid of what the fu-ture holds for me, O Lord. Let me
hide, Lord, in the sha-dow of your wings. Let me
hide, Lord, in the sha-dow of your wings.

2. If only I had wings to fly I would escape, Lord:
I'd fly as far as I could go to find some peace of mind.

3. I feel defeated by life's trials and disappointments.
My days and nights are spent in fear, with no one I can trust.

4. But all of this I can survive if you are with me:
my life is here, my life is now, and I must carry on.

5. Within the shadow of your wings I find my refuge.
You are the only one I have; I count on you, O Lord.

Text: Frances M. Kelly based on Psalm 54
Music: Frances M. Kelly arr. Keith Stent
© Copyright 1999 Kevin Mayhew Ltd.

LITURGICAL

HYMNS OLD & NEW

516 O God, we give ourselves today

IRISH CM

1. O God, we give our-selves to - day with
this pure host to thee, the self - same gift which
thy dear Son gave once on Cal - va - ry.

2. Entire and whole, our life and love
with heart and soul and mind,
for all our errors, faults and needs,
thy Church and humankind.

3. With humble and with contrite heart
this bread and wine we give
because thy Son once gave himself
and died that we might live.

4. Though lowly now, soon by thy word
these offered gifts will be
the very body of our Lord,
his soul and deity.

5. His very body, offered up,
a gift beyond all price,
he gives to us, that we may give,
in loving sacrifice.

6. O Lord, who took our human life,
as water mixed with wine,
grant through this sacrifice that we
may share thy life divine.

Text: Anthony Nye (b.1932) alt.
Music: Melody from 'Hymns and Sacred Poems', Dublin (1749)

517 O God, your people gather

TUNE 1: THORNBURY 76 76 D

1. O God, your peo-ple ga-ther, o-be-dient to your word, a-round your ho-ly al-tar to praise your name, O Lord. For all your lov-ing kind-ness our grate-ful hearts we raise; but par-don first the blind-ness of all our sin-ful ways.

2. You are our loving Father,
you are our holiest Lord,
but we have sinned against you,
by thought and deed and word.
Before the court of heaven
we stand and humbly pray
our sins may be forgiven,
our faults be washed away.

3. Though sinful, we implore you
to turn and make us live,
that so we may adore you,
and our due off'ring give,
and may the prayers and voices
of your glad people rise,
as your whole Church rejoices
in this great sacrifice.

TUNE 2: PINNER 76 76 D

1. O God, your peo-ple ga - ther, o - be-dient to your word, a -

round your ho - ly al - tar to praise your name, O Lord. For

all your lov - ing kind - ness our grate - ful hearts we raise; but

par-don first the blind - ness of all our sin - ful ways.

Text: Anthony Nye (b.1932)
Music: Tune 1 – Basil Harwood (1859-1949)
Tune 2 – Wilfrid Trotman

518 O healing river

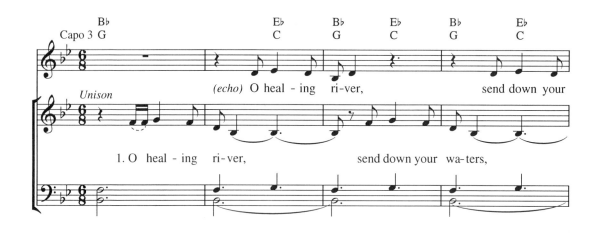

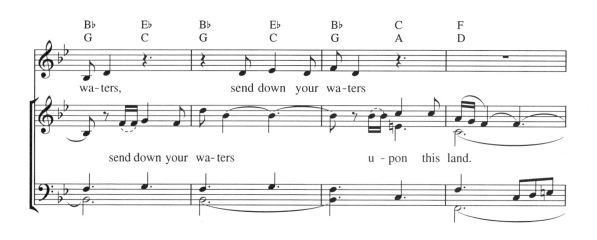

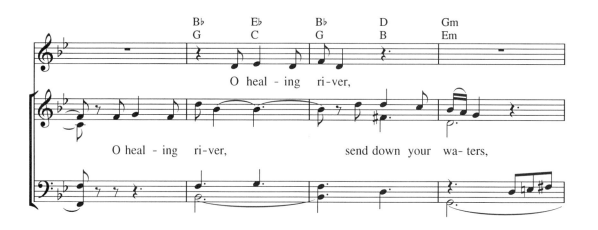

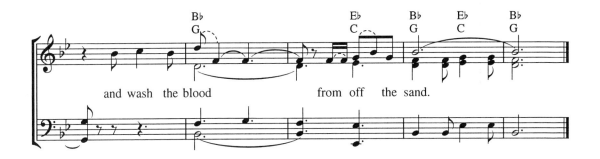

and wash the blood ... from off the sand.

2. This land is parching, this land is burning,
   no seed is growing in the barren ground.
   O healing river, send down your waters,
   O healing river, send your waters down.

3. Let the seed of freedom awake and flourish,
   let the deep roots nourish, let the tall stalks rise.
   O healing river, send down your waters,
   O healing river, from out of the skies.

Text: traditional Baptist hymn
Music: traditional Baptist hymn, arr. Keith Stent

LITURGICAL

HYMNS OLD & NEW

519 O holy Lord, by all adored

MIT FREUDEN ZART 87 87 887

1. O ho-ly Lord, by all a-dored, our tres-pas-ses con - fess - ing, to thee this day thy chil-dren pray, our ho-ly faith pro - fess - ing! Ac - cept, O King, the gifts we bring, our songs of praise, the prayers we raise, and grant us, Lord, thy bless - ing.

2. To God on high be thanks and praise,
   who deigns our bond to sever;
   his care shall guide us all our days,
   and harm shall reach us never;
   on him we rest with faith assured
   of all that live he is the Lord,
   for ever and for ever.

Text: Maurice F. Bell (1862-1947) alt.
Music: The Bohemian Brethren's 'Kirchengesang' (1566)

520 O, how good is the Lord

2. He gives us his Spirit, how good is the Lord. *(x3)*
   I never will forget what he has done for me.

3. He gives us his healing, how good is the Lord. *(x3)*
   I never will forget what he has done for me.

4. He gives us his body, how good is the Lord. *(x3)*
   I never will forget what he has done for me.

5. He gives us his freedom, how good is the Lord. *(x3)*
   I never will forget what he has done for me.

6. He gives us each other, how good is the Lord. *(x3)*
   I never will forget what he has done for me.

7. He gives us his glory, how good is the Lord. *(x3)*
   I never will forget what he has done for me.

Text: traditional
Music: traditional arr. Elaine Irwin

LITURGICAL

HYMNS OLD & NEW

521 O Jesus Christ, remember

AURELIA 76 76 D

1. O Jesus Christ, re-mem-ber, when thou shalt come a-gain upon the clouds of hea-ven, with all thy shi-ning train; when
ev-'ry eye shall see thee in de-i-ty re-vealed, who
now up-on this al-tar in si-lence art con-cealed.

A higher setting will be found at No. 513

2. Remember then, O Saviour,
   I supplicate of thee,
   that here I bowed before thee
   upon my bended knee;
   that here I owned thy presence,
   and did not thee deny,
   and glorified thy greatness
   though hid from human eye.

3. Accept, divine Redeemer,
   the homage of my praise;
   be thou the light and honour
   and glory of my days.
   Be thou my consolation
   when death is drawing nigh;
   be thou my only treasure
   through all eternity.

This hymn may be sung to the tune 'Kings Lynn' at No. 512

Text: Edward Caswall (1814-1878)
Music: Samuel Sebastian Wesley (1810-1876)

522 O Jesus, I have promised

HATHEROP CASTLE 76 76 D

1. O Je-sus, I have pro-mised to serve thee to the end;
be thou for e - ver near me, my Ma-ster and my friend:
I shall not fear the bat - tle if thou art by my side, nor
wan-der from the path-way if thou wilt be my guide.

Verses 1 to 4

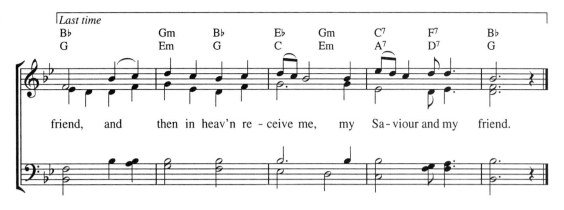

Last time

| Bb | | Gm | Bb | Eb | Gm | C7 | F7 | Bb |
| G | | Em | G | C | Em | A7 | D7 | G |

friend, and then in heav'n re - ceive me, my Sa - viour and my friend.

2. O let me feel thee near me:
    the world is ever near;
    I see the sights that dazzle,
    the tempting sounds I hear;
    my foes are ever near me,
    around me and within;
    but, Jesus, draw thou nearer,
    and shield my soul from sin.

3. O let me hear thee speaking
    in accents clear and still,
    above the storms of passion,
    the murmurs of self-will;
    O speak to reassure me,
    to hasten or control;
    O speak and make me listen,
    thou guardian of my soul.

4. O Jesus, thou hast promised,
    to all who follow thee,
    that where thou art in glory
    there shall thy servant be;
    and, Jesus, I have promised
    to serve thee to the end:
    O give me grace to follow,
    my Master and my friend.

5. O let me see thy foot-marks,
    and in them plant mine own;
    my hope to follow duly
    is in thy strength alone:
    O guide me, call me, draw me,
    uphold me to the end;
    and then in heav'n receive me,
    my Saviour and my friend.

Text: John E. Bode (1816-1874)
Music: Geoffrey Beaumont (1903-1970) arr. Norman Warren (b.1934)

523 O King of might and splendour

O KING OF MIGHT 76 76 D

1. O King of might and splen-dour, cre-a-tor most a-dored, this
sac-ri-fice we ren-der to thee as sov-'reign Lord. May
these our gifts be pleas-ing un-to thy ma-jes-ty, our
hearts from sin re-leas-ing who have of-fen-ded thee.

2. Thy body thou hast given,
   thy blood thou hast outpoured,
   that sin might be forgiven,
   O Jesus, loving Lord.
   As now with love most tender,
   thy death we celebrate,
   our lives in self-surrender
   to thee we consecrate.

524 O lady, full of God's own grace

GRACE DLM

1. O la-dy, full of God's own grace, whose car-ing hands the child em-braced, who lis-tened to the Spi-rit's word, be-lieved and trust - ed in the Lord. O Vir-gin fair, star of the sea, my dear-est mo - ther, pray for me. O Vir-gin me.

2. O lady, who felt daily joy
   in caring for the holy boy,
   whose home was plain and shorn of wealth,
   yet was enriched by God's own breath.

3. O lady, who bore living's pain
   but still believed that love would reign,
   who on a hill watched Jesus die,
   as on the cross they raised him high.

4. O lady, who, on Easter day,
   had all your sorrow wiped away
   as God the Father's will was done
   when from death's hold he freed your Son.

Text and Music: Estelle White (b.1925)

525 O let all who thirst
Come to the water

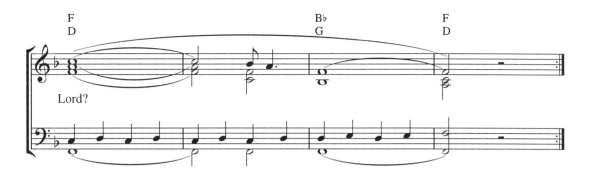

Lord?

2. And let all who seek,
   let them come to the water.
   And let all who have nothing,
   let them come to the Lord:
   without money, without strife.
   Why should you spend your life,
   except for the Lord?

3. And let all who toil,
   let them come to the water.
   And let all who are weary,
   let them come to the Lord:
   all who labour, without rest.
   How can your soul find rest,
   except for the Lord?

4. And let all the poor,
   let them come to the water.
   Bring the ones who are laden,
   bring them all to the Lord:
   bring the children without might.
   Easy the load and light:
   oh come to the Lord.

Text: John Foley based on Isaiah 55:1,2 and Matthew 11:28-30
Music: John Foley arr. Keith Stent

526 O little town of Bethlehem

FOREST GREEN DCM

1. O lit - tle town of Beth - le - hem, how still we see thee lie! A - bove thy deep and dream - less sleep the si - lent stars go by. Yet in thy dark streets shi - neth the e - ver - last - ing light; the hopes and fears of all the years are met in thee to - night.

2. O morning stars, together
proclaim the holy birth,
and praises sing to God the King,
and peace to all the earth;
For Christ is born of Mary;
and, gathered all above,
while mortals sleep, the angels keep
their watch of wond'ring love.

3. How silently, how silently,
the wondrous gift is giv'n!
So God imparts to human hearts
the blessings of his heav'n.
No ear may hear his coming;
but in this world of sin,
where meek souls will receive him, still
the dear Christ enters in.

4. O holy child of Bethlehem,
descend to us, we pray;
cast out our sin, and enter in,
be born in us today.
We hear the Christmas angels
the great glad tidings tell:
O come to us, abide with us,
our Lord Emmanuel.

Text: Phillips Brooks (1835-1893) alt.
Music: traditional English melody collected and arr. Ralph Vaughan Williams (1872-1958)
Music © Copyright Oxford University Press, Great Clarendon Street, Oxford OX2 6DP.
Used by permission from the 'English Hymnal'.

527 O living water

2. O set us free. O set us free.

3. Come, pray in us. Come, pray in us.

Text: Virginia Vissing
Music: Virginia Vissing arr. Andrew Moore

528 O Lord, be not mindful

Refrain
Unison

O Lord, be not mind-ful of our guilt and our sins;

O Lord, do not judge us for our faults and of-fen-ces. May your mer - ci-ful love be up-on us.

Fine

1. Help your peo - ple, Lord, O God our Sa - viour, de - liv - er us for the glo - ry of your name!

D.C.

2. Par - don us, O Lord, all our sins, de - liv - er us for the glo - ry of your name!

3. Praise to you, O Lord, through all a - ges with - out end, de - li - ver us for the glo - ry of your name!

Text: Lucien Deiss (b.1921) based on Psalm 102:17-18 (Refrain) and Psalm 78:9 (verses)
Music: Lucien Deiss (b.1921)

529 O Lord, my God
How great thou art

HOW GREAT THOU ART 11 10 11 10 and Refrain

1. O Lord, my God, when I in awe-some won-der con-si-der

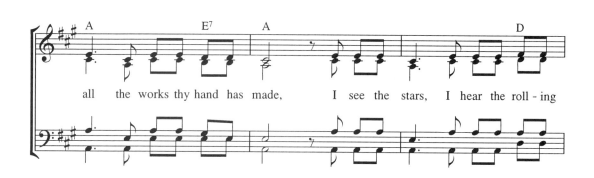

all the works thy hand has made, I see the stars, I hear the roll-ing

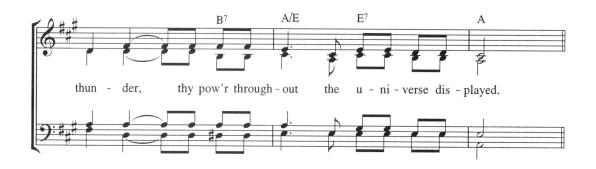

thun-der, thy pow'r through-out the u-ni-verse dis-played.

Refrain

Then sings my soul, my Sa-viour God, to thee: how great thou

art, how great thou art. Then sings my soul, my Sa-viour God, to

thee; how great thou art, how great thou art.

2. When through the woods and forest glades I wander
   and hear the birds sing sweetly in the trees;
   when I look down from lofty mountain grandeur,
   and hear the brook, and feel the gentle breeze.

3. And when I think that God, his Son not sparing,
   sent him to die, I scarce can take it in
   that on the cross, my burden gladly bearing,
   he bled and died to take away my sin.

4. When Christ shall come with shout of acclamation
   and take me home, what joy shall fill my heart;
   when I shall bow in humble adoration,
   and there proclaim: my God, how great thou art.

Text: 'O Støre Gud' by Karl Boberg (1859-1940) trans. Stuart K. Hine (1899-1989)
Music: Swedish folk melody arr. Stuart K. Hine (1899-1989)

530 O Lord, your tenderness

O Lord, your ten - der-ness, melt-ing all my
bit - ter - ness, O Lord, I re - ceive your
love. O Lord, your love - li-ness,
chang-ing all my ug - li-ness, O Lord, I re -

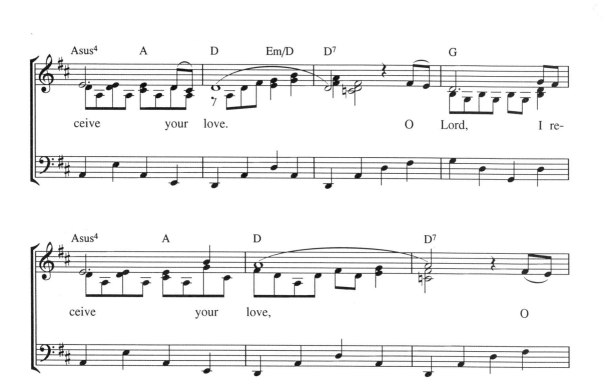

ceive   your   love.   O   Lord,   I re-

ceive   your   love,   O

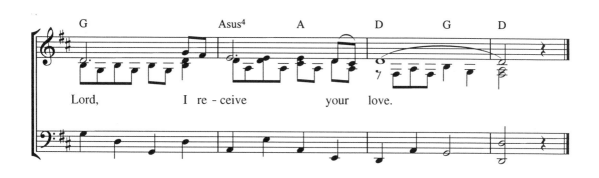

Lord,   I re - ceive   your   love.

Words and Music: Graham Kendrick (b.1950)

531 O Mary, when our God chose you

1. O Ma - ry, when our God chose you to bring his on - ly Son to birth, a new cre - a - tion made in you gave joy to all the earth.

2. When he was born on Christmas night
   and music made the rafters ring,
   the stars were dancing with delight;
   now all God's children sing.

3. One winter's night, a heap of straw
   becomes a place where ages meet,
   when kings come knocking at the door
   and kneeling at your feet.

4. In you, our God confounds the strong
   and makes the crippled dance with joy;
   and to our barren world belong
   his mother and her boy.

5. In empty streets and broken hearts
   you call to mind what he has done;
   where all his loving kindness starts
   in sending you a Son.

6. And, Mary, while we stand with you,
   may once again his Spirit come,
   and all his people follow you
   to reach our Father's home.

Text: Damian Lundy (1944-1997)
Music: Swiss folk melody arr. Christopher Tambling
Text and this arrangement © Copyright 1978 Kevin Mayhew Ltd.

532 O Mother blest

ST URSULA 86 86 and Refrain

1. O Mo - ther blest, whom God be-stows on sin-ners and on just, what joy, what hope thou giv - est those who in thy mer - cy trust.

Refrain

Thou art cle-ment, thou art chaste, Ma - ry, thou art fair; of all mo - thers sweet-est, best, none with thee com - pare.

2. O heav'nly mother, maiden sweet!
   It never yet was told
   that suppliant sinner left thy feet
   unpitied, unconsoled.

3. O mother pitiful and mild,
   cease not to pray for me;
   for I do love thee as a child
   and sigh for love of thee.

4. O mother blest, for me obtain,
   ungrateful though I be,
   to love that God who first could deign
   to show such love for me.

Text: 'Sei pura, sei pia' by St Alphonsus (1696-1787) trans. Edmund Vaughan (1827-1908)
Music: F. Westlake (1840-1898)

533 O my Lord, within my heart

2. Lord, my eyes do not look high
   nor my thoughts take wings,
   I can find such treasures in
   ordinary things.

3. Great affairs are not for me,
   deeds beyond my scope.
   In the simple things I do
   I find joy and hope.

Text: Estelle White (b.1925) based on Psalm 130
Music: Estelle White (b.1925) arr. Christopher Tambling
© Copyright 1976, 1997 Kevin Mayhew Ltd.

534 O my people, what have I done to you?

REPROACHES 7 8 9 8 and Refrain

Refrain
Unison

O my peo - ple, what have I done to you? How have I hurt you? An - swer me. 1. I led you out of E - gypt; from sla - ve - ry I set you free. I brought you in - to a land of prom - ise; you have pre - pared a cross for me.

Fine

D.C.

2. I led you as a shepherd,
   I brought you safely through the sea,
   fed you with manna in the desert;
   you have prepared a cross for me.

3. I fought for you in battles,
   I won you strength and victory,
   gave you a royal crown and sceptre:
   you have prepared a cross for me.

4. I planted you, my vineyard,
   and cared for you most tenderly,
   looked for abundant fruit, and found none
   – only the cross you made for me.

5. Then listen to my pleading,
   and do not turn away from me.
   You are my people: will you reject me?
   For you I suffer bitterly.

Text: Damian Lundy (1944-1997) based on the Good Friday 'Reproaches'
Music: Damian Lundy (1944-1997) arr. Christopher Tambling
© Copyright 1978 Kevin Mayhew Ltd.

535 On a hill far away
The old rugged cross

THE OLD RUGGED CROSS 66 8 D and Refrain

1. On a hill far a - way stood an old rug - ged cross, the em - blem of suff -'ring and shame; and I loved that old cross where the dear - est and best for a world of lost sin -ners was slain. So I'll cher - ish the old rug - ged cross, till my tro - phies at last I lay

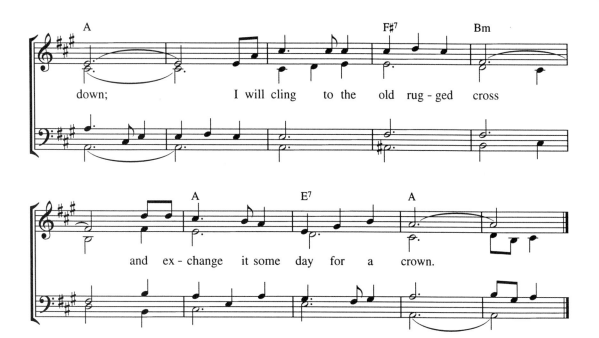

down; I will cling to the old rug-ged cross

and ex-change it some day for a crown.

2. O that old rugged cross,
   so despised by the world,
   has a wondrous attraction for me:
   for the dear Lamb of God
   left his glory above
   to bear it to dark Calvary.

3. In the old rugged cross,
   stained with blood so divine,
   a wondrous beauty I see.
   For 'twas on that old cross
   Jesus suffered and died
   to pardon and sanctify me.

4. To the old rugged cross
   I will ever be true,
   its shame and reproach gladly bear.
   Then he'll call me some day
   to my home far away;
   there his glory for ever I'll share.

Text and Music: George Bennard (1873-1958)

536 Once in royal David's city

IRBY 87 87 77

1. Once in roy-al Da-vid's ci-ty stood a low-ly cat-tle shed, where a
mo-ther laid her ba-by in a man-ger for his bed: Ma-ry
was that mo-ther mild, Je-sus Christ her lit-tle child.

2. He came down to earth from heaven,
   who is God and Lord of all,
   and his shelter was a stable,
   and his cradle was a stall;
   with the needy, poor and lowly,
   lived on earth our Saviour holy.

3. For he is our childhood's pattern,
   day by day like us he grew;
   he was little, weak and helpless,
   tears and smiles like us he knew;
   and he feeleth for our sadness,
   and he shareth in our gladness.

4. And our eyes at last shall see him
   through his own redeeming love,
   for that child so dear and gentle
   is our Lord in heav'n above;
   and he leads his children on
   to the place where he is gone.

Text: Cecil Frances Alexander (1818-1895)
Music: Henry John Gauntlett (1805-1876)

2. Many the gifts,
   many the works,
   one in the Lord of all.

3. Grain for the fields,
   scattered and grown,
   gathered to one, for all.

Text: John Foley based on 1 Cor. 10:16, 17; 12:4, Gal. 3:28; Didaché 9
Music: John Foley

539 One cold night in spring

ONE COLD NIGHT 97 87

1. One cold night in spring the wind blew strong; then the dark-ness had its hour. A man was eat - ing with his friends, for he knew his death was near.

2. And he broke a wheaten loaf to share,
   for his friends a last goodbye.
   'My body is the bread I break.
   O, my heart will break and die.'

3. Then he poured good wine into a cup,
   blessed it gently, passed it round.
   'This cup is brimming with my blood.
   Soon the drops will stain the ground.'

4. See a dying man with arms outstretched
   at the setting of the sun.
   He stretches healing hands to you.
   Will you take them for your own?

5. Soon a man will come with arms outstretched
   at the rising of the sun.
   His wounded hands will set you free
   if you take them for your own.

Text: Damian Lundy (1944-1997)
Music: Damian Lundy (1944-1997) arr. Christopher Tambling
© Copyright 1978 Kevin Mayhew Ltd.

540 One Father
One God

2. Lord Jesus, now enthroned in glory,
   what God is this who gives his life
   to set me free?

3. O loving breath of God almighty,
   what God is this who through my weakness
   sings his praise?

Text: Gerard Markland (b.1953)
Music: Gerard Markland (b.1953) arr. Keith Stent

541 On Jordan's bank the Baptist's cry

WINCHESTER NEW LM

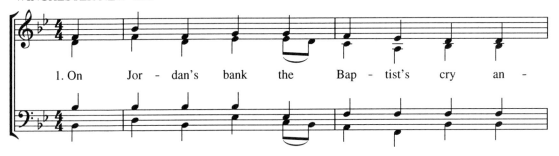

1. On Jor - dan's bank the Bap - tist's cry an -

noun - ces that the Lord is nigh; a - wake, and hear - ken,

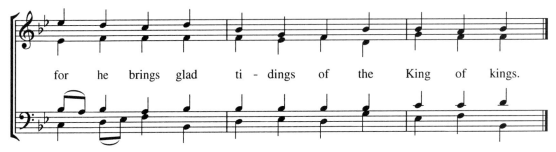

for he brings glad ti - dings of the King of kings.

A lower setting will be found at No. 593

2. Then cleansed be ev'ry breast from sin;
make straight the way for God within;
prepare we in our hearts a home,
where such a mighty guest may come.

3. For thou art our salvation, Lord,
our refuge and our great reward;
without thy grace we waste away,
like flow'rs that wither and decay.

4. To heal the sick stretch out thine hand,
and bid the fallen sinner stand;
shine forth and let thy light restore
earth's own true loveliness once more.

5. All praise, eternal Son, to thee
whose advent doth thy people free,
whom with the Father we adore
and Holy Ghost for evermore.

Text: Charles Coffin (1676-1749) trans. John Chandler (1806-1876) alt.
Music: from 'Musikalisches Handbuch' (1690)

542 On this day of joy

On this day of joy, on this day of hope, we come to you in love, O Lord, on this

day of joy, on this day of hope, we come to you in love.

1. With this bread and wine we come to this eu - cha - ri - stic feast. On this

day of joy, on this day of hope, we come to you in love.

2. Bread to be your body, Lord,
   wine to be your saving blood;
   on this day of joy, on this day of hope,
   we come to you in love.

Text: Marie Lydia Pereira (b.1920)
Music: Marie Lydia Pereira (b.1920) arr. Keith Stent

LITURGICAL

HYMNS OLD & NEW

543 On this house your blessing, Lord

1. On this house your bless-ing, Lord, on this house your grace be-stow. On this house your bless-ing, Lord, may it come and ne-ver go. Bring-ing peace and joy and hap-pi-ness, bring-ing love that knows no end. On this house your bless-ing, Lord, on this house your bless-ing send.

2. On this house your loving, Lord,
   may it overflow each day.
   On this house your loving, Lord,
   may it come and with us stay.
   Drawing us in love and unity
   by the love received from you.
   On this house your loving, Lord,
   may it come each day anew.

3. On this house your giving, Lord,
   may it turn and ever flow.
   On this house your giving, Lord,
   on this house your wealth bestow.
   Filling all our hopes and wishes, Lord,
   in the way you know is best.
   On this house your giving, Lord,
   may it come and with us rest.

4. On this house your calling, Lord,
   may it come to us each day.
   On this house your calling, Lord,
   may it come to lead the way.
   Filling us with nobler yearnings, Lord,
   calling us to live in you.
   On this house your calling, Lord,
   may it come each day anew.

The word 'house' may be replaced throughout by 'school', 'church', etc.

Text: Marie Lydia Pereira (b.1920)
Music: Marie Lydia Pereira (b.1920) arr. Christopher Tambling
© Copyright 1976 Kevin Mayhew Ltd.

544 Onward, Christian pilgrims

ST GERTRUDE 65 65 D and Refrain

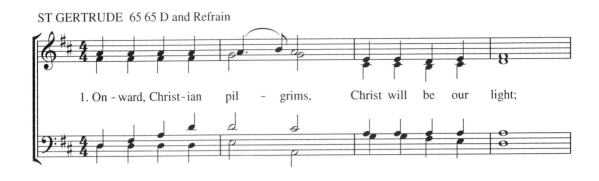

1. On-ward, Christ-ian pil - grims, Christ will be our light;

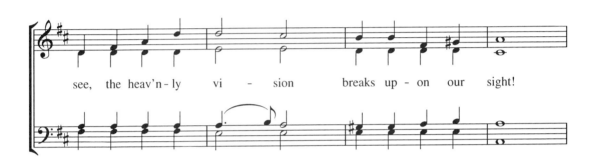

see, the heav'n-ly vi - sion breaks up-on our sight!

Out of death's en - slave - ment Christ has set us free,

on then to sal - va - tion, hope and li - ber - ty.

Refrain

On - ward, Christ-ian pil - grims, Christ will be our light; *(Tenor)* see, the

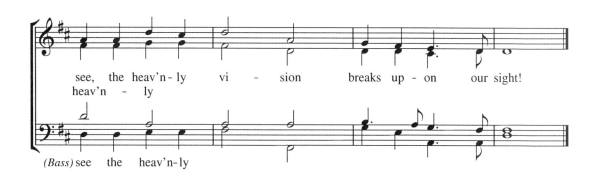

see, the heav'n-ly vi - sion breaks up - on our sight!
heav'n - ly

(Bass) see the heav'n-ly

2. Onward, Christian pilgrims,
   up the rocky way,
   where the dying Saviour
   bids us watch and pray.
   Through the darkened valley
   walk with those who mourn,
   share the pain and anger,
   share the promised dawn!

3. Onward, Christian pilgrims,
   in the early dawn;
   death's great seal is broken,
   life and hope reborn!
   Faith in resurrection
   strengthens pilgrim's hearts,
   ev'ry load is lightened,
   ev'ry fear departs.

4. Onward, Christian pilgrims,
   hearts and voices raise,
   till the whole creation
   echoes perfect praise:
   swords are turned to ploughshares,
   pride and envy cease,
   truth embraces justice,
   hope resolves in peace.

Text: Michael Forster (b.1946)
Music: Arthur Seymour Sullivan (1842-1900)

545 Open our eyes, Lord

Text: Robert Cull (b.1949)
Music: Robert Cull (b.1949) arr. David Peacock

© Copyright 1976 Maranatha! Music. Administered by CopyCare, P.O. Box 77,
Hailsham, East Sussex BN27 3EF, UK. Used by permission.

546 Open your ears, O Christian people

1. O - pen your ears, O Christ - ian peo - ple, o - pen your ears and hear Good News! O - pen your hearts, O roy - al priest - hood, God has come to you!

Refrain
God has spo - ken to his peo - ple, al - le - lu - ia, and his words are words of wis - dom, al - le - lu - ia.

2. Israel comes to greet the Saviour,
Judah is glad to see his day.
From east and west the peoples travel,
he will show the way.

3. All who have ears to hear his message,
all who have ears then let them hear.
All who would learn the way of wisdom,
let them hear God's words.

Text: Willard F. Jabusch (b.1930)
Music: Israeli melody arr. Christopher Tambling

547 O perfect love

TUNE 1: STRENGTH AND STAY 11 10 11 10

1. O per-fect love, all hu-man thought tran - scend - ing,
low - ly we kneel in prayer be - fore thy throne,
that theirs may be the love which knows no end - ing,
whom thou for e - ver-more dost join in one.

2. O perfect life,
be thou their full assurance
of tender charity
and steadfast faith,
of patient hope
and quiet, brave endurance,
with childlike trust
that fears not pain nor death.

3. Grant them the joy
which brightens earthly sorrow,
grant them the peace
which calms all earthly strife;
and to life's day
the glorious unknown morrow
that dawns upon
eternal love and life.

TUNE 2: HIGHWOOD 11 10 11 10

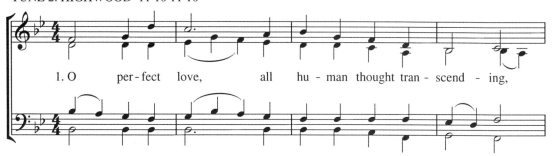

1. O per-fect love, all hu - man thought tran - scend - ing,

low - ly we kneel in prayer be - fore thy throne,

that theirs may be the love which knows no end - ing,

whom thou for e - ver - more dost join in one.

Text: Dorothy F. Gurney (1858-1932)
Music: Tune 1 – John Bacchus Dykes (1823-1876)
Tune 2 – Richard Runciman Terry (1865-1938)

548 O praise ye the Lord!

LAUDATE DOMINUM (PARRY) 10 10 11 11

1. O praise ye the Lord! praise him in the height; rejoice in his word, ye an - gels of light; ye
hea - vens, a - dore him, by whom ye were made, and
wor - ship be - fore him, in bright - ness ar - rayed.

A higher setting will be found at No. 669

2. O praise ye the Lord! praise him upon earth,
in tuneful accord, all you of new birth;
praise him who hath brought you his grace from above,
praise him who hath taught you to sing of his love.

3. O praise ye the Lord! all things that give sound;
each jubilant chord re-echo around;
loud organs his glory forth tell in deep tone,
and, sweet harp, the story of what he hath done.

4. O praise ye the Lord! thanksgiving and song
to him be outpoured all ages along:
for love in creation, for heaven restored,
for grace of salvation, O praise ye the Lord!

Text: Henry Williams Baker (1821-1877) based on Psalms 148 and 150 alt.
Music: Charles Hubert Hastings Parry (1848-1918)

549 O purest of creatures

MARIA ZU LIEBEN 11 11 11 11

1. O pur-est of crea-tures! Sweet mo-ther, sweet maid: the one spot-less womb where-in Je-sus was laid. Dark night hath come down on us, mo-ther, and we look out for thy shi-ning, sweet star of the sea.

2. Earth gave him one lodging;
   'twas deep in thy breast,
   and God found a home where
   the sinner finds rest;
   his home and his hiding-place,
   both were in thee;
   he was won by thy shining,
   sweet star of the sea.

3. O, blissful and calm
   was the wonderful rest
   that thou gavest thy God
   in thy virginal breast;
   for the heaven he left
   he found heaven in thee,
   and he shone in thy shining,
   sweet star of the sea.

Text: Frederick William Faber (1814-1863)
Music: from 'Paderborn Gesangbuch' (1765)

LITURGICAL

HYMNS OLD & NEW

550 O Queen of heaven

1. O Queen of heav'n, to you the an-gels sing, the Maid-en-
Mo-ther of their Lord and King. O Wo-man raised a-bove the stars, receive the ho-mage of your chil-dren, sin-less Eve.

2. O full of grace, in grace your womb did bear
Emmanuel, King David's promised heir.
O Eastern Gate, whom God had made his own,
by you, God's glory came to Zion's throne.

3. O Burning Bush, you gave the world its light,
when Christ, your Son, was born on Christmas night.
O Mary Queen, who bore God's holy one,
for us your children, pray to God your Son.

Text: James Quinn (b.1919)
Music: Gregory Murray (1905-1992)

551 O sacred head ill-used

PASSION CHORALE 76 76 D

1. O sa-cred head ill-us - ed, by reed and bram-ble
scarred, that i-dle blows have bruis - ed, and
mock - ing lips have marred, how dimmed that eye so
ten - der, how wan those cheeks ap-pear, how

o - ver - cast the splen - dour that an - gel hosts re - vere!

2. What marvel if thou languish,
vigour and virtue fled,
wasted and spent with anguish,
and pale as are the dead?
O by thy foes' derision,
that death endured for me,
grant that thy open vision
a sinner's eyes may see.

3. Good Shepherd, spent with loving,
look on me, who have strayed,
oft by those lips unmoving
with milk and honey stayed;
spurn not a sinner's crying
nor from thy love outcast,
but rest thy head in dying
on these frail arms at last.

4. In this thy sacred passion
O that some share had I!
O may thy Cross's fashion
o'erlook me when I die!
For these dear pains that rack thee
a sinner's thanks receive;
O, lest in death I lack thee,
a sinner's care relieve.

5. Since death must be my ending,
in that dread hour of need,
my friendless cause befriending,
Lord, to my rescue speed;
thyself, dear Jesus, trace me
that passage to the grave,
and from thy cross embrace me
with arms outstretched to save.

Another arrangement will be found at No. 552

Text: Paul Gerhardt (1607-1676) based on 'Salve caput cruentatum'
trans. Ronald Arbuthnott Knox (1888-1957)
Music: Hans Leo Hassler (1564-1612) harmonised by Johann Sebastian Bach (1685-1750)

552 O sacred head sore wounded

PASSION CHORALE 76 76 D

1. O sacred head sore wounded, defiled and put to scorn; O kingly head surrounded with mocking crown of thorn: what sorrow mars thy grandeur? Can death thy bloom deflower? O

coun - ten - ance whose splen - dour the hosts of heav'n a - dore.

2. Thy beauty, long-desirèd,
   hath vanished from our sight;
   thy pow'r is all expirèd,
   and quenched the light of light.
   Ah me, for whom thou diest,
   hide not so far thy grace:
   show me, O love most highest,
   the brightness of thy face.

3. I pray thee, Jesus, own me,
   me, shepherd good, for thine;
   who to thy fold hast won me,
   and fed with truth divine.
   Me guilty, me refuse not,
   incline thy face to me,
   this comfort that I lose not,
   on earth to comfort thee.

4. In thy most bitter passion
   my heart to share doth cry,
   with thee for my salvation
   upon the cross to die.
   Ah, keep my heart thus movèd,
   to stand thy cross beneath,
   to mourn thee, well-belovèd,
   yet thank thee for thy death.

5. My days are few, O fail not,
   with thine immortal power,
   to hold me that I quail not
   in death's most fearful hour:
   that I may fight befriended,
   and see in my last strife
   to me thine arms extended
   upon the cross of life.

Another arrangement will be found at No. 551

Text: Paul Gerhardt (1607-1676) based on 'Salve caput cruentatum' trans. Robert Bridges (1844-1930)
Music: Hans Leo Hassler (1564-1612) harmonised by Johann Sebastian Bach (1685-1750)

553 O Sacred Heart

LAURENCE 4 6 88 4

1. O Sacred Heart, our home lies deep in thee; on earth thou art an exile's rest, in heav'n the glory of the blest, O Sacred Heart.

2. O Sacred Heart,
thou fount of contrite tears;
where'er those living waters flow,
new life to sinners they bestow,
O Sacred Heart.

3. O Sacred Heart,
our trust is all in thee,
for though earth's night be dark and drear,
thou breathest rest where thou art near,
O Sacred Heart.

4. O Sacred Heart,
lead exiled children home,
where we may ever rest near thee,
in peace and joy eternally,
O Sacred Heart.

Text: Francis Stanfield (1835-1914)
Music: Richard Runciman Terry (1865-1938)

556 O that today you would listen to his voice

O that to-day you would lis-ten to his voice, 'Hard - en not your hearts.'

1. Come let us joy - ful-ly sing to the Lord, sa - lut- ing the rock who pre-serves us.

Let us ap-proach him to of - fer him thanks, with songs let us wel-come our God.

2. Let us come in, let us kneel and adore
in rev'rence for God who has made us.
We are his people, the sheep of his flock,
we graze in the pastures of God.

3. Out in the desert they hardened their hearts,
at Massah they tested their Saviour,
O that today you would listen to him,
and open your hearts to his love.

Text: Susan Sayers (b.1946) based on Psalm 94
Music: Andrew Moore (b.1954)

557 O, the love of my Lord
As gentle as silence

AS GENTLE AS SILENCE 10 9 12 10

1. O, the love of my Lord is the es-sence of all that I love here on earth. All the beau-ty I see he has gi-ven to me, and his giv-ing is gen-tle as si-lence.

2. Ev'ry
3. There've been

2. Ev'ry day, ev'ry hour, ev'ry moment
   have been blessed by the strength of his love.
   At the turn of each tide he is there at my side,
   and his touch is as gentle as silence.

3. There've been times when I've turned from his presence,
   and I've walked other paths, other ways;
   but I've called on his name in the dark of my shame,
   and his mercy was gentle as silence.

Text and Music: Estelle White (b.1925)

558 O the word of my Lord

2. I know that you are very young,
   but I will make you strong,
   I'll fill you with my word;
   and you will travel through the land,
   fulfilling my command which you have heard.

3. And ev'rywhere you are to go
   my hand will follow you;
   you will not be alone.
   In all the danger that you fear
   you'll find me very near, your words my own.

4. With all my strength you will be filled:
   you will destroy and build,
   for that is my design.
   You will create and overthrow,
   reap harvests I will sow, your word is mine.

Text: Damian Lundy (1944-1997) based on Jeremiah 1
Music: Damian Lundy (1944-1997) arr. Christopher Tambling

559 O thou, who at thy Eucharist didst pray

SONG 1 10 10 10 10 10 10

O thou, who at thy Eu – cha – rist didst pray

that all thy Church might be for e – ver one, grant us at

ev – 'ry eu – cha – rist to say, with long – ing heart and

soul, 'Thy will be done.' O may we all one bread, one

bo - dy be,   through this blest sa - cra - ment of u - ni - ty.

2. For all thy Church, O Lord, we intercede;
make thou our sad divisions soon to cease;
draw us the nearer each to each, we plead,
by drawing all to thee, O Prince of Peace:
thus may we all one bread, one body be,
through this blest sacrament of unity.

3. We pray thee too for wand'rers from thy fold;
O bring them back, good Shepherd of the sheep,
back to the faith which saints believed of old,
back to the Church which still that faith doth keep:
soon may we all one bread, one body be,
through this blest sacrament of unity.

4. So, Lord, at length when sacraments shall cease,
may we be one with all thy Church above,
one with thy saints in one unbroken peace,
one with thy saints in one unbounded love:
more blessèd still, in peace and love to be
one with the Trinity in unity.

Text: William Harry Turton (1856-1938) based on John 17
Music: Orlando Gibbons (1583-1625)

560 Our God loves us

PLAISIR D'AMOUR 4 6 6 5

1. Our God loves us, his love will never end. He rests with in our hearts for our God loves us.

2. His gentle hand
   he stretches over us.
   Though storm-clouds threaten the day,
   he will set us free.

3. He comes to us
   in sharing bread and wine.
   He brings us life that will reach
   past the end of time.

4. Our God loves us,
   his faithful love endures,
   and we will live like his child
   held in love secure.

5. The joys of love
   as off'rings now we bring.
   The pains of love will be lost
   in the praise we sing.

Text: v.1 unknown; vs. 2-5 Sandra Joan Billington (b.1946)
Music: traditional arr. Christopher Tambling

561 Our God sent his Son long ago

GOOD NEWS Irregular

1. Our God sent his Son long a-go, and he came to bring joy to us all. For the Lord wants his chil-dren to know he loves them.

Refrain

So sing the good news to the poor and the young! Praise to the Lord for his Word! Sha-ring the gos-pel with all those in need, be-come the good news you have heard!

2. But how will the good news be heard?
   When we answer the call of our Lord,
   when we live so our faith can be shared with others.

3. From the Spirit of God comes our call,
   bringing pow'r to be joyful and free,
   to be brothers and sisters to all: to love them.

4. Praise and glory to God for his Word,
   always living in those who believe,
   still made flesh in our lives to be shared with others.

Text: Damian Lundy (1944-1997)
Music: Damian Lundy (1944-1997) arr. Andrew Moore
© Copyright 1982 Kevin Mayhew Ltd.

562 Our hearts were made for you

2. I will take you from the nations,
   and will bring you to your land.
   From your idols I will cleanse you
   and you'll cherish my command.

3. I will put my law within you,
   I will write it on your heart;
   I will be your God and Saviour,
   you, my people set apart.

Text: Aniceto Nazareth based on Scripture
Music: Aniceto Nazareth
© Copyright 1984 Kevin Mayhew Ltd.

563 Our Saviour, Christ

ST CLEMENT 98 98

1. Our Saviour, Christ, of Godly nature and equal in the Father's eyes, refused to clutch his rightful glory the way a miser grasps the prize.

A lower setting will be found at No. 161

2. Of all his heav'nly glory emptied,
   his very self he freely gave,
   to clothe himself in human nature
   and wear the mantle of a slave.

3. Immortal God for us made mortal,
   the God-breathed Word drew human breath,
   then gave up even that to save us,
   obedient to the very death.

4. From death to life did God exalt him,
   to heaven's joy and earth's acclaim;
   on him, and him alone, bestowing
   the Name above all other names:

5. That at the glorious Name of Jesus
   all nations shall acclaim his worth,
   and every knee shall bow before him
   above, below and on the earth.

6. Let ev'ry tongue in earth and heaven
   proclaim that Jesus Christ is Lord,
   who shows the glory of the Father,
   our God for evermore adored.

Text: Michael Forster (b.1946) based on Philippians 2:6-11
Music: Clement Cotterill Scholefield (1839-1904)

564 Ours were the sufferings he bore

Refrain

Ours were the suf-fer-ings he bore,

ours were the sor-ows he car-ried.

He bears a pun-ish-ment that brings us peace,

and through his wounds we are healed. ... healed.

1. Come, Lord, and heal us;

O Lamb of God, O Lamb of God.
Come, Lord, and heal us;
O Lamb of God, O Lamb of God.

2. Come, Lord, and heal us;
   you died for us, you died for us.
   Come, Lord, and heal us;
   you died for us, you died for us.

3. Come, Lord, and heal us;
   grant us your peace, grant us your peace.
   Come, Lord, and heal us;
   grant us your peace, grant us your peace.

Text: Francesca Leftley (b.1955)
Music: Francesca Leftley (b.1955) arr. Keith Stent

565 Out of darkness

1. Let us take the words you give,
strong and faith - ful words to live,
words that in our hearts are sown,
words that bind us as your own.

2. Let us take the Christ you give,
Broken Body Christ we live,
Christ, the risen from the tomb,
Christ, who calls us as your own.

3. Let us take the love you give,
that the way of love we live,
love to bring your people home,
love to make us all your own.

Text and Music: Christopher Walker (b.1947)

LITURGICAL

HYMNS OLD & NEW

566 O Wisdom, source of harmony

O WALY WALY LM

1. O Wis-dom, source of har-mo-ny, the Word of God who made the

world, sus-tain-ing life and li-ber - ty, come, liv-ing Lord, and set us free.

2. O sov'reign Lord who long ago
   led Israel to liberty,
   come once again! On earth below
   your pow'r and loving-kindness show.

3. O Root of Jesse, hope for all
   who long to see a new life grow,
   come, raise your people when we fall,
   come, flow'r among us when we call.

4. Oh shine on us, dear Morning Star!
   Your radiant light be over all,
   for death is banished where you are.
   Come, shine in darkness from afar!

5. O David's key, your people wait
   to know your faithfulness and care.
   Come, save us from our gloomy state!
   Oh come and open heaven's gate!

6. O King of ev'ry nation, come
   and bring the joy for which we wait.
   Lord, to the earth you made us from
   come once again and be at home.

7. Emmanuel, God with us, Lord,
   the ancient Word dispelling gloom,
   in human flesh the living Word,
   fulfil the promise we have heard.

8. Lord Jesus, come again, we pray,
   come, live with us! Lord, with us stay!
   Take all our shame and fear away.
   Come, Lord! Be born again today.

Text: Damian Lundy (1944-1997) based on the 'O' Antiphons
Music: Somerset folk song collected by Cecil Sharp (1859-1924) arr. Richard Lloyd
Text and this arrangement © Copyright 1987, 1996 Kevin Mayhew Ltd.

567 O Word, in uncreated light

CREATOR ALME SIDERUM LM

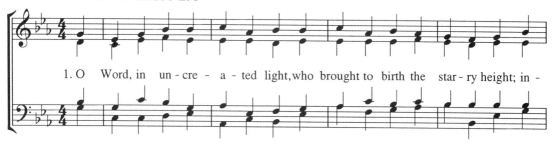

1. O Word, in un-cre-a-ted light, who brought to birth the star-ry height; in-

car-nate Sa-viour of us all, hear us, God's peo-ple, when we call.

2. Attentive to our helpless cry
   as mortals, so afraid to die,
   you took our flesh in truth and grace
   to save the fallen human race.

3. When earth was in its crisis' hour,
   you came in love's redeeming pow'r,
   with life and grace to burst the tomb,
   unsealing first the Virgin's womb.

4. Now to the glory of your Name
   let praise be sung and due acclaim;
   let all on earth and all above
   declare you Lord of life and love.

5. Prepare us, Lord and Judge, we pray
   to face you on the final day;
   and keep us in this present hour
   from yielding to temptation's pow'r.

6. To God the Father, God the Son,
   and God the Spirit, Three in One,
   all glory, praise and honour be,
   from age to age eternally.

Alternative plainsong setting

CREATOR ALME SIDERUM

1. O Word, in un-cre-a-ted light, who brought to birth the star-ry height;

in-car-nate Sa-viour of us all, hear us, God's peo-ple, when we call.

Text: Michael Forster (b.1946) based on 'Creator alme siderum' (7th century)
Music: Version 1 – Plainsong melody arr. Gregory Murray (1905-1992)
Version 2 – Plainsong melody arr. Andrew Moore

568 O worship the King

HANOVER 10 10 11 11

1. O wor-ship the King all glo-rious a-bove; O grate-ful-ly sing his pow'r and his love: our shield and de-fend-er, the An-cient of Days, pa-vil-ioned in splen-dour, and gird-ed with praise.

2. O tell of his might, O sing of his grace,
whose robe is the light, whose canopy space;
his chariots of wrath the deep thunder-clouds form,
and dark is his path on the wings of the storm.

3. This earth, with its store of wonders untold,
almighty, thy pow'r hath founded of old:
hath stablished it fast by a changeless decree,
and round it hath cast, like a mantle, the sea.

4. Thy bountiful care what tongue can recite?
It breathes in the air, it shines in the light;
it streams from the hills, it descends to the plain,
and sweetly distils in the dew and the rain.

5. Frail children of dust, and feeble as frail,
in thee do we trust, nor find thee to fail;
thy mercies how tender, how firm to the end!
Our maker, defender, redeemer, and friend.

6. O measureless might, ineffable love,
while angels delight to hymn thee above,
thy humbler creation, though feeble their lays,
with true adoration shall sing to thy praise.

Text: Robert Grant (1779-1838) based on Psalm 103
Music: melody and bass by William Croft (1678-1727)
in 'A Supplement to the New Version' (1708)

569 O worship the Lord in the beauty of holiness

WAS LEBET 13 10 13 10

1. O wor-ship the Lord in the beau-ty of ho-li-ness;
bow down be-fore him, his glo-ry pro-claim; with
gold of o-be-dience and in-cense of low-li-ness,
kneel and a-dore him: the Lord is his name.

2. Low at his feet lay thy burden of carefulness:
   high on his heart he will bear it for thee,
   comfort thy sorrows, and answer thy prayerfulness,
   guiding thy steps as may best for thee be.

3. Fear not to enter his courts in the slenderness
   of the poor wealth thou wouldst reckon as thine:
   truth in its beauty, and love in its tenderness,
   these are the off'rings to lay on his shrine.

4. These, though we bring them in trembling and fearfulness,
   he will accept for the name that is dear;
   mornings of joy give for evenings of tearfulness,
   trust for our trembling and hope for our fear.

Text: John Samuel Bewley Monsell (1811-1875)
Music: melody from the 'Rheinhardt MS', Üttingen (1754)

570 Pange lingua gloriosi

PANGE LINGUA 87 87 87

Unison

Pan-ge lin-gua glo-ri-o-si, Cor-po-ris My-ste-ri-um,

San-gui-nis-que pre-ti-o-si quem in mun-di pre-ti-um,

fru-ctus ven-tris ge-ne-ro-si Rex ef-fu-dit gen-ti-um. A - men.

Last time

2. Nobis datus, nobis natus
   ex intacta Virgine;
   et in mundo conversatus,
   sparso verbi semine,
   sui moras incolatus
   miro clausit ordine.

3. In supremæ nocte coenæ
   recumbens cum fratribus,
   observata lege plene
   cibis in legalibus:
   cibum turbæ duodenæ
   se dat suis manibus.

4. Verbum caro, panem verum,
   verbo carnem efficit:
   fitque sanguis Christi merum;
   et si sensus deficit,
   ad firmandum cor sincerum
   sola fides sufficit.

5. Tantum ergo Sacramentum
   veneremur cernui:
   et antiquum documentum
   novo cedat ritui;
   præstet fides supplementum
   sensuum defectui.

6. Genitori, genitoque
   laus, et jubilatio,
   salus, honor, virtus quoque
   sit et benedictio;
   procedenti ab utroque
   compar sit laudatio. Amen.

Text: St Thomas Aquinas (1227-1274)
Music: Plainsong arr. Andrew Moore
Music © Copyright 1994 Kevin Mayhew Ltd.

571 Peace I leave with you

Peace I leave with you, peace I give to you;

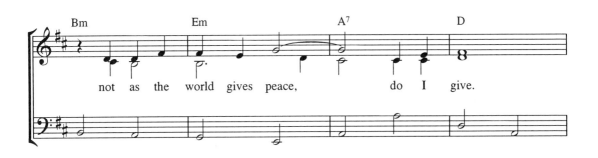

not as the world gives peace, do I give.

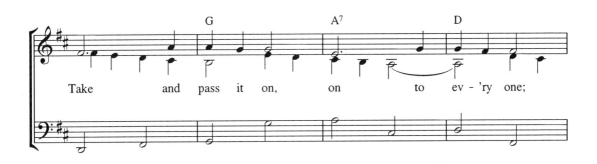

Take and pass it on, on to ev-'ry one;

thus the world will know, you are my friends.

Text: Peter Madden
Music: Peter Madden arr. Christopher Tambling

572 Peace is flowing like a river

VERSION 1

1. Peace is flow-ing like a ri - ver, flow - ing out through you and me, spread - ing out in - to the des - ert, set - ting all the cap - tives free.

2. Love is flowing like a river,
   flowing out through you and me,
   spreading out into the desert,
   setting all the captives free.

3. Joy is flowing like a river,
   flowing out through you and me,
   spreading out into the desert,
   setting all the captives free.

4. Hope is flowing like a river,
   flowing out through you and me,
   spreading out into the desert,
   setting all the captives free.

5. Christ brings peace to all creation,
   flowing out through you and me,
   love, joy, hope and true salvation,
   setting all the captives free.

VERSION 2: with Refrain

1. Peace is flow-ing like a ri - ver,

Text: vs.1-4 unknown; v.5 the Editors
Music: unknown arr. Andrew Moore

573 Peace is the gift

1. Peace is the gift of hea-ven to earth,
soft - ly en-fold-ing our fears.
Peace is the gift of Christ to the world,
gi - ven for us: he is the
Lamb who bore the pain of peace.

2. Peace is the gift of Christ to his Church,
   wound of the lance of his love.
   Love is the pain he suffered for all,
     offered to us:
   O, to accept the wound that brings us peace!

3. Joy is the gift the Spirit imparts,
   born of the heavens and earth.
   We are his children, children of joy,
     people of God:
   he is our Lord, our peace, our love, our joy!

Text: John Glynn (b.1948)
Music: John Glynn (b.1948) arr. Christopher Tambling
© Copyright 1976 Kevin Mayhew Ltd.

574 Peace, perfect peace

2. Love, perfect love, is the gift of Christ our Lord. *(x2)*
   Thus, says the Lord, will the world know my friends.
   Love, perfect love, is the gift of Christ our Lord.

3. Faith, perfect faith, is the gift of Christ our Lord. *(x2)*
   Thus, says the Lord, will the world know my friends.
   Faith, perfect faith, is the gift of Christ our Lord.

4. Hope, perfect hope, is the gift of Christ our Lord. *(x2)*
   Thus, says the Lord, will the world know my friends.
   Hope perfect hope, is the gift of Christ our Lord.

5. Joy, perfect joy, is the gift of Christ our Lord. *(x2)*
   Thus, says the Lord, will the world know my friends.
   Joy, perfect joy, is the gift of Christ our Lord.

Text and Music: Kevin Mayhew (b.1942)

LITURGICAL

HYMNS OLD & NEW

575 Praise him

1. Praise him, praise him, praise him in the morn - ing, praise him in the noon - time. Praise him, praise him, praise him, praise him when the sun goes down.

2. Love him, love him,
   love him in the morning,
   love him in the noontime.
   Love him, love him,
   love him when the sun goes down.

3. Trust him, trust him,
   trust him in the morning,
   trust him in the noontime.
   Trust him, trust him,
   trust him when the sun goes down.

4. Serve him, serve him,
   serve him in the morning,
   serve him in the noontime.
   Serve him, serve him,
   serve him when the sun goes down.

5. Jesus, Jesus,
   Jesus in the morning,
   Jesus in the noontime.
   Jesus, Jesus,
   Jesus when the sun goes down.

Text: unknown
Music: unknown arr. Christopher Tambling
This arrangement © Copyright 1994 Kevin Mayhew Ltd.

576 Praise, my soul, the King of heaven

PRAISE, MY SOUL 87 87 87

Unison

1. Praise, my soul, the King of hea - ven! To his feet thy tri - bute bring; ran - somed, healed, re - stored, for - giv - en, who like me his praise should sing? Praise him! Praise him! Praise him! Praise him! Praise the e - ver - last - ing King!

Harmony

2. Praise him for his grace and fa - vour to our fa - thers

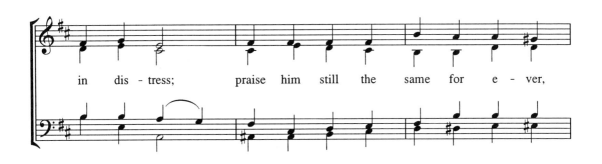

in dis - tress; praise him still the same for e - ver,

slow to chide and swift to bless. Praise him! Praise him!

Praise him! Praise him! Glo - rious in his faith - ful - ness!

4. An-gels, help us to a-dore him; ye be-hold him face to face; sun and moon, bow down be-fore him, dwell-ers all in time and space. Praise him! Praise him! Praise him! Praise him! Praise with us the God of grace!

Text: Henry Francis Lyte (1793-1847) alt. based on Psalm 103
Music: John Goss (1800-1880)

LITURGICAL

HYMNS OLD & NEW

577 Praise the Lord

Bouncy

Refrain

Praise the Lord, all of you peo-ples, praise the Lord,

shout for joy! Praise the Lord, sing him a new song,

praise the Lord and bless his name!

1. Clap your hands, now all of you na - tions, shout for

joy, ac - claim the Lord.

2. He goes up to shouts which acclaim him;
   he goes up to trumpet blast.

3. Let the music sound for the Lord, now;
   let your chords resound in praise.

4. He is King of all the nations;
   honour him by singing psalms.

Text: Mike Anderson (b.1956) based on Psalm 46
Music: Mike Anderson (b.1956)

578 Praise the Lord in his holy house

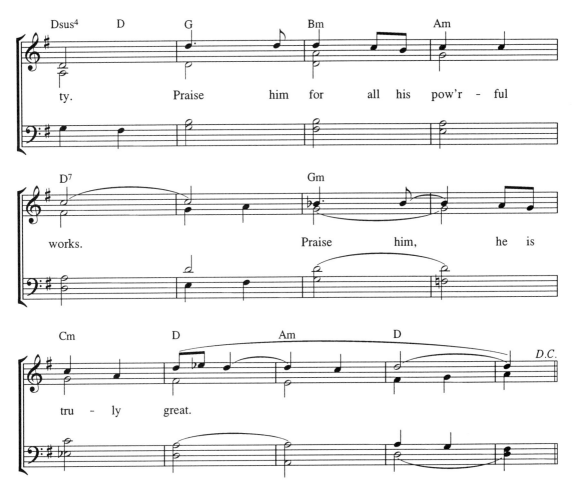

ty. Praise him for all his pow'r - ful works. Praise him, he is tru - ly great.

2. Praise him with your resounding horns,
   praise him with your lutes,
   your guitars and harps.
   Praise with dancing and tambourines,
   tune your strings and play your flute!

3. Praise with cymbals and pounding drums,
   praise him, brass and woodwind,
   let choirs rejoice.
   Alleluia, alleluia!
   All living, sing praise to God!

Text: Frances M. Kelly based on Psalm 150
Music: Frances M. Kelly arr. Christopher Tambling

LITURGICAL

HYMNS OLD & NEW

579 Praise the Lord, ye heavens, adore him

AUSTRIA 87 87 D

1. Praise the Lord, ye heav'ns, a-dore him! Praise him, an-gels, in the height; sun and moon, re-joice be-fore him, praise him, all ye stars and light. Praise the Lord, for he hath spo-ken; worlds his migh-ty voice o-beyed: laws, which ne-ver shall be bro-ken, for their gui-dance he hath made.

2. Praise the Lord, for he is glorious:
   never shall his promise fail.
   God hath made his saints victorious;
   sin and death shall not prevail.
   Praise the God of our salvation,
   hosts on high, his pow'r proclaim;
   heav'n and earth and all creation,
   laud and magnify his name!

3. Worship, honour, glory, blessing,
   Lord, we offer to thy name;
   young and old, thy praise expressing,
   join their Saviour to proclaim.
   As the saints in heav'n adore thee,
   we would bow before thy throne;
   as thine angels serve before thee,
   so on earth thy will be done.

Text: vs. 1 & 2: from 'Foundling Hospital Collection' (1796)
v. 3: Edward Osler (1798-1863)
Music: Croatian folk melody adapted by Franz Joseph Haydn (1732-1809)

580 Praise to God for saints and martyrs

TUNE 1: IN BABILONE 87 87 D

1. Praise to God for saints and mar-tyrs, in-spi-ra-tion to us all;
in the pre-sence of our Sa-viour, their ex-am-ple we re-call:
lives of ho-ly con-tem-pla-tion, sac-ri-fice or sim-ple love,
wit-nes-ses to truth and jus-tice, hon-oured here and crowned a-bove.

2. How we long to share their story, faithful in response to grace,
signs of God's eternal presence in the realm of time and space.
Now, their pilgrimage completed, cross of Christ their only boast,
they unite their own rejoicing with the great angelic host.

3. Saints and martyrs, now in glory, robed before your Saviour's face,
let us join your intercession for God's holy human race.
Let us join with you in singing Mary's liberation song,
till a just and free creation sings, with the angelic throng:

4. Praise and honour to the Father, adoration to the Son,
with the all-embracing Spirit wholly Three and holy One.
All the universe, united in complete diversity,
sings as one your endless praises, ever-blessèd Trinity!

TUNE 2: EBENEZER (TON -Y- BOTEL) 87 87 D

1. Praise to God for saints and mar - tyrs, in - spi - ra - tion

to us all; in the pre - sence of our Sa - viour, their ex - am - ple

we re - call: lives of ho - ly con - tem - pla - tion,

sac - ri - fice or sim - ple love, wit - nes - ses to

truth and jus - tice, ho - noured here and crowned a - bove.

Text : Michael Forster (b.1946)
Music: Tune 1 − traditional Dutch melody arr. Julius Röntgen
Tune 2 − from an anthem by Thomas Williams (1869 - 1944))

581 Praise to God in the highest

1. Praise to God in the highest!

Bless us, O Father! Praise to you!

2. Guide and prosper the nations, rulers and peoples.

3. May the truth in its beauty flourish triumphant.

4. May the mills bring us bread for food and for giving.

5. May the good be obeyed and evils be conquered.

6. Give us laughter and set all your people rejoicing.

7. Peace on earth and goodwill be ever among us.

Text: unknown
Music: unknown arr. Michael Irwin

582 Praise to the Holiest

BILLING CM

1. Praise to the Ho - liest in the height, and in the depth be praise; in all his words most won - der - ful, most sure in all his ways.

A higher setting will be found at No. 704

2. O loving wisdom of our God!
   when all was sin and shame,
   a second Adam to the fight,
   and to the rescue came.

3. O wisest love! that flesh and blood,
   which did in Adam fail,
   should strive afresh against the foe,
   should strive and should prevail.

4. And that a higher gift than grace
   should flesh and blood refine,
   God's presence and his very self,
   and essence all-divine.

5. And in the garden secretly,
   and on the cross on high,
   should teach his brethren, and inspire
   to suffer and to die.

6. Praise to the Holiest in the height,
   and in the depth be praise;
   in all his words most wonderful,
   most sure in all his ways.

Text: John Henry Newman (1801-1890)
Music: Richard Runciman Terry (1865-1938)
Music © Copyright Burns & Oates Ltd, Wellwood, North Farm Road,
Tunbridge Wells, Kent TN2 3QR. Used by permission.

LITURGICAL

HYMNS OLD & NEW

583 Praise to the Lord, the Almighty (Version A)

LOBE DEN HERREN 14 14 4 7 8

1. Praise to the Lord, the Almighty, the King of creation! O my soul, praise him, for he is your health and salvation. All you who hear, now to his altar draw near; join in profound adoration.

2. Praise to the Lord, let us offer our gifts at his altar;
let not our sins and transgressions now cause us to falter.
Christ, the High Priest,
bids us all join in his feast;
victims with him on the altar.

3. Praise to the Lord, O, let all that is in us adore him!
All that has life and breath, come now with praises before him.
Let the 'Amen'
sound from his people again,
now as we worship before him.

Text: Joachim Neander (1650-1680) trans. Catherine Winkworth (1827-1878) alt.
Music: from 'Praxis Pietatis Melica' (1668)

584 Praise to the Lord, the Almighty (Version B)

For use on Ecumenical occasions

LOBE DEN HERREN 14 14 4 7 8

1. Praise to the Lord, the Al - migh - ty, the King of cre -

a - tion! O my soul, praise him, for he is thy

health and sal - va - tion. All ye who hear, now to his

tem - ple draw near; join - ing in glad a - do - ra - tion.

2. Praise to the Lord, who o'er all things so wondrously reigneth,
   shieldeth thee gently from harm, or when fainting sustaineth:
   hast thou not seen
   how thy heart's wishes have been
   granted in what he ordaineth?

3. Praise to the Lord, who doth prosper thy work and defend thee,
   surely his goodness and mercy shall daily attend thee:
   ponder anew
   what the Almighty can do,
   if to the end he befriend thee.

4. Praise to the Lord, O let all that is in us adore him!
   All that hath life and breath, come now with praises before him.
   Let the 'Amen'
   sound from his people again,
   gladly for ay we adore him.

Text: Joachim Neander (1650-1680) trans. Catherine Winkworth (1827-1878)
Music: from 'Praxis Pietatis Melica' (1668)

585 Praise to you, O Christ, our Saviour

Praise to you, O Christ, our Sa - viour, Word of the Fa - ther,

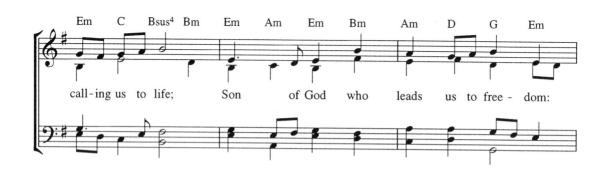

call-ing us to life; Son of God who leads us to free - dom:

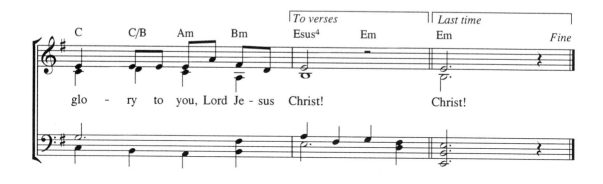

glo - ry to you, Lord Je - sus Christ! Christ!

1. You are the Word who calls us out of dark - ness; you are the Word who

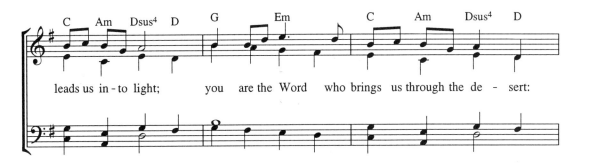

leads us in-to light; you are the Word who brings us through the de - sert:

glo - ry to you, Lord Je - sus Christ!

2. You are the one whom prophets hoped and longed for;
   you are the one who speaks to us today;
   you are the one who leads us to our future:
   glory to you, Lord Jesus Christ!

3. You are the Word who calls us to be servants;
   you are the Word whose only law is love;
   you are the Word-made-flesh who lives among us:
   glory to you, Lord Jesus Christ!

4. You are the Word who binds us and unites us;
   you are the Word who calls us to be one;
   you are the Word who teaches us forgiveness:
   glory to you, Lord Jesus Christ!

Text: Bernadette Farrell
Music: Bernadette Farrell arr. Paul Inwood

586 Praise we our God with joy

NUN DANKET 67 67 66 66

1. Praise we our God with joy and glad-ness ne-ver-
end - ing; an - gels and saints with us their grate-ful voi - ces
blend - ing. He is our Fa - ther dear, o'er - filled with par-ent's
love; mer - cies un - sought, un - known, he show-ers from a - bove.

A higher setting will be found at No. 497

2. He is our shepherd true;
   with watchful care unsleeping,
   on us, his erring sheep,
   an eye of pity keeping;
   he with a mighty arm
   the bonds of sin doth break,
   and to our burdened hearts
   in words of peace doth speak.

3. Graces in copious stream
   from that pure fount are welling,
   where, in our heart of hearts,
   our God hath set his dwelling.
   His word our lantern is;
   his peace our comfort still;
   his sweetness all our rest;
   our law, our life, his will.

Text: Frederick Oakeley (1802-1880) and others
Music: Johann Crüger (1598-1662)

587 Reap me the earth

JUCUNDA LAUDATIO 10 7 10 7 and Refrain

Reap me the earth as a har-vest to God, ga-ther and bring it a-gain,
all that is his, to the Ma-ker of all. Lift it and of-fer it
high. Bring bread, bring wine, give glo-ry to the Lord;
whose is the earth but God's, whose is the praise but his?

2. Go with your song and your music with joy,
go to the altar of God.
Carry your offerings, fruits of the earth,
work of your labouring hands.

3. Gladness and pity and passion and pain,
all that is mortal in man,
lay all before him, return him his gift,
God, to whom all shall go home.

Text: Luke Connaughton (1917-1979)
Music: Gregory Murray (1905-1992)
© Copyright McCrimmon Publishing Co. Ltd, 10-12 High Street, Great Wakering, Southend-on-Sea, Essex SS3 0EQ.
Used by permission.

588 Regina cæli

Re - gi - na cæ - li, læ - ta - re, al - le - lu - ia,

qui - a quem me - ru - i - sti por - ta - re, al - le - lu - ia,

re - sur - re - xit si - cut di - xit, al - le - lu - ia, O - ra pro no - bis De - um, al - le - lu - ia.

Text: unknown, 12th century
Music: Plainsong arr. Andrew Moore
This arrangement © Copyright 1994 Kevin Mayhew Ltd.

589 Rejoice, all heavenly powers

DARWALL'S 148TH 66 66 44 44

1. Re - joice, all heav'n -ly pow'rs, O choirs of an - gels sing! and let the u - ni -verse with al - le - lu - ias ring! For Je - sus lives in glo - ry bright, and end - less light to us he gives.

2. Rejoice, O shining earth,
   in glorious hope reborn,
   and praise the Light who wrought
   the first creation's dawn.
   Redeemed and free,
   in Christ we rise,
   and darkness dies
   eternally.

3. Rejoice, O Mother church;
   on you the Saviour shines:
   then let the vaults resound
   with joy and peace divine!
   His truth proclaim,
   and loud and long,
   in glorious song,
   exalt his name.

4. The people who have walked
   in terror through the night,
   from shades of death released,
   have seen a glorious light.
   God's word is sure,
   and he will bless
   with righteousness
   the humble poor.

5. O God of hope and love,
   who lit the desert way,
   and led from slav'ry's night
   to liberation's day:
   still go before,
   till we rejoice,
   with heart and voice,
   on Canaan's shore.

6. We light these gentle flames
   to be our pledge and sign:
   we share the risen life
   of Christ, the light divine.
   Throughout the earth,
   oppression's night
   shall flee the light
   of human worth.

7. Arise, O Morning Star,
   O Sun who never sets,
   and bring these humble flames
   to greater glory yet.
   Let all adore,
   in glorious strains,
   the Christ who reigns
   for evermore.

Text: Michael Forster (b.1946) based on the 'Exsultet' from the Easter Vigil Liturgy
Music: John Darwall (1731-1789) arr. William Henry Monk (1823-1889)

590 Rejoice in the Lord always

Text: based on Philippians 4:4
Music: unknown arr. Christopher Tambling

591 Rejoice, the Lord is King

GOPSAL 66 66 and Refrain

1. Re - joice, the Lord is King! Your Lord and King a -
dore; mor - tals, give thanks and sing, and
tri - umph e - ver - more.

Refrain

Lift up your heart, lift
up your voice; re - joice, a - gain I say, re - joice.

Org.

2. Jesus the Saviour reigns,
   the God of truth and love;
   when he had purged our stains,
   he took his seat above.

3. His kingdom cannot fail;
   he rules o'er earth and heav'n;
   the keys of death and hell
   are to our Jesus giv'n.

4. He sits at God's right hand
   till all his foes submit,
   and bow to his command,
   and fall beneath his feet.

Text: Charles Wesley (1707-1788)
Music: George Frideric Handel (1685-1759)

592 Remember your mercy, Lord

Cantor

Re-mem-ber, re-mem-ber your mer-cy, Lord. Re-mem-ber, re-mem-ber your mer-cy, Lord. Hear your peo-ple's prayer as they call to you: re-mem-ber, re-mem-ber your mer-cy, Lord.

Fine

1. Lord, make me know your ways. Lord, teach me your paths. Make me

walk in your truth, and teach me: for you are God my Sa-viour.

D.S.

2. mem-ber your mer-cy, Lord, and the love you have shown from of old.

Do not re-mem-ber the sins of my youth.

In your love re-mem-ber me, in your love re-mem-ber me, be - cause of your good-ness, O Lord.

3. Lord is good and up - right. He shows the path to all who stray, he guides the hum-ble in the right path; he teach-es his way to the poor.

Text: Psalm 24, Grail Translation
Music: Paul Inwood

LITURGICAL

HYMNS OLD & NEW

593 Ride on, ride on in majesty

WINCHESTER NEW LM

1. Ride on, ride on in majesty! Hark, all the tribes hosanna cry; thy humble beast pursues his road with palms and scattered garments strowed.

A higher setting will be found at No. 541

2. Ride on, ride on in majesty!
In lowly pomp ride on to die;
O Christ, thy triumphs now begin
o'er captive death and conquered sin.

3. Ride on, ride on in majesty!
The wingèd squadrons of the sky
look down with sad and wond'ring eyes
to see th'approaching sacrifice.

4. Ride on, ride on in majesty!
Thy last and fiercest strife is nigh;
the Father, on his sapphire throne,
awaits his own appointed Son.

5. Ride on, ride on in majesty!
In lowly pomp ride on to die;
bow thy meek head to mortal pain,
then take, O God, thy pow'r, and reign.

Text: Henry Hart Milman (1791-1868) alt.
Music: from 'Musikalisches Handbuch' (1690)

594 Ring out your joy

more! Blest be your ho - ly, glo - rious, great name;

glo - ry and praise for e - ver - more!

2. Blest in the temple of your glory;
 glory and praise for evermore!
 Blessèd, enthroned over your kingdom;
 glory and praise for evermore!

3. Blest, you who know the deeps and highest;
 glory and praise for evermore!
 Blest in the firmament of heaven;
 glory and praise for evermore!

4. All things the Lord has made, now bless him;
 glory and praise for evermore!
 Angels and saints, now bless and praise him;
 glory and praise for evermore!

Text: Aniceto Nazareth based on the Canticle of Daniel
Music: Aniceto Nazareth

595 Said Judas to Mary
Judas and Mary

1. Said Judas to Mary, 'Now what will you do with your oint-ment so rich and so rare?' 'I'll pour it all o-ver the feet of the Lord, and I'll wipe it a-way with my hair,' she said, 'I'll wipe it a-way with my hair.'

2. 'Oh Mary, oh Mary, oh think of the poor,
this ointment, it could have been sold,
and think of the blankets and think of the bread
you could buy with the silver and gold,' he said,
'you could buy with the silver and gold.'

3. 'Tomorrow, tomorrow, I'll think of the poor,
tomorrow,' she said, 'not today;
for dearer than all of the poor in the world
is my love who is going away,' she said,
'my love who is going away.'

4. Said Jesus to Mary, 'Your love is so deep,
today you may do as you will.
Tomorrow you say I am going away,
but my body I leave with you still,' he said,
'my body I leave with you still.'

5. 'The poor of the world are my body,' he said,
'to the end of the world they shall be.
The bread and the blankets you give to the poor
you'll find you have given to me,' he said,
'you'll find you have given to me.'

6. 'My body will hang on the cross of the world,
tomorrow,' he said, 'and today,
and Martha and Mary will find me again
and wash all my sorrow away,' he said,
'and wash all my sorrow away.'

Text: Sydney Carter (b.1915)
Music: Sydney Carter (b.1915) arr. Andrew Moore

596 Salvation is God's

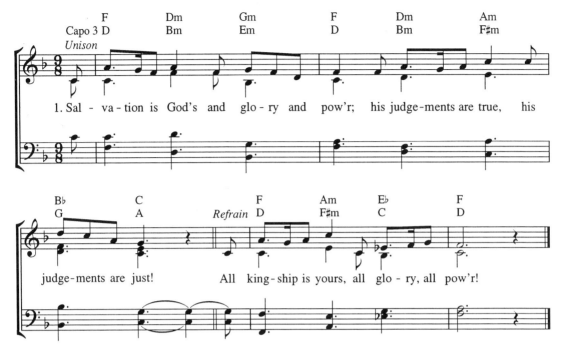

1. Sal - va - tion is God's and glo - ry and pow'r; his judge-ments are true, his judge-ments are just! *Refrain* All king-ship is yours, all glo - ry, all pow'r!

2. Give praise to our God,
   you servants of God,
   both little and great,
   revering his name!

3. The Lord is now King,
   the Ruler of all;
   give glory to him,
   in him take your joy!

4. The wedding day dawns
   for Lamb and for Bride;
   in beauty adorned,
   she waits for the Lamb.

5. The grace of the Lamb
   has robed her in white;
   in glory she shines,
   fit Bride for the Lamb.

6. How happy are those
   invited to share
   the Supper prepared
   for Bridegroom and Bride!

Text: James Quinn (b.1919) based on Revelation 19:1, 2, 5-9
Music: Noel Donnelly (b.1932)

597 Salve, Regina

il - los tu - os mi - se - ri - cor - des o - cu - los ad nos con - ver - te.

Et Je - sum, be - ne - di - ctum fru - ctum ven - tris tu - i,

no - bis post hoc ex - i - li - um o - sten - de.

O cle - mens, O pi - a,

O dul - cis Vir - go Ma - ri - a.

Text: Hermann the Lame (d.1054)
Music: Plainsong, accompaniment by Gregory Murray (1905-1992)
revised by Andrew Moore (b.1954)

LITURGICAL

HYMNS OLD & NEW

598 Save us, O Lord

Save us, O Lord, while we are a-wake, and guard us while we sleep, that a-wake we may watch with Christ, and a-sleep we may rest in peace, in Je - sus' name, in Je - sus' name.

Text: The Office of Night Prayer
Music: Kevin Mayhew (b.1942)
Music © Copyright 1996 Kevin Mayhew Ltd.

599 Save us, O Lord
Song of Simeon

Refrain
Unison

Save us, O Lord, while we're a-wake. Guard us, O

Lord, when we're a-sleep that we may watch with Christ and rest in

peace, that we may watch with Christ and rest in peace. *Fine*

1. At last, all-powerful Mas-ter, you give leave to your ser - vant
2. – – For my eyes have seen your sal - va - tion
3. – – The light to enlighten the Gen - tiles
4. – – Give glory to the Father al - migh-ty,
5. – – to the Spirit who dwells in our hearts,

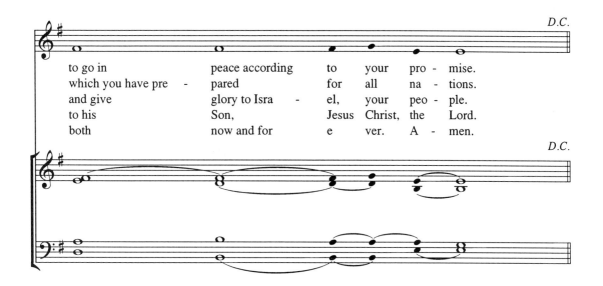

D.C.

to go in   peace according   to   your   pro - mise.
which you have pre - pared   for   all   na - tions.
and give   glory to Isra - el,   your   peo - ple.
to his   Son,   Jesus Christ, the   Lord.
both   now and for   e ver.   A - men.

D.C.

Text: Luke 2:29-32 trans. The Grail
Music: Aniceto Nazareth

600 Save us, O Lord

Text: Bob Dufford
Music: Bob Dufford arr. Keith Stent

601 See, amid the winter's snow

TUNE 1: HUMILITY (OXFORD) 77 77 and Refrain

1. See, a-mid the win – ter's snow, born for us on earth be-low,

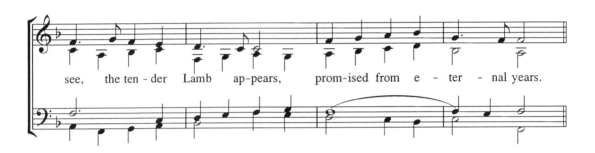

see, the ten – der Lamb ap-pears, prom-ised from e – ter – nal years.

Hail, thou e – ver – bles-sed morn, hail, re-demp-tion's hap – py dawn!

Sing through all Je – ru – sa-lem, Christ is born in Beth – le – hem.

2. Lo, within a manger lies
   he who built the starry skies;
   he who, throned in heights sublime,
   sits amid the cherubim.

3. Say, you holy shepherds, say,
   what your joyful news today?
   Wherefore have you left your sheep
   on the lonely mountain steep?

4. 'As we watched at dead of night,
   there appeared a wondrous light;
   angels, singing peace on earth,
   told us of the Saviour's birth.'

5. Sacred infant, all divine,
   what a tender love was thine,
   thus to come from highest bliss,
   down to such a world as this!

6. Virgin mother, Mary, blest,
   by the joys that fill thy breast,
   pray for us, that we may prove
   worthy of the Saviour's love.

TUNE 2: CHRISTMAS MORN 77 77 and Refrain

1. See, a-mid the win-ter's snow, born for us on earth be-low,
see, the ten-der Lamb ap-pears, prom-ised from e-ter-nal years.

Refrain
Hail, thou e-ver-bles-sed morn, hail, re-demp-tion's hap-py dawn!
Sing through all Je-ru-sa-lem Christ is born in Beth-le-hem.

Text: Edward Caswall (1814-1878)
Music: Tune 1 – John Goss (1800-1880)
Tune 2 – traditional melody

LITURGICAL

HYMNS OLD & NEW

602 See, Christ was wounded

EISENACH LM

1. See, Christ was wound-ed for our sake, and bruised and beat-en for our sin, so by his suff-'rings we are healed, for God has laid our guilt on him.

2. Look on his face, come close to him
   – see, you will find no beauty there;
   despised, rejected, who can tell
   the grief and sorrow he must bear?

3. Like sheep that stray we leave God's path,
   to choose our own and not his will;
   like lamb to slaughter he has gone,
   obedient to his Father's will.

4. Cast out to die by those he loved,
   reviled by those he died to save,
   see how sin's pride has sought his death,
   see how sin's hate has made his grave.

5. For on his shoulders God has laid
   the weight of sin that we should bear;
   so by his passion we have peace,
   through his obedience and his prayer.

Text: Brian Foley (b.1919)
Music: melody by Johann Hermann Schein (1586-1630) harmonised by Johann Sebastian Bach (1685-1750)
Text © Copyright 1971 Faber Music Ltd, 3 Queen Square, London WC1N 3AU.
Used by permission from 'New Catholic Hymnal.'

603 See him lying on a bed of straw

CALYPSO CAROL *Irregular and Refrain*

1. See him ly-ing on a bed of straw: a draugh-ty sta-ble with an o-pen door.

Ma-ry cra-dl-ing the babe she bore: the Prince of Glo-ry is his name.

Refrain

O now car-ry me to Beth-le-hem to see the Lord of love a-gain:

To verses

just as poor as was the sta-ble then, the Prince of Glo-ry when he came!

Last time D.C.

sta-ble then, the Prince of Glo-ry when he came!

2. Star of silver, sweep across the skies,
   show where Jesus in the manger lies;
   shepherds, swiftly from your stupor rise
   to see the Saviour of the world!

3. Angels, sing again the song you sang,
   sing the glory of God's gracious plan;
   sing that Bethl'em's little baby can
   be salvation to the soul.

4. Mine are riches, from your poverty;
   from your innocence, eternity;
   mine, forgiveness by your death for me,
   child of sorrow for my joy.

Text: Michael Perry (1942-1996)
Music: Michael Perry (1942-1996) arr. Christopher Tambling

604 Seek ye frst

SEEK YE FIRST Irregular

This may be sung as a round, the second entry beginning at the double bar

1. Seek ye first the king - dom of God, and his right - eous - ness, and all these things shall be add - ed un - to you; al - le - lu, al - le - lu - ia. Al - le - lu - ia, al - le - lu - ia, al - le - lu - ia, al - le - lu, al - le - lu - ia.

2. You shall not live by bread alone,
   but by ev'ry word
   that proceeds from the mouth of God;
   allelu, alleluia.

3. Ask and it shall be given unto you,
   seek and ye shall find;
   knock, and it shall be opened unto you;
   allellu, alleluia.

Text: v.1 Karen Lafferty (b.1948); vs. 2 & 3 unknown, based on Matthew 6:33, 7:7
Music: Karen Lafferty (b.1948) arr. Adrian Vernon Fish

605 See the holy table, spread for our healing

NICAEA 11 12 12 10

1. See the ho-ly ta - ble, spread for our heal - ing;
hear the in - vi - ta - tion to share in bread and wine.
Catch the scent of good - ness, taste and touch sal - va - tion;
all mor - tal sen - ses tell of love di -vine!

2. As the bread is broken, Christ is remembered;
   as the wine is flowing, his passion we recall;
   as redemption's story opens up before us,
   hope is triumphant, Christ is all in all.

3. Tell again the story, wonder of wonders:
   Christ, by grace eternal, transforms the simplest food!
   Sign of hope and glory, life in all its fullness,
   God's whole creation ransomed and renewed!

Text: Michael Forster (b.1946)
Music: John Bacchus Dykes (1823-1876)
Text © Copyright 1993 Kevin Mayhew Ltd.

LITURGICAL

HYMNS OLD & NEW

606 See us, Lord, about your altar

LAUS DEO (Redhead No. 46) 87 87

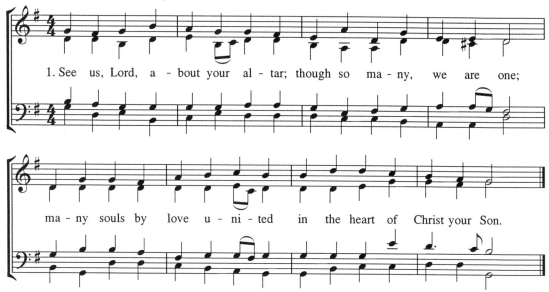

1. See us, Lord, a - bout your al - tar; though so ma - ny, we are one;
ma - ny souls by love u - ni - ted in the heart of Christ your Son.

A lower setting will be found at No. 340

2. Hear our prayers, O loving Father,
   hear in them your Son, our Lord;
   hear him speak our love and worship,
   as we sing with one accord.

3. Once were seen the blood and water;
   now he seems but bread and wine;
   then in human form he suffered,
   now his form is but a sign.

4. Wheat and grape contain the meaning;
   food and drink he is to all;
   one in him, we kneel adoring,
   gathered by his loving call.

5. Hear us yet; so much is needful
   in our frail, disordered life;
   stay with us and tend our weakness
   till that day of no more strife.

6. Members of his mystic body,
   now we know our prayer is heard,
   heard by you, because your children
   have received th'eternal Word.

Text: John Greally
Music: German melody adapted by Richard Redhead (1820-1901)
Text © Copyright Trustees for Roman Catholic Purposes Registered, 114 Mount Street, London W1Y 6AH.
Used by permission.

607 See, your Saviour comes

an - gry and rest - less. When will you know the

things that would make for your peace?

2. Father of mercy, hear as we cry
   for all who live in this place;
   show here your glory, come satisfy
   your longing that all should be saved.

3. Where lives are broken, let there be hope,
   where there's division bring peace;
   where there's oppression, judge and reprove,
   and rescue the crushed and the weak.

4. Lord, let your glory dwell in this land,
   in mercy restore us again:
   pour out salvation, grant us your peace,
   and strengthen the things that remain.

Words and Music: Graham Kendrick (b.1950)

608 Send forth your Spirit

Send forth, send forth your Spi-rit, O Lord, to re-new, re-new the face of the earth, send your Spi-rit to re-new the earth.

Fine

1. Send the Spi-rit of wis-dom and un-der-stand-ing, the Spi-rit of right judge-ment and cou-rage, send the Spi-rit of know-ledge and

D.C.

re - ve - rence, send your Spi - rit to re - new us all.

2. Send your Spi - rit up - on us as help - er and guide, may he

fill us with won - der and awe. Seal us, O Lord, with your

D.C.

ho - ly gift, send your Spi - rit to re - new our lives.

Text: from the Rite of Confirmation
Music: Alan Rees (b.1941)

609 Send forth your Spirit

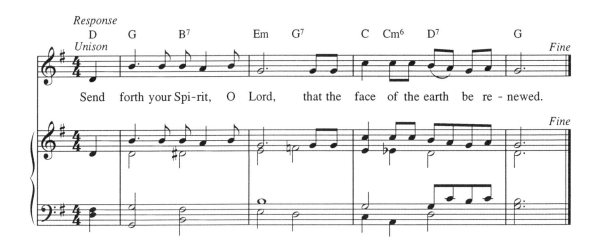

Send forth your Spi-rit, O Lord, that the face of the earth be re - newed.

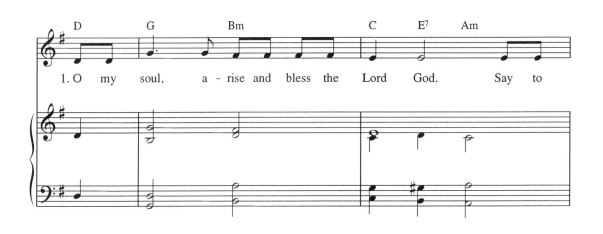

1. O my soul, a - rise and bless the Lord God. Say to

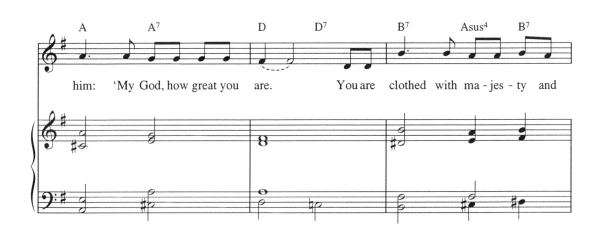

him: 'My God, how great you are. You are clothed with ma - jes - ty and

splen - dour, and light is the gar - ment you wear.'

2. 'You have built your palace on the waters.
   Like the winds, the angels do your word.
   you have set the earth on its foundations,
   so firm, to be shaken no more.'

3. 'All your creatures look to you for comfort;
   from your open hand they have their fill,
   you send forth your Spirit and revive them,
   the face of the earth you renew.'

4. While I live, I sing the Lord God's praises;
   I will thank the author of these marvels.
   Praise to God, the Father, Son and Spirit
   both now and for ever. Amen.

Text: Aniceto Nazareth based on Psalm 104
Music: Aniceto Nazareth

610 Send forth your Spirit, Lord

glo - ry, you set the world on its foun - da - tions.

2. Lord, how great are your works,
   in wisdom you made them all;
   all the earth is full of your creatures,
   your hand always open to feed them.

3. May your wisdom endure,
   rejoice in your works, O Lord.
   I will sing for ever and ever,
   in praise of my God and my King.

Text: Michael Forster (b.1946) based on Psalm 104
Music: Margaret Rizza (b.1929)

611 Send me, Lord
Thuma mina

Leader

1. Send me, Lord.
Thu - ma mi - na.

All

1. Send me, Je - sus. Send me, Je - sus. Send me,
Thu - ma mi - na, thu - ma mi - na, thu - ma

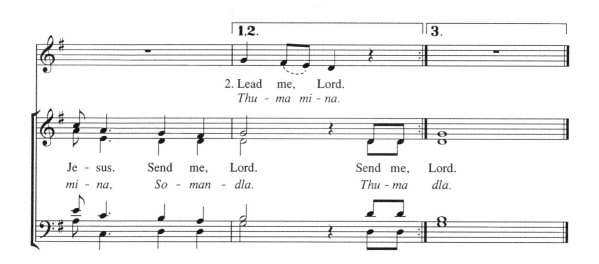

1,2.

2. Lead me, Lord.
Thu - ma mi - na.

3.

Je - sus. Send me, Lord. Send me, Lord.
mi - na, So - man - dla. Thu - ma dla.

2. Lead me, Lord.
   Lead me, Jesus. *(x3)*
   Lead me, Lord.

3. Fill me, Lord.
   Fill me, Jesus. *(x3)*
   Fill me, Lord.

Text and Music: traditional South African, collected and translated by Anders Nyberg
© Copyright 1990 WGRG, Iona Community, 840 Govan Road, Glasgow G51 3UU, Scotland.
Used by permission from 'Freedom is coming' (Wild Goose Publications, 1990).

612 Shalom, my friend

VERSION 1: ROUND

This may be sung as a round, the second part entering at [B]

VERSION 2: ALTERNATIVE HARMONISATION

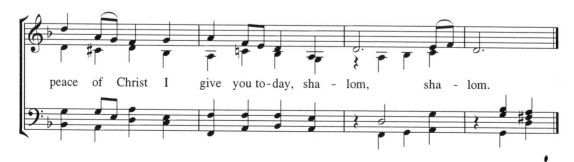

Text: Sandra Joan Billington (b.1946)
Music: traditional Hebrew melody arr. Andrew Moore

613 She sits like a bird
Enemy of apathy

THAINAKE 11 11 11 11

1. She sits like a bird, brood-ing on the wa-ters, hov-'ring on the cha-os of the world's first day; she sighs and she sings, mo-ther-ing cre-a-tion, wait-ing to give birth to all the Word will say.

2. She wings over earth, resting where she wishes,
   lighting close at hand or soaring through the skies;
   she nests in the womb, welcoming each wonder,
   nourishing potential hidden to our eyes.

3. She dances in fire, startling her spectators,
   waking tongues of ecstasy where dumbness reigned;
   she weans and inspires all whose hearts are open,
   nor can she be captured, silenced or restrained.

4. For she is the Spirit, one with God in essence,
   gifted by the Saviour in eternal love;
   she is the key opening the scriptures,
   enemy of apathy and heav'nly dove.

Text and Music: John L. Bell (b.1949) and Graham Maule (b.1958)

614 Silent night

STILLE NACHT Irregular

2. Silent night, holy night.
   Shepherds quake at the sight,
   glories stream from heaven afar,
   heav'nly hosts sing alleluia:
   Christ, the Saviour is born,
   Christ, the Saviour is born.

3. Silent night, holy night.
   Son of God, love's pure light,
   radiant beams from thy holy face,
   with the dawn of redeeming grace:
   Jesus, Lord, at thy birth,
   Jesus, Lord, at thy birth.

Text: Joseph Mohr (1792-1848) trans. John Freeman Young (1820-1885)
Music: Franz Grüber (1787-1863) arr. Colin Hand
This arrangement © Copyright 1994 Kevin Mayhew Ltd.

615 Sing, all creation

CHRISTE SANCTORUM 11 11 11 5

1. Sing, all cre-a-tion, sing to God in glad-ness! Joy-ous-ly serve him, sing-ing hymns of hom-age! Chant-ing his prai-ses, come be-fore his pre-sence! Praise the Al-migh-ty!

A higher setting will be found at No. 284

2. Know that our God is Lord of all the ages!
   He is our maker; we are all his creatures,
   people he fashioned, sheep he leads to pasture!
   Praise the Almighty!

3. Enter his Temple, ringing out his praises!
   Sing in thanksgiving as you come before him!
   Blessing his bounty, glorify his greatness!
   Praise the Almighty!

4. Great in his goodness is the Lord we worship;
   steadfast his kindness, love that knows no ending!
   Faithful his word is, changeless, everlasting!
   Praise the Almighty!

Text: James Quinn (b. 1919) based on Psalm 99
Music: from the 'Paris Antiphoner' (1681)

616 Sing a new song

Sing a new song un-to the Lord, let your

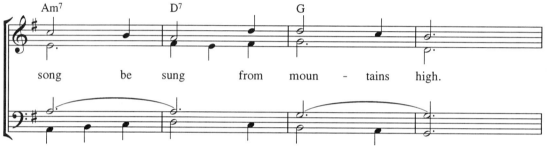

song be sung from moun - tains high.

Sing a new song un - to the Lord, sing - ing

al - le - lu - ia.

2. Rise, O children, from your sleep,
   your Saviour now has come,
   and he has turned your sorrow to joy,
   and filled your soul with song.

3. Glad my soul, for I have seen
   the glory of the Lord.
   The trumpet sounds, the dead shall be raised.
   I know my Saviour lives.

Text: Dan Schutte based on Psalm 97
Music: Dan Schutte arr. Adrian Vernon Fish

LITURGICAL

HYMNS OLD & NEW

grace; hold-ing the hopes of cre - a - tion in your ma - ter-nal em - brace.

2. Stand with the lost and the lonely,
   those whom the vain world denies,
   join with the weak and the foolish,
   humbling the strong and the wise!

3. Sing of the values of heaven,
   shame our respectable pride!
   Sing to the spurned and the faithful,
   tell them no longer to hide!

Text: Michael Forster (b.1946)
Music: Kevin Mayhew (b.1942)

619 Sing it in the valleys

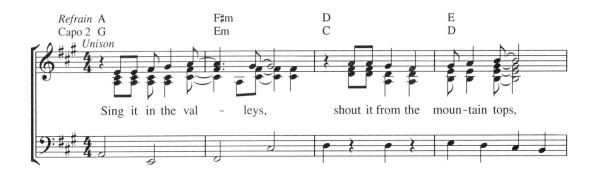

Sing it in the val - leys, shout it from the moun-tain tops,

Je - sus came to save us, and his sav - ing ne-ver stops.

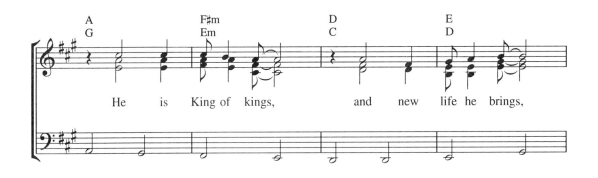

He is King of kings, and new life he brings,

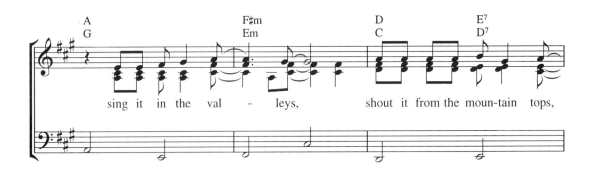

sing it in the val - leys, shout it from the moun-tain tops,

2. You have not deserted me,
   though I go astray.
   Jesus, take me in your arms,
   help me walk with you today.

3. Jesus, you are living now,
   Jesus, I believe;
   Jesus, take me, heart and soul,
   yours alone I want to be.

Text and Music: Mike Anderson (b.1956)

620 Sing, my soul

When ci - ty lights would blind my eyes.

He hears my si - lent call. His hands help when I fall.

His gen - tle voice stills my sighs.

D.C.

2. The Lord is good to me.
   His word will set me free
   when men would tie me to the ground.
   He mocks my foolish ways
   with love that never fails.
   When I'm most lost then I'm found.

3. The Lord is good to me.
   I hear him speak to me.
   His voice is in the rain that falls.
   He whispers in the air
   of his unending care.
   If I will hear, then he calls.

Text: Michael Cockett (b.1938)
Music: Estelle White (b.1925) arr. Keith Stent

621 Sing, my tongue, the song of triumph

ST THOMAS 87 87 87

1. Sing, my tongue, the song of triumph, tell the story far and wide;

tell of dread and final battle, sing of Saviour crucified;

how upon the cross a victim vanquishing in death he died.

A lower setting will be found at No. 509

2. He endured the nails, the spitting,
   vinegar and spear and reed;
   from that holy body broken
   blood and water forth proceed;
   earth and stars and sky and ocean
   by that flood from stain are freed.

3. Faithful Cross, above all other,
   one and only noble tree,
   none in foliage, none in blossom,
   none in fruit your peer may be;
   sweet the wood and sweet the iron
   and your load, most sweet is he.

4. Bend your boughs, O Tree of glory!
   all your rigid branches, bend!
   For a while the ancient temper
   that your birth bestowed, suspend;
   and the King of earth and heaven
   gently on your bosom tend.

This may also be sung to the tune 'Westminster Abbey' at No. 197

Text: translation of 'Pange, lingua, gloriosi proelium certaminis'
by Venantius Fortunatus (c.530-609) from 'The Three Days' (1981)
Music: Samuel Webbe (1740-1816)

622 Sing of Mary, pure and lowly

PLEADING SAVIOUR 87 87 D

Unison

1. Sing of Ma-ry, pure and low-ly, vir-gin mo-ther un-de-filed.
Sing of God's own Son most ho-ly, who be-came her lit-tle child.
Fair-est child of fair-est mo-ther, God, the Lord, who came to earth,
Word made flesh, our ve-ry bro-ther, takes our na-ture by his birth.

2. Sing of Jesus, son of Mary,
   in the home at Nazereth.
   Toil and labour cannot weary
   love enduring unto death.
   Constant was the love he gave her,
   though he went forth from her side,
   forth to preach and heal and suffer,
   till on Calvary he died.

3. Glory be to God the Father,
   glory be to God the Son,
   glory be to God the Spirit,
   glory to the Three in One.
   From the heart of blessèd Mary,
   from all saints the song ascends,
   and the Church the strain re-echoes
   unto earth's remotest ends.

Text: anonymous (c.1914)
Music: from 'The Christian Lyre (1831) arr. Christopher Tambling

623 Sing praises to the living God

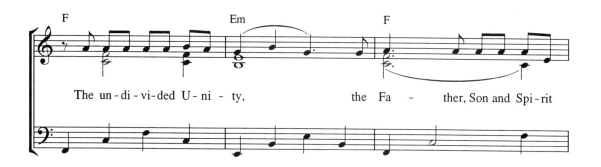

The un-di-vi-ded U-ni-ty, the Fa - ther, Son and Spi-rit

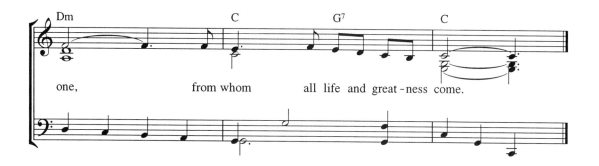

one, from whom all life and great-ness come.

2. And to the living God we sing,
   glory, alleluia.
   Let our love and praises ring,
   glory, alleluia.
   To all of us he always gives
   his mercy and his love.
   So praise him now for evermore,
   glory, alleluia.

3. And to the God who cannot die,
   glory, alleluia.
   To the living God we cry,
   glory, alleluia.
   He promised to be with us and
   he lives in ev'ryone.
   We love him now for evermore,
   glory, alleluia.

Text: Sebastian Temple (1928-1997)
Music: Sebastian Temple (1928-1997) arr. Keith Stent

624 Sing the gospel of salvation

AUSTRIA 87 87 D

1. Sing the gospel of salvation, tell it out to all the earth;
to the ones so long ex-clud-ed, speak of hope and hu-man worth.
All the dark-ness of in-ju-stice can-not dim sal-va-tion's light,
for the out-cast and ex-ploit-ed count as wor-thy in God's sight.

2. Christ, the one eternal Shepherd,
   calls creation to rejoice,
   and the victims of oppression
   thrill to hear salvation's voice.
   All who recognise the Saviour
   take their place within the fold,
   there, in perfect truth and freedom,
   life's eternal joys to hold.

3. See, the host that none can number
   gathers in from ev'ry side,
   once the victims of injustice,
   now redeemed and glorified.
   Fear and weeping here are ended,
   hunger and oppression cease.
   Now the Lamb becomes the Shepherd!
   Now begins the reign of peace!

Text: Michael Forster (b.1946)
Music: Croatian folk melody adapted by Franz Joseph Haydn (1732-1809)
Text © Copyright 1993 Kevin Mayhew Ltd.

625 Sing to the Lord, alleluia

2. Give to him, you fam'lies of peoples,
   glory and praise, alleluia.

3. Great is he and worthy of praises,
   day after day, alleluia.

4. He it is who gave us the heavens,
   glory to God, alleluia.

5. Tell his glories, tell all the nations,
   day after day, alleluia.

6. Bring your gifts and enter his temple,
   worship the Lord, alleluia.

Text: John Foley based on Psalm 95
Music: John Foley arr. Andrew Moore

626 Sing to the mountains

Refrain
Unison

Sing to the moun-tains, sing to the sea, raise your voi - ces, lift your hearts. This is the day the Lord has made, let all the earth re-joice.

1. I will give thanks to you, my Lord, you have an-swered my plea; you have saved my soul from death, you are my strength and my song.

Text: Bob Dufford based on Psalm 117
Music: Bob Dufford arr. Adrian Vernon Fish

627 Sleep, holy babe

EDGBASTON 46 886

1. Sleep, ho - ly babe, u - pon thy mo -ther's breast; great

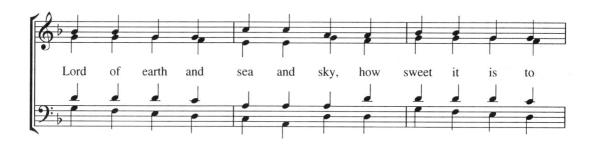

Lord of earth and sea and sky, how sweet it is to

see thee lie in such a place of rest.

2. Sleep, holy babe, thine angels watch around,
all bending low, with folded wings,
before th'incarnate King of kings,
in reverent awe profound.

3. Sleep, holy babe, while I with Mary gaze
in joy upon thy face awhile,
upon the loving infant smile,
which there divinely plays.

4. Sleep, holy babe, ah, take thy brief repose;
too quickly will thy slumbers break,
and thou to lengthened pains awake,
that death alone shall close.

5. O lady blest, sweet virgin, hear my cry;
forgive the wrong that I have done
to thee, in causing thy dear Son
upon the cross to die.

Text: Edward Caswall (1814-1878)
Music: traditional English melody arr. Alan Ridout (1934-1997)

628 Soul of my Saviour

ANIMA CHRISTI 10 10 10 10

1. Soul of my Sa - viour, san - cti - fy my breast;
Bo - dy of Christ, be thou my sav - ing guest;
Blood of my Sa - viour, bathe me in thy tide,
wash me with wa - ter flow - ing from thy side.

2. Strength and protection may thy passion be;
   O blessèd Jesus, hear and answer me;
   deep in thy wounds, Lord, hide and shelter me;
   so shall I never, never part from thee.

3. Guard and defend me from the foe malign;
   in death's dread moments make me only thine;
   call me, and bid me come to thee on high,
   where I may praise thee with thy saints for aye.

Text: 'Anima Christi' ascribed to John XXII (1249-1334) trans. unknown
Music: W.J. Maher (1823-1877)

629 Spirit hovering o'er the waters
Veni, veni, Sancte Spiritus

2. Spirit speaking through the prophets
when they cried for justice and peace,
living Spirit, come renew us,
fill the earth with peace and love.

3. Spirit hov'ring o'er the virgin,
Word and flesh are mothered in her.
living Spirit, breath of Yahweh,
bring the Word to life in us.

4. Spirit breathed on John and Mary
as they stood here under the cross,
living Spirit, strengthen, comfort,
guide, unite your church today.

5. Spirit hov'ring o'er apostles,
wind and fire of Pentecost Day,
living Spirit, now confirm us,
come inspire us, come, we pray.

Text and Music: Noel Donnelly (b.1932)
© Copyright Noel Donnelly. Used by permission.

630 Spirit of the living God

LIVING GOD 75 75 44 75

1. Spi - rit of the liv - ing God, fall a-fresh on me.
Spi - rit of the liv - ing God, fall a-fresh on me.
Melt me, mould me, fill me, use me.
Spi - rit of the liv - ing God, fall a-fresh on me.

2. Spirit of the living God, fall afresh on us.
   Spirit of the living God, fall afresh on us.
   Melt us, mould us, fill us, use us.
   Spirit of the living God, fall afresh on us.

When appropriate, a third verse may be added,
singing 'on them', for example, before Confirmation,
or at a service for the sick.

Text and Music: Daniel Iverson (1890-1972)

631 Springs of water, bless the Lord

2. At the wat'ry dawn of all,
   order out of chaos came,
   when your Spirit hovered there.

3. With the waters of the flood
   you renewed baptismal sign.
   Sin gave way to spring of life.

4. Through the waters of the sea
   you led Israel, set her free,
   image of your baptised Church.

5. In the Jordan waters, John
   saw your Son baptised and sealed
   with your Spirit resting there.

6. Blood and water from his side,
   symbols of his life outpoured,
   as he hung upon the cross.

7. Then the risen Lord proclaimed:
   'Go and teach, baptising all.
   I will always be with you!'

Text: Noel Donnelly (b.1932) based on the Blessing of baptismal waters (Roman Missal)
Music: Noel Donnelly (b.1932)

632 Star of sea and ocean

AVE MARIS STELLA 66 66

1. Star of sea and o - cean, gate-way to God's ha - ven,
mo - ther of our Mak - er, hear our pray'r, O mai - den.

2. Welcoming the Ave
   of God's simple greeting,
   you have borne a Saviour,
   far beyond all dreaming.

3. Loose the bonds that hold us
   bound in sin's own blindness
   that with eyes now opened
   God's own light may guide us.

4. Show yourself our mother;
   he will hear your pleading
   whom your womb has sheltered
   and whose hand brings healing.

5. Gentlest of all virgins,
   that our love be faithful
   keep us from all evil
   gentle, strong and grateful.

6. Guard us through life's dangers,
   never turn and leave us.
   May our hope find harbour
   in the calm of Jesus.

7. Sing to God our Father
   through the Son who saves us,
   joyful in the Spirit,
   everlasting praises.

Text: 'Ave Maris Stella' (9th century) trans. Ralph Wright (b.1938)
Music: Casper Ett (1788-1847)

LiTURGiCAL

HYMNS OLD & NEW

633 Steal away

Steal a-way, steal a-way, steal a-way to Je - sus.

Steal a-way, steal a-way home. I ain't got long to stay here.

1. My Lord, he calls me, he calls me by the thun-der. The

trum-pet sounds with-in my soul; I ain't got long to stay here.

2. Green trees are bending,
the sinner stands a-trembling.
The trumpet sounds within my soul;
I ain't got long to stay here.

3. My Lord, he calls me,
he calls me by the lightning.
The trumpet sounds within my soul;
I ain't got long to stay here.

Text: Spiritual
Music: Spiritual arr. Christopher Tambling
This arrangement © Copyright 1994 Kevin Mayhew Ltd.

634 Sweet heart of Jesus

FONS AMORIS 11 10 11 10 88 and Refrain

Unison

1. Sweet heart of Je - sus, fount of love and mer-cy, to-day we

come, thy bless-ing to im - plore; O touch our hearts, so cold and so un -

grate - ful, and make them, Lord, thine own for e - ver - more.

Refrain
Harmony

Sweet heart of Je - sus, we im - plore,

O make us love thee more and more.

2. Sweet heart of Jesus, make us know and love thee,
   unfold to us the treasures of thy grace;
   that so our hearts, from things of earth uplifted,
   may long alone to gaze upon thy face.

3. Sweet heart of Jesus, make us pure and gentle,
   and teach us how to do thy blessèd will;
   to follow close the print of thy dear footsteps,
   and when we fall – sweet heart, O love us still.

4. Sweet heart of Jesus, bless all hearts that love thee,
   and may thine own heart ever blessèd be;
   bless us, dear Lord, and bless the friends we cherish,
   and keep us true to Mary and to thee.

Text: Sister Marie Josephine
Music: traditional melody

635 Sweet sacrament divine

TUNE 1: DIVINE MYSTERIES 66 66 88 6

1. Sweet sa - cra - ment di - vine, hid in thy earth - ly home, lo, round thy low - ly shrine, with sup - pliant hearts we come; Je - sus, to thee our voice we raise, in songs of love and heart-felt praise, sweet sa - cra - ment di - vine, sweet sa - cra - ment di - vine.

2. Sweet sacrament of peace,
   dear home of ev'ry heart,
   where restless yearnings cease,
   and sorrows all depart,
   there in thine ear all trustfully
   we tell our tale of misery,
   sweet sacrament of peace.

3. Sweet sacrament of rest,
   Ark from the ocean's roar,
   within thy shelter blest
   soon may we reach the shore;
   save us, for still the tempest raves;
   save, lest we sink beneath the waves,
   sweet sacrament of rest.

4. Sweet sacrament divine,
   earth's light and jubilee,
   in thy far depths doth shine
   thy Godhead's majesty;
   sweet light, so shine on us, we pray,
   that earthly joys may fade away,
   sweet sacrament divine.

TUNE 2: SANCTISSIMUM 66 66 88 6

1. Sweet sa - cra - ment di - vine, hid in thy earth - ly home, lo, round thy low - ly shrine, with sup - pliant hearts we come; Je - sus, to thee our voice we raise, in songs of love and heart-felt praise, sweet sa - cra - ment di - vine.

Text: Francis Stanfield (1835-1914)
Music:Tune 1 – Francis Stanfield (1835-1914)
Tune 2 – Gregory Murray (1905-1992)

636 Sweet Saviour, bless us

SUNSET 88 88 88

1. Sweet Sa - viour, bless us ere we go,
thy word in - to our minds in - stil;
and make our luke - warm hearts to glow
with low - ly love and fer - vent will.

Refrain

Through life's long day and death's dark

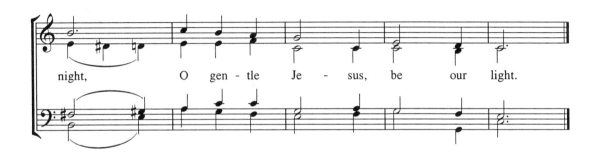

night, O gen - tle Je - sus, be our light.

2. The day is done; its hours have run,
   and thou hast taken count of all
   the scanty triumphs grace has won,
   the broken vow, the frequent fall.

3. Grant us, dear Lord, from evil ways,
   true absolution and release;
   and bless us more than in past days
   with purity and inward peace.

4. Do more than pardon; give us joy,
   sweet fear and sober liberty,
   and loving hearts without alloy,
   that only long to be like thee.

5. Labour is sweet, for thou hast toiled,
   and care is light, for thou hast cared;
   let not our works with self be soiled,
   nor in unsimple ways ensnared.

6. For all we love – the poor, the sad,
   the sinful – unto thee we call;
   O let thy mercy make us glad,
   thou art our Jesus and our all.

Text: Frederick William Faber (1814-1863)
Music: George Herbert (1817-1906)

637 Take and bless our gifts

2. Blessed are you, Lord, God of all creation.
   Through your goodness we offer you this wine,
   fruit of the vine and work of human hands.
   It will become for us the wine of life.

3. Blessed are you, Lord, God of all creation.
   Through your goodness we offer you our lives.
   Accept, make holy all we try to do,
   offered in praise and glory of your name.

Text: Christine McCann (b.1951)
Music: Christine McCann (b.1951) arr. Andrew Moore

638 Take me, Lord

1. Take me, Lord, use my life in the way you wish to do.
Fill me, Lord, touch my heart till it al - ways thinks of you.
Take me now, as I am, this is all I can of-fer.

Refrain
Here to - day I, the clay, will be mould - ed by my Lord.

2. Lord, I pray that each day I will listen to your will.
   Many times I have failed but I know you love me still.
   Teach me now, guide me, Lord, keep me close to you always.

3. I am weak, fill me now with your strength and set me free.
   Make me whole, fashion me so that you will live in me.
   Hold me now in your hands, form me now with your Spirit.

Text: Francesca Leftley (b.1955)
Music: Francesca Leftley (b.1955) arr. Andrew Moore

639 Take my hands

1. Take my hands and make them as your own, and use them for your king-dom here on earth. Con-se-crate them to your care, a-noint them for your ser-vice where you may need your gos-pel to be sown.

2. Take my hands, they speak now for my heart,
and by their actions they will show their love.
Guard them on their daily course,
be their strength and guiding force
to ever serve the Trinity above.

3. Take my hands, I give them to you, Lord.
Prepare them for the service of your name.
Open them to human need
and by their love they'll sow your seed
so all may know the love and hope you give.

Text: Sebastian Temple (1928-1997)
Music: Sebastian Temple (1928-1997) arr. Andrew Moore

640 Take my hands, Lord
Take my life

2. Give me someone to feed when I'm hungry,
   when I'm thirsty give water for their thirst.
   When I stand in need of tenderness,
   give me someone to hold who longs for love.

3. Keep my heart ever open to others,
   may my time, Lord, be spent with those in need;
   may I tend to those who need your care.
   Take my life, Lord, and make it truly yours.

Text: vs. 1 & 3 Margaret Rizza (b.1929); v.2 unknown
Music: Margaret Rizza (b.1929)

641 Take our bread

Refrain
Unison

Take our bread, we ask you, take our hearts, we love you, take our lives, O Fa-ther, we are yours, we are yours.

1. Yours as we stand at the ta - ble you set, yours as we eat the bread our hearts can't for - get. We are the signs of your life with us yet; we are yours, we are yours.

2. Your holy people stand washed in your blood,
   Spirit-filled, yet hungry, we await your food.
   Poor though we are, we have brought ourselves to you:
   we are yours, we are yours.

Text: Joe Wise (b.1939)
Music: Joe Wise (b.1939) arr. Andrew Moore

642 Take this and eat

Refrain

Take this and eat it, for this is my bo-dy.
Take this and drink it, for this is my blood.

1. Taste and see that the Lord is all good-ness.
Hap-py those who take re-fuge in him.

2. 'Come to me, you who are heavy laden;
   take my yoke, for my burden is light.'

3. When you eat and you drink at this table,
   Jesus' death you proclaim, till he comes.

4. Eat, you poor, and be filled, you afflicted.
   Those who seek him, give praise to the Lord.

5. Come, be filled as you sit at my table;
   quench your thirst as you drink of my wine.

6. You who eat, break your bread with the hungry;
   you who drink of his Spirit, give praise.

7. Beautiful is the place of your dwelling;
   how my soul longs for you, O my God.

8. See how good and delightful that brethren
   share this meal to bring true unity.

9. You commanded the heavens to open,
   raining manna upon Israel.

10. This, indeed, is the bread come from heaven;
    those who eat it will never know death.

Text: Aniceto Nazareth based on Scripture
Music: Aniceto Nazareth
© 1984 Kevin Mayhew Ltd.

643 Taste and see the goodness of the Lord

Response
Unison

Taste and see the good-ness of the Lord, the good-ness of the Lord.

1. I sing God's prai - ses all my days, his

name is al - ways on my lips; he is my one and

on - ly boast, the pride and joy of all the poor.

2. So come with me to sing his praise,
   together let us praise his name.
   I seek the Lord, he answers me,
   and rescues me from all my fears.

3. The Lord is quick to heed the poor
   and liberate them from their chains.
   The Lord is close to broken hearts,
   he rescues slaves and sets them free.

Text: Hubert J. Richards (b.1921) based on Psalm 33
Music: Andrew Moore (b.1954)
© Copyright 1996 Kevin Mayhew Ltd.

644 Tell out, my soul

WOODLANDS 10 10 10 10

1. Tell out, my soul, the great-ness of the Lord: un-num-bered bless-ings, give my spi-rit voice; ten-der to me the pro-mise of his word; in God my Sa-viour shall my heart re-joice.

2. Tell out, my soul, the greatness of his name:
   make known his might, the deeds his arm has done;
   his mercy sure, from age to age the same;
   his holy name, the Lord, the mighty one.

3. Tell out, my soul, the greatness of his might:
   pow'rs and dominions lay their glory by;
   proud hearts and stubborn wills are put to flight,
   the hungry fed, the humble lifted high.

4. Tell out, my soul, the glories of his word:
   firm is his promise, and his mercy sure.
   Tell out, my soul, the greatness of the Lord
   to children's children and for evermore.

Text: Timothy Dudley Smith (b.1926) based on Luke 1:46-55
Music: Walter Greatorex (1877-1949)

645 Thanks for the fellowship

Thanks for the fel-low-ship found at this meal, thanks for a day re-freshed;

thanks to the Lord for his pre-sence we feel, thanks for the food he blessed.

Joy-ful-ly sing praise to the Lord, praise to the ri - sen Son,

al - le - lu - ia, e - ver a-dored, pray that his will be done.

As he was known in the break-ing of bread, now is he known a - gain,

and by his hand have the hun-gry been fed, thanks be to Christ. A - men!

Text: Jean Holloway (b.1939)
Music: traditional Scottish melody arr. Colin Hand

646 The angel Gabriel from heaven came

BIRJINA GAZTETTOBAT ZEGOEN 10 10 12 10

1. The an-gel Ga-bri-el from hea-ven came, his
wings as drift-ed snow, his eyes as flame. 'All
hail,' said he, 'thou low-ly maid-en, Ma - ry, most
high-ly fa-voured la - dy.' Glo - ri - a!

2. 'For known a blessèd Mother thou shalt be.
All generations laud and honour thee.
Thy Son shall be Emmanuel, by seers foretold,
most highly favoured lady.' Gloria!

3. Then gentle Mary meekly bowed her head.
'To me be as it pleaseth God,' she said.
'My soul shall laud and magnify his holy name.'
Most highly favoured lady! Gloria!

4. Of her, Emmanuel, the Christ, was born
in Bethlehem, all on a Christmas morn;
and Christian folk throughout the world will ever say:
'Most highly favoured lady.' Gloria!

Text: Sabine Baring-Gould (1843-1924) based on 'Birjina gaztettobat zegoen'
Music: traditional Basque melody arr. Richard Lloyd
This arrangement © Copyright 1996 Kevin Mayhew Ltd.

647 The Church's one foundation

AURELIA 76 76 D

1. The Church's one foundation is Jesus Christ, her Lord; she is his new creation, by water and the word; from heav'n he came and sought her to be his holy bride, with his own blood he bought her, and for her life he died.

A lower setting will be found at No. 521

2. Elect from ev'ry nation, yet one o'er all the earth,
   her charter of salvation, one Lord, one faith, one birth;
   one holy name she blesses, partakes one holy food,
   and to one hope she presses, with ev'ry grace endued.

3. 'Mid toil and tribulation, and tumult of her war,
   she waits the consummation of peace for evermore;
   till with the vision glorious her longing eyes are blest,
   and the great Church victorious shall be the Church at rest.

4. Yet she on earth hath union with God the Three in One,
   and mystic sweet communion with those whose rest is won:
   O happy ones and holy! Lord, give us grace that we
   like them, the meek and lowly, on high may dwell with thee.

Text: Samuel John Stone (1839-1900)
Music: Samuel Sebastian Wesley (1810-1876)

648 The coming of our God

TUNE 1: FRANCONIA SM

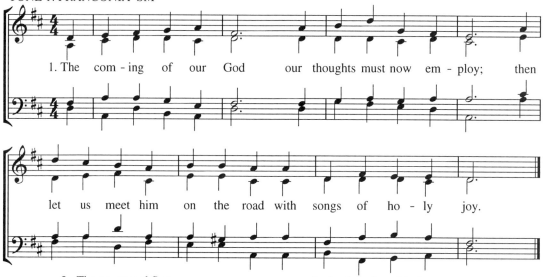

1. The com-ing of our God our thoughts must now em-ploy; then let us meet him on the road with songs of ho-ly joy.

2. The co-eternal Son,
   a maiden's offspring see;
   a servant's form Christ putteth on,
   to set his people free.

3. Daughter of Sion, rise
   to greet thine infant king,
   nor let thy stubborn heart despise
   the pardon he doth bring.

4. In glory from his throne
   again will Christ descend,
   and summon all that are his own
   to joys that never end.

5. Let deeds of darkness fly
   before th'approaching morn,
   for unto sin 'tis ours to die,
   and serve the virgin-born.

6. Our joyful praises sing
   to Christ, that set us free;
   like tribute to the Father bring
   and, Holy Ghost, to thee.

TUNE 2: BELLWOODS SM

1. The com-ing of our God our thoughts must now em-ploy; then let us meet him on the road with songs of ho-ly joy.

Text: 'Instantis adventum Dei' by Charles Coffin (1676-1749) trans. Robert Campbell (1814-1868) and others
Music: Tune 1 – traditional melody arr. William Henry Havergal (1793-1870)
Tune 2 – James Hopkirk (b.1908)
Tune 2 © Copyright control

649 The day of resurrection

ELLACOMBE 76 76 D

1. The day of re-sur-rec-tion! Earth, tell it out a-broad; the pass-o-ver of glad-ness, the pass-o-ver of God! From death to life e-ter-nal, from earth un-to the sky, our Christ hath brought us o-ver with hymns of vic-to-ry.

2. Our hearts be pure from evil, that we may see aright
the Lord in rays eternal of resurrection-light;
and list'ning to his accents, may hear so calm and plain
his own 'All hail' and, hearing, may raise the victor strain.

3. Now let the heav'ns be joyful, and earth her song begin,
the round world keep high triumph, and all that is therein;
let all things, seen and unseen, their notes of gladness blend,
for Christ the Lord hath risen, our joy that hath no end.

Text: St. John of Damascus (c.750) trans. John Mason Neale (1818-1866)
Music: 'Württemberg Gesangbuch' (1784)

LITURGICAL

HYMNS OLD & NEW

650 The day thou gavest, Lord, is ended

ST CLEMENT 98 98

1. The day thou gav - est, Lord, is end - ed: the dark - ness falls at thy be - hest; to thee our morn - ing hymns a - scend - ed; thy praise shall san - cti - fy our rest.

A higher setting will be found at No. 563

2. We thank thee that thy Church unsleeping,
   while earth rolls onward into light,
   through all the world her watch is keeping,
   and rests not now by day or night.

3. As o'er each continent and island
   the dawn leads on another day,
   the voice of prayer is never silent,
   nor dies the strain of praise away.

4. The sun that bids us rest is waking
   our brethren 'neath the western sky,
   and hour by hour fresh lips are making
   thy wondrous doings heard on high.

5. So be it, Lord; thy throne shall never,
   like earth's proud empires, pass away;
   thy kingdom stands, and grows for ever,
   till all thy creatures own thy sway.

Text: John Ellerton (1826-1893)
Music: Clement Cotterill Scholefield (1839-1904)

THE FIRST NOWELL Irregular

1. The first No-well the an-gel did say was to cer-tain poor shep-herds in fields as they lay: in fields where they lay keep-ing their sheep, on a cold win-ter's night that was so deep.

Refrain

No - well, No - well, No - well, No - well, born is the King of Is - ra - el!

2. They lookèd up and saw a star,
   shining in the east, beyond them far,
   and to the earth it gave great light,
   and so it continued both day and night.

3. And by the light of that same star,
   three wise men came from country far;
   to seek for a king was their intent,
   and to follow the star wherever it went.

4. This star drew nigh to the north-west,
   o'er Bethlehem it took its rest,
   and there it did both stop and stay
   right over the place where Jesus lay.

5. Then entered in those wise men three,
   full rev'rently upon their knee,
   and offered there in his presence,
   their gold and myrrh and frankincense.

6. Then let us all with one accord
   sing praises to our heav'nly Lord,
   who with the Father we adore
   and Spirit blest for evermore.

Text: from William Sandys' 'Christmas Carols, Ancient and Modern' (1833) alt.
Music: traditional English melody arr. John Stainer (1840-1901)

652 The head that once was crowned with thorns

ST MAGNUS CM

1. The head that once was crowned with thorns is crowned with glo - ry now: a roy - al di - a - dem a - dorns the migh - ty vic - tor's brow.

2. The highest place that heav'n affords
   is his, is his by right.
   The King of kings and Lord of lords,
   and heav'n's eternal light.

3. The joy of all who dwell above,
   the joy of all below,
   to whom he manifests his love,
   and grants his name to know.

4. To them the cross, with all its shame,
   with all its grace is giv'n;
   their name an everlasting name,
   their joy the joy of heav'n.

5. They suffer with their Lord below,
   they reign with him above,
   their profit and their joy to know
   the myst'ry of his love.

6. The cross he bore is life and health,
   though shame and death to him;
   his people's hope, his people's wealth,
   their everlasting theme.

Text: Thomas Kelly (1769-1855)
Music: Jeremiah Clarke (1670-1707)

653 The holly and the ivy

THE HOLLY AND THE IVY 76 86 (Irregular) and Refrain

1. The hol-ly and the i-vy, when they are both full grown, of all the trees that are in the wood the hol-ly bears the crown.

Refrain

The ri-sing of the sun and the run-ning of the deer, the play-ing of the mer-ry or-gan, sweet sing-ing in the choir.

2. The holly bears a blossom,
   white as the lily flower,
   and Mary bore sweet Jesus Christ
   to be our sweet Saviour.

3. The holly bears a berry,
   as red as any blood,
   and Mary bore sweet Jesus Christ
   to do poor sinners good.

4. The holly bears a prickle,
   as sharp as any thorn,
   and Mary bore sweet Jesus Christ
   on Christmas day in the morn.

5. The holly bears a bark,
   as bitter as any gall,
   and Mary bore sweet Jesus Christ
   for to redeem us all.

6. The holly and the ivy,
   when they are both full grown,
   of all the trees that are in the wood
   the holly bears the crown.

Text: traditional
Music: English folk carol arr. Adrian Vernon Fish
This arrangement © Copyright 1994 Kevin Mayhew Ltd.

654 The kingdom of heaven
The Beatitudes

2. Blessed are you who hunger for right,
   for you shall be satisfied;
   blessed are you the merciful ones,
   for you shall be pardoned too.

3. Blessed are you whose hearts are pure,
   your eyes shall gaze on the Lord;
   blessed are you who strive after peace,
   the Lord will call you his own.

4. Blessed are you who suffer for right,
   the heav'nly kingdom is yours;
   blessed are you who suffer for me,
   for you shall reap your reward.

Text: Mike Anderson (b.1956) based on Matthew 5:3-10
Music: Mike Anderson (b.1956)

LITURGICAL
HYMNS OLD & NEW

655 The King of glory comes

Refrain
Unison

The King of glo-ry comes, the na-tion re - joi - ces, o - pen the gates be-fore him, lift up your voi - ces. 1. Who is the King of glo-ry, how shall we call him? He is Em - ma-nu - el, the pro-mised of a - ges.

2. In all of Galilee,
   in city and village,
   he goes among his people,
   curing their illness.

3. Sing then of David's Son,
   our Saviour and brother;
   in all of Galilee
   was never another.

4. He gave his life for us,
   the pledge of salvation.
   He took upon himself
   the sins of the nation.

5. He conquered sin and death;
   he truly has risen;
   and he will share with us
   his heavenly vision.

Text: Willard F. Jabusch (b.1930)
Music: Israeli melody arr. Andrew Moore

656 The King of love my shepherd is

TUNE 1: DOMINUS REGIT ME 87 87

1. The King of love my shep - herd is, whose

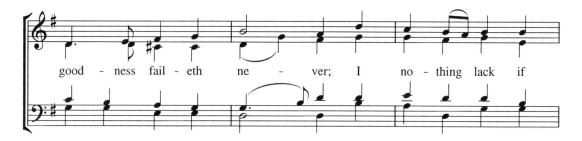

good - ness fail - eth ne - ver; I no - thing lack if

I am his and he is mine for e - ver.

A lower setting will be found at No. 671

2. Where streams of living water flow
   my ransomed soul he leadeth,
   and where the verdant pastures grow
   with food celestial feedeth.

3. Perverse and foolish oft I strayed,
   but yet in love he sought me,
   and on his shoulder gently laid,
   and home, rejoicing, brought me.

4. In death's dark vale I fear no ill
   with thee, dear Lord, beside me;
   thy rod and staff my comfort still,
   thy cross before to guide me.

5. Thou spread'st a table in my sight,
   thy unction grace bestoweth:
   and O what transport of delight
   from thy pure chalice floweth!

6. And so through all the length of days
   thy goodness faileth never;
   good Shepherd, may I sing thy praise
   within thy house for ever.

TUNE 2: ST COLUMBA 87 87

1. The King of love my shep - herd is, whose

good - ness fail - eth ne - ver; I no - thing lack if

I am his and he is mine for e - ver.

Text: Henry Williams Baker (1821-1877) based on Psalm 22
Music: Tune 1 – John Bacchus Dykes (1823-1876)
Tune 2 – Irish melody (Petrie Collection)

657 The light of Christ

Text: Donald Fishel (b.1950)
Music: Donald Fishel (b.1950) arr. Andrew Moore

658 The Lord hears the cry of the poor

Refrain
Unison

The Lord hears the cry of the poor. Bles-sed be the Lord.

1. I will bless the Lord at all times, his praise e-ver in my mouth. Let my

soul glo-ry in the Lord, for he hears the cry of the poor.

2. Let the lowly hear and be glad:
   the Lord listens to their pleas;
   and to hearts broken he is near,
   for he hears the cry of the poor.

3. Ev'ry spirit crushed he will save;
   will be ransom for their lives;
   will be safe shelter for their fears,
   for he hears the cry of the poor.

4. We proclaim the greatness of God,
   his praise ever in our mouth;
   ev'ry face brightened in his light,
   for he hears the cry of the poor.

Text: John Foley based on Psalm 33
Music: John Foley arr. Andrew Moore

LITURGICAL

HYMNS OLD & NEW

659 The Lord is alive

The division between Cantor and Congregation is suggested for responsorial use.
Verse 5 may be used as a Memorial Acclamation after the Consecration.

2. He brings us great joy! Alleluia!
   He fills us with hope! Alleluia!
   He comes as our food,
   he gives us our life!
   Alleluia! Alleluia!

3. So let us rejoice! Alleluia!
   Give praise to the Lord! Alleluia!
   He showed us his love,
   by him we are saved!
   Alleluia! Alleluia!

4. The Lord is alive! Alleluia!
   So let us proclaim, alleluia,
   the Good News of Christ
   throughout all the world!
   Alleluia! Alleluia!

5. Christ Jesus has died! Alleluia!
   Christ Jesus is ris'n! Alleluia!
   Christ Jesus will come
   again as the Lord!
   Alleluia! Alleluia!

6. Sing praises to God, alleluia,
   who reigns without end! Alleluia!
   The Father, the Son,
   and Spirit – all One!
   Alleluia! Alleluia!

Text: Jean-Paul Lécot (b.1947) trans. W.R. Lawrence (1925-1997)
Music: J. Herrera
© Copyright 1988 Kevin Mayhew Ltd.

660 The Lord is my life

whom shall I fear? The Lord is the ref-uge of my

on-ly one thing I seek: to live in the pre-sence of the

land where the liv - ing dwell. Wait for the Lord and be

Am | F⁷ | G | D | Em

life; of whom should I be a - fraid? The

Lord, to dwell in the house of my God. The

brave; yes, wait for the liv - ing God! The

C | C♯dim | G | D⁷ | G

D.S.

Text: Michael Joncas (b.1951) based on Psalm 27
Music: Michael Joncas (b.1951) arr. Keith Stent

661 The Lord's my shepherd

TUNE 1: CRIMOND CM

1. The Lord's my shep - herd, I'll not want. He

makes me down to lie in pas - tures green. He

lead - eth me the qui - et wa - ters by.

2. My soul he doth restore again,
and me to walk doth make
within the paths of righteousness,
e'en for his own name's sake.

3. Yea, though I walk in death's dark vale,
yet will I fear no ill.
For thou art with me, and thy rod
and staff me comfort still.

4. My table thou has furnishèd
in presence of my foes,
my head thou dost with oil anoint,
and my cup overflows.

5. Goodness and mercy all my life
shall surely follow me.
And in God's house for evermore
my dwelling-place shall be.

TUNE 2: BROTHER JAMES'S AIR CM

1. The Lord's my shep-herd, I'll not want. He makes me down to lie in

pas-tures green. He lead-eth me the qui-et wa - ters by. In

pas-tures green, he lead-eth me the qui-et wa - ters by.

Text: Psalm 22 from 'The Scottish Psalter' (1650)
Music: Tune 1 – melody by Jessie Seymour Irvine (1836-1887)
Tune 2 – Brother James Leith Macbeth Bain (d.1925) arr. Christopher Tambling

662 The love I have for you
Only a shadow

1. The love I have for you, my Lord, is on-ly a sha-dow of your love for me; on-ly a sha-dow of your love for me; your deep a-bid-ing love.

3. My life is in your hands; my life is in your hands. My love for you will grow, my God. Your light in me will shine.

2. My own belief in you, my Lord,
   is only a shadow of your faith in me;
   only a shadow of your faith in me;
   your deep and lasting faith.

3. *See music above.*

4. The dream I have today, my Lord,
   is only a shadow of your dreams for me;
   only a shadow of all that will be;
   if I but follow you.

5. The joy I feel today, my Lord,
   is only a shadow of your joys for me;
   only a shadow of your joys for me;
   when we meet face to face.

6. *Repeat verse 3.*

Text: Carey Landry
Music: Carey Landry arr. Christopher Tambling

663 The Mass is ended

1. The Mass is end-ed, all go in peace.
We must di-min-ish, and Christ in-crease.
We take him with us where-e'er we go,
that through our ac-tions his life may show.

2. We witness his love to ev'ryone
by our communion with Christ the Son.
We take the Mass to where people are
that Christ may shine forth, their Morning Star.

3. Thanks to the Father who shows the way.
His life within us throughout each day.
Let all our living and loving be
to praise and honour the Trinity.

4. *Repeat verse 1.*

Text: Sebastian Temple (1928-1997) alt.
Music: Sebastian Temple (1928-1997) arr. Andrew Moore

664 The night was dark
Come and see

1. The night was dark and filled with gloom. (Come and see. Come and see.) They
hid with - in a se - cret room. (Come and see. Come and see.) Now
Thom - as had not seen the Lord, (Come and see. Come and see.) he
doubt - ed ev - 'ry sing - le word. (Come and see. Come and see.)
I be - lieve this is Je - sus. (Come and see. Come and see.) Oh,

I be-lieve this is Je - sus. (Come and see. Come and see.)

2. Then suddenly the Lord appeared
   (Come and see. Come and see.)
   to see his friends and calm their fears.
   (Come and see. Come and see.)
   'Now Thomas,' he said, 'see my hand,'
   (Come and see. Come and see.)
   'it happened just as God had planned.'

3. 'Well,' Thomas said, 'my God, my Lord.
   (Come and see. Come and see.)
   'Now I believe the living Word.'
   (Come and see. Come and see.)
   Go tell the people far and wide,
   (Come and see. Come and see.)
   twas for their sins that Jesus died.

Text: John Ylvisaker
Music: Traditional American arr. Andrew Moore

665 The race that long in darkness pined

TUNE 1: ST FULBERT CM

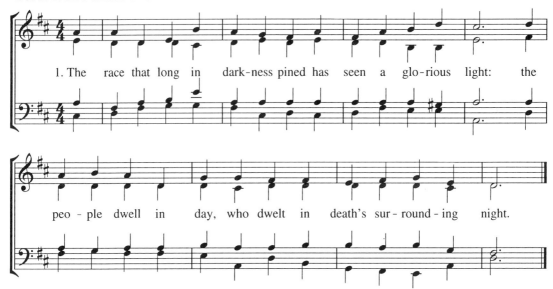

1. The race that long in darkness pined has seen a glorious light: the
people dwell in day, who dwelt in death's surrounding night.

2. To hail thy rise, thou better sun,
   the gath'ring nations come,
   joyous as when the reapers bear
   the harvest treasures home.

3. To us a child of hope is born,
   to us a Son is giv'n;
   him shall the tribes of earth obey,
   him all the hosts of heav'n.

4. His name shall be the Prince of Peace
   for evermore adored,
   the Wonderful, the Counsellor,
   the great and mighty Lord.

5. His pow'r increasing still shall spread,
   his reign no end shall know;
   justice shall guard his throne above,
   and peace abound below.

TUNE 2: DUNDEE CM

1. The race that long in darkness pined has seen a glorious light: the
people dwell in day, who dwelt in death's surrounding night.

Text: John Morrison (1750-1798) based on Isaiah 9:2-7
Music: Tune 1 – Henry John Gauntlett (1805-1876)
Tune 2 – melody from 'Psalms', Edinburgh (1615)

666 There is a green hill far away

HORSLEY CM

1. There is a green hill far a-way, out-side a ci-ty wall, where the dear Lord was cru-ci-fied who died to save us all.

2. We may not know, we cannot tell
   what pains he had to bear,
   but we believe it was for us
   he hung and suffered there.

3. He died that we might be forgiv'n,
   he died to make us good;
   that we might go at last to heav'n,
   saved by his precious blood.

4. There was no other good enough
   to pay the price of sin;
   he only could unlock the gate
   of heav'n, and let us in.

5. O, dearly, dearly has he loved,
   and we must love him too,
   and trust in his redeeming blood,
   and try his works to do.

Text: Cecil Frances Alexander (1818-1895) alt.
Music: William Horsley (1774-1858)

LITURGICAL

HYMNS OLD & NEW

667 There is a river

Unison

1. There is a ri-ver that flows from God a-bove;
there is a foun-tain that's filled with his great love.

Refrain

Come to the wa-ters, there is a great sup-ply;
there is a ri-ver that ne-ver shall run dry.

2. Wash me with water, and then I shall be clean;
white as the new snow, if you remove my sin.

3. Plunged in the water, the tomb of our rebirth,
so may we rise up to share in Christ's new life.

4. All who are thirsty, now hear God as he calls;
come to the Lord's side, his life pours out for all.

5. Safe in the new Ark, the Church of Christ our Lord,
praise God for water, his sign to save the world.

Text: v.1 Unknown; vs. 2-5 Robert B. Kelly (b.1948) from Scripture
Music: Traditional melody arr. Andrew Moore (b.1954)

668 The royal banners forward go

TUNE 1: TRURO LM

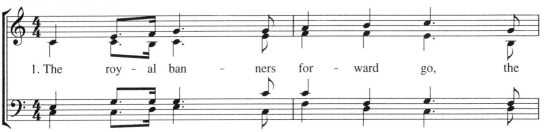

1. The roy - al ban - ners for - ward go, the

cross shines forth in mys - tic glow, where he in flesh, our

flesh who made, our sen - tence bore, our ran - som paid.

2. There whilst he hung, his sacred side
by soldier's spear was opened wide,
to cleanse us in the precious flood
of water mingled with his blood.

3. Fulfilled is now what David told
in true prophetic song of old,
how God the heathen's king should be;
for God is reigning from the tree.

4. O tree of glory, tree most fair,
ordained those holy limbs to bear,
how bright in purple robe it stood,
the purple of a Saviour's blood!

5. Upon its arms, like balance true,
he weighed the price for sinners due,
the price which none but he could pay:
and spoiled the spoiler of his prey.

6. To thee, eternal Three in One,
let homage meet by all be done,
as by the cross thou dost restore,
so rule and guide us evermore.

TUNE 2: WINCHESTER NEW LM

1. The roy - al ban - ners for - ward go, the
cross shines forth in mys - tic glow, where he in flesh, our
flesh who made, our sen - tence bore, our ran - som paid.

A lower setting will be found at No. 593

Text: 'Vexilla regis prodeunt' by Venantius Fortunatus (530-609) trans. John Mason Neale (1818-1866) and others
Music: Tune 1 – from 'Psalmodia Evangelica' (1789)
Tune 2 – from 'Musikalisches Handbuch' (1690)

669 The Saviour will come, resplendent in joy

LAUDATE DOMINUM 10 10 11 11

A lower setting will be found at No. 548

2. The Saviour will come, like rain on the earth,
   to harvest at last his crop of great worth.
   In patience await him, with firmness of mind;
   both mercy and judgement his people will find.

3. The Saviour will come, his truth we shall see:
   where lepers are cleansed and captives set free.
   No finely clad princeling in palace of gold,
   but Christ with his people, O wonder untold!

Text: Michael Forster (b.1946) based on Isaiah 35
Music: Hubert Parry (1848-1918)
Text © Copyright 1993 Kevin Mayhew Ltd.

670 The seed is Christ's

AG CRÍOST AN SÍOL Irregular

The seed is Christ's, the har-vest his: may we be stored with-in God's barn. The
sea is Christ's, the fish are his: may we be caught with-in God's net. From
birth to age, from age to death, en-fold us, Christ, with-in your arms. Until the end, the great re-birth, Christ be our joy in pa-ra-dise.

Text: James Quinn (b.1919)
Music: Seán Ó Riada

671 The sign of hope, creation's joy

DOMINUS REGIT ME 87 87

1. The sign of hope, cre - a - tion's joy, is
born of pur - est beau - ty: the vir - gin's womb, now
glo - ri - fied, where grace u - nites with du - ty.

A higher setting will be found at No. 656

2. Emmanuel shall be his name,
   a title pure and holy,
   for God with us will truly be
   among the poor and lowly.

3. Where love divine concurs with trust
   to share redemption's story,
   Emmanuel in hope is born,
   and earth exults in glory.

4. Now we, by grace and duty called,
   proclaim to ev'ry nation
   the Sign of hope which Mary bore,
   and promise of salvation.

Text: Michael Forster (b.1946)
Music: John Bacchus Dykes (1823-1876)
Text © Copyright 1993 Kevin Mayhew Ltd.

672 The Spirit lives to set us free
Walk in the light

Unison

1. The Spi-rit lives to set us free, walk, walk in the light. He

binds us all in u-ni-ty, walk, walk in the light.

Refrain

Walk in the light, walk in the light,

walk in the light, walk in the light of the Lord. Lord.

To verses D.C. / *Last time*

2. Jesus promised life to all,
   walk, walk in the light.
   The dead were wakened by his call,
   walk, walk in the light.

3. He died in pain on Calvary,
   walk, walk in the light,
   to save the lost like you and me,
   walk, walk in the light.

4. We know his death was not the end,
   walk, walk in the light.
   He gave his Spirit to be our friend,
   walk, walk in the light.

5. By Jesus' love our wounds are healed,
   walk, walk in the light.
   The Father's kindness is revealed,
   walk, walk in the light.

6. The Spirit lives in you and me,
   walk, walk in the light.
   His light will shine for all to see,
   walk, walk in the light.

Text: Damian Lundy (1944-1997)
Music: unknown arr. Christopher Tambling

673 The Spirit of the Lord

The Spi - rit of the Lord is now up - on me
to heal the bro - ken heart and set the cap - tives free,
to op - en pri - son doors and make the blind to see.
The Spi - rit of the Lord is now on me.

Text: Luke 4:18 and Isaiah 61:1-2
Music: unknown, arr. John Rombaut

674 The table's set, Lord

2. At this same table in other places,
   so many people here in Christ's name.
   Those gone before us, who will succeed us,
   one single table throughout all time.

3. One Lord inviting, one Church responding;
   one single bread and one cup of wine.
   May what we do here change and transform us,
   one single presence, Christ through all time.

Text: Robert B. Kelly (b.1948)
Music: Robert B. Kelly (b.1948) arr. Keith Stent

LITURGICAL

HYMNS OLD & NEW

675 The temple of the living God

ELLACOMBE DCM

1. The tem-ple of the liv-ing God is built of liv-ing stones, a
ho-ly peo-ple, called to live by light of Christ a - lone. With
spe-cial joy we ce-le-brate the word the psalm-ist said: 'The
stone the build-ers cast a-side is now the cor-ner's head!'

2. The temple of the living God
   is set secure above,
   where Christ invites the world to share
   his perfect reign of love.
   And we who seek the Father's face
   are summoned to obey,
   and follow where he goes before,
   the Life, the Truth, the Way.

3. The temple of the living God
   upon the earth must grow,
   and those of ev'ry race and class
   his true compassion know.
   The widow and the fatherless
   receive a special care,
   till all creation, just and free,
   his perfect peace will share.

Text: Michael Forster (b.1946)
Music: 'Württemberg Gesangbuch' (1784)

676 The Virgin Mary had a baby boy

2. The angels sang when the baby was born, *(x3)*
   and proclaimed him the Saviour Jesus.

3. The wise men saw where the baby was born, *(x3)*
   and they saw that his name was Jesus.

Text: traditional West Indian
Music: traditional West Indian arr. Christopher Tambling

677 The wandering flock of Israel

smile is our peace, his word our hope.

2. I walk on the heights, I climb and cling,
   the terrors beneath, the ice aloft.
   I look for his tracks, await his hand
   to help and to hold, to guide and save.

3. I thirst for his word as grass in drought,
   dry, brittle and barren, parched and brown;
   no shower can fall, no sap rise green
   no hope, if the Lord should send no rain.

4. Creator of all, your craftsman's care
   with fashioning hand caressed our clay;
   this vine is the work your hands have wrought,
   your love is the sun, our soil of growth.

Text: Luke Connaughton (1917-1979)
Music: Gregory Murray (1905-1992)

678 Thine be the glory

MACCABAEUS 10 11 11 11 and Refrain

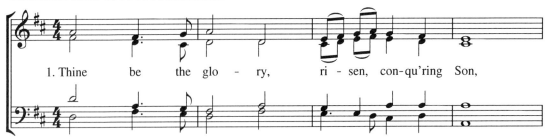

1. Thine be the glo - ry, ri - sen, con-qu'ring Son,

end - less is the vic - t'ry thou o'er death hast won;

an - gels in bright rai - ment rolled the stone a - way,

kept the fold - ed grave - clothes where thy bo - dy lay.

Refrain
Unison

Thine be the glo - ry, ri - sen, con-qu'ring Son,

end - less is the vic - t'ry thou o'er death hast won.

2. Lo! Jesus meets us, risen from the tomb;
   lovingly he greets us, scatters fear and gloom.
   Let the Church with gladness hymns of triumph sing,
   for her Lord now liveth; death hath lost its sting.

3. No more we doubt thee, glorious Prince of Life!
   Life is naught without thee: aid us in our strife.
   Make us more than conqu'rors through thy deathless love.
   Bring us safe through Jordan to thy home above.

Text: 'À toi la gloire' by Edmond Louis Budry (1854-1932) trans. Richard Birch Hoyle (1875-1939)
Music: George Frideric Handel (1685-1759)

679 This Child

near to this hea - ven-ly Child.

2. This Child.
3. This

2. This Child, rising on us like the sun,
   O this Child, given to light everyone,
   O this Child, guiding our feet on the pathway
   to peace on earth.

3. This Child, raising the humble and poor,
   O this Child, making the proud ones to fall;
   O this Child, filling the hungry with good things,
   this heavenly Child.

Text and Music: Graham Kendrick (b.1950)

680 This day God gives me

BUNESSAN 55 54 D

1. This day God gives me strength of high hea - ven, sun and moon shi - ning, flame in my hearth, flash - ing of light - ing, wind in its swift - ness, deeps of the o - cean, firm - ness of earth.

2. This day God sends me
strength to sustain me,
might to uphold me,
wisdom as guide.
Your eyes are watchful,
your ears are list'ning,
your lips are speaking,
friend at my side.

3. God's way is my way,
God's shield is round me,
God's host defends me,
saving from ill.
Angel of heaven,
drive from me always
all that would harm me,
stand by me still.

4. Rising, I thank you,
mighty and strong One,
King of creation,
giver of rest,
firmly confessing
Threeness of persons,
Oneness of Godhead,
Trinity blest.

Text: ascribed to St. Patrick (372-466) adapted by James Quinn (b.1919)
Music: traditional Gaelic melody arr. Colin Hand

681 This is my body

2. This is my blood, poured out for you,
   bringing forgiveness, making you free.
   Take it and drink it, and when you do,
   do it in love for me.

3. Back to my Father soon I shall go.
   Do not forget me; then you will see
   I am still with you, and you will know
   you're very close to me.

4. Filled with my Spirit, how you will grow!
   You are my branches; I am the tree.
   If you are faithful, others will know
   you are alive in me.

5. Love one another; I have loved you,
   and I have shown you how to be free;
   serve one another, and when you do,
   do it in love for me.

Text: vs. 1 & 2 Jimmy Owens; vs. 3-5 Damian Lundy (1944-1997)
Music: Peter Jacobs arr. Christopher Tambling

682 This is my will

Unison

1. This is my will, my one com- mand, that love should

dwell a - mong you all. This is my will that

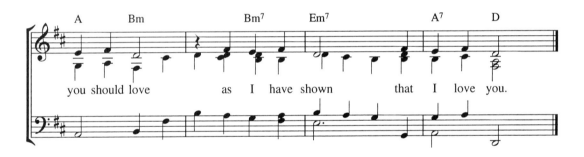

you should love as I have shown that I love you.

2. No greater love can be than this:
   to choose to die to save one's friends.
   You are my friends if you obey
   all I command that you should do.

3. I call you now no longer slaves;
   no slave knows all his master does.
   I call you friends, for all I hear
   my Father say, you hear from me.

4. You chose not me, but I chose you,
   that you should go and bear much fruit.
   I called you out that you in me
   should bear much fruit that will abide.

5. All that you ask my Father dear
   for my name's sake you shall receive.
   This is my will, my one command,
   that love should dwell in each, in all.

Text: James Quinn (b.1919)
Music: traditional Irish melody arr. Christopher Tambling

683 This is our faith

This may be sung as a round, the voices entering as indicated.

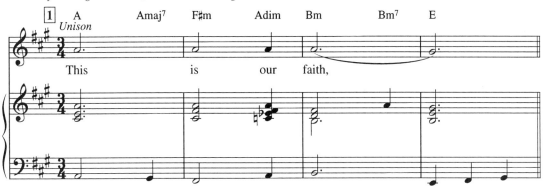

This is our faith,

this is our faith in Christ Je-sus our Lord

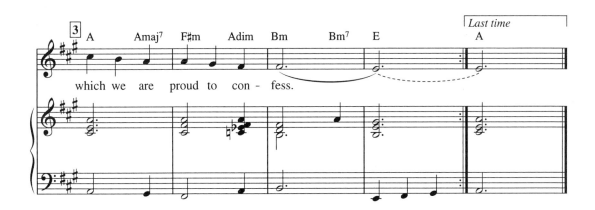

which we are proud to con-fess.

Text: from the Renewal of Baptismal Promises
Music: Robert B. Kelly (b.1948)

684 This is the day

1. This is the day, this is the day that the Lord has made, that the Lord has made;
we will re-joice, we will re-joice and be glad in it, and be glad in it.
This is the day that the Lord has made; we will re-joice and be glad in it.
This is the day, this is the day that the Lord has made.

2. This is the day, this is the day
   when he rose again, when he rose again;
   we will rejoice, we will rejoice
   and be glad in it, and be glad in it.
   This is the day when he rose again;
   we will rejoice and be glad in it.
   This is the day, this is the day
   when he rose again.

3. This is the day, this is the day
   when the Spirit came, when the Spirit came;
   we will rejoice, we will rejoice
   and be glad in it, and be glad in it.
   This is the day when the Spirit came;
   we will rejoice and be glad in it.
   This is the day, this is the day
   when the Spirit came.

Text: Les Garrett (b.1944)
Music: Les Garrett (b.1944) arr. Christopher Tambling

685 This is the image of the queen

IVER 86 86 87 86

1. This is the im-age of the queen who reigns in bliss a-
bove; of her who is the hope of men, whom men and
an-gels love. Most ho-ly Ma-ry, at thy feet
I bend a sup-pli-ant knee; in this thy own sweet
month of May, do thou re-mem-ber me.

2. The homage offered at the feet
of Mary's image here
to Mary's self at once ascends
above the starry sphere.
Most holy Mary, at thy feet
I bend a suppliant knee;
in all my joy, in all my pain,
do thou remember me.

3. How fair soever be the form
which here your eyes behold,
its beauty is by Mary's self
excelled a thousandfold.
Most holy Mary, at thy feet
I bend a suppliant knee;
in my temptations, each and all,
do thou remember me,

Text: Edward Caswall (1814-1878)
Music: Henri Friedrich Hémy (1818-1888)

686 This joyful Eastertide

THIS JOYFUL EASTERTIDE (VREUCHTEN) 67 67 and Refrain

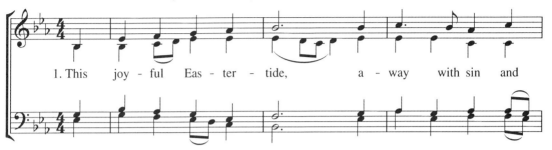

1. This joy-ful Eas-ter-tide, a - way with sin and

sor - - row. My love, the Cru - ci -

fied, hath sprung to life this mor -

Refrain

- row. Had Christ, that once was slain, ne'er burst his

three-day pri - son, our faith had been in vain: but now hath Christ a - ri - sen, a - ri - sen, a - ri - sen, a - ri - sen.

2. My flesh in hope shall rest,
   and for a season slumber;
   till trump from east to west
   shall wake the dead in number.

3. Death's flood hath lost its chill,
   · since Jesus crossed the river:
   lover of souls, from ill
   my passing soul deliver.

Text: George Ratcliffe Woodward (1848-1934)
Music: 17th century Dutch melody arr. Charles Wood (1866-1926)

687 This, then, is my prayer

strong in your in - ner-most self.

1. May Christ live in your hearts and may your lives, root - ed in love, grow strong in him.

2. May you, with all the saints,
   grow in the pow'r to understand
   how he loves you.

3. O how can I explain
   in all its depth and all its scope
   his love, God's love!

The Refrain is not sung after verse 3.

4. For his love is so full,
   it is beyond all we can dream:
   his love, in Christ!

5. And so, glory to him
   working in us, who can do more
   than we can pray!

Text: Damian Lundy (1944-1997) based on Eph. 3:14-21
Music: Gerard Markland (b.1953) arr. Christopher Tambling

688 Though the mountains may fall

Though the moun - tains may fall and the hills turn to dust,

yet the love of the Lord will stand

as a shel - ter for all who will call on his name.

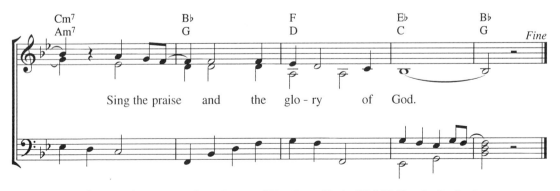

Sing the praise and the glo - ry of God.

1. Could the Lord e - ver leave you? Could the Lord for - get his love?

Though the mo - ther for - sake her child, he will not a - ban - don you.

2. Should you turn and forsake him,
   he will gently call your name.
   Should you wander away from him,
   he will always take you back.

3. Go to him when you're weary;
   he will give you eagle's wings.
   You will run, you will never tire,
   for your God will be your strength.

4. As he swore to your fathers,
   when the flood destroyed the land,
   he will never forsake you;
   he will swear to you again.

Text: Dan Schutte based on Isaiah
Music: Dan Schutte arr. Christopher Tambling

LITURGICAL

HYMNS OLD & NEW

689 Thou, whose almighty word

MOSCOW 664 6664

1. Thou, whose al-migh-ty word cha-os and dark-ness heard, and took their flight; hear us, we hum-bly pray, and where the gos-pel day sheds not its glo-rious ray, let there be light.

2. Thou, who didst come to bring
on thy redeeming wing,
healing and sight,
health to the sick in mind,
sight to the inly blind,
O now to humankind
let there be light.

3. Spirit of truth and love,
life-giving, holy Dove,
speed forth thy flight;
move on the water's face,
bearing the lamp of grace,
and in earth's darkest place
let there be light.

4. Holy and blessèd Three,
glorious Trinity,
Wisdom, Love, Might;
boundless as ocean's tide
rolling in fullest pride,
through the earth far and wide
let there be light.

Text: John Marriott (1780-1825) alt.
Music: melody from Madan's 'Collection' (1769) adapted by Felice de Giardini (1716-1796)

690 Thy hand, O God, has guided

THORNBURY 76 76 D

1. Thy hand, O God, has guid - ed thy flock, from age to age; the wond - rous tale is writ - ten, full clear, on ev - 'ry page; our fore - bears owned thy good - ness, and we their deeds re - cord; and both of this bear wit - ness: one

Church, one Faith, one Lord.

2. Thy heralds brought glad tidings
   to greatest, as to least;
   they bade them rise, and hasten
   to share the great King's feast;
   and this was all their teaching,
   in ev'ry deed and word,
   to all alike proclaiming:
   one Church, one Faith, one Lord.

3. Through many a day of darkness,
   through many a scene of strife,
   the faithful few fought bravely
   to guard the nation's life.
   Their gospel of redemption,
   sin pardoned, hope restored,
   was all in this enfolded:
   one Church, one Faith, one Lord.

4. And we, shall we be faithless?
   Shall hearts fail, hands hang down?
   Shall we evade the conflict,
   and cast away our crown?
   Not so: in God's deep counsels
   some better thing is stored:
   we will maintain, unflinching,
   one Church, one Faith, one Lord.

5. Thy mercy will not fail us,
   nor leave thy work undone;
   with thy right hand to help us,
   the vict'ry shall be won;
   and then by all creation,
   thy name shall be adored.
   And this shall be their anthem:
   One Church, one Faith, one Lord.

Text: Edward Hayes Plumptre (1821-1891) alt.
Music: Basil Harwood (1859-1949)

691 To be in your presence
My desire

1. To be in your pre - sence, to sit at your feet,
where your love sur - rounds me and makes me com - plete.

Refrain
This is my de - sire, O Lord, this is my de - sire,
this is my de - sire, O Lord, this is my de - sire.

2. To rest in your presence,
   not rushing away,
   to cherish each moment,
   here I would stay.

Text and Music: Noel Richards

692 To Christ, the Prince of peace

NARENZA SM

1. To Christ, the Prince of peace, and Son of God most high, the

Fa - ther of the world to come, sing we with ho - ly joy.

2. Deep in his heart for us
   the wound of love he bore;
   that love wherewith he still inflames
   the hearts that him adore.

3. O Jesu, victim blest,
   what else but love divine
   could thee constrain to open thus
   that sacred heart of thine?

4. O fount of endless life,
   O spring of water clear,
   O flame celestial, cleansing all
   who unto thee draw near!

5. Hide us in thy dear heart,
   for thither we do fly;
   where seek thy grace through life, in death
   thine immortality.

6. Praise to the Father be,
   and sole-begotten Son;
   praise, holy Paraclete, to thee,
   while endless ages run.

Text: 'Summi parentis filio' from 'Catholicum Hymnologium' (1587) trans. Edward Caswall (1814-1878)
Music: melody from J. Leisentritt's 'Catholicum Hymnologium Germanicum' (1584)
adapted by William Henry Havergal (1793-1870)

693 To Jesus' heart, all burning

COR JESU 76 76 and Refrain

1. To Jesus' heart, all burn - ing with fer - vent love for men, my heart with fond - est yearn - ing shall raise its joy - ful strain.

Refrain

While a - ges course a - long, blest be with loud - est song the sa - cred heart of Je - sus by ev - 'ry heart and tongue, the sa - cred heart of Je - sus by ev - 'ry heart and tongue.

2. O heart, for me on fire
with love that none can speak,
my yet untold desire
God gives me for thy sake.

3. Too true, I have forsaken
thy love for wilful sin;
yet now let me be taken
back by thy grace again.

4. As thou art meek and lowly,
and ever pure of heart,
so may my heart be wholly
of thine the counterpart.

5. When life away is flying,
and earth's false glare is done,
still, Sacred Heart, in dying,
I'll say I'm all thine own.

Text: 'Dem Herzen Jesu singe' by Aloys Schlör (1805-1852) trans. A.J. Christie (1817-1891) alt.
Music: traditional

694 To you, O Lord, I lift up my soul

Refrain
Unison

To you, O Lord, I lift up my soul, I lift up my soul.

1. Teach me, Lord, your ho-ly ways and help me learn your paths.
Guide my foot-steps in your truth, my Sa-viour and my God.

2. Good and upright is the Lord
   who guides the wand'rer back,
   leads the humble in this path
   and shows the poor his ways.

3. Faithfulness and love abound
   for all who keep his word;
   those who love him have a friend
   whose promise is made clear.

Text: Susan Sayers (b.1946) based on Psalm 24
Music: Andrew Moore (b.1954)
© Copyright 1996 Kevin Mayhew Ltd.

695 To your altar we bring

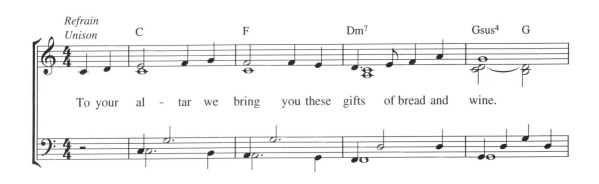

To your al - tar we bring you these gifts of bread and wine.

Take, Lord, re - ceive, make them ho - ly and di - vine. They're our

joys and our hopes, all our fail - ures and our strife.

Take, Lord, and make these gifts our food of life.

1. Take and bless these gifts we of - fer;

make them pleas - ing to you, O Lord.

2. Take these gifts and make them holy
   by the pow'r of your Holy Spirit.

3. They'll become the body and blood
   of your Son, Jesus Christ, our Lord.

Text and Music: Julian Wiener

LITURGICAL

HYMNS OLD & NEW

696 Turn to me

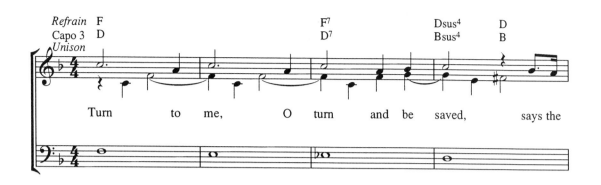

Turn to me, O turn and be saved, says the

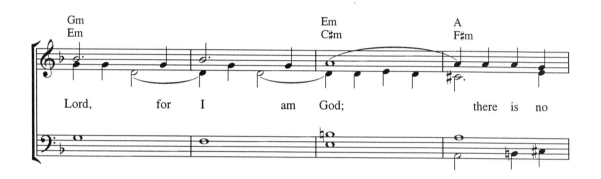

Lord, for I am God; there is no

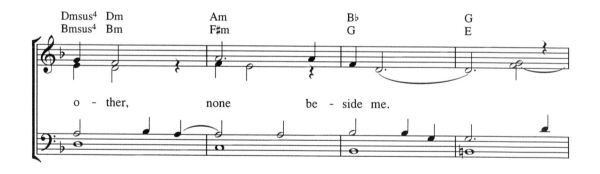

o - ther, none be - side me.

I call your name.

1. I am he that com-forts you;

2. Lis - ten to me, my peo - ple, give

3. Lift up your eyes to the hea - vens, and

F	Fmaj⁷	Dm	Dm⁷
D	Dmaj⁷	Bm	Bm⁷

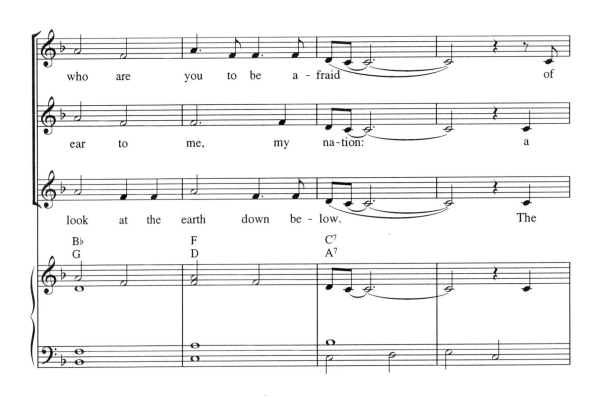

who are you to be a - fraid of

ear to me, my na - tion: a

look at the earth down be - low. The

B♭	F	C⁷
G	D	A⁷

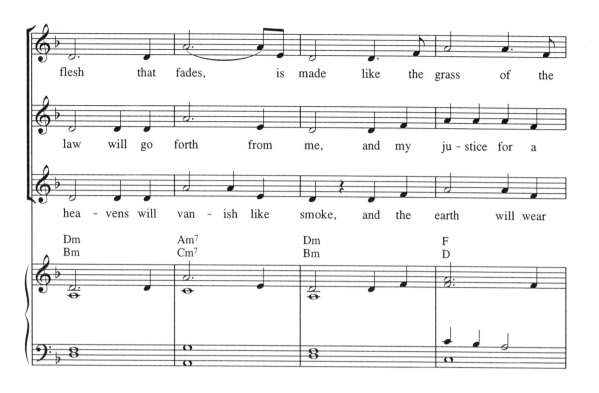

flesh that fades, is made like the grass of the

law will go forth from me, and my ju - stice for a

hea - vens will van - ish like smoke, and the earth will wear

Dm   Am⁷   Dm   F
Bm   Cm⁷   Bm   D

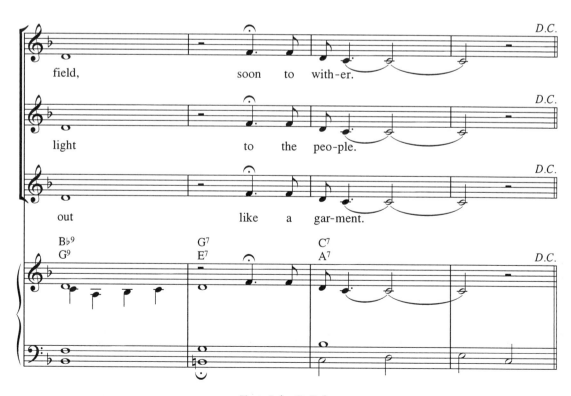

field, soon to with-er.

light to the peo-ple.

out like a gar-ment.

B♭⁹   G⁷   C⁷
G⁹   E⁷   A⁷

Text: John B. Foley
Music: John B. Foley arr. Keith Stent

697 Unless a grain of wheat

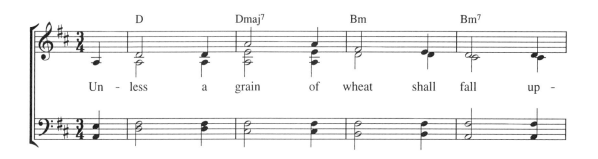

Un - less a grain of wheat shall fall up -

on the ground and die, it re - mains

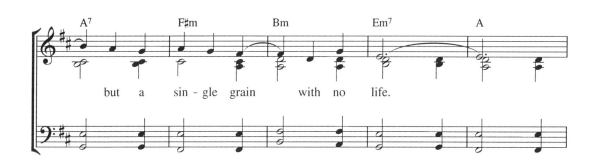

but a sin - gle grain with no life.

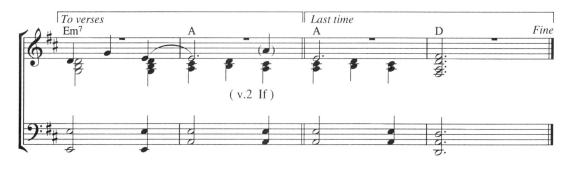

(v.2 If)

Text: based on Scripture
Music: Bernadette Farrell

698 Unto us a boy is born

PUER NOBIS 76 77

Unison

1. Un - to us a boy is born! King of all cre -

a - tion; came he to a world for-lorn, the Lord of ev - 'ry

na - tion, the Lord of ev - 'ry na - tion.

2. Cradled in a stall was he,
   watched by cows and asses;
   but the very beasts could see
   that he the world surpasses,
   that he the world surpasses.

3. Then the fearful Herod cried,
   'Pow'r is mine in Jewry!'
   So the blameless children died
   the victims of his fury,
   the victims of his fury.

4. Now may Mary's Son, who came
   long ago to love us,
   lead us all with hearts aflame
   unto the joys above us,
   unto the joys above us.

5. Omega and Alpha he!
   Let the organ thunder,
   while the choir with peals of glee
   shall rend the air asunder,
   shall rend the air asunder.

Text: 'Puer nobis nascitur' (15th century) trans. Percy Dearmer (1867-1936) alt.
Music: from 'Piae Cantiones' (1582) arr. Adrian Vernon Fish

699 Upon thy table, Lord

DAWBY LM

U - pon thy ta - ble, Lord, we place these sym - bols of our work and thine, life's food won on - ly by thy grace, who giv'st to all the bread and wine.

2. Within these simple things there lie
the height and depth of human life,
the thought of all, our tears and toil,
our hopes and fears, our joy and strife.

3. Accept them, Lord; from thee they come:
we take them humbly at thy hand.
These gifts of thine for higher use
we offer, as thou dost command.

Text: M.F.C. Wilson (1884-1944) alt.
Music: traditional English melody arr. Andrew Moore

700 Vaster far than any ocean

Vaster far than any ocean, deeper than the deepest sea
is the love of Christ my Saviour, reaching through eternity.

2. But my sins are truly many,
   is God's grace so vast, so deep?
   Yes, there's grace o'er sin abounding,
   grace to pardon, grace to keep.

3. Can he quench my thirst for ever?
   Will his Spirit strength impart?
   Yes, he gives me living water,
   springing up within my heart.

Text: unknown
Music: Russian folk melody arr. John Rombaut
This arrangement © Copyright 1973 Kevin Mayhew Ltd.

701 Veni, Creator Spiritus

PLAINSONG (MODE VIII)

1. Ve - ni, Cre - a - tor Spi - ri - tus,
men - tes tu - o - rum vi - si - ta,
im - ple su - per - na gra - ti - a,
quæ tu cre - a - sti pe - cto - ra. A - men.

2. Qui diceris Paraclitus,
Altissimi donum Dei,
fons vivus, ignis, caritas,
et spiritalis unctio.

3. Tu septiformis munere,
digitus paternæ dexteræ,
tu rite promissum Patris,
sermone ditans guttura.

4. Accende lumen sensibus,
infunde amorem cordibus,
infirma nostri corporis
virtute firmans perpeti.

5. Hostem repellas longius,
pacemque dones protinus:
ductore sic te prævio,
vitemus omne noxium.

6. Per te sciamus da Patrem,
noscamus atque Filium,
teque utriusque Spiritum
credamus omni tempore.

7. Deo Patri sit gloria,
et Filio, qui a mortuis
surrexit, ac Paraclito,
in sæculorum sæcula. Amen.

Text: ascribed to Rabanus Maurus (776-856)
Music: Plainsong, accompaniment by Gregory Murray (1905-1992)

702 Veni, Sancte Spiritus

PLAINSONG (MODE I)

1. Ve - ni, San - cte Spi - ri - tus, et e - mit - te cæ - li - tus
2. Ve - ni, pa - ter pau - pe - rum, ve - ni, da - tor mu - ne - rum,

lu - cis tu - æ ra - di - um. 3. Con - so - la - tor op - ti - me,
ve - ni, lu - men cor - di - um. 4. In la - bo - re re - qui - es,

dul - cis hos - pes a - ni - mæ, dul - ce re - fri - ge - ri - um.
in æ - stu tem - pe - ri - es, in fle - tu so - la - ti - um.

5. O lux be - a - tis - si - ma re - ple cor - dis in - ti - ma
6. Si - ne tu - o nu - mi - ne, ni - hil est in ho - mi - ne,

tu – o-rum fi-de – li-um. 7. La-va quod est sor – di-dum,
ni – hil est in-no – xi-um. 8. Fle-cte quod est ri – gi-dum,

ri-ga quod est a – ri-dum, sa-na quod est sau-ci-um.
fo-ve quod est fri – gi-dum, re-ge quod est de-vi-um.

9. Da tu-is fi-de-li-bus, in te con-fi-den-ti-bus,
10. Da vir-tu-tis me-ri-tum, da sa-lu-tis ex-i-tum,

sa-crum sep-te-na-ri-um. A – men. Al-le-lu – ia.
da pe-ren-ne gau-di-um.

Text: sequence for Pentecost Sunday ascribed to Stephen Langton (d.1228)
Music: Plainsong (13th century), accompaniment by Gregory Murray (1905-1992)

703 Victimae Paschali laudes

PLAINSONG (MODE I)

1. Vic - ti - mæ Pa - scha - li lau - des im - mo - lent Chri - sti - a - ni.

2. A - gnus re - de - mit o - ves: Chri - stus in - no - cens Pa - tri

re - con - ci - li - a - vit pec - ca - to - res.

3. Mors et vi - ta du - el - lo con - fli - xe - re mi - ran - do:

dux vi - tae mor - tu - us, reg - nat vi - vus.

Text: attributed to Wipo (c.1030)
Music: Plainsong arr. Andrew Moore

LITURGICAL

HYMNS OLD & NEW

704 Waken, O sleeper, wake and rise

BILLING CM

1. Wa - ken, O sleep - er, wake and rise, sal - va - tion's day is near, and let the dawn of light and truth dis - pel the night of fear.

A lower setting will be found at No. 582

2. Let us prepare to face the day
of judgement and of grace,
to live as people of the light,
and perfect truth embrace.

3. Watch then and pray, we cannot know
the moment or the hour,
when Christ, unheralded, will come
with life-renewing power.

4. Then shall the nations gather round
to learn his ways of peace,
when spears to pruning-hooks are turned
and all our conflicts cease.

Text: Michael Forster (b.1946)
Music: Richard Runciman Terry (1865-1938)

705 Wake up, O people

2. The night of sin has passed. Wake up!
   The light is near at last. Wake up!
   The day star, Christ, the Son of God, will soon appear.

3. To live in love and peace. Wake up!
   To let all quarrels cease. Wake up!
   To live that all you do may stand the light of day.

4. That Christ may be your shield. Wake up!
   That death to life may yield. Wake up!
   That heaven's gate be opened wide again for you.

Text: Marie Lydia Pereira (b.1920) from Romans 13:11-14
Music: Marie Lydia Pereira (b.1920) arr. Christopher Tambling

706 Walk with me, O my Lord

2. Stones often bar my path
   and there are times I fall,
   but you are always there
   to help me when I call.

3. Just as you calmed the wind
   and walked upon the sea,
   conquer, my living Lord,
   the storms that threaten me.

4. Help me to pierce the mists
   that cloud my heart and mind,
   so that I shall not fear
   the steepest mountain-side.

5. As once you healed the lame
   and gave sight to the blind,
   help me when I'm downcast
   to hold my head up high.

Text and Music: Estelle White (b.1925)

LITURGICAL

HYMNS OLD & NEW

707 We are gathering together

1. We are ga-ther-ing to-ge-ther un-to him. We are ga-ther-ing to-ge-ther un-to him. Un-to him shall the gath-'ring of the peo-ple be, we are ga-ther-ing to-ge-ther un-to him.

2. We are offering together unto him.
   We are offering together unto him.
   Unto him shall the off'ring of the people be,
   we are offering together unto him.

3. We are singing together unto him.
   We are singing together unto him.
   Unto him shall the singing of the people be,
   we are singing together unto him.

4. We are praying together unto him.
   We are praying together unto him.
   Unto him shall the praying of the people be,
   we are praying together unto him.

Text: unknown
Music: traditional melody arr. Christopher Tambling

708 We are his children
Go forth in his name

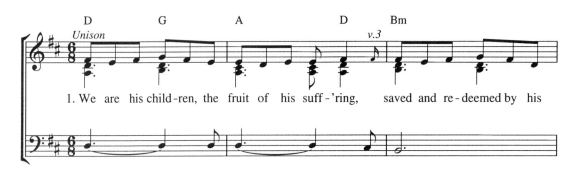

1. We are his child-ren, the fruit of his suff-'ring, saved and re-deemed by his

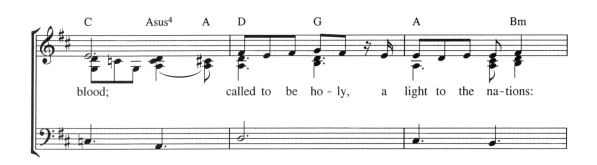

blood; called to be ho-ly, a light to the na-tions:

clothed with his pow'r, filled with his love.

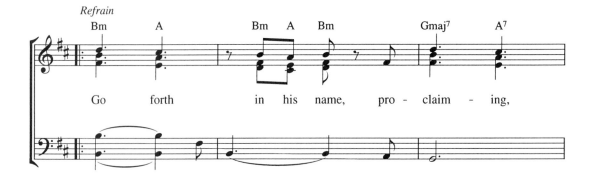

Refrain

Go forth in his name, pro-claim-ing,

'Je - sus reigns!' Now is the time for the church to a - rise and pro-

claim him 'Je - sus, Sa - viour, Re - deem - er and Lord.'

2. Countless the souls that are stumbling in darkness,
   why do we sleep in the light?
   Jesus commands us to go make disciples,
   this is our case, this is our fight.

3. Listen, the wind of the Spirit is blowing,
   the end of the age is so near;
   powers in the earth and the heavens are shaking,
   Jesus our Lord soon shall appear!

Text and Music: Graham Kendrick (b.1950)

LITURGICAL
HYMNS OLD & NEW

709 We are his people

Response

We are his peo - ple, the

sheep of his flock, his peo - ple, the sheep of his flock. *Fine*

1. Shout with glad-ness to God all the earth, joy - ful-ly o - bey him.

D.C.

Come and ga - ther be-fore him now, sing-ing songs of glad - ness.

2. Understand that the Lord is our God;
   he it is who made us.
   We his people belong to him,
   he our loving shepherd.

3. O how faithful and good is the Lord,
   loving us for ever;
   rich in mercy and faithfulness,
   true through all the ages.

Text: Susan Sayers (b.1946) based on Psalm 99
Music: Andrew Moore (b.1954)
© Copyright 1995 Kevin Mayhew Ltd.

710 We are marching

Text: traditional South African trans. Anders Nyberg
Music: traditional South African arr. Anders Nyberg

711 We behold the splendour of God

Text: Carey Landry
Music: Carey Landry arr. Christopher Tambling

LiTURGiCAL

HYMNS OLD & NEW

712 We believe

KENTSTOWN 87 87 87

Unison

1. We be-lieve in one al-migh-ty God and Fa-ther of us all,
ma - ker of the earth and hea-ven, hold-ing worlds and stars in thrall.
All things seen and all things un-seen come to be - ing at his call.

2. We believe in one Redeemer,
   Christ, the Father's only Son.
   Timelessly in love begotten,
   through him all God's work is done.
   Light from Light and God from Godhead,
   with the Father's Being, one.

3. All for us and our salvation,
   Christ his glory set aside,
   by the Holy Spirit's power,
   and the womb of virgin bride;
   suffered under Pilate's sentence,
   for our sake was crucified.

4. He has burst the grave asunder,
   rising as the prophets said;
   seated in the Father's presence,
   he is our exalted head.
   He will come again with glory,
   judge the living and the dead.

5. We acclaim the Holy Spirit,
   of all life the source and Lord;
   with the Son and Father worshipped,
   ever honoured and adored;
   speaking through the holy prophets,
   pow'r of sacrament and word.

6. Holy Church, and universal,
   apostolic company!
   In one sacrament forgiven,
   signed by water, his to be.
   In the resurrection body
   we shall share eternity.

Text: Michael Forster (b.1946) based on the Creed
Music: Colin Mawby (b.1936)

713 We cannot measure

YE BANKS AND BRAES DLM

1. We can-not mea-sure how you heal or ans-wer ev-'ry suff-'rer's prayer, yet we be-lieve your grace res-ponds where faith and doubt un-ite to care. Your hands, though blood-ied on the cross, sur-vive to hold and

heal and warn, to car - ry all through death to

life and cra - dle child - ren yet un - born.

2. The pain that will not go away,
   the guilt that clings from things long past,
   the fear of what the future holds,
   are present as if meant to last.
   But present too is love which tends
   the hurt we never hoped to find,
   the private agonies inside,
   the memories that haunt the mind.

3. So some have come who need your help
   and some have come to make amends,
   as hands which shaped and saved the world
   are present in the touch of friends.
   Lord, let your Spirit meet us here
   to mend the body, mind and soul,
   to disentangle peace from pain
   and make your broken people whole.

Text: The Iona Community
Music: traditional Scottish melody arr. John L.Bell (b.1949) and Graham Maule (b.1958)

714 We celebrate the new creation

ST CLEMENT 98 98

1. We ce - le - brate the new cre - a - tion, to God, in
Christ, now re - con - ciled, and re - cog - nise our full sal -
va - tion in him whom peo - ple once re - viled.

A higher setting will be found at No.563

2. In token of our liberation,
   within God's presence now we stand,
   to share the banquet of salvation,
   the harvest of the promised land.

3. The news of reconciliation
   is now entrusted to our care;
   so spread the word throughout creation,
   the feast is here for all to share.

4. Begin the joyful celebration:
   the lost return, the dead arise,
   to see the light of exultation
   which shines from God's forgiving eyes.

Text: Michael Forster (b.1946) based on 2 Corinthians 5:17-21
Music: Clement Cotterill Scholefield (1839-1904)

715 We celebrate this festive day

FESTIVE DAY 86 86 and Refrain

1. We ce-le-brate this fes-tive day with pray'r and joy-ful song. Our
Fa-ther's house is home to us, we know that we be-long.
Refrain The bread is bro-ken, wine is poured, a feast to lift us up! Then
thank the Lord who gives him-self as food and sa-ving cup!

2. The door is open, enter in,
and take your place by right.
For you've been chosen as his guest
to share his love and light.

3. We come together as the twelve
came to the Upper Room.
Our host is Jesus Christ the Lord,
now risen from the tomb.

4. Who travels needs both food and drink
to help them on their way.
Refreshed and strong we'll journey on
and face another day.

5. Who shares this meal receives the Lord
who lives, though he was dead.
So death can hold no terrors now
for those who eat his bread.

Text: Willard F. Jabusch (b.1930)
Music: melody by Johann Sebastian Bach (1685-1750)
adapted by Willard F. Jabusch (b.1950) arr. Andrew Moore

LITURGICAL

HYMNS OLD & NEW

716 We have a dream

WOODLANDS 10 10 10 10

2. We have a dream that one day we shall see
a world of justice, truth and equity,
where children of the slaves and of the free
will share the banquet of community.

3. We have a dream of deserts brought to flow'r,
once made infertile by oppression's heat,
when love and truth shall end oppressive pow'r,
and streams of righteousness and justice meet.

4. We have a dream: our children shall be free
from judgements based on colour or on race;
free to become whatever they may be,
of their own choosing in the light of grace.

5. We have a dream that truth will overcome
the fear and anger of our present day;
that black and white will share a common home,
and hand in hand will walk the pilgrim way.

6. We have a dream: each valley will be raised,
and ev'ry mountain, ev'ry hill brought down;
then shall creation echo perfect praise,
and share God's glory under freedom's crown!

Text: Michael Forster (b.1946) based on the speech by Martin Luther King Jr.
Music: Walter Greatorex (1877-1949)

717 We hold a treasure
Earthen vessels

Refrain

We hold a trea - sure, not made of gold, in earth - en ves - sels, wealth un - told; one trea - sure on - ly: the Lord, the Christ, in earth - en ves - sels. - sels.

1. Light has shone in our dark-ness; God has shone in our heart, with the light of the glo-ry of Je - sus, the Lord.

2. He has chosen the lowly,
who are small in this world;
in his weakness is glory,
in Jesus the Lord.

Text: John Foley based on 2 Corinthians 4 and 1 Corinthians 1
Music: John Foley arr. Christopher Tambling

718 We plough the fields and scatter

WIR PFLÜGEN 76 76 D and Refrain

1. We plough the fields and scat - ter the good seed on the land, but it is fed and wa - tered by God's al - migh - ty hand: he sends the snow in win - ter, the warmth to swell the grain, the breez - es and the sun - shine, and soft, re - fresh - ing rain.

Refrain

All good gifts a - round us are sent from heav'n a - bove; then

thank the Lord, O thank the Lord, for all his love.

2. He only is the maker
   of all things near and far;
   he paints the wayside flower,
   he lights the evening star;
   he fills the earth with beauty,
   by him the birds are fed;
   much more to us, his children,
   he gives our daily bread.

3. We thank thee then, O Father,
   for all things bright and good:
   the seed-time and the harvest,
   our life, our health, our food.
   Accept the gifts we offer
   for all thy love imparts,
   and, what thou most desirest,
   our humble, thankful hearts.

Text: Matthias Claudius (1740-1815) trans. Jane Montgomery Campbell (1817-1878) alt.
Music: Johann Abraham Peter Schulz (1747-1800) harmonised by John Bacchus Dykes (1823-1876)

LITURGICAL

HYMNS OLD & NEW

719 Were you there when they crucified my Lord?

WERE YOU THERE 10 10 14 10

2. Were you there when they nailed him to a tree? . . .

3. Were you there when they pierced him in the side? . . .

4. Were you there when they laid him in the tomb? . . .

5. Were you there when he rose to glorious life? . . .

Text: Spiritual alt.
Music: Spiritual arr. Richard Lloyd
This arrangement © Copyright 1996 Kevin Mayhew Ltd.

720 We shall draw water joyfully

Text and Music: Paul Inwood (b.1947)

LITURGICAL

HYMNS OLD & NEW

721 We shall stay awake
Advent acclamations

Advent 1
We shall stay a-wake and pray at all times, rea - dy to wel-come
Christ, the Prince of Jus - tice. We shall set a - side all
fears and wor - ries, rea - dy to wel - come Christ, the Prince of Peace.

Advent 2
We shall set our sights on what is righteous,
ready to welcome Christ, the Prince of Justice.
We shall smooth the path, prepare the Lord's way,
ready to welcome Christ, the Prince of Peace.

Advent 3
We shall plunge into the saving water,
ready to welcome Christ, the Prince of Justice.
We shall be reborn and rise to new life,
ready to welcome Christ, the Prince of Peace.

Advent 4
We shall hold with faith to what God promised,
ready to welcome Christ, the Prince of Justice.
We shall be attentive to his Spirit,
ready to welcome Christ, the Prince of Peace.

Text: Pierre-Marie Hoog and Robert B. Kelly (b.1948)
Music: Jacques Berthier (1923-1994)

722 We three kings of Orient are

KINGS OF ORIENT 88 86 and Refrain

1. We three kings of O - ri - ent are; bear - ing
gifts we tra - verse a - far; field and foun - tain,
moor and moun - tain, fol - low - ing yon - der star.

Refrain

O star of won - der, star of night,
star with roy - al beau - ty bright, west - ward lead - ing,

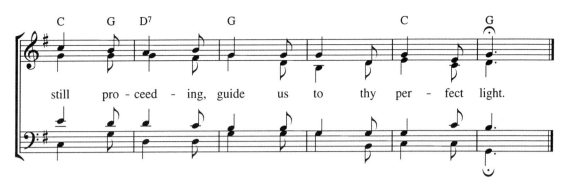

still pro - ceed - ing, guide us to thy per - fect light.

2. Born a King on Bethlehem plain,
gold I bring, to crown him again,
King for ever, ceasing never,
over us all to reign.

3. Frankincense to offer have I,
incense owns a Deity nigh,
prayer and praising, gladly raising,
worship him, God most high.

4. Myrrh is mine, its bitter perfume
breathes a life of gathering gloom;
sorrowing, sighing, bleeding, dying,
sealed in the stone-cold tomb.

5. Glorious now behold him arise,
King and God and sacrifice;
alleluia, alleluia,
earth to heav'n replies.

Text and Music: John Henry Hopkins (1820-1891) alt.

723 What child is this

GREENSLEEVES 87 87 68 67

1. What child is this who, laid to rest, on Ma-ry's lap is sleep-ing? Whom an-gels greet with an-thems sweet, while shep-herds watch are keep-ing? This, this is Christ the King, whom shep-herds guard and an-gels sing: come, greet the in-fant Lord, the babe, the Son of Ma-ry!

2. Why lies he in such mean estate,
   where ox and ass are feeding?
   Good Christians, fear: for sinners here
   the silent Word is pleading.
   Nails, spear, shall pierce him through,
   the cross be borne for me, for you;
   hail, hail the Word made flesh,
   the babe, the Son of Mary!

3. So bring him incense, gold and myrrh,
   come rich and poor, to own him.
   The King of kings salvation brings,
   let loving hearts enthrone him.
   Raise, raise the song on high,
   the Virgin sings her lullaby:
   joy, joy for Christ is born,
   the babe, the Son of Mary!

Text: William Chatterton Dix (1837-1898) alt.
Music: traditional English melody arr. John Stainer (1840-1901)

724 What feast of love

GREENSLEEVES 87 87 68 67

1. What feast of love is of-fered here, what ban-quet come from hea - ven? What
food of e - ver-last - ing life, what gra-cious gift is giv - en?
This, this is Christ the King, the bread come down from hea - ven.
O taste and see and sing! How sweet the man - na giv - en!

2. What light of truth is offered here,
what covenant from heaven?
What hope of everlasting life,
what wondrous word is given?
This, this is Christ the King,
the Sun come down from heaven.
O see, and list'ning, sing!
The Word of God is given!

3. What wine of love is offered here,
what crimson drink from heaven?
What stream of everlasting life,
what precious blood is given?
This, this is Christ the King,
the sweetest wine of heaven.
O taste and see and sing!
The Son of God is given!

Text: Delores Dufner
Music: Traditional English melody arr. John Stainer (1840-1901)

725 What kind of greatness

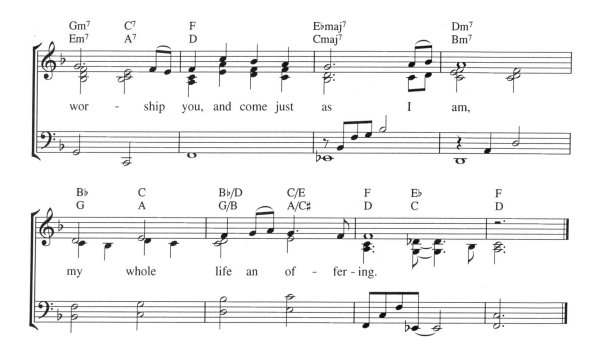

wor - ship you, and come just as I am,

my whole life an of - fer-ing.

2. The One in whom we live and move
   in swaddling cloths lies bound.
   The voice that cried, 'Let there be light',
   asleep without a sound.
   The One who strode among the stars,
   and called each one by name,
   lies helpless in a mother's arms
   and must learn to walk again.

3. What greater love could he have shown
   to shamed humanity,
   yet human pride hates to believe
   in such deep humility.
   But nations now may see his grace
   and know that he is near,
   when his meek heart, his words, his works
   are incarnate in us here.

Text and Music: Graham Kendrick (b.1950)

726 Whatsoever you do

Refrain
Unison

What-so-e-ver you do to the least of my peo-ple, that you do un-to me. 1. When I was hun-gry you gave me to eat. When I was thir-sty you gave me to drink. Now en-ter in-to the home of my Fa - ther.

2. When I was homeless you opened your door.
   When I was naked you gave me your coat.
   Now enter into the home of my Father.

3. When I was weary you helped me find rest.
   When I was anxious you calmed all my fears.
   Now enter into the home of my Father.

4. When in a prison you came to my cell.
   When on a sick-bed you cared for my needs.
   Now enter into the home of my Father.

5. When I was aged you bothered to smile.
   When I was restless you listened and cared.
   Now enter into the home of my Father.

6. When I was laughed at you stood by my side.
   When I was happy you shared in my joy.
   Now enter into the home of my Father.

Text: Willard F. Jabusch (b.1930)
Music: Willard F. Jabusch (b.1930) arr. Christopher Tambling

727 When Christ our Lord to Andrew cried

ST ANDREW DCM

1. When Christ our Lord to And - rew cried: 'Come, thou and fol - low me,' the fish - er left his net be-side the Sea of Ga - li - lee. To teach the truth his Mas - ter taught, to tread the path he trod was all his will, and thus he brought un - num - bered souls to God.

2. When Andrew's hour had come, and he
   was doomed like Christ to die,
   he kissed his cross exultingly,
   and this his loving cry:
   'O noble cross! O precious wood!
   I long have yearned for thee;
   uplift me to my only good
   who died on thee for me.'

3. Saint Andrew, now in bliss above,
   thy fervent prayers renew
   that Scotland yet again may love
   the faith, entire and true;
   that I the cross allotted me
   may bear with patient love!
   'Twill lift me, as it lifted thee,
   to reign with Christ above.

Text: E.M. Barrett
Music: traditional

728 When from bondage we are summoned

FREEDOM 87 87 D

1. When from bond-age we are sum-moned out of dark-ness in-to light, we must go in hope and pa-tience, walk by faith and not by sight.

Refrain
Let us throw off all that hin-ders; let us run the race to win! Let us has-ten to our home-land and, re-joic-ing, en-ter in.

2. When our God names us a people,
   Jesus leads us by the hand
   through a lonely, barren desert,
   to a great and glorious land.

3. Through all stages of the journey
   Christ is with us, night and day,
   with compassion for our weakness
   ev'ry step along the way.

4. We must not lose sight of Jesus
   who accepted pain and loss;
   who, for joy of love unmeasured,
   dared embrace the shameful cross.

5. See the prize our God has promised:
   endless life with with Christ the Lord.
   Now we fix our eyes on Jesus
   walk by faith in Jesus' word.

Text: Delores Dufner
Music: Jay F. Hunstiger

729 When I feel the touch

When I feel the touch of your hand up-on my life, it caus-es

me to sing a song that I love you, Lord.

So from deep with - in my spi-rit sing - eth un - to thee, you are my

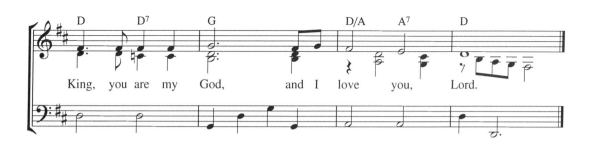

King, you are my God, and I love you, Lord.

Text and Music: Keri Jones and David Matthew

LITURGICAL

HYMNS OLD & NEW

730 When I needed a neighbour

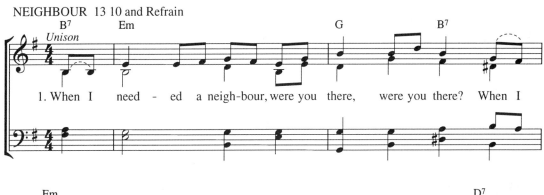

NEIGHBOUR 13 10 and Refrain

1. When I need - ed a neigh-bour, were you there, were you there? When I

need - ed a neigh-bour, were you there? And the

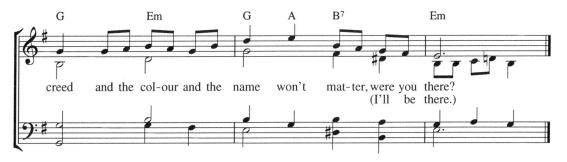

creed and the col-our and the name won't mat-ter, were you there?
(I'll be there.)

2. I was hungry and thirsty,
   were you there, were you there?
   I was hungry and thirsty,
   were you there?

3. I was cold, I was naked,
   were you there, were you there?
   I was cold, I was naked,
   were you there?

4. When I needed a shelter,
   were you there, were you there?
   When I needed a shelter,
   were you there?

5. When I needed a healer,
   were you there, were you there?
   When I needed a healer,
   were you there?

6. Wherever you travel,
   I'll be there, I'll be there,
   wherever you travel,
   I'll be there.

Text: Sydney Carter (b.1915)
Music: Sydney Carter (b.1915) arr. Andrew Moore

731 When I survey the wondrous cross

TUNE 1: ROCKINGHAM LM

1. When I sur-vey the won-drous cross on which the Prince of Glo-ry died, my rich-est gain I count but loss, and pour con-tempt on all my pride.

A lower setting will be found at No. 480

2. Forbid it, Lord, that I should boast,
   save in the death of Christ, my God:
   all the vain things that charm me most,
   I sacrifice them to his blood.

3. See from his head, his hands, his feet,
   sorrow and love flow mingling down:
   did e'er such love and sorrow meet,
   or thorns compose so rich a crown?

4. Were the whole realm of nature mine,
   that were an off'ring far too small;
   love so amazing, so divine,
   demands my soul, my life, my all.

TUNE 2: O WALY WALY LM

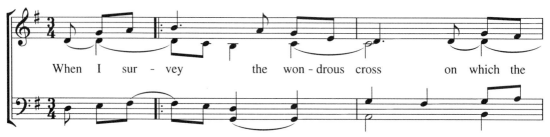

When I sur-vey the won-drous cross on which the

Text: Isaac Watts (1674-1748)
Music: Tune 1 – adapted by Edward Miller (1735-1807)
Tune 2 – Somerset folk song collected by Cecil Sharp (1859-1924) arr. Richard Lloyd

732 When the time came

1. When the time came to stretch out his arms,
and to lay down his life for his friends,
God's only Son, in breaking the bread,
gave his own flesh as food for us all;
gave his own flesh as food for us all.

2. This is my flesh, O take it and eat.
   This is my blood, O take it and drink,
   and to proclaim my death for you all,
   this must you do until I return,
   this must you do until I return.

3. Hunger and thirst no longer we fear,
   Christ's holy flesh becomes now our food.
   And when we raise his chalice to drink,
   joy overflows, our hope is renewed,
   joy overflows, our hope is renewed.

4. O bread of life, O banquet divine,
   sign of the love that makes us all one;
   we who now share this gift from above,
   surely have seen the goodness of God,
   surely have seen the goodness of God.

5. Through Jesus Christ, the perfect high Priest,
   and in the Spirit, source of our peace,
   for this great feast which you have prepared,
   Father above, O praised be your name,
   Father above, O praised be your name.

Text: Didier Rimaud trans. Margaret Foley and Robert B. Kelly (b.1948)
Music: Jo Akepsimas arr. Andrew Moore

LITURGICAL

HYMNS OLD & NEW

733 Where are you bound, Mary

Refrain

Unison

Where are you bound, Ma - ry, Ma - ry, where are you bound, Mo - ther of God?

1. Beau-ty is a dove sit-ting on a sun - lit bough, beau-ty is a prayer with-

out the need of words. Words are more than sounds fall-ing off an emp-ty tongue:

let it be ac - cor-ding to his word.

2. Mary heard the word spoken in her inmost heart.
   Mary bore the Word and held him in her arms.
   Sorrow she has known, seeing him upon the cross:
   greater joy to see him rise again.

3. Where are we all bound, carrying the Word of God?
   Time and place are ours to make his glory known.
   Mary bore him first, we will tell the whole wide world:
   let it be according to his word.

Text: John Glynn (b.1948)
Music: John Glynn (b.1948) arr. Andrew Moore
© Copyright 1976 Kevin Mayhew Ltd.

734 Where is love and loving kindness

Refrain
Unison

Fine

Where is love and lov-ing kind - ness, God is there.

1. The love of Christ has ga-thered us to - ge - ther in one:

D.C.

let us then re - joice and be glad in him.

D.C.

2. Let us fear and love the liv-ing God; let us love each o-ther in the depths of our hearts.

D.C.

3. There-fore when we are to-ge - ther let us take heed not to be di-vid-ed in mind.

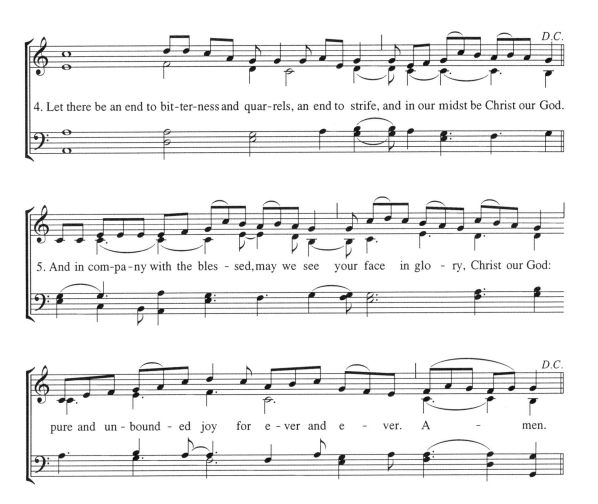

4. Let there be an end to bit-ter-ness and quar-rels, an end to strife, and in our midst be Christ our God.

5. And in com-pa-ny with the bles - sed, may we see your face in glo - ry, Christ our God:

pure and un - bound - ed joy for e - ver and e - ver. A - men.

Text: based on 'Ubi Caritas'
Music: Alan Rees (b.1941)

735 Where love and charity endure

Refrain
Unison

Where love and char-i-ty en-dure, God dwells there-in. *Fine*

1. The love of Christ has bound us all in-to one

fold: let us re-joice and ren-der thanks for his great love. *D.C.*

2. Let us revere and love the ever-living God,
   and by our love for one another prove that love.

3. It is together in one Body that we live:
   make sure that we do not divide it by our deeds.

4. May conflicts, quarrels, bitterness all disappear:
   let Jesus Christ be ever-present in our midst.

5. In heav'n amid the saints may we behold you, Lord,
   and there before the Father's throne your love enjoy.

6. Thus may we have unending happiness and joy
   in heav'n with God through endless ages evermore.

Text: Jean-Paul Lécot (b.1947) based on 'Ubi caritas', trans. W.R. Lawrence (1925-1997)
Music: Paul Décha
© Copyright 1988 Kevin Mayhew Ltd.

736 Where the love of Christ unites us

AR HYD Y NOS 84 84 88 84

1. Where the love of Christ u-nites us, there God is found.

When we meet as love in-vites us, there God is found.

Let us come with ju - bi-la - tion to the God of our sal-va - tion;

love en- li - vens all cre-a - tion; there God is found.

A higher setting will be found at No. 232

2. Where we meet without division,
   there God is found,
   free from anger and derision,
   there God is found.
   Let all bitter feuds be ended,
   strife resolved and foes befriended,
   pride and fear by love transcended:
   there God is found.

3. Where the blessèd live for ever,
   there God is found;
   bonds of love no pain can sever,
   there God is found.
   Christ in glory, we implore you,
   let us with the saints adore you,
   love resplendent flows before you;
   there God is found.

Text: Michael Forster (b.1946) based on 'Ubi Caritas'
Music: traditional Welsh melody arr. Colin Hand
Text and this arrangement © Copyright 1993 Kevin Mayhew Ltd.

737 Where true love is found with charity

UBI CARITAS 12 12 12 12 and Refrain

1. Where true love is found with cha-ri-ty, God is pre-sent there.

Christ's own love has called us, ga-thered us to-ge-ther,

Let us come with songs of hope and ju-bi-la-tion,

wor-ship and a-dore him, God of our sal-va-tion,

lov-ing one a-no-ther, lov-ing one a-no-ther.

2. Where true love is found with charity,
   God is present there.
   As his holy people, gathering together,
   let us be united, strife and discord ending.
   Christ, our God, among us, ev'ry fear transcending,
   known in one another, known in one another.

3. Where true love is found with charity,
   God is present there.
   With the saints and martyrs, one in faith together,
   let us see your glory, Christ our great salvation,
   sharing in the great eternal celebration,
   there with one another, there with one another.

Text: Michael Forster (b.1946) based on 'Ubi Caritas'
Music: Gregory Murray (1905-1992) arr. Andrew Moore

738 Where true love is present
Leave your gift

MAKE PEACE 65 65 and Refrain

1. Where true love is pre-sent, God is pre-sent there.

When we meet to-ge-ther let all quar-rels cease.

Refrain

Leave your gift, and make peace with each o-ther.

Leave your gift, and make peace with each o-ther.

2. God is loving kindness;
   those who love like him
   live in God most truly,
   and he lives in them.

3. Let us put behind us
   bitterness and strife,
   recognising Jesus
   present in our midst.

Text: H.J. Richards (b.1921) based on Scripture and 'Ubi Caritas'
Music: Christopher Tambling (b.1964)

739 While shepherds watched

WINCHESTER OLD CM

1. While shep - herds watched their flocks by night, all seat - ed on the ground, the an - gel of the Lord came down, and glo - ry shone a - round.

2. 'Fear not,' said he, (for mighty dread
   had seized their troubled mind)
   'glad tidings of great joy I bring
   to you and all mankind.'

3. 'To you in David's town this day
   is born of David's line
   a Saviour, who is Christ the Lord;
   and this shall be the sign:'

4. 'The heav'nly babe you there shall find
   to human view displayed,
   all meanly wrapped in swathing bands,
   and in a manger laid.'

5. Thus spake the seraph, and forthwith
   appeared a shining throng
   of angels praising God, who thus
   addressed their joyful song:

6. 'All glory be to God on high,
   and on the earth be peace,
   goodwill henceforth from heav'n to all
   begin and never cease.'

Text: Nahum Tate (1652-1715)
Music: from Este's 'Psalter' (1592)

740 Will you come and follow me
The Summons

KELVINGROVE 76 76 77 76

1. Will you come and fol-low me if I but call your name? Will you go where you don't know, and ne-ver be the same? Will you let my love be shown, will you let my name be known, will you let my life be grown in you, and you in me?

2. Will you leave yourself behind
   if I but call your name?
   Will you care for cruel and kind,
   and never be the same?
   Will you risk the hostile stare
   should your life attract or scare,
   will you let me answer prayer
   in you, and you in me?

3. Will you let the blinded see
   if I but call your name?
   Will you set the pris'ners free,
   and never be the same?
   Will you kiss the leper clean
   and do such as this unseen,
   and admit to what I mean
   in you, and you in me?

4. Will you love the 'you' you hide
   if I but call your name?
   Will you quell the fear inside,
   and never be the same?
   Will you use the faith you've found
   to reshape the world around
   through my sight and touch and sound
   in you, and you in me?

5. Lord, your summons echoes true
   when you but call my name.
   Let me turn and follow you,
   and never be the same.
   In your company I'll go
   where your love and footsteps show.
   Thus I'll move and live and grow
   in you, and you in me.

Text: John L. Bell (b.1949) and Graham Maule (b.1958)
Music: traditional Scottish melody arr. Christopher Tambling

741 With the Lord there is mercy

2. If you only saw our guilt, Lord, who would live?
   But forgiveness flows from you, and so we praise your name.

3. How my soul awaits the Lord! In him I trust.
   Longingly I wait for him as watchers for the dawn.

4. Since our great forgiving God comes to redeem,
   all his people will be saved from all their sin and shame.

Text: Susan Sayers (b.1946) based on Psalm 129
Music: Andrew Moore (b.1954)

742 With you, O God

Response

1. With you, O God, my high - est good,
with you
(with you I am se - cure.)
I am se - cure.
With you, I am al - ways with you, my God,
you hold me tight, your hand in mine.

2. All things come to their fulfilment in you;
   you lead me on in your great love.

3. Heaven, what is that if you are not there?
   And here on earth you are my joy.

4. And when life on earth has come to an end,
   then I will be with you, my God.

Text: Huub Oosterhuis based on Psalm 72
Music: Frances M. Kelly (b.1952) arr. Christopher Tambling

LITURGICAL

HYMNS OLD & NEW

743 Word made flesh

2. Lord and Saviour, Son of God.

3. Prince of Peace, Son of God.

4. Alleluia, Son of God.

5. Bread of Life, Son of God.

6. Light of the World, Son of God.

7. Jesus Christ, Son of God.

Text: Virginia Vissing
Music: Virginia Vissing arr. Christopher Tambling

744 Yahweh, I know you are near

Refrain
Unison

Yah-weh, I know you are near, stand-ing al-ways at my side. You guard me from the foe and you lead me in ways e-ver-last-ing.

1. Lord, you have searched my heart, and you know when I sit and when I stand, Your hand is up-on me, pro-tec-ting me from death,

keep-ing me from harm.

2. Where can I run from your love?
   If I climb to the heavens you are there.
   If I fly to the sunrise or sail beyond the sea,
   still I'd find you there.

3. You know my heart and its ways,
   you who formed me before I was born,
   in the secret of darkness, before I saw the sun
   in my mother's womb.

4. Marv'llous to me are your works;
   how profound are your thoughts, my Lord!
   Even if I could count them, they number as the stars,
   you would still be there.

Text: Dan Schutte based on Psalm 138
Music: Dan Schutte arr. Christopher Tambling

745 Yahweh is the God of my salvation

Yah-weh is the God of my sal-va-tion: I trust in him and have no fear. I sing of the joy which his love gives to me, and I draw deep-ly from the springs of his great kind-ness.

1. O - pen our eyes to the won - der of this mo - ment, the be -
2. Be with us, Lord, as we break through with each o - ther to
3. When ev - 'ning comes, and our day of toil is o - ver, give us
4. Take us be - yond the vi - sion of this day to the

Dm   B♭   C⁷
Bm   G   A⁷

gin - ning of a - no - ther day.
find the truth and beau - ty of each friend.
rest, O Lord, in the joy of ma - ny friends.
deep and wide ways of your in - fi - nite love and life.

Dm   B♭   C⁷
Bm   G   A⁷

D.C.

Text: Gregory Norbet based on Isaiah 12
Music: Gregory Norbet arr. Andrew Moore

746 Ye choirs of new Jerusalem

ST FULBERT CM

1. Ye choirs of new Je - ru - sa - lem, your sweet - est notes em - ploy, the

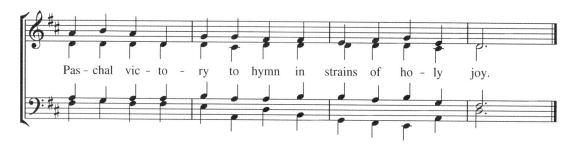

Pas - chal vic - to - ry to hymn in strains of ho - ly joy.

2. For Judah's Lion burst his chains,
   and crushed the serpent's head;
   and brought with him, from death's domain,
   the long-imprisoned dead.

3. From hell's devouring jaws the prey
   alone our leader bore;
   his ransomed hosts pursue their way
   where he hath gone before.

4. Triumphant in his glory now
   his sceptre ruleth all:
   earth, heav'n and hell before him bow
   and at his footstool fall.

5. While joyful thus his praise we sing,
   his mercy we implore,
   into his palace bright to bring,
   and keep us evermore.

6. All glory to the Father be,
   all glory to the Son,
   all glory, Holy Ghost, to thee,
   while endless ages run.

Text: 'Chorus novæ Jerusalem' by St Fulbert of Chartres (c.1028) trans. Robert Campbell (1814-1868)
Music: Henry John Gauntlett (1805-1876)

747 Ye sons and daughters of the Lord

O FILLII ET FILIAE 888 and Alleluias

Al - le - lu - ia, al - le - lu - ia, al - le - lu - ia.

1. Ye sons and daugh - ters of the Lord, the King of glo - ry,

King a - dored, this day him - self from death re - stored. Al - le - lu - ia.

2. All in the early morning grey
went holy women on their way
to see the tomb where Jesus lay.
Alleluia.

3. Then straightway one in white they see,
who saith, 'Ye seek the Lord; but he
is ris'n, and gone to Galilee.'
Alleluia.

4. That self-same night, while out of fear
the doors were shut, their Lord most dear
to his apostles did appear.
Alleluia.

5. But Thomas, when of this he heard,
was doubtful of his brethren's word;
wherefore again there comes the Lord.
Alleluia.

6. 'Thomas, behold my side,' saith he;
'my hands, my feet, my body see,
and doubt not, but believe in me.'
Alleluia.

7. When Thomas saw that wounded side,
the truth no longer he denied:
'Thou art my Lord and God!' he cried.
Alleluia.

8. Now let us praise the Lord most high,
and strive his name to magnify
on this great day, through earth and sky.
Alleluia.

Text: Jean Tisserand (d.1494) trans. Edward Caswall (1814-1878)
Music: Samuel Webbe (1740-1816) arr. Andrew Moore
This arrangement © Copyright 1999 Kevin Mayhew Ltd.

748 You are beautiful
I stand in awe

You are beau-ti-ful be-yond de-scrip - tion, too mar-vel-lous for words, too won-der-ful for com-pre-hen- - sion, like no-thing e - ver seen or heard. Who can grasp your in-fi-nite wis - dom? Who can

Words and Music: Mark Altrogge

749 You are salt for the earth
Bring forth the kingdom

1. You are salt for the earth, O peo-ple: salt for the

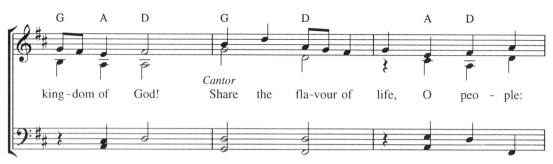

king-dom of God! Share the fla-vour of life, O peo - ple:

life in the king-dom of God! Bring forth the

king-dom of mer - cy, bring forth the king-dom of peace;

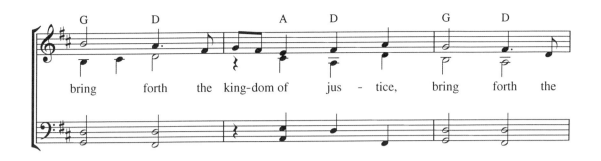

bring   forth   the   king-dom of   jus   -   tice,   bring   forth   the

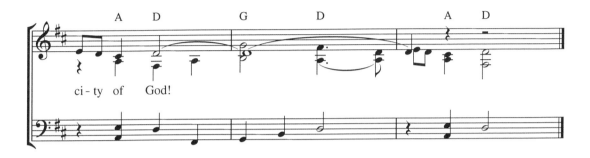

ci - ty   of   God!

2. You are a light on the hill, O people:
   light for the city of God!
   Shine so holy and bright, O people:
   shine for the kingdom of God!

3. You are a seed of the Word, O people:
   bring forth the kingdom of God!
   Seeds of mercy and seeds of justice,
   grow in the kingdom of God!

4. We are a blest and a pilgrim people:
   bound for the kingdom of God!
   Love our journey and love our homeland:
   love is the kingdom of God!

Text and Music: Marty Haugen (b.1950)

750 You are the King of Glory
Hosanna to the Son of David

You are the King of Glo-ry, you are the Prince of Peace, you are the Lord of heav'n and earth, you're the Son of right-eous-ness. An-gels bow down be-fore you, wor-ship and a-dore, for you have the words of e-ter-nal life, you are Je-sus Christ the

Text and Music: Mavis Ford

751 You are the light
Enfold me in your love

1. You are the light that is e- ver bright,
you fill my heart, giv- ing life;
you give the work I en- dea- vour to do,
mean- ing and pur- pose are bles- sings from you. O

hold me, en - fold me in your love.

2. You are the beauty that fills my soul,
   you, by your wound, make me whole.
   You paid the price to redeem me from death;
   yours is the love that sustains my ev'ry breath.

3. You still the storms and the fear of night,
   you turn despair to delight.
   You feel the anguish, and share in my tears,
   you give the hope from the depth of my fears.

4. You are the word full of life and truth,
   you guide my feet since my youth;
   you are my refuge, my firm cornerstone,
   you I will worship and honour alone.

5. You have restored me and pardoned sin,
   you give me strength from within.
   You called me forth, and my life you made new.
   Love is the binding that holds me to you.

6. You are the Way, you are Truth and Life,
   you keep me safe in the strife.
   You give me love I cannot comprehend,
   you guide the way to a life without end.

Text and Music: Margaret Rizza (b.1929)

752 You give, Lord
Nunc Dimitis

1. You give, Lord, the sign to your ser-vant to go in your peace; your pro-mise of old has been ho-noured, your word is ful-filled.

Refrain

May God give his grace in our wa-king and watch as we sleep; may Christ be our friend in the day-light, our peace through the night.

2. At last I have seen your salvation,
   your gift to the world:
   the light of the Gentiles,
   the glory in Israel's midst.

3. Give thanks to the Father of mercies,
   give thanks to his Son,
   give thanks to the joy-giving Spirit,
   give thanks to one God.

Text: Gregory Murray (1905-1992) based on Luke 2:29-32
Music: Gregory Murray (1905-1992)
© Copyright 1999 Kevin Mayhew Ltd.

753 You have been baptised in Christ

hope of e - ter - nal life.   *Last time* life.

- ter   have hope of e - ter - nal life.

1,2,3.

1. God the Fa - ther has freed you and giv - en you a new

2. You are a new cre - a - tion. In Christ you have been

3. Re - ceive the light of Christ; keep it burn - ing

birth, and to be a mem - ber of his ho - ly peo - ple he

clothed. See in this gar - ment the out - ward sign of your

bright - ly. Al - ways walk as a child of the light, with his

now a - noints you with oil.

dig - ni - ty in him.

flame a - live in your heart.

Text: Carey Landry from the Rite of Baptism
Music: Carey Landry arr. Keith Stent

754 You have called us

roy - al priest - hood by your grace. We are a ho -
- ly na - tion set a - part for you. You have called
CODA
We re - joice in your pow - er and might.

2. We are to take your light
   to ev'ry nation, tongue and tribe,
   so they may see your glory
   shining through our lives.

Text and Music: Lynn DeShazo and Martin J. Nystrom

LiTURGiCAL

HYMNS OLD & NEW

755 You have the message of eternal life

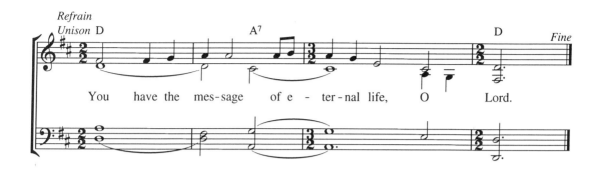

You have the mes-sage of e - ter-nal life, O Lord.

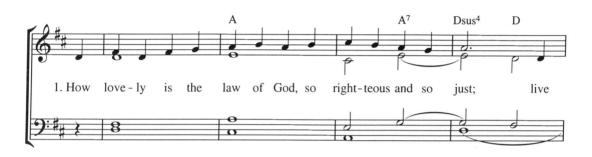

1. How love-ly is the law of God, so right-teous and so just; live

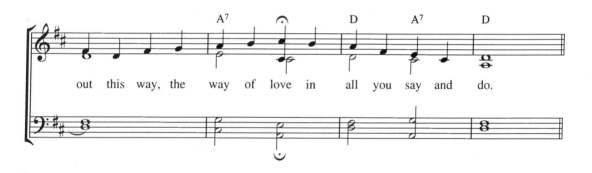

out this way, the way of love in all you say and do.

2. This law alone can soothe the soul,
   give peace and inner joy;
   like solid ground that we may trust,
   and light to travel by.

3. As worldly values shift and slide,
   the love of God holds fast,
   and though our world will pass away
   his faithfulness remains.

Text: Susan Sayers (b.1946) based on Psalm 18
Music: Andrew Moore (b.1954)

756 Your love's greater

1. You made the hea-vens, the earth and sea;

your pow'r is awe-some, and you still love me.

2. Your ways are righteous,
   your laws are just,
   love is your promise,
   and in you I trust.

3. Your love is healing,
   your love endures;
   my life is changed,
   Lord, now I know I'm yours.

Text: Mike Anderson (b.1956)
Music: Mike Anderson (b.1956) arr. Keith Stent

LITURGICAL

HYMNS OLD & NEW

757 You shall cross the barren desert
Be not afraid

1. You shall cross the bar-ren des-ert, but you shall not die of thirst. You shall wan-der far in safe-ty though you do not know the way. You shall speak your words in fo-reign lands and they will un-der-stand. You shall see the face of God and live.

Refrain
Be not a-fraid. I go be-fore you al-ways.

Text: Bob Dufford based on Isaiah 43:2-3, Luke 6:20
Music: Bob Dufford

LITURGICAL

HYMNS OLD & NEW

Text: Michael Joncas (b.1951) based on Psalm 90
Music: Michael Joncas (b.1951)

LITURGICAL

HYMNS OLD & NEW

Children's Hymns and Songs

760 A butterfly, an Easter egg
Signs of new life

Lively

Leader 1. A but-ter-fly, *All* a but-ter-fly, *Leader* an Eas-ter egg, *All* an Eas-ter egg, *Leader* a

foun-tain flow-ing in the park, *All* a foun-tain flow-ing in the park.

Refrain

All These are signs of new life; the life of Je-sus the Lord. And we

sing to him, al-le-lu-ia! We give to him our praise! We

sing to him, al-le - lu - ia! *Leader* Glo-ry be to him! *All* Glo-ry be to

him! Glo-ry be to Je - sus the Lord!

2. A helping hand,
   a helping hand,
   a happy smile,
   a happy smile,
   a heart so full of hope and joy,
   a heart so full of hope and joy.

3. A cup of wine,
   a cup of wine,
   a loaf of bread,
   a loaf of bread,
   now blest and broken for us all,
   now blest and broken for us all.

Text: Carey Landry
Music: Carey Landry arr. Norman Warren

761 All in an Easter garden

1. All in an Eas-ter gar-den, be-fore the break of day, an
an-gel came from hea-ven and rolled the stone a-way. When
Je-sus' friends came seek-ing, with myrrh and spi-ces rare, they
found the an-gels at the door, but Je-sus was not there.

2. All in an Easter garden,
   where water lilies bloom,
   the angels gave their message
   beside an empty tomb:
   'The Lord is here no longer,
   come, see where once he lay;
   the Lord of life is ris'n indeed,
   for this is Easter day.'

Text: traditional
Music: traditional arr. Andrew Moore
This arrangement © Copyright 1999 Kevin Mayhew Ltd.

762 All of my heart

Text: Doug Marks-Smirchirch
Music: Doug Marks-Smirchirch arr. Keith Stent

763 All of the people

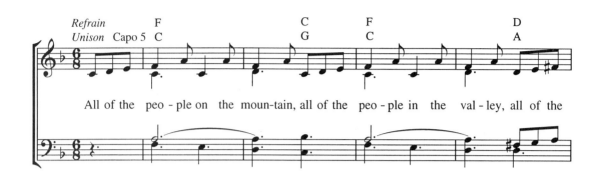

All of the peo - ple on the moun-tain, all of the peo - ple in the val - ley, all of the

peo - ple in the vil - la - ges and the town, say to each

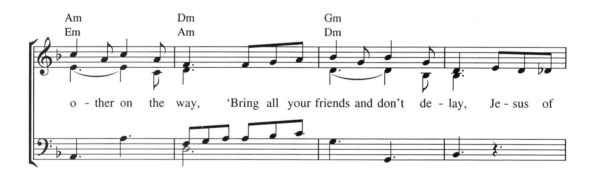

o - ther on the way, 'Bring all your friends and don't de - lay, Je - sus of

Na - za - reth is com - ing here to - day.' day.'

2. Jesus, Jesus, healing as you go,
   your loving seems to flow
   like water from a fountain,
   and as we are touched we want to grow
   in love towards each other –
   just because you love us so!

3. Jesus, Jesus, we have come to see
   that you must really be
   the Son of God our Father.
   We've been with you and we all agree
   that only in your service
   can the world be truly free!

Text: Susan Sayers (b.1946)
Music: Susan Sayers (b.1946) arr. Andrew Moore

764 All the nations of the earth

2. Snow-capped mountains, praise the Lord,
   alleluia.
   Rolling hills, praise the Lord,
   alleluia.

3. Deep sea water, praise the Lord,
   alleluia.
   Gentle rain, praise the Lord,
   alleluia.

4. Roaring lion, praise the Lord,
   alleluia.
   Singing birds, praise the Lord,
   alleluia.

5. Earthly monarchs, praise the Lord,
   alleluia.
   Young and old, praise the Lord,
   alleluia.

Text: Michael Cockett (b.1938)
Music: Kevin Mayhew (b.1942) arr. Andrew Moore

765 And everyone beneath the vine and fig tree

This can be sung as a round with the second voices entering at **B**

Text: unknown

Music: unknown arr. Andrew Moore

This arrangement © Copyright 1999 Kevin Mayhew Ltd.

766 As Jacob with travel was weary one day

2. This ladder is long, it is strong and well-made,
   has stood hundreds of years and is not yet decayed;
   many millions have climbed it and reached Zion's hill,
   and thousands by faith are climbing it still:

3. Come let us ascend! all may climb it who will;
   for the angels of Jacob are guarding it still:
   and remember, each step that by faith we pass o'er,
   some prophet or martyr has trod it before:

4. And when we arrive at the haven of rest
   we shall hear the glad words, 'Come up hither, ye blest,
   here are regions of light, here are mansions of bliss.'
   O who would not climb such a ladder as this?

Text: 18th century
Music: 18th century English carol melody arr. Andrew Moore

LiTURGiCAL

HYMNS OLD & NEW

767 Be the centre of my life

Unison

1. Be the cen-tre of my life, Lord Je - sus, be the cen-tre of my life, I pray; be my Sa-viour to for-give me, be my friend to be with me, be the cen-tre of my life to - day!

2. Let the power of your presence, Lord Jesus,
   from the centre of my life shine through;
   oh, let ev'rybody know it,
   I really want to show it,
   that the centre of my life is you!

Text: Alan J. Price
Music: Alan J. Price arr. Andrew Moore
© Copyright 1990 Daybreak Music Ltd, Silverdale Road, Eastbourne, East Sussex BN20 7AB. Used by permission.

768 Caterpillar, caterpillar

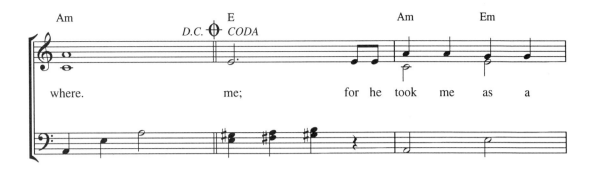

where.   me;   for he took   me   as   a

cat - er - pil - lar, and he made a but - ter - fly   of   me.'

2. Caterpillar, caterpillar, feeling sleepy,
   fixed up a silken bed.
   Then caterpillar, caterpillar climbed inside
   and covered up his sleepy head.
   In the dark he slept and rested
   as the days and nights went by,
   till on a sunny morning when the silk bed burst,
   he was a butterfly!

3. Butterfly, oh butterfly, a-flitt'ring, flutt'ring;
   oh what a sight to see.
   And as the lovely butterfly was flutt'ring by,
   I heard him sing a song to me:
   'Oh I never knew God could do
   such a wondrous thing for me;
   for he took me as a caterpillar and he made
   a butterfly of me.'

Text: Susan Sayers (b.1946)
Music: Susan Sayers (b.1946) arr. Andrew Moore

769 Change my heart, O God

Text: Eddie Espinosa
Music: Eddie Espinosa arr. Andrew Moore

770 'Cheep!' said the sparrow
The birds' song

1. 'Cheep!' said the sparrow on the chimney top, 'All my feathers are known to God.' 'Caw!' said the rook in a tree so tall, 'I know that God gladly made us all.'

2. 'Coo!' said the gentle one, the grey-blue dove,
   'I can tell you that God is love.'
   High up above sang the lark in flight,
   'I know the Lord is my heart's delight.'

3. 'Chirp!' said the robin with his breast so red,
   'I don't work at all, yet I'm fed.'
   'Whoo!' called the owl in a leafy wood,
   'Our God is wonderful, wise and good.'

Text: Estelle White (b.1925)
Music: Estelle White (b.1925) arr. Noel Rawsthorne
© Copyright 1977 Kevin Mayhew Ltd.

771 Christ is our King

blind, let - ting the sun - light pour in - to their minds.

Vi - sion is wait - ing for those who have hope. He is the

light of the world.

2. He came to speak tender words to the poor,
   he is the gateway and he is the door.
   Riches are waiting for all those who hope.
   He is the light of the world.

3. He came to open the doors of the gaol;
   he came to help the downtrodden and frail.
   Freedom is waiting for all those who hope.
   He is the light of the world.

4. He came to open the lips of the mute,
   letting them speak out with courage and truth.
   His words are uttered by all those who hope.
   He is the light of the world.

5. He came to heal all the crippled and lame,
   sickness took flight at the sound of his name.
   Vigour is waiting for all those who hope.
   He is the light of the world.

6. He came to love everyone on this earth
   and through his Spirit he promised rebirth.
   New life is waiting for all those who hope.
   He is the light of the world.

Text: Estelle White (b.1925)
Music: Estelle White (b.1925) arr. Andrew Moore

772 Clap your hands, all you people

This can be sung as a round with the second voices entering at **B**

Text: Jimmy Owens
Music: Jimmy Owens, arr. Noel Rawsthorne

773 Clap your hands and sing this song

MICHAEL ROW THE BOAT 74 74

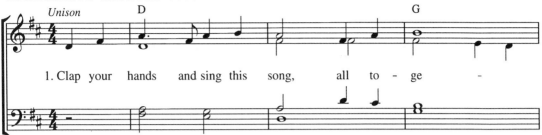

2. Raise your hands up in the air, all together,
   God can reach you anywhere, all together.

3. Fold your arms across your chest, all together,
   in the arms of God you're blessed, all together.

4. Close your eyes and shut them tight, all together,
   God will keep you in his sight, all together.

5. Now sing softly, whisper low, all together,
   God will hear you even so, all together.

6. Sing out loud and strong and clear, all together,
   so that ev'ryone can hear, all together.

7. Sing with harmony and joy, all together,
   God loves ev'ry girl and boy, all together.

Text: Jean Holloway (b.1939)
Music: traditional arr. Andrew Moore
Text and this arrangement © Copyright 1997, 1999 Kevin Mayhew Ltd.

774 Come and praise the Lord our King

MICHAEL ROW THE BOAT 74 74

1. Come and praise the Lord our King, al - le - lu -

ia, come and praise the Lord our King, al - le - lu - ia!

2. Christ was born in Bethlehem, alleluia,
   Son of God and Son of Man, alleluia.

3. He grew up an earthly child, alleluia,
   in the world, but undefiled, alleluia.

4. He who died at Calvary, alleluia,
   rose again triumphantly, alleluia.

5. He will cleanse us from our sin, alleluia,
   if we live by faith in him, alleluia.

Text: unknown
Music: traditional melody arr. Christopher Tambling
This arrangement © Copyright 1994 Kevin Mayhew Ltd.

775 Come, God's children

MICHAEL ROW THE BOAT 74 74

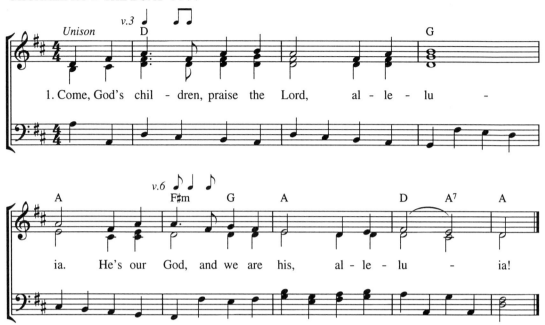

1. Come, God's chil - dren, praise the Lord, al - le - lu - ia. He's our God, and we are his, al - le - lu - ia!

2. Come to him with songs of praise, alleluia,
   songs of praise, rejoice in him, alleluia.

3. For the Lord is a mighty God, alleluia,
   he is King of all the world, alleluia.

4. In his hands are valleys deep, alleluia,
   in his hands are mountain peaks, alleluia.

5. In his hands are all the seas, alleluia,
   and the lands which he has made, alleluia.

6. Praise the Father, praise the Son, alleluia,
   praise the Spirit, the Holy One, alleluia.

Text: unknown
Music: traditional melody arr. Christopher Tambling
This arrangement © Copyright 1994 Kevin Mayhew Ltd.

LITURGICAL

HYMNS OLD & NEW

776 Come into his presence

Unison

1. Come in-to his pre-sence, sing-ing, 'Al – le – lu – ia, al – le – lu – ia, al – le – lu – ia.'

2. Come into his presence, singing,
   'Jesus is Lord, Jesus is Lord, Jesus is Lord.'
   Come into his presence, singing,
   'Jesus is Lord, Jesus is Lord, Jesus is Lord.'

3. Come into his presence, singing,
   'Glory to God, glory to God, glory to God.'
   Come into his presence, singing,
   'Glory to God, glory to God, glory to God.'

Text: unknown
Music: unknown arr. Andrew Moore
This arrangement © Copyright 1999 Kevin Mayhew Ltd.

777 Come, they told me
The little drummer boy

1. Come, they told me, pah-
rum-pum-pum-pum! our new-born King to see, pah-
rum-pum-pum-pum! Our fi-nest gifts we bring, pah-
rum-pum-pum-pum! to lay be-fore the King, pah-
rum-pum-pum-pum! Rum-pum-pum-pum! Rum-pum-pum-pum!

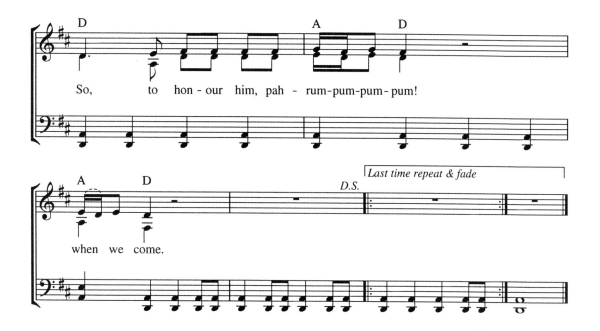

So, to hon-our him, pah-rum-pum-pum-pum!

Last time repeat & fade

D.S.

when we come.

2. Baby Jesus, pah-rum-pum-pum-pum!
I am a poor child too, pah-rum-pum-pum-pum!
I have no gift to bring, pah-rum-pum-pum-pum!
that's fit to give a King, pah-rum-pum-pum-pum!
Rum-pum-pum-pum! Rum-pum-pum-pum!
Shall I play for you, pah-rum-pum-pum-pum!
on my drum?

3. Mary nodded, pah-rum-pum-pum-pum!
The ox and lamb kept time, pah-rum-pum-pum-pum!
I played my drum for him, pah-rum-pum-pum-pum!
I played my best for him, pah-rum-pum-pum-pum!
Rum-pum-pum-pum! Rum-pum-pum-pum!
Then he smiled at me, pah-rum-pum-pum-pum!
me and my drum.

Text: Katherine K. Davis, Henry V. Onorati and Harry Simeone
Music: Katherine K. Davis, Henry V. Onorati and Harry Simeone arr. Noel Rawsthorne

LiTURGiCAL

HYMNS OLD & NEW

778 Dear child divine

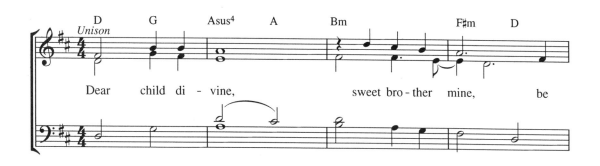

Dear child di-vine, sweet bro-ther mine, be

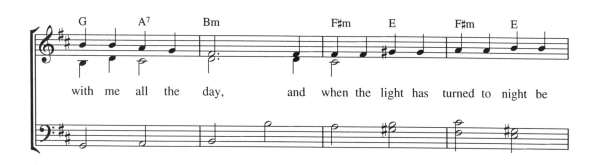

with me all the day, and when the light has turned to night be

with me still, I pray. Where-'er I be, come

down to me and ne-ver go a-way.

Text: unknown
Music: Alan Rees (b.1941) arr. Andrew Moore

779 Do not worry over what to eat

Sol - o-mon was not ar - rayed like one of these. The
birds of the air, they do not sow or reap, but
God tends to them like a shep - herd tends his sheep.

2. The Lord will guide you in his hidden way,
   show you what to do and tell you what to say.
   When you pray for rain, go build a dam to store
   ev'ry drop of water you have asked him for.

3. The Lord knows all your needs before you ask.
   Only trust in him for he will do the task
   of bringing in your life whatever you must know.
   He'll lead you through the darkness wherever you must go.

Text: Sebastian Temple (1928-1998)
Music: Sebastian Temple (1928-1998) arr. Andrew Moore

780 Don't build your house on the sandy land

Don't build your house on the san - dy land, don't build it too near the shore. Well, it might look kind of nice, but you'll have to build it twice, oh, you'll have to build your house once more. You'd bet-ter build your house up-on a rock, make a good foun-da - tion on a sol - id spot. Oh, the storms may come and go but the peace of God you will know.

This song can be sung as a round with the second voice entering at B

Text: Karen Lafferty
Music: Karen Lafferty arr. Andrew Moore

781 Do what you know is right

Leader: Do what you know is right. All: Do what you know is right.

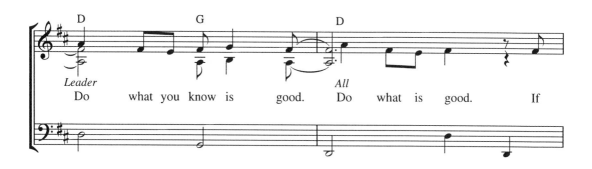

Leader: Do what you know is good. All: Do what is good. If

no one else does it, don't be a-fraid. Je - sus says, 'I am

with you al - ways.'

Text: Bev Gammon
Music: Bev Gammon arr. Noel Rawsthorne

782 Each of us is a living stone
Living stones

Brightly (swinging)

Each of us is a liv-ing stone, no one needs to stand a-lone,

joined to o-ther liv-ing stones, we're build-ing the tem-ple of God. *Fine*

1. We're build-ing, we're build-ing the tem-ple of God on earth, but it

needs no walls or stee - ple, for we're ma-king a house of grea-ter worth, we're

build-ing it with peo - ple!

D.C.

2. The stone that, the stone that the builders once cast aside
has been made the firm foundation,
and the carpenter who was crucified
now offers us salvation.

Text: Michael Forster (b.1946)
Music: James Patten (b.1936)
© Copyright 1997 Kevin Mayhew Ltd.

783 Every bird, every tree

1. Ev - 'ry bird, ev - 'ry tree helps me know, helps me
see, helps me feel God is love and love's a - round.
From each riv - er pain - ted blue to the ear - ly morn - ing
dew this is love, God is love, love's a - round.

2. Ev'ry prayer, ev'ry song
   makes me feel I belong
   to a world filled
   with love that's all around.
   From each daybreak to each night,
   out of darkness comes the light,
   this is love, God is love, love's around.

3. Ev'ry mountain, ev'ry stream,
   ev'ry flower, ev'ry dream
   comes from God,
   God is love and love's around.
   From the ever-changing sky
   to a new-born baby's cry,
   this is love, God is love, love's around.

Text: Peter Watcyn-Jones
Music: Peter Watcyn-Jones arr. Andrew Moore

784 Father welcomes all his children

Fa - ther wel-comes all his chil-dren to his fam - 'ly

through his Son. Fa - ther giv-ing his sal - va - tion,

life for e - ver has been won. won.

1. Lit - tle chil-dren, come to me, for my king-dom is of these.

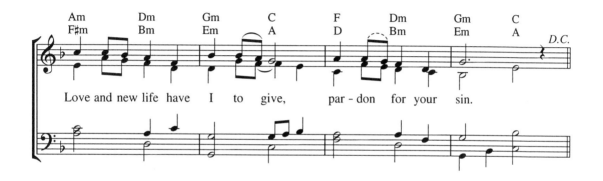

Love and new life have I to give, par - don for your sin.

2. In the water, in the word,
   in his promise, be assured:
   all who believe and are baptised
   shall be born again.

3. Let us daily die to sin;
   let us daily rise with him –
   walk in the love of Christ our Lord,
   live in the peace of God.

Text: Robin Mann
Music: Robin Mann arr. Andrew Moore

785 Fishes of the ocean

Unison

1. Fish-es of the o-cean and the birds of the air, they all declare the won-der-ful works of God who has cre-a-ted ev-'rything, ev-'ry-where; let the whole earth sing of his love!

2. Apples in the orchard and the corn in the field,
   the plants all yield their fruit in due season,
   so the generosity of God is revealed;
   let the whole earth sing of his love!

3. Energy and colour from the sun with its light,
   the moon by night; the patterns of the stars
   all winking in the darkness on a frosty cold night;
   let the whole earth sing of his love!

4. Muddy hippopotamus and dainty gazelle,
   the mice as well, are of his making,
   furry ones and hairy ones and some with a shell;
   let the whole earth sing of his love!

5. All that we can hear and ev'rything we can see,
   including me, we all of us spring from God
   who cares for ev'rybody unendingly;
   let the whole earth sing of his love!

Text: Susan Sayers (b.1946)
Music: Susan Sayers (b.1946) arr. Noel Rawsthorne

786 Forward in faith

1. For-ward in faith, for-ward in Christ, we are tra-vel-ling on - ward;
for-ward in faith, for-ward in Christ, we are trav' - ling on.

Refrain

On - ward, on - ward, we are trav' - ling on,

1, 2.

on - ward, on - ward, we are trav' - ling on.

Last time

on.

2. Jesus is Lord,
   Jesus is Lord,
   we are travelling onward;
   Jesus is Lord,
   Jesus is Lord,
   we are trav'ling on.

3. He is our King,
   he is our King,
   we are travelling onward;
   he is our King,
   he is our King,
   we are trav'ling on.

Text: Graham Jeffery
Music: Kevin Mayhew (b.1942) arr. Andrew Moore

787 Friends, all gather here in a circle
Circle of friends

Friends, all ga-ther here in a cir-cle. It has no be-gin-ning and it has no end.

Face to face, we all have a place in God's own cir-cle of friends.

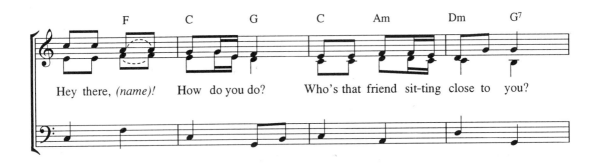

Hey there, *(name)!* How do you do? Who's that friend sit-ting close to you?

Thank the Lord, for *(name)* has a place in the cir - cle too.

Take a look a-round. Find some-one near. Take her/him by the hand, say,

'Glad you're here.' We're to - ge-ther and when we've gone, God's

love like a cir-cle rolls on and on and on.

Last time

Text: David Morstad
Music: David Morstad arr. Noel Rawsthorne

788 Give me peace, O Lord

1. Give me peace, O Lord, I pray, in my work and in my play; and in-side my heart and mind, Lord, give me peace.

2. Give peace to the world, I pray
   let all quarrels cease today.
   May we spread your light and love:
   Lord, give us peace.

Text: Estelle White (b.1925)
Music: Estelle White (b.1925) arr. Andrew Moore
© Copyright 1976 Kevin Mayhew Ltd.

789 God almighty set a rainbow

1. God al-migh-ty set a rain-bow arch-ing in the sky a-
bove, and his peo-ple un-der-stand it as a sig-nal of his love.

Refrain after each verse:
Thank you, Father, thank you, Father,
thank you, Father, for your care,
for your warm and loving kindness
to your people ev'rywhere.

2. Clouds will gather, storms come streaming
on the darkened earth below –
too much sunshine makes a desert,
without rain no seed can grow.

3. Through the stormcloud shines your rainbow,
through the dark earth springs the wheat.
In the future waits your harvest
and the food for all to eat.

4. God almighty, you have promised
after rain the sun will show;
bless the seeds and bless the harvest.
Give us grace to help us grow.

Text: Caroline Somerville
Music: traditional melody arr. Andrew Moore
Text © Copyright 1976 The Central Board of Finance of the Church of England, Church House,
Great Smith Street, London SW1P 3NZ. Used by permission from 'Together for Harvest' (CIO, 1976)
This arrangement © Copyright 1999 Kevin Mayhew Ltd.

790 God gives his people strength

1. God gives his peo-ple strength. If we believe in his way he's swift to re-pay all
those who bear the bur-den of the day.
God gives his peo-ple strength.

2. God gives his people hope.
If we but trust in his word
our prayers are always heard.
He warmly welcomes anyone who's erred.
God gives his people hope.

3. God gives his people love.
If we but open wide our heart
he's sure to do his part.
He's always the first to make a start.
God gives his people love.

4. God gives his people peace.
When sorrow fills us to the brim
and courage grows dim
he lays to rest our restlessness in him.
God gives his people peace.

Text: Miriam Thérèse Winter
Music: Miriam Thérèse Winter arr. Andrew Moore

791 God our Father gave us life

2. When we're frightened, hurt or tired,
   there's always someone there.
   Make us thankful for their love:
   Lord, hear our prayer;
   Lord, hear our prayer.

3. All God's children need his love,
   a love that we can share.
   So, we pray for ev'ryone:
   Lord, hear our prayer;
   Lord, hear our prayer.

Text: Kathleen Middleton
Music: Kathleen Middleton arr. Noel Rawsthorne
© Copyright 1986 Kevin Mayhew Ltd.

792 God sends a rainbow
Colours of hope

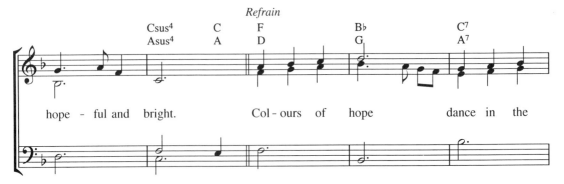

sun, while it yet rains the hope has be - gun;

col - ours of hope shine through the rain,

col - ours of love, noth - ing is vain.

2. When we are lonely, when we're afraid,
   though it seems dark, rainbows are made;
   even when life itself has to end,
   God is our rainbow, God is our friend.

3. Where people suffer pain or despair,
   God can be seen in those who care;
   even where war and hatred abound,
   rainbows of hope are still to be found.

4. People themselves like rainbows are made,
   colours of hope in us displayed;
   old ones and young ones, women and men,
   all can be part of love's great 'Amen'!

Text: Michael Forster (b.1946)
Music: Christopher Tambling (b.1964)

LITURGICAL

HYMNS OLD & NEW

793 God turned darkness into light

2. God divided land and sea,
   filled the world with plants and trees,
   all so beautiful to see,
   and declared that it was good.

3. God made animals galore,
   fishes, birds and dinosaurs,
   heard the splashes, songs and roars,
   and declared that it was good.

4. God made people last of all,
   black and white, and short and tall,
   male and female, large and small,
   and declared that it was good.

Text: Michael Forster (b.1946)
Music: Christopher Tambling (b.1964) arr. Keith Stent
© Copyright 1997 Kevin Mayhew Ltd.

794 Goliath was big and Goliath was strong
Biggest isn't always best

With vigour

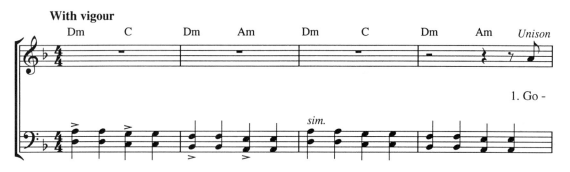

1. Go -

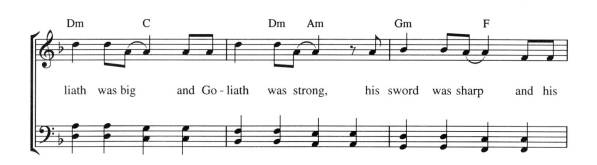

liath was big and Go-liath was strong, his sword was sharp and his

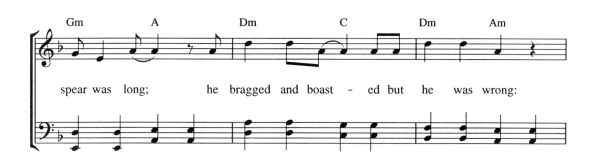

spear was long; he bragged and boast – ed but he was wrong:

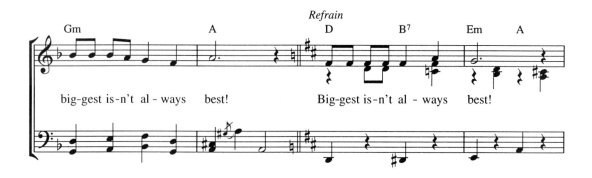

big-gest is-n't al - ways best! Big-gest is-n't al - ways best!

Big-gest is-n't al-ways best! God told Da-vid,

'Don't be a-fraid, big-gest is-n't al-ways best!'

2. A shepherd boy had a stone and sling;
   he won the battle and pleased the King!
   Then all the people began to sing:
   'Biggest isn't always best!'

3. So creatures made in a smaller size,
   like tiny sparrows and butterflies,
   are greater than we may realise:
   biggest isn't always best!

Text: Michael Forster (b.1946)
Music: Christopher Tambling (b.1964)

795 Hail, Mary, full of grace

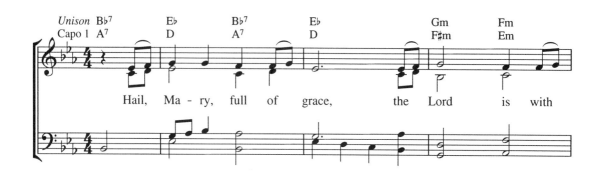

Hail, Ma-ry, full of grace, the Lord is with

thee. Bless-ed art thou a-mong wo-men, and bless-ed is the fruit of thy womb,

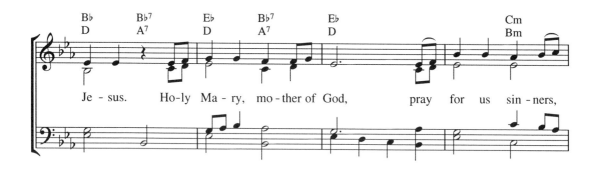

Je - sus. Ho-ly Ma - ry, mo-ther of God, pray for us sin-ners,

now and at the hour of our death. A - men.

Text: Luke 1:28
Music: Julian Wiener arr. Andrew Moore

796 Hallelu, hallelu

Hal - le - lu, hal-le-lu, hal - le - lu, hal-le-lu - jah; we'll praise the
Lord! Hal - le - lu, hal - le - lu, hal - le - lu, hal - le - lu - jah;
we'll praise the Lord! We'll praise the Lord, hal-le-lu - jah!
We'll praise the Lord, hal-le-lu - jah! We'll praise the
Lord, hal-le - lu - jah! We'll praise the Lord!

Text: unknown
Music: unknown arr. Keith Stent

797 Have you heard the raindrops
Water of life

2. There's a busy worker digging in the desert,
digging with a spade that flashes in the sun;
soon there will be water rising in the well-shaft,
spilling from the bucket as it comes.

3. Nobody can live who hasn't any water,
when the land is dry, then nothing much grows;
Jesus gives us life if we drink the living water,
sing it so that ev'rybody knows.

Text: Christian Strover
Music: Christian Strover arr. Noel Rawsthorne

798 He is the King

He is the King of kings, he is the Lord of lords, his name is Je-sus, Je-sus, Je-sus, Je-sus, O, he is the King.

Text: unknown
Music: unknown arr. Andrew Moore
This arrangement © Copyright 1999 Kevin Mayhew Ltd.

799 Hey, now, everybody sing

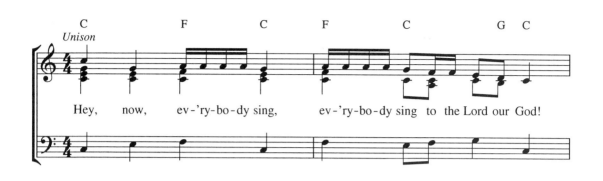

Hey, now, ev-'ry-bo-dy sing, ev-'ry-bo-dy sing to the Lord our God!

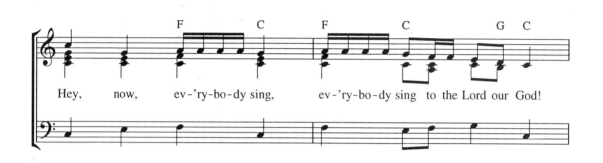

Hey, now, ev-'ry-bo-dy sing, ev-'ry-bo-dy sing to the Lord our God!

Ev-'ry-bo-dy join in a song of praise, come and sing a-long with me!

Glo-ry, al-le-lu-ia, glo-ry, al-le-lu-ia, I'm so glad I'm free!

Text: Orien Johnson
Music: Orien Johnson arr. Keith Stent

800 If I were a butterfly

1. If I were a but-ter-fly, I'd thank you, Lord, for giv-ing me wings, and if I were a ro-bin in a tree, I'd thank you, Lord, that I could sing, and if I were a fish in the sea, I'd wig-gle my tail and I'd gig-gle with glee, but I just thank you, Fa-ther, for mak-ing me 'me'.

Refrain

For you gave me a heart, and you gave me a smile, you gave me Je-sus and you made me your child, and I just thank you, Fa - ther, for mak - ing me 'me'.

2. If I were an elephant,
   I'd thank you, Lord, by raising my trunk,
   and if I were a kangaroo,
   you know I'd hop right up to you,
   and if I were an octopus,
   I'd thank you, Lord, for my fine looks,
   but I just thank you, Father, for making me 'me'.

3. If I were a wiggly worm,
   I'd thank you, Lord, that I could squirm,
   and if I were a billy goat,
   I'd thank you, Lord, for my strong throat,
   and if I were a fuzzy wuzzy bear,
   I'd thank you, Lord, for my fuzzy wuzzy hair,
   but I just thank you, Father, for making me 'me'.

Text: Brian Howard
Music: Brian Howard arr. Andrew Moore

801 I give my hands

in my soul and the joy of the Lord is my strength.

2. I give my eyes to see the world
   and ev'ryone, in just the way you do.
   I give my tongue to speak your words,
   to spread your name and freedom-giving truth.

3. I give my mind in every way
   so that each thought I have will come from you.
   I give my spirit to you, Lord,
   and every day my prayer will spring anew.

4. I give my heart that you may love
   in me your Father and the human race.
   I give myself that you may grow
   in me and make my life a song of praise.

Text: Estelle White (b.1925)
Music: Estelle White (b.1925) arr. Andrew Moore

802 I'm black, I'm white, I'm short, I'm tall

1. I'm black, I'm white, I'm short, I'm tall, I'm all the hu-man race. I'm young, I'm old, I'm large, I'm small, and Je-sus knows my face. The love of God is free to ev-'ry-one, free to ev-'ry-one, free to ev-'ry-one. The love of God is free, oh yes! That's what the gos-pel says.

2. I'm rich, I'm poor, I'm pleased, I'm sad,
I'm ev'ry-one you see.
I'm quick, I'm slow, I'm good, I'm bad,
I know that God loves me.

3. So tall and thin, and short and wide,
and any shade of face,
I'm one of those for whom Christ died,
part of the human race.

Text: Michael Forster (b.1946)
Music: Christopher Tambling (b.1964)

803 In the upper room
You must do for others

Unison
Capo 3

1. In the up-per room, Je-sus and his friends

met to ce-le-brate their fi-nal sup - per.

Je-sus took a bowl, knelt to wash their feet, told them:

'You must do for o - thers as I do for you.'

2. Peter was annoyed: 'This will never do!
You, as Master, should not play the servant!'
Jesus took a towel, knelt to dry their feet, told them:
'You must do for others as I do for you.'

Text: Gerard Fitzpatrick
Music: Gerard Fitzpatrick arr. Andrew Moore
© Copyright 1986 Kevin Mayhew Ltd.

804 Isn't it good

Text: Alan J. Price
Music: Alan J. Price arr. Keith Stent

805 It's me, O Lord

Refrain
Unison

It's me, it's me, it's me, O Lord, stand-ing in the need of prayer. It's me, it's me, it's me, O Lord, stand-ing in the need of prayer.

1. Not my bro-ther or my sis-ter, but it's me, O Lord, stand-ing in the need of prayer. Not my bro-ther or my sis-ter, but it's me, O Lord, stand-ing in the need of prayer.

2. Not my mother or my father,
   but it's me, O Lord,
   standing in the need of prayer.
   Not my mother or my father,
   but it's me, O Lord,
   standing in the need of prayer.

3. Not the stranger or my neighbour,
   but it's me, O Lord,
   standing in the need of prayer.
   Not the stranger or my neighbour,
   but it's me, O Lord,
   standing in the need of prayer.

Text: Spiritual
Music: Spiritual arr. Keith Stent
This arrangement © Copyright 1999 Kevin Mayhew Ltd.

806 I've got peace like a river

Unison

1. I've got peace like a ri-ver, I've got peace like a ri-ver, I've got peace like a ri-ver in my soul.

To verses 2 & 3

Last time

I've got o-cean in my soul.

2. I've got joy like a fountain,
   I've got joy like a fountain,
   I've got joy like a fountain in my soul.

3. I've got love like an ocean,
   I've got love like an ocean,
   I've got love like an ocean in my soul.

Text: Spiritual
Music: Spiritual arr. Andrew Moore
This arrangement © Copyright 1999 Kevin Mayhew Ltd.

807 I will wave my hands

I will wave my hands in praise and a-dor-a-tion, I will

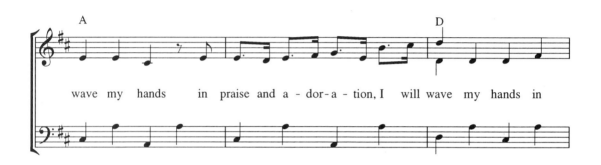

wave my hands in praise and a-dor-a-tion, I will wave my hands in

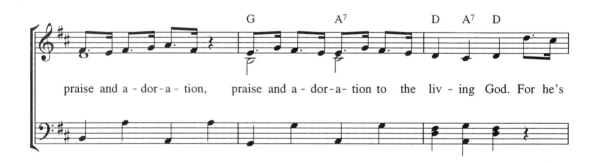

praise and a-dor-a-tion, praise and a-dor-a-tion to the liv-ing God. For he's

gi-ven me hands that just love clap-ping: one, two,

Text: Ian Smale
Music: Ian Smale arr. Keith Stent

LITURGICAL

HYMNS OLD & NEW

808 Jesus had all kinds of friends

Moderately

Refrain

Unison

Je - sus had all kinds of friends, so the gos - pel sto - ries say.

Je - sus had all kinds of friends, and there's room for us to - day.

1. Some were hap-py, some were sad, some were good and some were bad,

some were short and some were tall, Je - sus said he loved them all.

2. Some were humble, some were proud,
some were quiet, some were loud,
some were fit and some were lame,
Jesus loved them all the same.

3. Some were healthy, some were sick,
some were slow and some were quick,
some were clever, some were not,
Jesus said he loved the lot!

Text: Michael Forster (b.1946)
Music: Christopher Tambling (b.1964)

809 Jesus is greater

his way. He's the truth that we can be - lieve in, and

he's the life, he's liv - ing to - day. Son of

1. **2.**

D.S.

Text: Gill Hutchinson
Music: Gill Hutchinson arr. Andrew Moore

LITURGICAL

HYMNS OLD & NEW

810 Jesus put this song

'Hebrew' style, getting faster

Unison

1. Je-sus put this song in-to our hearts, Je-sus put this song in-to our hearts; it's a song of joy no one can take a-way. Je-sus put this song in-to our hearts.

dance.

Each verse should be sung faster

2. Jesus taught us how to live in harmony,
   Jesus taught us how to live in harmony;
   diff'rent faces, diff'rent races, he made us one.
   Jesus taught us how to live in harmony.

3. Jesus turned our sorrow into dancing,
   Jesus turned our sorrow into dancing;
   changed our tears of sadness into rivers of joy.
   Jesus turned our sorrow into a dance.

Text: Graham Kendrick (b.1950)
Music: Graham Kendrick (b.1950) arr. Keith Stent

811 Jesus went away to the desert

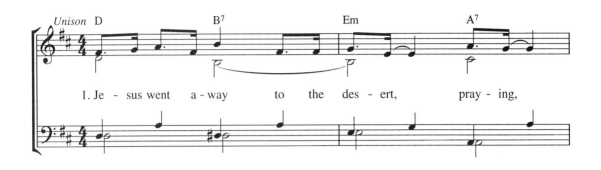

Unison

1. Je - sus went a - way to the des - ert, pray - ing,

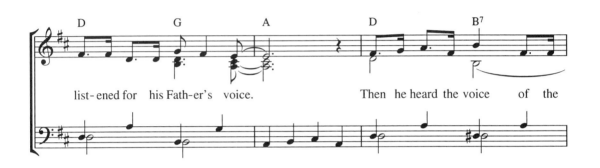

list - ened for his Fath - er's voice. Then he heard the voice of the

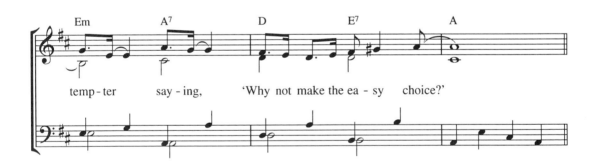

temp - ter say - ing, 'Why not make the ea - sy choice?'

Refrain

Ain't list - 'nin' to no temp - ta - tion, ain't fall - in' for

no per - sua - sion, ain't gon - na turn a - way from sal-va-tion, I'm a-

To verses 2-4 *Last time*

wait - in' on the word of the Lord.

2. 'There's an easy way if only you'd only choose it,
   you can turn the stones to bread!
   What's the good of pow'r if you don't abuse it?
   Gotta keep yourself well fed!'

3. 'What about a stunt to attract attention,
   showing off your special pow'r?
   You'd get more applause than I'd care to mention
   jumping from the Temple tow'r!'

4. 'Ev'rything you want will be right there for you,
   listen to the words I say!
   Nobody who matters will dare ignore you;
   my way is the easy way.'

Text: Michael Forster (b.1946)
Music: Christopher Tambling (b.1964) arr. Keith Stent

812 Jesus will never, ever

Text: Greg Leavers
Music: Greg Leavers arr. Noel Rawsthorne

LITURGICAL

HYMNS OLD & NEW

813 Jesus, you love me

Je - sus, you love me more than I can know. Jesus, you love me more than words can say. I'm spe - cial, I'm planned; I'm born with a fu - ture, I'm in your hands.

Words: David Hind
Music: David Hind arr. Andrew Moore

814 Joseph was an honest man

1. Jo - seph was an hon-est man, he was an hon-est

man. He pleased the Lord in all his ways

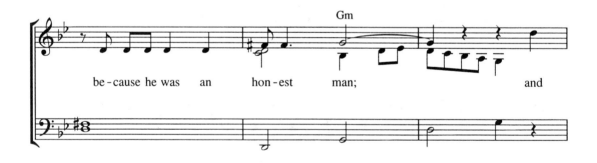

be - cause he was an hon-est man; and

God said: 'I am choos - ing you, be-cause you are an hon-est

man, to care for the one who'll bear my Son, be-cause you

are an hon-est man.'

2. Joseph was a faithful man,
   he was a faithful man.
   He kept the trust the Lord had given
   because he was a faithful man.
   He cared for Mary and her Son,
   because he was a faithful man,
   through days of pain and days of fun,
   because he was a faithful man.

3. Joseph was a working man,
   he was a working man.
   He laboured as a carpenter
   because he was a working man.
   And daily at his work he'd be,
   because he was a working man,
   no idler or a shirker he,
   because he was a working man.

4. Joseph was a praying man,
   he was a praying man.
   He walked with God each single day
   because he was a praying man.
   In joy or pain he'd turn to him,
   because he was a praying man,
   if fear did rage or hope grew dim,
   because he was a praying man.

5. Joseph was an honest man,
   he was an honest man.
   His blameless life won its reward
   because he was an honest man.
   The Lord was pleased and called him home,
   because he was an honest man,
   with him to rest, no more to roam,
   because he was an honest man.

6. Joseph is a helping man,
   he is a helping man.
   He rescues those who turn to him
   because he is a helping man.
   So go to Joseph in your need,
   because he is a helping man,
   you'll see him work with speed and power,
   because he is a helping man.

Text: Marie Lydia Pereira
Music: Marie Lydia Pereira arr. Andrew Moore

815 Kum ba yah

Unison

1. Kum ba yah, my Lord, kum ba yah, kum ba yah, my Lord, kum ba

yah, kum ba yah, my Lord, kum ba yah, O Lord, kum ba yah.

2. Someone's crying, Lord, kum ba yah,
   someone's crying, Lord, kum ba yah,
   someone's crying, Lord, kum ba yah,
   O Lord, kum ba yah.

3. Someone's singing, Lord, kum ba yah,
   someone's singing, Lord, kum ba yah,
   someone's singing, Lord, kum ba yah,
   O Lord, kum ba yah.

4. Someone's praying, Lord, kum ba yah,
   someone's praying, Lord, kum ba yah,
   someone's praying, Lord, kum ba yah,
   O Lord, kum ba yah.

Text: Spiritual
Music: Spiritual arr. Andrew Moore

816 Let the mountains dance and sing

1. Let the moun-tains dance and sing! Let the trees all sway and swing! All cre-a-tion praise its King! Al – le – lu – ia!

2. Let the water sing its song!
   And the pow'rful wind so strong
   whistle as it blows along!
   Alleluia!

3. Let the blossom all break out
   in a huge unspoken shout,
   just to show that God's about!
   Alleluia!

Text: Susan Sayers (b.1946)
Music: Susan Sayers (b.1946) arr. Andrew Moore
© Copyright 1984 Kevin Mayhew Ltd.

817 Life for the poor was hard and tough
Jesus turned the water into wine

Never hurrying

1. Life for the poor was hard and tough, Je-sus said, 'That's not good e-nough; life should be great and here's the sign: I'll turn the wa-ter in-to wine.' Je-sus turned the wa-ter in-to wine, Je-sus turned the wa-ter in-to wine,

Je-sus turned the wa- ter in - to wine, and the peo - ple saw that life was good.

2. Life is a thing to be enjoyed,
   not to be wasted or destroyed.
   Laughter is part of God's design;
   let's turn the water into wine!

3. Go to the lonely and the sad,
   give them the news to make them glad,
   helping the light of hope to shine,
   turning the water into wine!

Text: Michael Forster (b.1946)
Music: Christopher Tambling (b.1964)

818 Little donkey

fol - low that star to - night, Beth - le - hem, Beth - le - hem.

Lit-tle don - key, lit-tle don - key, had a hea - vy day,

lit - tle don - key, car-ry Ma - ry safe-ly on her way.

2. Little donkey, little donkey,
   on the dusty road,
   there are wise men, waiting for a
   sign to bring them here.
   Do not falter, little donkey,
   there's a star ahead;
   it will guide you, little donkey,
   to a cattle shed.

Text: Eric Boswell
Music: Eric Boswell arr. Andrew Moore

819 Little Jesus, sleep away

1. Lit-tle Je-sus, sleep a-way, in the hay, while we wor-ship, watch and pray. We will ga-ther at the man-ger, wor-ship this a-maz-ing stran-ger: lit-tle Je-sus born on earth, sign of grace and hu-man worth.

2. Little Jesus, sleep away,
   while you may;
   pain is for another day.
   While you sleep, we will not wake you,
   when you cry we'll not forsake you.
   Little Jesus, sleep away,
   we will worship you today.

Text: Christopher Massey (b.1956)
Music: traditional Czech carol, arr. Christopher Tambling

820 Lord of the future

1. Lord of the fu - ture, Lord of the past, Lord of our lives, we a -
dore you. Lord of for-e - ver, Lord of our hearts,
we give all praise to you. you.

2. Lord of tomorrow,
   Lord of today,
   Lord over all, you are worthy.
   Lord of creation,
   Lord of all truth,
   we give all praise to you.

Text: Ian D. Craig
Music: Ian D. Craig arr. Noel Rawsthorne

LITURGICAL

HYMNS OLD & NEW

821 Lord, we've come to worship you

Text: Ian Smale
Music: Ian Smale arr. Keith Stent

822 Lord, you've promised, through your Son
Lord, forgive us

Lord, we're sor - ry.

Last refrain

Lord, you've pro-mised, through your Son, you'll for - give the wrongs

we've done; we re - ceive your par - don,

Lord, as you for - give us.

2. Sinful and unkind thoughts too,
   all of these are known to you.
   Lord, we're sorry.
   Lord, we're sorry.

3. And the things we've left undone,
   words and deeds we should have done.
   Lord, we're sorry.
   Lord, we're sorry.

Last refrain:
*Lord, you've promised, through your Son,
you'll forgive the wrongs we've done;
we receive your pardon,
Lord, as you forgive us.*

Text: Alan J. Price
Music: Alan J. Price arr. Norman Warren

LITURGICAL

HYMNS OLD & NEW

823 My mouth was made for worship

2. My heart was made for loving,
   my mind to know God's ways,
   my body was made a temple,
   my life is one of praise to Jesus.
   And all God's people said: Amen,
   hallelujah, amen, praise and glory,
   amen, amen, amen, amen,
   Wo,wo,wo,wo,wo.

Text: Ian Smale
Music: Ian Smale arr. Norman Warren

824 Nobody's a nobody

2. I'm no car-toon, I'm hu-man, I have feel-ings, treat me right. I'm

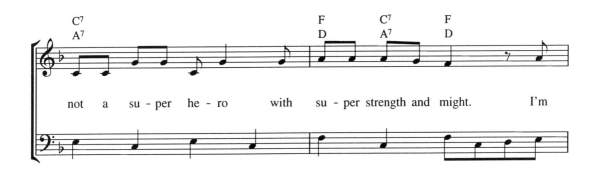

not a su-per he-ro with su-per strength and might. I'm

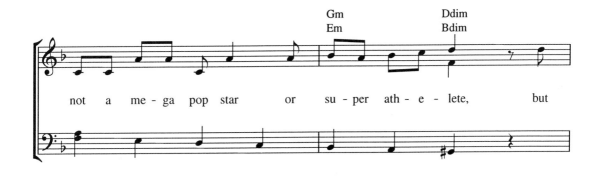

not a me-ga pop star or su-per ath-e-lete, but

did you know I'm spec-ial, in fact I'm quite u-nique!

Text: John Hardwick
Music: John Hardwick arr. Noel Rawsthorne

LITURGICAL

HYMNS OLD & NEW

825 Now the Mass is ended

Unison
Capo 3

1. Now the Mass is end-ed, Lord, now it's time to go,
but we will not leave a-lone, we will take you too.
In our work, in our play, all through-out our bu-sy day,
we will not be left a-lone, we'll live this day with you.

2. Through this Mass we have received blessing, grace and pow'r
loving truly as you did, loving hour by hour,
to be kind, to be true, just like you in all we do.
Stay with us, we ask you, Lord, and help us stay with you.

Text: Marie Lydia Pereria
Music: Marie Lydia Pereria arr. Keith Stent

826 O come and join the dance

As a Scottish folk-dance

1. O come and join the dance that all be-gan so long a-go, when Christ the Lord was born in Beth-le-hem. Through all the years of dark-ness still the dance goes on and on, oh, take my hand and come and join the song. Re-joice! Re-joice! Re-joice! Re-joice! O lift your voice and sing, and

2. Come shed your heavy load and dance your worries away,
   for Christ the Lord was born in Bethlehem.
   He came to break the pow'r of sin and turn your night to day,
   oh, take my hand and come and join the song.

3. Let laughter ring and angels sing and joy be all around,
   for Christ the Lord was born in Bethlehem.
   And if you seek with all your heart he surely can be found,
   oh, take my hand and come and join the song.

Text: Graham Kendrick (b.1950)
Music: Graham Kendrick (b.1950) arr. Keith Stent

827 O give thanks

O give thanks to the Lord, all you his

peo-ple, O give thanks to the Lord, for he is good.

Let us praise, let us thank, let us ce - le-brate and

dance, O give thanks to the Lord, for he is good.

Text: Joanne Pond
Music: Joanne Pond arr. Keith Stent

828 O Lord, all the world

1. O Lord, all the world be-longs to you, and you are al-ways mak-ing all things new. What is wrong you for-give, and the new life you give is what's turn-ing the world up - side down.

2. The world's only loving to its friends,
   but you have brought us love that never ends;
   loving enemies too,
   and this loving with you
   is what's turning the world upside down.

3. This world lives divided and apart.
   You draw us all together and we start,
   in your body, to see
   that in a fellowship we
   can be turning the world upside down.

4. The world wants the wealth to live in state,
   but you show us a new way to be great:
   like a servant you came,
   and if we do the same,
   we'll be turning the world upside down.

5. O Lord, all the world belongs to you,
   and you are always making all things new.
   Send your Spirit on all
   in your Church, whom you call
   to be turning the world upside down.

Text: Patrick Appleford
Music: Patrick Appleford arr. Andrew Moore

829 One hundred and fifty-three!

One hun-dred and fif - ty - three! One

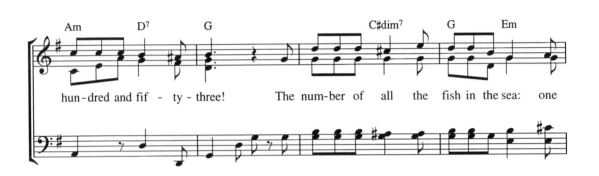

hun-dred and fif - ty - three! The num-ber of all the fish in the sea: one

hun-dred and fif - ty - three! 1. We'd fished all the night for

no-thing, but Je-sus said, 'Try once more.' So we doubt-ful-ly tried on the

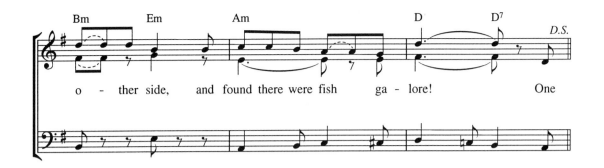

o - ther side, and found there were fish ga - lore! One

2. We got all the fish to the shore,
   we wondered how many there'd be.
   So we started to count,
   and what an amount:
   one hundred and fifty-three!

3. Now here was a wonderful sight
   we'd never expected to see;
   and the net didn't break,
   it was able to take
   the hundred and fifty-three!

4. So whether you're rich or you're poor,
   whatever your race or your sect,
   be you black, white or brown,
   Jesus wants you around,
   there's plenty of room in the net!

Text: Michael Forster (b.1946)
Music: Christopher Tambling (b.1964)

830 Our God is so great

Our God is so great, so strong and so migh-ty, there's

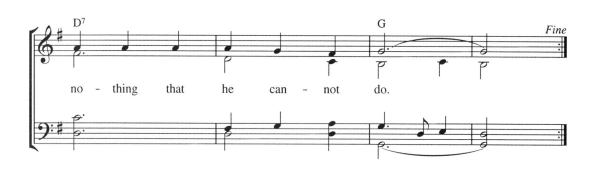

no - thing that he can - not do.

The ri - vers are his, the moun - tains are his, the

stars are his han - di - work too.

Text: unknown
Music: unknown arr. Andrew Moore
This arrangememt © Copyright 1999 Kevin Mayhew Ltd.

831 Out to the great wide world we go

Joyfully

Out to the great wide world we go! Out to the great wide world we go!

Out to the great wide world we go and we sing of the love of Je - sus.

1. Go and tell our neigh-bours, go and tell our friends,

Je - sus gives his peo - ple love that ne - ver ends. So:

2. People sad and lonely,
   wond'ring how to cope;
   let's find ways of showing
   Jesus gives us hope. So:

Text: Michael Forster (b.1946)
Music: Christopher Tambling (b.1964)

LITURGICAL

HYMNS OLD & NEW

832 O when the saints go marching in

2. O when they crown him Lord of all,
   O when they crown him Lord of all,
   I want to be in that number
   when they crown him Lord of all.

3. O when all knees bow at his name,
   O when all knees bow at his name,
   I want to be in that number
   when all knees bow at his name.

4. O when they sing the Saviour's praise,
   O when they sing the Saviour's praise,
   I want to be in that number
   when they sing the Saviour's praise.

5. O when the saints go marching in,
   O when the saints go marching in,
   I want to be in that number
   when the saints go marching in.

Text: traditional
Music: traditional arr. Keith Stent (b.1934)
This arrangement © Copyright 1999 Kevin Mayhew Ltd.

833 Peter and John went to pray
Silver and gold

Peter and John went to pray, they met a lame man on the way. He asked for alms and held out his palms and this is what Peter did say: 'Sil-ver and gold have I none, but such as I have I give thee, in the name of Je-sus Christ of Na-za-reth, rise up and

walk!' He went walk-ing and leap-ing and prais - ing God,

walk-ing and leap-ing and prais - ing God. 'In the name of Je - sus

Christ of Na - za-reth, rise up and walk.'

Text: unknown based on Acts 3
Music: unknown arr. Colin Hand

834 Praise and thanksgiving

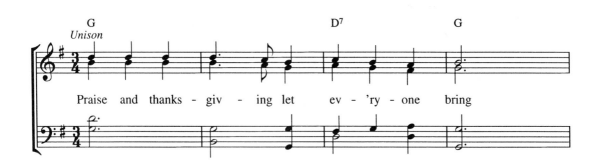

Praise and thanks - giv - ing let ev - 'ry - one bring

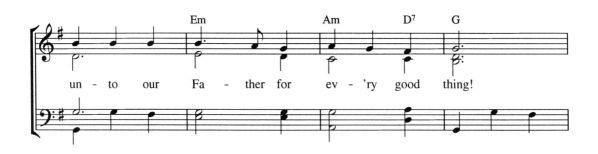

un - to our Fa - ther for ev - 'ry good thing!

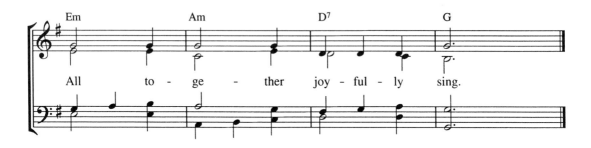

All to - ge - ther joy - ful - ly sing.

Text: unknown
Music: unknown arr. Andrew Moore

835 Praise God in his holy place

Lively

1. Praise God in his ho-ly place! He's the God of time and space. Praise him, all the hu-man race! Let ev-'ry-thing praise our God!

To next verse · *Last time* · *D.C.*

2. Praise him with the ol' wood block!
   Let it swing and let it rock,
   praising God around the clock!
   Let ev'rything praise the Lord!

3. Praise him with the big bass drum,
   if you've got guitars, then strum!
   Now let's make those rafters hum!
   Let ev'rything praise our God!

4. Praise him with the chime bars' chime,
   tell the bells it's party time,
   help those singers find a rhyme!
   Let ev'rything praise our God!

5. Violin or xylophone,
   trumpets with their awesome tone;
   bowed or beaten, bashed or blown,
   let ev'rything praise our God!

6. Cymbals, triangles and things,
   if it crashes, howls or rings,
   ev'rybody shout and sing!
   Let ev'rything praise our God!

Text: Michael Forster (b.1946)
Music: Christopher Tambling (b.1964)
© Copyright 1997 Kevin Mayhew Ltd.

LiTURGiCAL

HYMNS OLD & NEW

836 Put your trust

1. Put your trust in the man who tamed the sea,
   put your trust in the man who calmed the waves,
   put your trust in the Lord Jesus,
   it is he who rescues and saves.

2. Put your trust in the man who cured the blind,
   put your trust in the man who helped the lame,
   put your trust in the Lord Jesus,
   there is healing strength in his name.

3. Put your trust in the man who died for you,
   put your trust in the man who conquered fear,
   put your trust in the Lord Jesus,
   for he rose from death and he's near.

4. Put your trust in the man who understands,
   put your trust in the man who is your friend,
   put your trust in the Lord Jesus,
   who will give you life without end.

Text: Estelle White (b.1925)
Music: Estelle White (b.1925) arr. Andrew Moore

837 Rise and shine

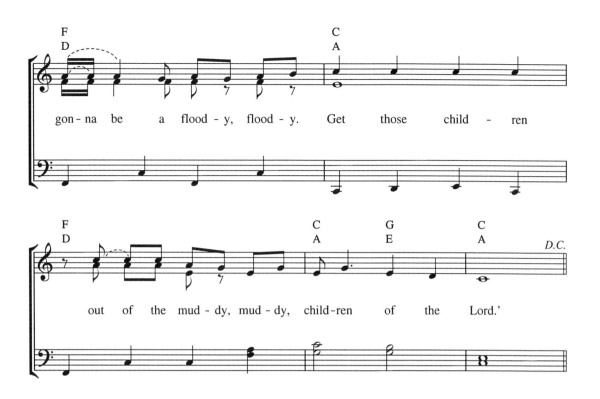

2. So Noah, he built him, he built him an arky, arky,
   Noah, he built him, he built him an arky, arky,
   built it out of hickory barky, barky,
   children of the Lord.

3. The animals, they came on, they came on, by twosies, twosies,
   animals, they came on, they came on by twosies, twosies,
   elephants and kangaroosies, roosies,
   children of the Lord.

4. It rained and poured for forty daysies, daysies,
   rained and poured for forty daysies, daysies,
   nearly drove those animals crazies, crazies,
   children of the Lord.

5. The sun came out and dried up the landy, landy,
   sun came out and dried up the landy, landy,
   ev'rything was fine and dandy, dandy,
   children of the Lord.

6. If you get to heaven before I do-sies, do-sies,
   you get to heaven before I do-sies, do-sies,
   tell those angels I'm comin' too-sies, too-sies,
   children of the Lord.

Text: unknown based on Genesis 6:4
Music: traditional arr. Noel Rawsthorne (b. 1929)

LITURGICAL

HYMNS OLD & NEW

838 Sing a simple song

2. Say a simple prayer unto the Lord,
   say a simple prayer unto the Lord,
   say it with your heart, say it with your soul,
   say a simple prayer unto the Lord.

3. Give a simple gift unto the Lord,
   give a simple gift unto the Lord,
   give it with your heart, give it with your soul,
   give a simple gift unto the Lord.

Text: Carey Landry
Music: Carey Landry arr. Andrew Moore

839 Sing praise to God

2. Lift up your eyes to see the works of God,
   in ev'ry blade of grass, in ev'ry human face.
   Lift up your eyes to see the works of God,
   through all life, in all time and all space.

3. Open your ears to hear the cries of pain
   arising from the poor and all who are oppressed.
   Open your mind and use your wits to find
   who are the causes of this world's unjust ways.

4. Reach out your hands to share the wealth God gave
   with those who are oppressed, and those who feel alone.
   Reach out your hands and gently touch with Christ
   each frozen heart which has said 'No' to love.

5. Open our hearts to love the world with Christ,
   each person in this world, each creature of this earth.
   Open our hearts to love the ones who hate,
   and in their hearts find a part of ourselves.

6. Live life with love, for love encircles all,
   it casts out all our fears, it fills the heart with joy.
   Live life with love, for love transforms our life,
   as we praise God with our eyes, hands and hearts.

Text: W.L. Wallace
Music: Noel Rawsthorne (b.1929)

840 Step by step, on and on
Jesus is the living way

Step by step, on and on, we will walk with Je - sus till the
jour - ney's done. Step by step, day by day, be - cause Je - sus is the liv - ing
way. 1. He's the one to fol - low, in his
foot - steps we will tread. Don't wor - ry a - bout to -
mor - row, Je - sus knows the way a - head. Oh,

2. He will never leave us,
   and his love he'll always show,
   so wherever Jesus leads us,
   that's the way we want to go. Oh,

Text: Gill Hutchinson
Music: Gill Hutchinson arr. Keith Stent

841 Thank you, Lord
Right where we are

1. Thank you, Lord, for this new day, thank you, Lord, for this new day, thank you, Lord, for this new day, right where we are.

Refrain
Alleluia, praise the Lord, alleluia, praise the Lord, alleluia, praise the Lord, right where we are.

2. Thank you, Lord, for food to eat,
   thank you, Lord, for food to eat,
   thank you, Lord, for food to eat,
   right where we are.

3. Thank you, Lord, for clothes to wear,
   thank you, Lord, for clothes to wear,
   thank you, Lord, for clothes to wear,
   right where we are.

4. Thank you, Lord, for all your gifts,
   thank you, Lord, for all your gifts,
   thank you, Lord, for all your gifts,
   right where we are.

Text: Diane Davis Andrew adapted by Geoffrey Marshall-Taylor
Music: Diane Davis Andrew arr. Noel Rawsthorne

LITURGICAL

HYMNS OLD & NEW

842 There are hundreds of sparrows
God knows me

1. There are hun-dreds of spar-rows, thou-sands, mil-lions, they're
two a pen-ny, far too ma-ny there must be; there are hun-dreds and thou-sands,
mil-lions of spar-rows, but God knows ev'-ry one, and God knows me.

2. There are hundreds of flowers, thousands, millions,
   and flowers fair the meadows wear for all to see;
   there are hundreds and thousands, millions of flowers,
   but God knows ev'ry one, and God knows me.

3. There are hundreds of planets, thousands, millions,
   way out in space each has a place by God's decree;
   there are hundreds and thousands, millions of planets,
   but God knows ev'ry one, and God knows me.

4. There are hundreds of children, thousands, millions,
   and yet their names are written on God's memory;
   there are hundreds and thousands, millions of children,
   but God knows ev'ry one, and God knows me.

Text: John Gowans
Music: John Larsson arr. Andrew Moore

843 There's a great big world out there

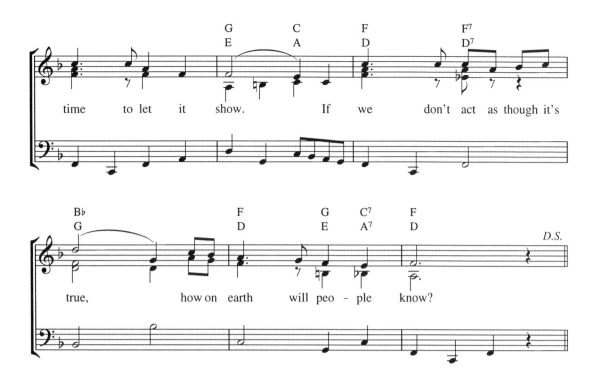

time to let it show. If we don't act as though it's

true, how on earth will peo - ple know?

2. We've brought to God our prayers and hymns,
   now it's time to live his life,
   to sow a little love and peace
   in the place of selfish strife.

3. We've listened to the word of God,
   now it's time to live it out,
   to show by ev'rything we do
   what the gospel is about.

This can be sung as a round during the third verse, with the second voices entering at the refrain
(using the accompaniment to the verse).

Text: Michael Forster (b.1946)
Music: Andrew Gant (b.1963)

LITURGICAL

HYMNS OLD & NEW

844 There's a rainbow in the sky

Refrain
Unison

There's a rain-bow in the sky, and it's o-kay! There's a rain-bow in the sky, and it's o-kay! There's a rain-bow in the sky, and it's o-kay! It's a sign that God is good.

1. For-ty days and nights a-float, all cooped up on No-ah's boat!

Now the rain is al-most done; wake up world, here comes the sun!

2. Now we've got another start,
ev'ryone can play a part:
make the world a better place,
put a smile on ev'ry face!

3. Sometimes, still, the world is bad,
people hungry, people sad.
Jesus wants us all to care,
showing people ev'rywhere:

Text: Michael Forster (b.1946)
Music: Christopher Tambling (b.1964)

845 There was one, there were two
The children's band

Refrain
Unison

There was one, there were two, there were three friends of Je-sus, there were four, there were five, there were six friends of Je-sus, there were sev'n, there were eight, there were nine friends of Je-sus, ten friends of Je-sus in the band.

1. Bells are going to ring in praise of Je-sus, praise of Je-sus, praise of Je-sus, bells are going to ring in praise of Je-sus, prais-ing Je-sus the Lord.

2. Drums are going to boom in praise of Jesus,
   praise of Jesus, praise of Jesus,
   drums are going to boom in praise of Jesus,
   praising Jesus the Lord.

3. Tambourines will shake in praise of Jesus,
   praise of Jesus, praise of Jesus,
   tambourines will shake in praise of Jesus,
   praising Jesus the Lord.

4. Trumpets will resound in praise of Jesus,
   praise of Jesus, praise of Jesus,
   trumpets will resound in praise of Jesus,
   praising Jesus the Lord.

Verses can be added ad lib, for example:

Clarinets will swing in praise of Jesus. . .

Play recorders, too. . .

Triangles will ting. . .

Fiddles will be scraped. . .

Let guitars be strummed. . .

Chime bars will be chimed. . .

Glockenspiels will play. . .

Vibraphones will throb. . .

Trombones slide about. . .

Words: Christina Wilde
Music: traditional American melody arr. Andrew Moore

846 The voice from the bush
Lead my people to freedom

2. The people of God were suff'ring and dying,
   sick and tired of slavery.
   All God could hear was the sound of their crying;
   Moses had to set them free:

3. We know that the world is still full of sorrow,
   people need to be set free.
   We've got to give them a better tomorrow,
   so God says to you and me:

Text: Michael Forster (b.1946)
Music: Christopher Tambling (b.1964)

847 The wise man

1. The wise man built his house upon the rock, the wise man built his house upon the rock, the wise man built his house upon the rock, and the rain came tumbling down. And the rain came down and the floods came up, the rain came down and the floods came up, the rain came down and the floods came up, and the house on the rock stood firm.

2. The foolish man built his house upon the sand, *(x3)*
and the rain came tumbling down,
And the rain came down and the floods came up,
the rain came down and the floods came up, *(x2)*
and the house on the sand fell flat.

Text: unknown
Music: unknown arr. Keith Stent
This arrangement © Copyright 1999 Kevin Mayhew Ltd.

LITURGICAL

HYMNS OLD & NEW

848 The world is full of smelly feet

Refrain
Capo 5

The world is full of smel-ly feet, wea-ry from the dus-ty street. The
world is full of smel-ly feet, we'll wash them for each oth-er.

1. Je-sus said to his dis-ci-ples, 'Wash those wea-ry toes!
Do it in a cheer-ful fash-ion, ne-ver hold your nose!'

2. People on a dusty journey
need a place to rest;
Jesus says, 'You say you love me,
this will be the test!'

3. We're his friends, we recognize him
in the folk we meet;
smart or scruffy, we'll still love him,
wash his smelly feet!

Text: Michael Forster (b.1946)
Music: Christopher Tambling (b.1964)

849 This little light of mine

2. On Monday he gave me the gift of love,
   Tuesday peace came from above.
   On Wednesday he told me to have more faith,
   on Thursday he gave me a little more grace.
   On Friday he told me to watch and pray,
   on Saturday he told me just what to say,
   on Sunday he gave me the power divine
   to let my little light shine.

Text: traditional
Music: traditional arr. Keith Stent

850 We will praise

We will praise, we will praise, we will praise the Lord, we will
praise the Lord be-cause he is good. We will praise, we will praise, we will
praise the Lord be - cause his love is e - ver-last - ing.
Bring on the trum-pets and harps, let's hear the cym-bals
ring, then in har - mo - ny

Text: Ian Smale
Music: Ian Smale arr. Keith Stent

851 When is he coming

2. Long years awaiting,
   many years here awaiting the Redeemer!
   Ready to greet him,
   always ready to meet him, the Redeemer!

3. Spare us from evil,
   from the clutches of evil, O Redeemer!
   Though we are sinners
   we have known your forgiveness, O Redeemer!

Text: David Palmer
Music: David Palmer arr. Andrew Moore

LiTURGiCAL

HYMNS OLD & NEW

852 When the Spirit of the Lord

1. When the Spi-rit of the Lord is with-in my heart I will sing as Dav-id sang. When the Spi-rit of the Lord is with-in my heart I will sing as Dav-id sang. I will sing, I will sing, I will sing, I will sing as Dav-id sang. I will sing, I will sing, I will sing as Dav-id sang.

2. When the Spirit of the Lord is within my heart
   I will clap as David clapped . . .

3. When the Spirit of the Lord is within my heart
   I will dance as David danced . . .

4. When the Spirit of the Lord is within my heart
   I will praise as David praised . . .

Text: unknown
Music: unknown arr. Andrew Moore

853 When your Father made the world
Care for your world

1. When your Fa-ther made the world, be-fore that world was old, in his eye what he had made was love-ly to be-hold. Help your peo-ple to care for your world.

Refrain

The world is a gar-den you made, and you are the one who plant-ed the seed, the world is a gar-den you

made, a life for our food, life for our joy,

life we could kill with our sel - fish greed.

2. All the world that he had made,
   the seas, the rocks, the air,
   all the creatures and the plants
   he gave into our care.
   Help your people to care for your world.

3. When you walked in Galilee,
   you said your Father knows
   when each tiny sparrow dies,
   each fragile lily grows.
   Help your people to care for your world.

4. And the children of the earth,
   like sheep within your fold,
   should have food enough to eat,
   and shelter from the cold.
   Help your people to care for your world.

Text: Anne Conlon
Music: Peter Rose arr. Andrew Moore

854 Who put the colours in the rainbow?

1. Who put the col-ours in the rain - bow? Who put the salt in-to the sea? Who put the cold in-to the snow - flake? Who made you and me? Who put the hump up-on the ca - mel? Who put the neck on the gi - raffe? Who put the tail up-on the mon - key? Who made hy - e - nas

2. Who put the gold into the sunshine?
   Who put the sparkle in the stars?
   Who put the silver in the moonlight?
   Who made Earth and Mars?
   Who put the scent into the roses?
   Who taught the honey-bee to dance?
   Who put the tree inside the acorn?
   It surely can't be chance!
   Who made seas and leaves and trees?
   Who made snow and winds that blow?
   Who made streams and rivers flow?
   God made all of these!

Text: Paul Booth
Music: Paul Booth arr. Keith Stent

855 Yesterday, today, for ever

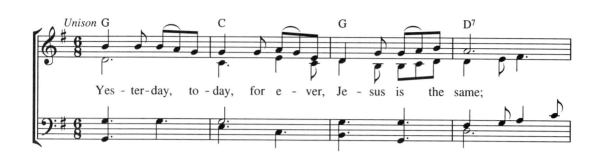

Yes - ter-day, to - day, for e - ver, Je - sus is the same;

all may change, but Je - sus ne - ver, glo - ry to his name!

Glo - ry to his name! Glo - ry to his name!

All may change, but Je - sus ne-ver, glo - ry to his name!

Text: unknown
Music: unknown arr. Andrew Moore
This arrangement © Copyright 1999 Kevin Mayhew Ltd.

856 You've got to move

2. You've got to sing . . .

3. You've got to clap . . .

4. You've got to shout . . .

5. You've got to move . . .

Text: traditional
Music: traditional arr. Keith Stent

LITURGICAL

HYMNS OLD & NEW

857 Zacchaeus was a very little man

Zac-chae-us was a ve-ry lit-tle man, and a ve-ry lit-tle man was he. He climbed up in-to a sy-ca-more tree, for the Sa-viour he wan-ted to see. And when the Sa-viour passed that way, he looked in-to the tree and said, 'Now Zac-chae-us, you come down, for I'm com-ing to your house for tea.'

Text: unknown
Music: unknown arr. Andrew Moore

858 Zip bam boo

work-ing man who shout-ed 'Yes' to life, but did-n't choose to set-tle down, or take him-self a wife. To live for God he made his task, 'Who is this man?' the peo-ple ask. Zip bam boo, za-ma la-ma la boo, there's free-dom in Je-sus Christ.

2. He'd come to share good news from God
and show that he is Lord.
He made folk whole who trusted him
and took him at his word.
He fought oppression, loved the poor,
gave the people hope once more.
Zip bam boo, zama lama la boo,
there's freedom in Jesus Christ.

3. 'He's mad! He claims to be God's Son
and give new life to men!
Let's kill this Christ, once and for all,
no trouble from him then!'
'It's death then, Jesus, the cross for you!'
Said, 'Man, that's what I came to do!'
Zip bam boo, zama lama la boo,
there's freedom in Jesus Christ.

Text: Sue McClellan, John Paculabo and Keith Ryecroft
Music: Sue McClellan, John Paculabo and Keith Ryecroft arr. Norman Warren

LITURGICAL

HYMNS OLD & NEW

Chants

859 Adoramus te, Domine

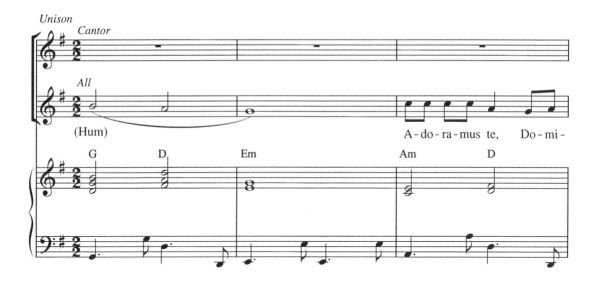

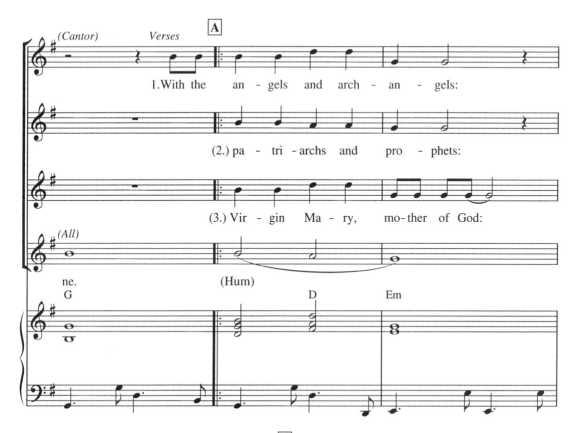

The cantor always enters on the upbeat so that the A marked in his/her part
in the melody edition coincides with the A indicated in the part above.

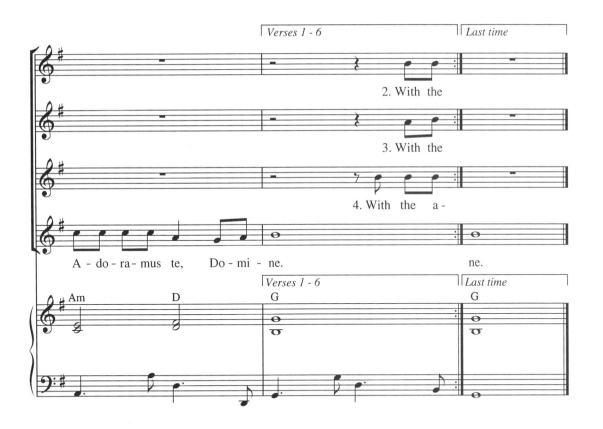

Verses 1 - 6   Last time

2. With the
3. With the
4. With the a-
A - do - ra - mus te, Do - mi - ne.   ne.

Verses 1 - 6   Last time

Am   D   G   G

Verses: Cantor

4. With the a - pos - tles and e - van - ge - lists:

5. With all the mar - tyrs of Christ:

6. With all who wit - ness to the Gos - pel of the Lord:

7. With all your peo - ple of the Church through-out the world.

* Choose either part.

Text: Taizé Community
Music: Jacques Berthier (1923-1994)

860 Adoramus te, Domine Deus

Slow and calm (♩ = c.52)

Capo 3 D

A - do - ra - mus te, Do - mi - ne De - us.

A - do - ra - mus te, Do - mi - ne De - us.

Last time

A - do - ra - mus te, a - do - ra - mus te, a - do - ra - mus te.

Hum

Translation: We adore you, O Lord God.

Text: Traditional
Music: Margaret Rizza (b.1929)
© Copyright 1997 Kevin Mayhew Ltd.

861 Benedictus qui venit

Be - ne - dic - tus qui ve - nit in

no - mi - ne Do - mi - ni. Be - ne - dic - tus qui

ve - nit in no - mi - ne Do - mi - ni. Ho - san - na, ho-

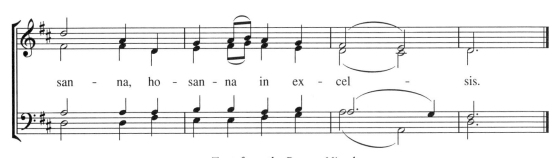

san - na, ho - san - na in ex - cel - sis.

Text: from the Roman Missal
Music: Noel Darros

862 Bless the Lord, my soul

Bless the Lord, my soul, and bless God's ho-ly name.

Bless the Lord, my soul, who leads me in-to life.

Verses: Cantor

1. It is God who for-gives all your guilt, who heals ev-'ry one of your ills, who re-deems your life from the grave, who crowns you with love and com-pas-sion.

2. The Lord is com-pas-sion and love, the Lord is pa-tient and rich in mer-cy. God does not

treat us ac-cord-ing to our sins, nor re - pay us ac-cord-ing to our faults.

3. As a fa-ther has com-pas-sion on his chil-dren, the Lord has mer-cy on those who re-

vere him; for God knows of what we are made, and re - mem-bers that we are dust.

Text: Taizé Community from Psalm 102
Music: Jacques Berthier (1923-1994)

863 Calm me, Lord

Tranquil (♩ = 108)

Calm me, Lord, as you calmed the storm; still me, Lord,

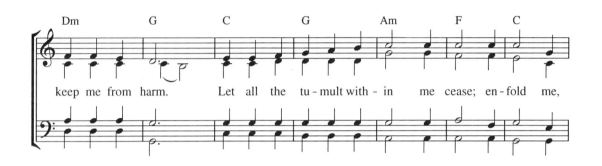

keep me from harm. Let all the tu-mult with-in me cease; en-fold me,

Lord, in your peace. Lord, en-fold me in your peace.

Text: David Adam
Music: Margaret Rizza (b.1929)

864 Confitemini Domino

Translation: Give thanks to the Lord for he is good.

Text: Psalm 117
Music: Jacques Berthier (1923-1994)

865 Eat this bread

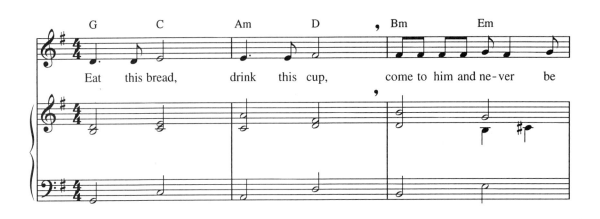

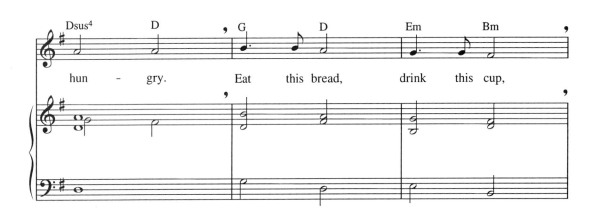

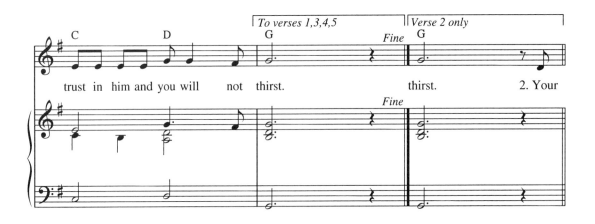

Verses: Cantor

1. Christ is the Bread of Life, the
2. an - ces - tors ate man - na in the des - ert, but
3. Eat his flesh, and drink his blood, and
4. A - ny - one who eats this bread will
5. If we be - lieve and eat this bread

Em   B

true bread sent from the Fa - ther.   D.C.
this is the bread come down from hea - ven.   D.C.
Christ will raise you up on the last day.   D.C.
live for e - ver.   D.C.
we will have e - ter - nal life.   D.C.

Em   D   D.C.

* Choose either part.

Text: Taizé Community based on Scripture
Music: Jacques Berthier (1923-1994)

866 Exaudi nos, Domine

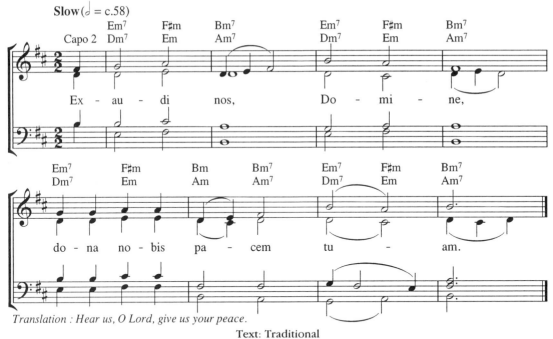

Ex-au-di nos, Do-mi-ne, do-na no-bis pa-cem tu-am.

Translation : Hear us, O Lord, give us your peace.

Text: Traditional
Music: Margaret Rizza (b.1929)
Music © Copyright 1998 Kevin Mayhew Ltd.

867 Holy God

Unison

Ho-ly God, we place our-selves in-to your hands. Bless us and care for us, be gra-cious and lov-ing to us; look kind-ly up-on us, and give us peace.

Text: Kevin Mayhew based on the Aaronic Blessing (Numbers 6:24-26)
Music: Kevin Mayhew (b.1942)

Music © Copyright 1996 Kevin Mayhew Ltd.

868 In the Lord I'll be ever thankful

Text: Taizé Community
Music: Jacques Berthier (1923-1994)

869 In the Lord is my joy

Text and Music: Margaret Rizza (b.1929)
© Copyright 1998 Kevin Mayhew Ltd.

870 Jesus, remember me

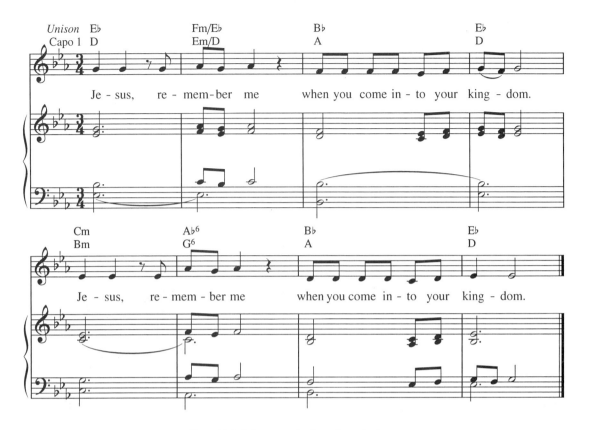

Je-sus, re-mem-ber me when you come in-to your king-dom.

Je-sus, re-mem-ber me when you come in-to your king-dom.

Text: Taizé Community based on Scripture
Music: Jacques Berthier (1923-1994)

871 Jubilate Deo

This may be sung as a round, the voices entering as indicated.

Ju - bi - la-te De-o, Ju-bi-la-te De-o, al - le-lu - ia.

Translation: Rejoice in God.

Text: from Psalm 32
Music: Michael Praetorius (1571-1621)

872 Jubilate Deo (Servite)

This may be sung as a 2-part round, the voices entering as indicated.

Joyfully

Ju - bi - la - te De - o om - nis ter - ra.

Ser - vi - te Do - mi - no in læ - ti - ti - a.

Al - le - lu - ia, al - le - lu - ia, in læ - ti - ti - a.

Last time

in læ - ti - ti - a!

Al - le - lu - ia, al - le - lu - ia, in læ - ti - ti - a.

Translation: Rejoice in God, all the earth. Serve the Lord with gladness.

Guitar

D   G   A

Text: Traditional
Music: Jacques Berthier (1923-1994)

873 Kindle a flame

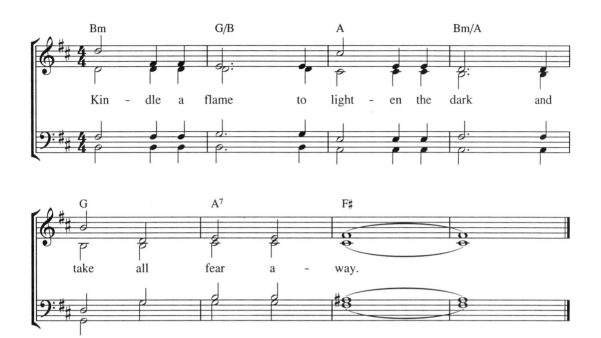

Kin - dle a flame to light - en the dark and take all fear a - way.

Text and Music: John L. Bell (b.1949) and Graham Maule (b.1958)

874 Laudate Dominum
Sing praise

Lau - da - te Do-mi-num, lau - da - te Do-mi-num, om - nes
Sing praise and bless the Lord, sing praise and bless the Lord, peo - ples,

gen - tes, al - le - lu - ia. Lau - da - te Do - mi - num,
na - tions, al - le - lu - ia. Sing praise and bless the Lord,

lau - da - te Do-mi-num, om - nes gen-tes, al - le - lu - ia.
sing praise and bless the Lord, peo-ples, na-tions, al - le - lu - ia.

These verses may be sung above the Refrain.

Verses: Cantor

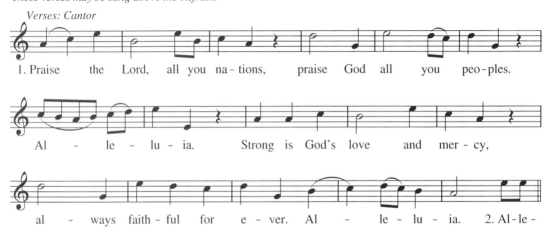

1. Praise the Lord, all you na-tions, praise God all you peo-ples.

Al - le - lu - ia. Strong is God's love and mer - cy,

al - ways faith-ful for e - ver. Al - le - lu - ia. 2. Al-le-

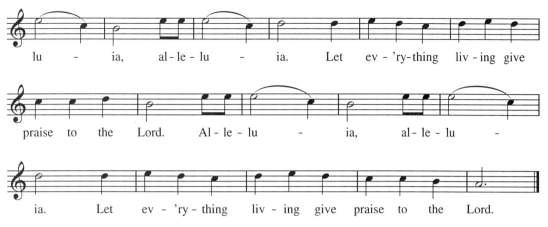

lu - ia, al-le-lu - ia. Let ev - 'ry-thing liv-ing give

praise to the Lord. Al-le-lu - ia, al-le-lu -

ia. Let ev - 'ry-thing liv-ing give praise to the Lord.

Text: Taizé Community, based on Scripture
Music: Jacques Berthier (1923-1994)

875 Laudate omnes gentes

Lau - da - te om-nes gen - tes, lau - da - te Do - mi - num. Lau -

da - te om-nes gen - tes, lau - da - te Do - mi - num.

Translation: All peoples, praise the Lord.

Text: from Psalm 116
Music: Jacques Berthier (1923-1994)

876 Lord of creation

Optional Soprano solo or flute

Ah,   ah,

Capo 1

| Fm | Eb | Fm | Eb | Fm | Gm | Fm | | Gm | | Fm |
| Em | D | Em | D | Em | F#m | Em | | F#m | | Em |

Cantor   *All*

Lord of cre - a - tion, may your will be done. Lord of cre -

| Bb | | Db | | Fm | Cm | F | | Bb |
| A | | C | | Em | Bm | E | | A |

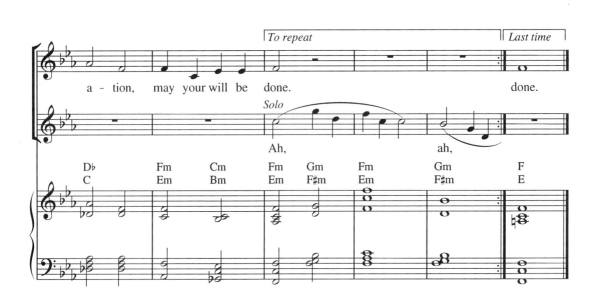

To repeat   *Last time*

a - tion, may your will be done.   done.

Solo

Ah,   ah,

| Db | | Fm | Cm | Fm | Gm | Fm | | Gm | | F |
| C | | Em | Bm | Em | F#m | Em | | F#m | | E |

Text and Music: Colin Mawby (b.1936)

877 Magnificat

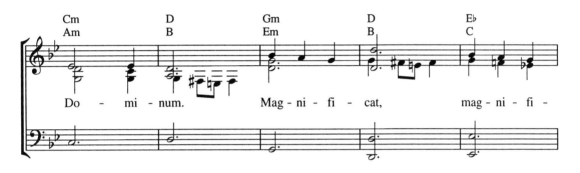

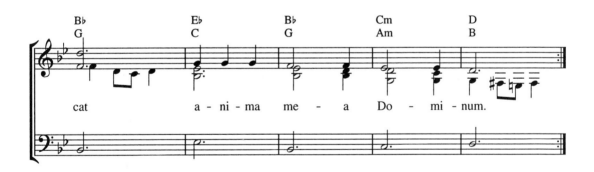

Translation: My soul praises and magnifies the Lord.

Text: Luke 1:46
Music: Margaret Rizza (b.1929)

878 May the Lord bless you
A Blessing

Text: Gaelic Blessing, adapted by Margaret Rizza (b.1929)
Music: Margaret Rizza (b.1929)

879 Misericordias Domini

Refrain

Mi- se- ri- cor- di- as Do- mi- ni in æ- ter- num can- ta- bo.

Translation: I will sing for ever of the mercy of the Lord

Verses: Cantor

1. From age to age, through all ge-ne-ra-tions, my mouth shall pro-claim your truth, O Lord.

2. Who, O God, who in the u-ni-verse can com-pare with you?

3. Blest be the Lord for e-ver through-out e-ter-ni-ty. A-men! A - men!

* Choose either part.

Accompaniment 1

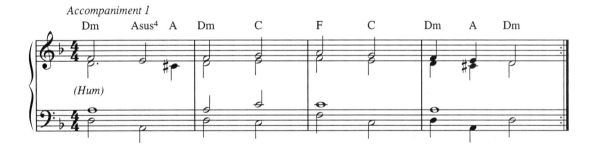

(Hum)

Accompaniment 2

Text: Psalm 88
Music: Jacques Berthier (1923-1994)

880 Nada te turbe
Nothing can trouble

Na - da te tur - be, na - da te es - pan - te.
No - thing can trou - ble, no - thing can fright - en.

Quien a Dios tie - ne na - da le fal - ta. Na - da te tur - be,
Those who seek God shall ne - ver go want - ing. No - thing can trou - ble,

na - da te es - pan - te. So - lo Dios ba - sta.
no - thing can fright - en. God a - lone fills us.

Text: St Teresa of Avila
Music: Jacques Berthier (1923-1994)

881 O Christe, Domine Jesu

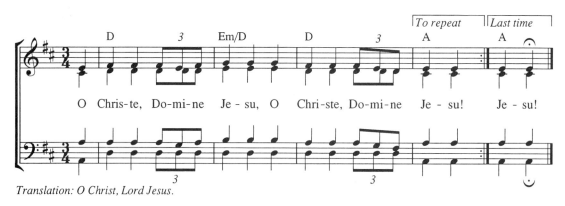

O Chris - te, Do - mi - ne Je - su, O Chri - ste, Do - mi - ne Je - su! Je - su!

Translation: O Christ, Lord Jesus.

These verses may be sung above the Refrain.

Verses: Cantor

1. The Lord is my shep - herd; there is no-thing I shall want.

Fresh and green are the pas - tures where he gives me re - pose. Near

rest-ful wa - ters he leads me, to re - vive my droop-ing spi - rit.

He guides me a - long the right path; he is true to his name. If I should

walk in the val- ley of dark - ness no e - vil would I fear.

2. You are there with your rod and staff; with these you give me com - fort.

You have pre-pared a ban - quet for me in the sight of my foes.

My head you have a - noin-ted with oil; my cup is o-ver - flow-ing. Sure-ly

good-ness and kind - ness shall fol-low me all the days of my life.

In the Lord's own house shall I dwell for e - ver and e - ver.

* *Choose either part.*

Text: Psalm 22
Music: Jacques Berthier (1923-1994)

882 O Lord, hear my prayer

Text: Taizé Community
Music: Jacques Berthier (1923-1994)

883 O Lord, my heart is not proud

Tru-ly I have set my soul in si - lence and peace; at rest, as a child in its mo-ther's arms, so is my soul. soul, so is my soul.

Text: Psalm 130
Music: Margaret Rizza (b.1929)

884 O Sacrament most holy

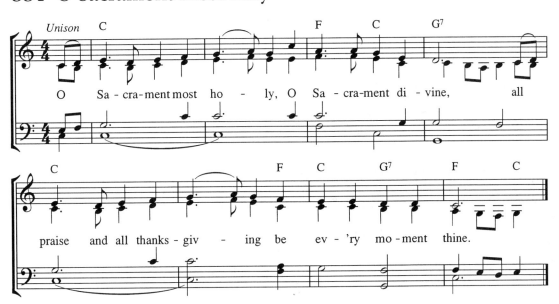

O Sa-cra-ment most ho - ly, O Sa-cra-ment di - vine, all praise and all thanks-giv - ing be ev-'ry mo-ment thine.

Text and Music: traditional arr. Nancy Benvenga
This arrangement © Copyright 1988 Kevin Mayhew Ltd.

885 Ostende nobis

This may be sung as a round, the voices entering as indicated.

Translation: *Lord, show us your mercy. Amen! Come soon!*

Text: Taizé Community
Music: Jacques Berthier (1923-1994)
© Copyright Ateliers et Presses de Taizé, Taizé-Communauté, F-71250, France. Used by permission.

886 Sanctum nomen Domini

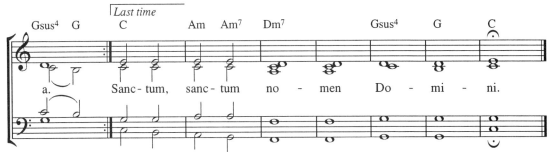

Translation: My soul magnifies the holy name of the Lord.

Text: Traditional
Music: Margaret Rizza (b.1929)

887 Silent, surrendered

Si-lent, sur-ren-dered, calm and still, o-pen to the
*Come, Ho-ly Spi-rit, bring us light, teach us, heal us,

word of God. Heart hum-bled to his will,
give us life. Come, Lord, O let our hearts

of-fered is the ser-vant of God. of-fered is the ser-vant of God.
flow with love and all that is true. flow with love and all that is true.

* *For use at Pentecost*

Text: v.1: Pamela Hayes; v.2: Margaret Rizza (b.1929)
Music: Margaret Rizza (b.1929)

888 Stay here and keep watch

Text: Taizé Community from Matthew 26
Music: Jacques Berthier (1923-1994)
© Copyright 1984 Ateliers et Presses de Taizé, Taizé-Communauté, F-71250, France. Used by permission.

889 Stay with me

*Choose either part

Text: Matthew 26: 36-42
Music: Jacques Berthier (1923-1994)

890 Surrexit Christus

Translation: *Christ is risen. Sing to the Lord.*

These verses may be sung above the Refrain.

* Choose either part.

4. Fire and heat, bless the Lord. And
you, light and dark - ness, bless the Lord.

5. Spi - rits and souls of the just, bless the Lord.
Saints and the hum- ble- heart- ed, bless the Lord.

Text: from Daniel 3
Music: Jacques Berthier (1923-1994)

891 The Lord is my light

The Lord is my light, in him I trust. The trust. The

Lord is my light, in him I trust, in him I trust.

Text: from Psalm 26
Music: Margaret Rizza (b.1929)
© Copyright 1998 Kevin Mayhew Ltd.

LITURGICAL

HYMNS OLD & NEW

892 The Lord is my song

The Lord is my song, the Lord is my praise: all my hope comes from God. The Lord is my song, the Lord is my praise: God, the well-spring of life.

Text: Taizé Community
Music: Jacques Berthier (1923-1994)

893 Ubi caritas

Cantor(s)

1. Your

2. May your

3. Let us *

4. Let us be

5. The love of *

6. The love of *

All
U – bi ca – ri – tas et a – mor.

F   C   Dm   Bb   D   G   C
Capo 3 D   A   Bm   G   B   E   A

* *Choose either part, or divide.*

© Copyright Ateliers et Presses de Taizé, Taizé-Communauté, F-71250, France. Used by permission.

(1) love, O Je - sus Christ, has ga-thered us to - geth-er.

(2) love, O Je - sus Christ, be fore-most in our lives.

(3) love one an - o - ther as God has loved us.

(4) one in love to - ge - ther in the one bread of Christ.

(5) God in Je - sus Christ bears e - ter - nal joy.

(6) God in Je - sus Christ will ne - ver have an end.

U - bi ca - ri - tas De - us i - bi est.

| F | C | Dm | | Gm | C | F |
| D | A | Bm | | Em | A | D |

Text: Taizé Community
Music: Jacques Berthier (1923-1994)

894 Veni, lumen cordium
Come, light of our hearts

Translation: Come, light of our hearts. Come, Holy Spirit, come.

Text: Stephen Langton (1160-1228)
Music: Margaret Rizza (b.1929)

895 Veni, Sancte Spiritus (Vogler)

Translation: Come, Holy Spirit.

Music: George Vogler (1749-1814)

896 Veni, Sancte Spiritus (Walker)

2. Thou, of all con - so - lers, the best. Thou the soul's de - light-ful
guest; re - fresh-ing peace be - stow. Thou, in toil, my com - fort sweet; thou,
cool-ness in the heat. Thou, my sol - ace in time of woe.

3. Light im - mor - tal, light di - vine; fire of love, our
hearts re - fine, our in - most be - ing fill. Take thy grace a - way and
no - thing pure in us will stay, all our good is turned to ill.

4. Heal our wounds, our strength re - new, on our dry - ness
pour thy dew; wash guilt a - way, bend the stub-born heart, melt the froz - en,
warm the chill and guide the steps that go a - stray.

5. Seven - fold gifts on us be pleased to pour, who thee con - fess and
thee a - dore; bring us thy com-fort when we die; give us life with thee on
high; give us joys, give us joys that ne - ver end.

Text: Stephen Langton (1160-1228), trans. Edward Caswall (1814-1878), alt. Christopher Walker
Music: Christopher Walker (b.1947)

897 Wait for the Lord

Wait for the Lord, whose day is near.

Wait for the Lord: keep watch, take heart!

These verses may be sung above the Refrain.

Verses: Cantor

1. Pre-pare the way for the Lord. Make a straight path for God.

Pre-pare the way for the Lord.

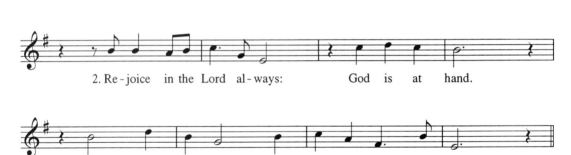

2. Re-joice in the Lord al-ways: God is at hand.

Joy and glad-ness for all who seek the Lord.

3. The glo-ry of the Lord shall be re-vealed. All the earth will see the Lord.

4. I wait-ed for the Lord. God heard my cry.

5. Our eyes are fixed on the Lord our God.

6. Seek first the king-dom of God. Seek and you shall find.

7. O Lord, show us your way. Guide us in your truth.

Text: Taizé Community, based on Scripture
Music: Jacques Berthier (1923-1994)

898 Within our darkest night

With-in our dark-est night, you kin - dle the fire that ne - ver dies a - way, that ne - ver dies a - way. With - in our dark-est night, you kin - dle the fire that ne - ver dies a - way, that ne - ver dies a - way.

Text: Taizé Community
Music: Jacques Berthier (1923-1994)
© Copyright Ateliers et Presses de Taizé, Taizé-Communauté, F-71250, France. Used by permission.

899 You are the centre

You are the cen - tre, you are my life, you are the cen - tre, O Lord, of my life. Come, Lord, and heal me, Lord of my life,

Text and Music: Margaret Rizza (b.1929)

LITURGICAL

HYMNS OLD & NEW

Responsorial Psalms

900 1st Advent (A)

Responsorial Psalm Psalm 121:1-2, 4-5, 6-9. ℟ cf. v.1

1. I rejoiced when I <u>heard</u> them say:
   'Let us go <u>to</u> God's house.'
   And now our <u>feet</u> are standing
   within your gates, <u>O</u> Jerusalem.

2. It is there that the <u>tribes</u> go up,
   the tribes <u>of</u> the Lord.
   For Israel's <u>law</u> it is,
   there to praise <u>the</u> Lord's name.

3. For the peace of Jeru<u>sa</u>lem pray:
   'Peace be <u>to</u> your homes!
   May peace reign <u>in</u> your walls,
   in your pal<u>a</u>ces, peace!'

4. For love of my bre<u>thren</u> and friends
   I say: 'Peace <u>upon</u> you!'
   For love of the house <u>of</u> the Lord
   I will ask <u>for</u> your good.

Gospel Acclamation Psalm 84.8
For musical setting see Nos 36 to 47

Alleluia.
Let us see, O <u>Lord</u>, your mercy
and give us your <u>saving</u> help.
Alleluia.

Response: Andrew Moore Psalm tone: Alan Rees

901 1st Advent (B)

Responsorial Psalm Psalm 79:2-3, 15-16, 18-19. Ry v.4

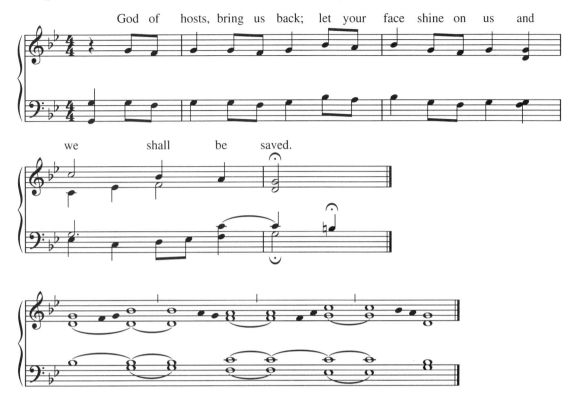

God of hosts, bring us back; let your face shine on us and we shall be saved.

1. O Shepherd of Israel, hear us,
   shine forth from your cherubim throne.
   O Lord, rouse up your might,
   O Lord, come to our help.

2. God of hosts, turn again, we implore,
   look down from heaven and see.
   Visit this vine and protect it,
   the vine your right hand has planted.

3. May your hand be on the one you have chosen,
   the one you have given your strength.
   And we shall never forsake you again:
   give us life that we may call upon your name.

Gospel Acclamation Psalm 84:8

For musical setting see Nos 36 to 47

Alleluia.
Let us see, O Lord, your mercy
and give us your saving help.
Alleluia.

Response: Andrew Moore Psalm tone: Gregory Murray

Text © 1963, 1986, 1993 The Grail, England, taken from 'The Psalms, a New Inclusive Language Version',
published by HarperCollins Religious. Used by permission of A.P. Watt Ltd, London.
Response © Copyright 1998 Kevin Mayhew Ltd.
Psalm tone © Copyright Downside Abbey, Stratton-on-the-Fosse, Bath BA3 4RH. Used by permission.

902　1st Advent (C)

Responsorial Psalm Psalm 24:4-5, 8-9, 10, 14. ℟ v.1

1. Lord, make me know your ways.
   Lord, teach me your paths.
   Make me walk in your truth, and teach me:
   for you are God my saviour.

2. The Lord is good and upright.
   He shows the path to those who stray,
   he guides the humble in the right path;
   he teaches his way to the poor.

3. His ways are faithfulness and love
   for those who keep his covenant and will.
   The Lord's friendship is for those who revere him;
   to them he reveals his covenant.

Gospel Acclamation Psalm 84:8
For musical setting see Nos 36 to 47

Alleluia.
Let us see, O Lord, your mercy
and give us your saving help.
Alleluia.

Response and Psalm tone: Alan Rees

903 2nd Advent (A)

Responsorial Psalm Psalm 71:1-2, 7-8, 12-13, 17. ℟ cf. v.7

In his days   jus-tice shall flou - rish and peace till the moon   fails.

1. O God, give your judgement to the king,
   to a king's son your justice,
   that he may judge your people in justice
   and your poor in right judgement.

2. In his days justice shall flourish
   and peace till the moon fails.
   He shall rule from sea to sea,
   from the Great River to earth's bounds.

3. For he shall save the poor when they cry
   and the needy who are helpless.
   He will have pity on the weak
   and save the lives of the poor.

4. May his name be blest for ever
   and endure like the sun.
   Every tribe shall be blest in him,
   all nations bless his name.

Gospel Acclamation Luke 3:4, 6
For musical setting see Nos 36 to 47

Alleluia.
Prepare a way for the Lord and make his paths straight,
and all mankind shall see the salvation of our God.
Alleluia.

Response: Stephen Dean   Psalm tone: Alan Rees

904 2nd Advent (B)

Responsorial Psalm Psalm 84:9-14. ℟ v.8

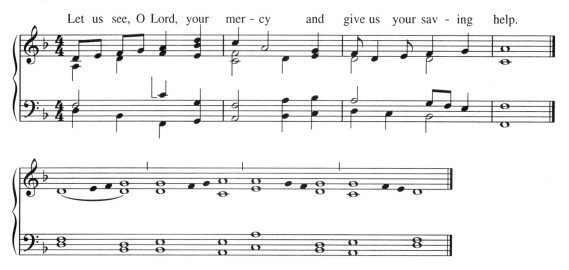

Let us see, O Lord, your mer - cy and give us your sav - ing help.

1. I will hear what the Lord God <u>has</u> to say,
   a voice that <u>speaks</u> of peace.
   His help is near for <u>those</u> who fear him
   and his glory will dwell <u>in</u> our land.

2. Mercy and faithful<u>ness</u> have met;
   justice and peace <u>have</u> embraced.
   Faithfulness shall spring <u>from</u> the earth
   and justice look <u>down</u> from heaven.

3. The Lord will <u>make</u> us prosper
   and our earth shall <u>yield</u> its fruit.
   Justice shall <u>march</u> before him
   and peace shall fo<u>llow</u> his steps.

Gospel Acclamation Luke 3:4, 6
For musical setting see Nos 36 to 47

Alleluia.
Prepare a way for the Lord and make <u>his</u> paths straight,
and all mankind shall see the salvation <u>of</u> our God.
Alleluia.

Response: Stephen Dean   Psalm tone: Laurence Bevenot

905 2nd Advent (C)

Responsorial Psalm Psalm 125. ℟ v.3

1. When the Lord delivered Z<u>io</u>n from bondage,
   it seemed <u>like</u> a dream.
   Then was our mouth <u>filled</u> with laughter,
   on our lips <u>there</u> were songs.

2. The heathens themselves <u>said</u>: 'What marvels
   the Lord <u>worked</u> for them!'
   What marvels the Lord <u>worked</u> for us!
   Indeed <u>we</u> were glad.

3. Deliver us, O Lord, <u>from</u> our bondage
   as streams <u>in</u> dry land.
   Those who are sow<u>ing</u> in tears
   will sing <u>when</u> they reap.

4. They go out, they go out, <u>full</u> of tears
   carrying seed <u>for</u> the sowing:
   they come back, they come back, <u>full</u> of song,
   carry<u>ing</u> their sheaves.

Gospel Acclamation Luke 3:4, 6
For musical setting see Nos 36 to 47

Alleluia.
Prepare a way for the Lord and make <u>his</u> paths straight,
and all mankind shall see the salvation <u>of</u> our God.
Alleluia.

Response: Martin Setchell Psalm tone: Gregory Murray

Text © 1963, 1986, 1993 The Grail, England, taken from 'The Psalms, a New Inclusive Language Version',
published by HarperCollins Religious. Used by permission of A.P. Watt Ltd, London.
Response © Copyright 1998 Kevin Mayhew Ltd.
Psalm tone © Copyright McCrimmon Publishing Co. Ltd, 10-12 High St, Great Wakering, Essex SS3 0EQ. Used by permission.

906 3rd Advent (A)

Responsorial Psalm Psalm 145:6-10. R/ cf. Isaiah 35:4

Come, Lord, and save us, come, Lord, and save us.

1. It is the Lord who keeps <u>faith</u> for ever,
   who is just to those who <u>are</u> oppressed.
   It is he who gives bread <u>to</u> the hungry,
   the Lord, who sets pri<u>son</u>ers free.

2. It is the Lord who gives sight <u>to</u> the blind,
   who raises up those who <u>are</u> bowed down,
   the Lord, who pro<u>tects</u> the stranger
   and upholds the wi<u>dow</u> and orphan.

3. It is the Lord who <u>loves</u> the just
   but thwarts the path <u>of</u> the wicked.
   The Lord will <u>reign</u> for ever,
   Zion's God, from <u>age</u> to age.

Gospel Acclamation Isaiah 61:1 (Luke 4:18)
For musical setting see Nos 36 to 47

Alleluia.
The spirit of the Lord has been <u>given</u> to me.
He has sent me to bring good news <u>to</u> the poor.
Alleluia.

Response: Richard Lloyd Psalm tone: Andrew Moore

907 3rd Advent (B)

Responsorial Psalm Luke 1:46-50, 53-54. ℟ Isaiah 61:10

1. My soul glorifies the Lord,
   my spirit rejoices in God, my Saviour.
   He looks on his servant in her nothingness;
   henceforth all ages will call me blessed.

2. The Almighty works marvels for me.
   Holy is his name!
   His mercy is from age to age,
   on those who fear him.

3. He fills the starving with good things,
   sends the rich away empty.
   He protects Israel, his servant,
   remembering his mercy.

Gospel Acclamation Isaiah 61:1 (Luke 4:18)
For musical setting see Nos 36 to 47

   Alleluia.
   The spirit of the Lord has been given to me.
   He has sent me to bring good news to the poor.
   Alleluia.

Response and Psalm tone: Andrew Moore

908 3rd Advent (C)

Responsorial Psalm Isaiah 12:2-6. R℣ v.6

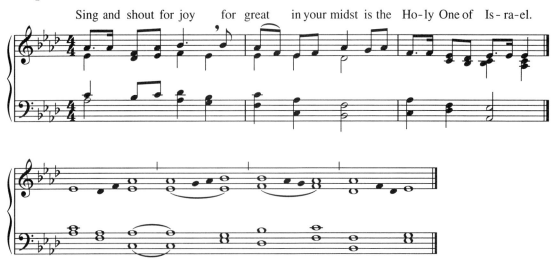

Sing and shout for joy   for great   in your midst is the Ho-ly One of Is-ra-el.

1. Truly, God is <u>my</u> salvation,
   I trust, I <u>shall</u> not fear.
   For the Lord is my <u>strength</u>, my song,
   he be<u>came</u> my saviour.

2. Give thanks <u>to</u> the Lord,
   give praise <u>to</u> his name!
   Make his mighty deeds known <u>to</u> the peoples!
   Declare the greatness <u>of</u> his name.

3. Sing a psalm to the Lord for he has done glor<u>i</u>ous deeds,
   make them known to <u>all</u> the earth!
   People of Zion, sing and <u>shout</u> for joy
   for great in your midst is the Holy <u>One</u> of Israel.

Gospel Acclamation Isaiah 61:1 (Luke 4:18)
For musical setting see Nos 36 to 47

Alleluia.
The spirit of the Lord has been <u>given</u> to me.
has sent me to bring good news <u>to</u> the poor.
Alleluia.

Response: Richard Lloyd   Psalm tone: Laurence Bevenot

909 4th Advent (A)

Responsorial Psalm Psalm 23:1-6. ℟ cf. vv. 7,10

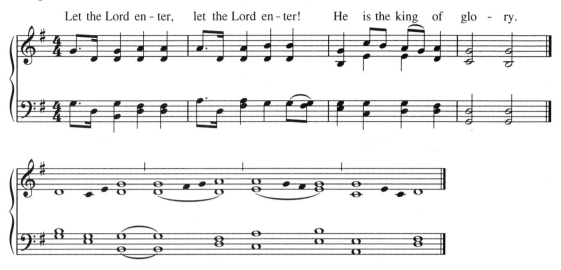

Let the Lord en-ter, let the Lord en-ter! He is the king of glo-ry.

1. The Lord's is the earth and its fullness,
   the world and all its peoples.
   It is he who set it on the seas;
   on the waters he made it firm.

2. Who shall climb the mountain of the Lord?
   Who shall stand in his holy place?
   Those with clean hands and pure heart,
   who desire not worthless things.

3. They shall receive blessings from the Lord
   and reward from the God who saves them.
   Such are the ones who seek him,
   seek the face of the God of Jacob.

Gospel Acclamation Matthew 1:23
For musical setting see Nos 36 to 47

Alleluia.
The virgin will conceive and give birth to a son
and they will call him Emmanuel, a name which means 'God-is-with-us'.
Alleluia.

Response: Alan Rees Psalm tone: Laurence Bevenot

910 4th Advent (B)

Responsorial Psalm Psalm 88:2-5, 27, 29. ℟ cf.v.2

1. I will sing for ever of your <u>love</u>, O Lord;
   through all ages my mouth will pro<u>claim</u> your truth.
   Of this I am sure, that your love <u>lasts</u> for ever,
   that your truth is firmly established <u>as</u> the heavens.

2. 'I have made a covenant <u>with</u> my chosen one;
   I have sworn to Da<u>vid</u> my servant:
   I will establish your dyna<u>sty</u> for ever
   and set up your throne <u>through</u> all ages.'

3. He will say to me: 'You <u>are</u> my father,
   my God, the <u>rock</u> who saves me.'
   I will keep my love <u>for</u> him always;
   for him my covenant <u>shall</u> endure.

Gospel Acclamation Luke 1:38
For musical setting see Nos 36 to 47

Alleluia.
I am the handmaid <u>of</u> the Lord:
let what you have <u>said</u> be done to me.
Alleluia.

Response and Psalm tone: Andrew Moore

911 4th Advent (C)

Responsorial Psalm Psalm 79:2-3, 15-16, 18-19. ℟ v.4

God of hosts, bring us back; let your face shine on us and we shall be saved.

1. O shepherd of Israel, hear us,
   shine forth from your che<u>ru</u>bim throne.
   O Lord, rouse <u>up</u> your might,
   O Lord, come <u>to</u> our help.

2. God of hosts, turn again, <u>we</u> implore,
   look down from hea<u>ven</u> and see.
   Visit this vine <u>and</u> protect it,
   the vine your right <u>hand</u> has planted.

3. May your hand be on the one <u>you</u> have chosen,
   the one you have gi<u>ven</u> your strength,
   and we shall never forsake <u>you</u> again:
   give us life that we may call u<u>pon</u> your name.

Gospel Acclamation Luke 1:38
For musical setting see Nos 36 to 47

Alleluia.
I am the handmaid <u>of</u> the Lord:
let what you have <u>said</u> be done to me.
Alleluia.

Response: Andrew Moore Psalm tone: Gregory Murray

912 The Nativity of Our Lord - Midnight Mass (A,B,C)

Responsorial Psalm Psalm 95:1-3, 11-13. ℟ Luke 2:11

1. O sing a new song to the Lord,
   sing to the Lord all the earth.
   O sing to the Lord, bless his name.
   Proclaim his help day by day,
   tell among the nations his glory
   and his wonders among all the peoples.

2. Let the heavens rejoice and earth be glad,
   let the sea and all within it thunder praise,
   let the land and all it bears rejoice,
   all the trees of the wood shout for joy
   at the presence of the Lord for he comes,
   he comes to rule the earth.

Gospel Acclamation Luke 2:10-11
For musical setting see Nos 36 to 47

> Alleluia.
> I bring you news of great joy:
> today a saviour has been born to us, Christ the Lord.
> Alleluia.

Response: Rosalie Bonighton Psalm tone: Andrew Moore

913 The Nativity of Our Lord - Mass During the Day (A,B,C)

Responsorial Psalm   Psalm 97:1-6. ℟ v.3

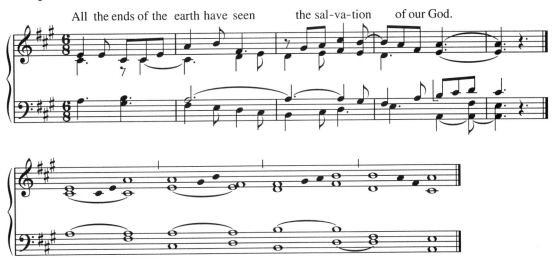

All the ends of the earth have seen   the sal-va-tion   of our God.

1. Sing a new song to the Lord
   for he has worked wonders.
   His right hand and his holy arm
   have brought salvation.

2. The Lord has made known his salvation;
   has shown his justice to the nations.
   He has remembered his truth and love
   for the house of Israel.

3. All the ends of the earth have seen
   the salvation of our God.
   Shout to the Lord all the earth,
   ring out your joy.

4. Sing psalms to the Lord with the harp,
   with the sound of music.
   With trumpets and the sound of the horn
   accalim the King, the Lord.

Gospel Acclamation
For musical setting see Nos 36 to 47

Alleluia.
Come, you nations, worship the Lord,
for today a great light has shone down upon the earth.
Alleluia.

Response: Richard Proulx   Psalm tone: Alan Rees

The Holy Family (A,B,C)

Responsorial Psalm Psalm 127:1-5. ℟ cf. v.1

1. O blessed are those who <u>fear</u> the Lord
   and walk <u>in</u> his ways!
   By the labour of your hands <u>you</u> shall eat.
   You will be hap<u>py</u> and prosper.

2. Your wife like a <u>fruit</u>ful vine
   in the heart <u>of</u> your house;
   your children like shoots <u>of</u> the olive,
   ar<u>ound</u> your table.

3. Indeed thus <u>shall</u> the blessed
   the man who <u>fears</u> the Lord.
   May the Lord bless <u>you</u> from Zion
   all the days <u>of</u> your life!

Gospel Acclamation Colossians 3:15, 16
For musical setting see Nos 36 to 47

Alleluia.
May the peace of Christ reign <u>in</u> your hearts;
let the message of Christ find a <u>home</u> within you.
Alleluia.

Response: Andrew Moore Psalm tone: Alan Rees

915 The Holy Family (B ad lib)

Responsorial Psalm Psalm 104:1-6, 8-9. ℟ vv. 7, 8

He, the Lord, is our God. He re-mem-bers his co-ven-ant for e - ver.

1. Give thanks to the Lord, <u>tell</u> his name,
   make known his deeds am<u>ong</u> the peoples.
   O sing to him, <u>sing</u> his praise;
   tell all his won<u>der</u>ful works!

2. Be proud of his <u>ho</u>ly name,
   let the hearts that seek the <u>Lord</u> rejoice.
   Consider the Lord <u>and</u> his strength;
   constantly <u>seek</u> his face.

3. Remember the wonders <u>he</u> has done,
   his miracles, the judg<u>ements</u> he spoke.
   O children of Abr<u>aham</u>, his servant,
   O sons of the Ja<u>cob</u> he chose.

4. He remembers his cove<u>nant</u> for ever,
   his promise for a thousand <u>generations</u>,
   the covenant he <u>made</u> with Abraham,
   the oath he <u>swore</u> to Isaac.

Gospel Acclamation Hebrews 1:1-2
For musical setting see Nos 36 to 47

Alleluia.
At various times <u>in</u> the past
and in various dif<u>ferent</u> ways,
God spoke to our ancestors <u>through</u> the prophets;
but in our own time, the last days, he has spoken to us <u>through</u> his Son.
Alleluia.

Note: the tone should be sung twice

Response: Stephen Dean Psalm tone: Laurence Bevenot

916 The Holy Family (C ad lib)

Responsorial Psalm Psalm 83:2-3, 5-6, 9-10. ℟ v.5

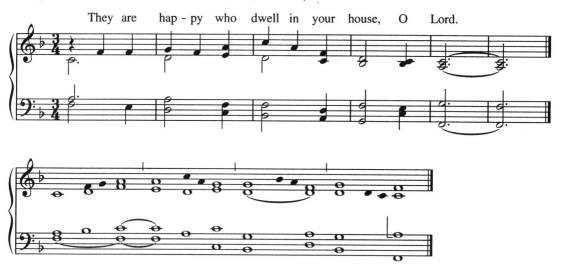

They are hap-py who dwell in your house, O Lord.

1. How lovely is your dwelling place,
   Lord God of hosts.
   My soul is longing and yearning,
   is yearning for the courts of the Lord.

2. They are happy, who dwell in your house,
   for ever singing your praise.
   They are happy, whose strength is in you;
   they walk with ever growing strength.

3. O Lord, God of hosts, hear my prayer,
   give ear, O God of Jacob.
   Turn your eyes, O God, our shield,
   look on the face of your anointed.

Gospel Acclamation cf. Acts 16:14
For musical setting see Nos 36 to 47

Alleluia.
Open our heart, O Lord,
to accept the words of your Son.
Alleluia.

Response: Rosalie Bonighton Psalm tone: Alan Rees

917 *1 January: Octave of Christmas*
Solemnity of Mary, Mother of God (A,B,C)

Responsorial Psalm Psalm 66:2-3, 5, 6, 8. ℟ v.2

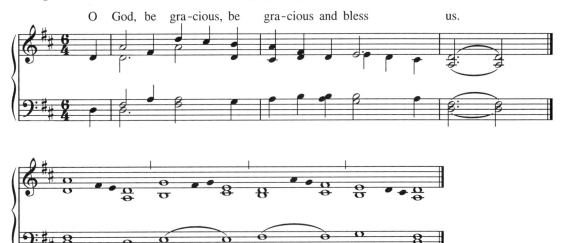

O God, be gra-cious, be gra-cious and bless us.

1. God, be gracious and bless us
   and let your face shed its light upon us.
   So will your ways be known upon earth
   and all nations learn your saving help.

2. Let the nations be glad and exult
   for you rule the world with justice.
   With fairness you rule the peoples,
   you guide the nations on earth.

3. Let the peoples praise you, O God;
   let all the peoples praise you.
   May God still give us his blessing
   till the ends of the earth revere him.

Gospel Acclamation Hebrews 1:1-2
For musical setting see Nos 36 to 47

Alleluia.
At various times in the past
and in various different ways,
God spoke to our ancestors through the prophets;
but in our own time, the last days, he has spoken to us through his Son.
Alleluia.

Note: the tone should be sung twice

Response: Alan Rees Psalm tone: Andrew Moore

918 2nd after Christmas (A,B,C)

Responsorial Psalm Psalm 147:12-15, 19-20. ℟ John 1:14

1. O praise the <u>Lord</u>, Jerusalem!
   Zion, <u>praise</u> your God!
   He has strengthened the bars <u>of</u> your gates,
   he has blessed the chil<u>dren</u> within you.

2. He established peace <u>on</u> your borders,
   he feeds you with <u>fin</u>est wheat.
   He sends out his word <u>to</u> the earth
   and swiftly runs <u>his</u> command.

3. He makes his word <u>known</u> to Jacob,
   to Israel his laws <u>and</u> decrees.
   He has not dealt thus with <u>other</u> nations;
   he has not taught them <u>his</u> decrees.

Gospel Acclamation cf. 1 Timothy 3:16
For musical setting see Nos 36 to 47

Alleluia.
Glory be to you, O Christ, proclaimed <u>to</u> the pagans;
Glory be to you, O Christ, believed in <u>by</u> the world.
Alleluia.

Response: Colin Mawby   Psalm tone: Gregory Murray

6 January or the Sunday between 2 January and 8 January
The Epiphany of the Lord (A,B,C)

Responsorial Psalm Psalm 71:1-2, 7-8, 10-13. ℟ cf. v.11

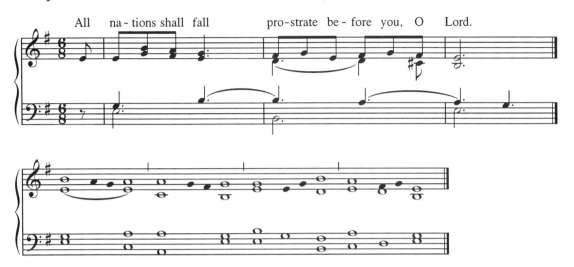

1. O God, give your judgement to the king,
   to a king's son your justice,
   that he may judge your people in justice
   and your poor in right judgement.

2. In his days justice shall flourish
   and peace till the moon fails.
   He shall rule from sea to sea,
   from the Great River to earth's bounds.

3. The kings of Tarshish and the sea coasts
      shall pay him tribute.
   The kings of Sheba and Seba shall bring him gifts.
   Before him all kings shall fall prostrate,
   all nations shall serve him.

4. For he shall save the poor when they cry
   and the needy who are helpless.
   He will have pity on the weak
   and save the lives of the poor.

Gospel Acclamation Matthew 2:2
For musical setting see Nos 36 to 47

Alleluia.
We saw his star as it rose
and have come to pay homage to the Lord.
Alleluia.

Response: Andrew Moore   Psalm tone: Gregory Murray

920 The Baptism of the Lord (A)

Responsorial Psalm Psalm 28:1-4, 9-10. ℟ v.11

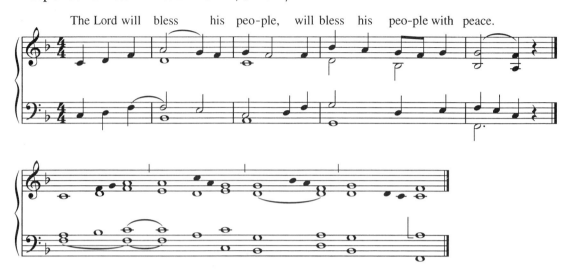

1. O give the Lord you chil<u>dren</u> of God,
   give the Lord glo<u>ry</u> and power;
   give the Lord the glory <u>of</u> his name.
   Adore the Lord in his <u>ho</u>ly court.

2. The Lord's voice resounding <u>on</u> the waters,
   the Lord on the immensi<u>ty</u> of waters;
   the voice of the Lord, <u>full</u> of power,
   the voice of the Lord, <u>full</u> of splendour.

3. The God of <u>glo</u>ry thunders.
   In his temple they <u>all</u> cry: 'Glory!'
   The Lord sat enthroned o<u>ver</u> the flood;
   the Lord sits as <u>king</u> for ever.

Gospel Acclamation cf. Mark 9:8
For musical setting see Nos 36 to 47

Alleluia.
The heavens opened and the Father's <u>voice</u> resounded:
'This is my Son, the Beloved. Lis<u>ten</u> to him.'
Alleluia.

Response: Richard Lloyd Psalm tone: Alan Rees

921 The Baptism of the Lord (B ad lib)

Responsorial Psalm Isaiah 12:2-6. ℞ v.6

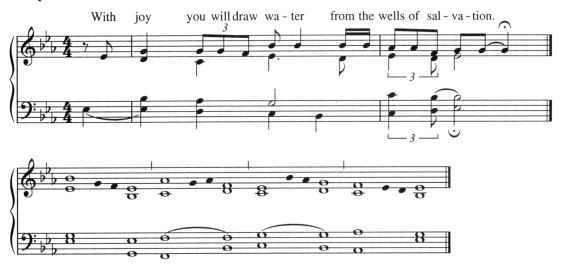

1. Truly, God is my salvation
   I trust, I shall not fear.
   For the Lord is my strength, my song,
   he became my saviour.

2. Give thanks to the Lord,
   give praise to his name!
   Make his mighty deeds known to the peoples!
   Declare the greatness of his name.

3. Sing a psalm to the Lord for he has done glorious deeds,
   make them known to all the earth!
   People of Zion, sing and shout for joy
   for great in your midst is the Holy One of Israel.

Gospel Acclamation cf. John 1:29
For musical setting see Nos 36 to 47

Alleluia.
John saw Jesus coming towards him, and said:
This is the Lamb of God who takes away the sin of the world.
Alleluia.

Response and Psalm tone: Andrew Moore

922 The Baptism of the Lord (C ad lib)

Responsorial Psalm Psalm 103:1-2, 3-4, 24-25, 27-30. ℟ v.1

Bless the Lord, my soul! Lord God, how great you are.

1. Lord God, how <u>great</u> you are,
   clothed in majes<u>ty</u> and glory,
   wrapped in light as <u>in</u> a robe!
   You stretch out the heavens <u>like</u> a tent.

2. The earth is full <u>of</u> your riches.
   There is the sea, <u>vast</u> and wide,
   with its moving <u>swarms</u> past counting,
   living things <u>great</u> and small.

3. All of these <u>look</u> to you
   to give them their food <u>in</u> due season.
   You give it, they <u>gather</u> it up:
   you open your hand, they <u>have</u> their fill.

4. You take back your sp<u>irit</u>, they die,
   returning to the dust from <u>which</u> they came.
   You send forth your spirit, they <u>are</u> created;
   and you renew the face <u>of</u> the earth.

Gospel Acclamation cf. Luke 3:16
For musical setting see Nos 36 to 47

Alleluia.
Someone is coming, said John, someone <u>greater</u> than I.
He will baptise you with the Holy Spirit <u>and</u> with fire.
Alleluia.

Response: Andrew Moore Psalm tone: Laurence Bevenot

923 Ash Wednesday (A,B,C)

Responsorial Psalm Psalm 50:3-6, 12-14, 17. ℟ v.3

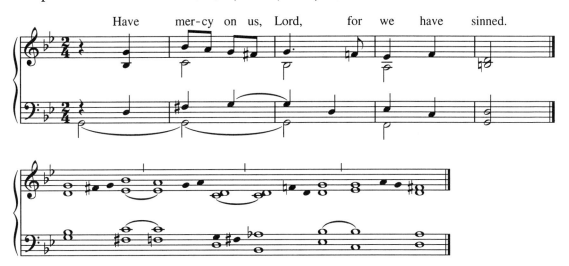

1. Have mercy on me, God, <u>in</u> your kindness.
   In your compassion blot out <u>my</u> offence.
   O wash me more and more <u>from</u> my guilt
   and cleanse me <u>from</u> my sin.

2. My offences tru<u>ly</u> I know them;
   my sin is al<u>ways</u> before me.
   Against you, you alone, <u>have</u> I sinned;
   what is evil in your sight <u>I</u> have done.

3. A pure heart create for <u>me</u>, O God,
   put a steadfast sp<u>ir</u>it within me.
   Do not cast me away <u>from</u> your presence,
   nor deprive me of your <u>ho</u>ly spirit.

4. Give me again the joy <u>of</u> your help;
   with a spirit of fer<u>vour</u> sustain me.
   O Lord, <u>op</u>en my lips
   and my mouth shall de<u>clare</u> your praise.

Gospel Acclamation Psalm 50:12, 14
*One of the responses Nos 53 to 55 should be
sung before and after this text.*

A pure heart create for <u>me</u>, O God,
and give me again the joy <u>of</u> your help.

or cf. Psalm 94:8

Harden not your <u>hearts</u> today,
but listen to the voice <u>of</u> the Lord.

Response and Psalm tone: Andrew Moore

924 1st Lent (A)

Responsorial Psalm Psalm 50:3-6, 12-14, 17. ℟ v.3

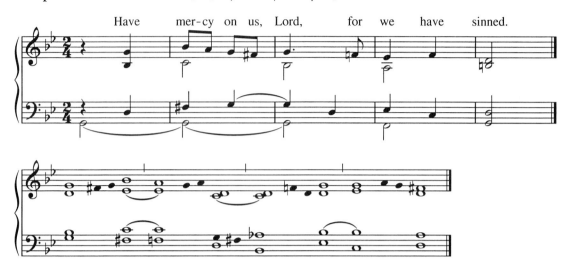

1. Have mercy on me, God, <u>in</u> your kindness.
   In your compassion blot out <u>my</u> offence.
   O wash me more and more <u>from</u> my guilt
   and cleanse me <u>from</u> my sin.

2. My offences tru<u>ly</u> I know them;
   my sin is al<u>ways</u> before me.
   Against you, you alone, <u>have</u> I sinned;
   what is evil in your sight <u>I</u> have done.

3. A pure heart create for <u>me</u>, O God,
   put a steadfast sp<u>irit</u> within me.
   Do not cast me away <u>from</u> your presence,
   nor deprive me of your <u>ho</u>ly spirit.

4. Give me again the joy <u>of</u> your help;
   with a spirit of fer<u>vour</u> sustain me.
   O Lord, o<u>pen</u> my lips

Gospel Acclamation Matthew 4:4
One of the responses Nos 53 to 55 should
be sung before and after this text.

   Man does not live on <u>bread</u> alone,
   but on every word that comes from the <u>mouth</u> of God.

Response and Psalm tone: Andrew Moore

925 1st Lent (B)

Responsorial Psalm Psalm 24:4-9. ℟ cf. v.10

1. Lord, make me <u>know</u> your ways.
   Lord, teach <u>me</u> your paths.
   Make me walk in your <u>truth</u>, and teach me:
   for you are <u>God</u> my saviour.

2. Remember your <u>mercy</u>, Lord,
   and the love you have shown <u>from</u> of old.
   In your <u>love</u> remember me,
   because of your good<u>ness</u>, O Lord.

3. The Lord is <u>good</u> and upright.
   He shows the path to <u>those</u> who stray,
   he guides the humble in <u>the</u> right path;
   he teaches his way <u>to</u> the poor.

Gospel Acclamation Matthew 4:4
*One of the responses Nos 53 to 55 should
be sung before and after this text.*

Man does not live on <u>bread</u> alone,
but on every word that comes from the <u>mouth</u> of God.

Response: Rosalie Bonighton   Psalm tone: Laurence Bevenot

926 1st Lent (C)

Responsorial Psalm Psalm 90:1-2, 10-15. ℟ v.15

1. He who dwells in the shelter of the Most High
   and abides in the shade of the Almighty,
   says to the Lord: 'My refuge,
   my stronghold, my God in whom I trust!'

2. Upon you no evil shall fall,
   no plague approach where you dwell.
   For you has he commanded his angels,
   to keep you in all your ways.

3. They shall bear you upon their hands
   lest you strike your foot against a stone.
   On the lion and the viper you will tread
   and trample the young lion and the dragon.

4. His love he set on me, so I will rescue him;
   protect him for he knows my name.
   When he calls I shall answer: 'I am with you.'
   I will save him in distress and give him glory.

Gospel Acclamation Matthew 4:4

*One of the responses Nos 53 to 55 should
be sung before and after this text.*

Man does not live on bread alone,
but on every word that comes from the mouth of God.

Response and Psalm tone: Andrew Moore

927 2nd Lent (A)

Responsorial Psalm Psalm 32:4-5, 18-20, 22. ℟ v.22

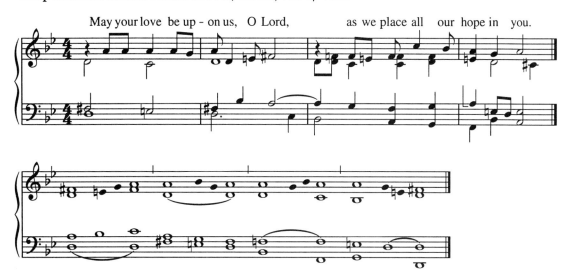

1. The word of the Lord is faithful
   and all his works to be trusted.
   The Lord loves justice and right
   and fills the earth with his love.

2. The Lord looks on those who revere him,
   on those who hope in his love,
   to rescue their souls from death,
   to keep them alive in famine.

3. Our soul is waiting for the Lord.
   The Lord is our help and our shield.
   May your love be upon us, O Lord,
   as we place all our hope in you.

Gospel Acclamation Matthew 17:5
*One of the responses Nos 53 to 55 should
be sung before and after this text.*

From the bright cloud the Father's voice was heard:
'This is my Son, the Beloved. Listen to him.'

Response: Rosalie Bonighton Psalm tone: Laurence Bevenot

928 2nd Lent (B)

Responsorial Psalm Psalm 115:10, 15-19. ℟ Psalm 114:9

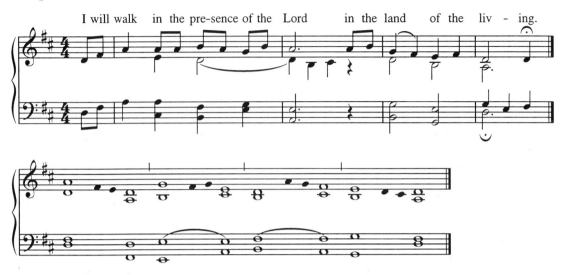

1. I trusted, even <u>when</u> I said:
   'I am sore<u>ly</u> afflicted.'
   O precious in the eyes <u>of</u> the Lord
   is the death <u>of</u> his faithful.

2. Your servant, Lord, your ser<u>vant</u> am I;
   you have loo<u>sened</u> my bonds.
   A thanksgiving sacri<u>fice</u> I make:
   I will call on <u>the</u> Lord's name.

3. My vows to the Lord I <u>will</u> fulfil
   before <u>all</u> his people,
   in the courts of the house <u>of</u> the Lord,
   in your midst, <u>O</u> Jerusalem.

Gospel Acclamation Matthew 17:5
*One of the responses Nos 53 to 55 should
be sung before and after this text.*

From the bright cloud the Father's <u>voice</u> was heard:
'This is my Son, the Beloved. Li<u>sten</u> to him.'

Response and Psalm tone: Andrew Moore

929 2nd Lent (C)

Responsorial Psalm Psalm 26:1, 7-9, 13-14. ℟ v.1

1. The Lord is my light <u>and</u> my help;
   whom <u>shall</u> I fear?
   The Lord is the stronghold <u>of</u> my life;
   before whom <u>shall</u> I shrink?

2. O Lord, hear my voice <u>when</u> I call;
   have mer<u>cy</u> and answer.
   Of you my <u>heart</u> has spoken:
   '<u>Seek</u> his face.'

3. It is your face, O Lord, <u>that</u> I seek;
   hide <u>not</u> your face.
   Dismiss not your ser<u>vant</u> in anger;
   you have <u>been</u> my help.

4. I am sure I shall see <u>the</u> Lord's goodness
   in the land <u>of</u> the living.
   Hope in him, hold firm <u>and</u> take heart.
   Hope <u>in</u> the Lord!

Gospel Acclamation Matthew 17:5
*One of the responses Nos 53 to 55 should
be sung before and after this text.*

From the bright cloud the Father's <u>voice</u> was heard:
'This is my Son, the Beloved. <u>Lis</u>ten to him.'

Response: Richard Lloyd Psalm tone: Alan Rees

930 3rd Lent (A)

Responsorial Psalm Psalm 94:1-2, 6-9. ℟ v.8

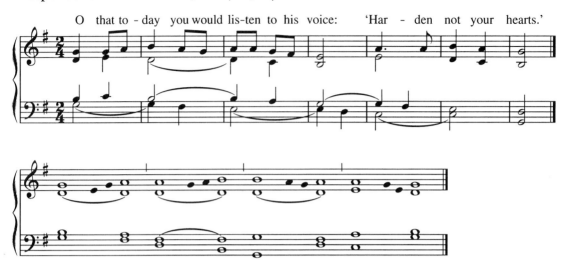

1. Come, ring out our joy to the Lord;
   hail the rock who saves us.
   Let us come before him, giving thanks,
   with songs let us hail the Lord.

2. Come in; let us bow and bend low;
   let us kneel before the God who made us
   for he is our God, and we the people who
      belong to his pasture,
   the flock that is led by his hand.

3. O that today you would listen to his voice!
   'Harden not your hearts as at Meribah,
   as on that day as Massah in the desert, when
      your fathers put me to the test;
   when they tried me, though they saw my work.'

Gospel Acclamation cf. John 4:42, 15
*One of the responses Nos 53 to 55 should be
sung before and after this text.*

Lord, you are really the saviour of the world;
give me the living water, so that I may never get thirsty.

Response and Psalm tone: Gregory Murray

931 3rd Lent (B)

Responsorial Psalm Psalm 18:8-11. ℟ John 6:68

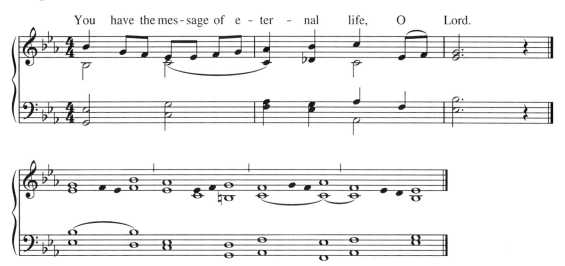

1. The law of the <u>Lord</u> is perfect,
   it re<u>vives</u> the soul.
   The rule of the Lord is <u>to</u> be trusted,
   it gives wisdom <u>to</u> the simple.

2. The precepts of the <u>Lord</u> are right,
   they <u>gladden</u> the heart.
   The command of the <u>Lord</u> is clear,
   it gives light <u>to</u> the eyes.

3. The fear of the <u>Lord</u> is holy,
   a<u>biding</u> for ever.
   The decrees of the <u>Lord</u> are truth
   and all <u>of</u> them just.

4. They are more to be de<u>sired</u> than gold,
   than the p<u>urest</u> of gold
   and sweeter are <u>they</u> than honey,
   than honey <u>from</u> the comb.

Gospel Acclamation John 11:25-26
*One of the responses Nos 53 to 55 should be
sung before and after this text.*

I am the resurrection and the life, <u>says</u> the Lord,
whoever believes in me will <u>never</u> die.

Response and Psalm tone: Andrew Moore

932 3rd Lent (C)

Responsorial Psalm Psalm 102:1-4, 6-8, 11. ℟ v.8

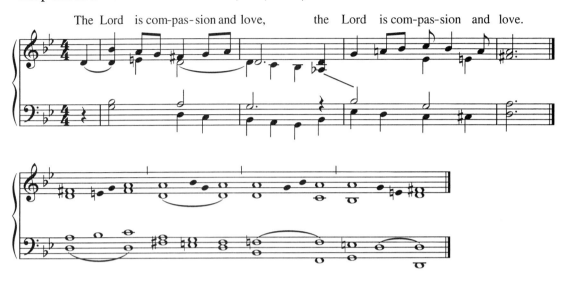

The Lord is com-pas-sion and love, the Lord is com-pas-sion and love.

1. My soul, give thanks <u>to</u> the Lord,
   all my being, bless his <u>ho</u>ly name.
   My soul give thanks <u>to</u> the Lord
   and never forget <u>all</u> his blessings.

2. It is he who forgives <u>all</u> your guilt,
   who heals every one <u>of</u> your ills,
   who redeems your life <u>from</u> the grave,
   who crowns you with love <u>and</u> compassion.

3. The Lord does <u>deeds</u> of justice,
   gives judgement for all who <u>are</u> oppressed.
   He made known his <u>ways</u> to Moses
   and his deeds to Is<u>ra</u>el's sons.

4. The Lord is compa<u>ssion</u> and love,
   slow to anger and <u>rich</u> in mercy,
   for as the heavens are high a<u>bove</u> the earth
   so strong is his love for <u>those</u> who fear him.

Gospel Acclamation Matthew 4:17
*One of the responses Nos 53 to 55 should be sung
before and after this text.*

Repent, <u>says</u> the Lord,
for the kingdom of heaven is <u>close</u> at hand.

Response: Andrew Moore Psalm tone: Laurence Bevenot

933 4th Lent (A)

Responsorial Psalm Psalm 22. ℟ v.1

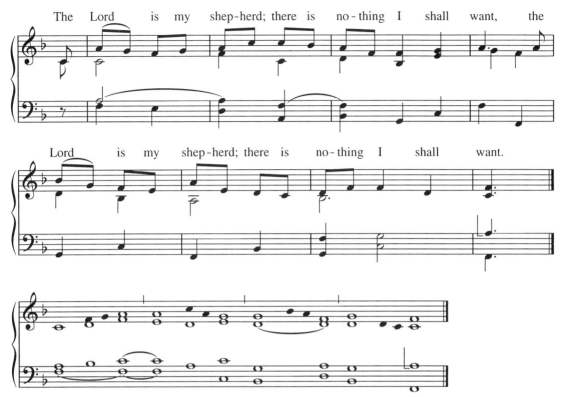

1. The Lord is my shepherd;
   there is nothing I shall want.
   Fresh and green are the pastures
   where he gives me repose.

2. Near restful waters he leads me,
   to revive my drooping spirit.
   He guides me along the right path;
   he is true to his name.

3. If I should walk in the valley of darkness
   no evil would I fear.
   You are there with your crook and your staff;
   with these you give me comfort.

4. You have prepared a banquet for me
   in the sight of my foes.
   My head you have anointed with oil;
   my cup is overflowing.

5. Surely goodness and kindness shall follow me
   all the days of my life.
   In the Lord's own house shall I dwell
   for ever and ever.

   Note: verse 3 may be omitted

Gospel Acclamation John 8:12
*One of the responses Nos 53 to 55 should
be sung before and after this text.*

I am the light of the world, says the Lord;
anyone who follows me will have the light of life.

Response: Andrew Moore Psalm tone: Alan Rees

934 4th Lent (B)

Responsorial Psalm Psalm 136. R℣ v.6

1. By the rivers of Babylon there we <u>sat</u> and wept,
   remem<u>ber</u>ing Zion;
   on the pop<u>lars</u> that grew there
   we hung <u>up</u> our harps.

2. For it was there that they asked us, our cap<u>tors</u>, for songs,
   our oppress<u>ors</u>, for joy.
   'Sing to <u>us</u>,' they said,
   'one of <u>Zion</u>'s songs.'

3. O how could we sing the song <u>of</u> the Lord
   on a<u>li</u>en soil?
   If I forget <u>you</u>, Jerusalem,
   let my <u>right</u> hand wither!

4. O let my tongue cleave <u>to</u> my mouth
   if I remem<u>ber</u> you not,
   if I prize <u>not</u> Jerusalem
   above <u>all</u> my joys!

Gospel Acclamation John 3:16
*One of the responses Nos 53 to 55 should
be sung before and after this text.*

God loved the world so much that he gave his <u>only</u> Son;
everyone who believes in him has e<u>ter</u>nal life.

Response and Psalm tone: Andrew Moore

935 4th Lent (C)

Responsorial Psalm Psalm 33:2-7. ℟ v.9

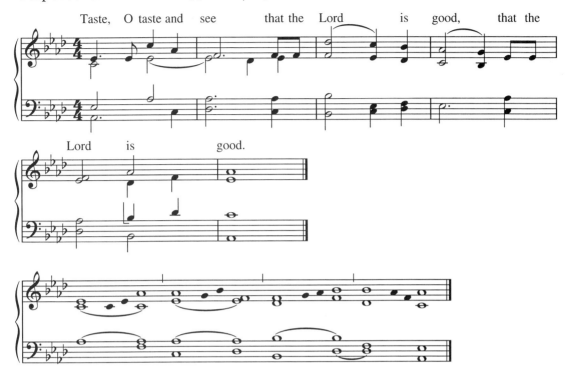

1. I will bless the Lord <u>at</u> all times,
   his praise always <u>on</u> my lips;
   in the Lord my soul shall <u>make</u> its boast.
   The humble shall hear <u>and</u> be glad.

2. Glorify the <u>Lord</u> with me.
   Together let us <u>praise</u> his name.
   I sought the Lord <u>and</u> he answered me;
   from all my terrors he <u>set</u> me free.

3. Look towards him <u>and</u> be radiant;
   let your faces not <u>be</u> abashed.
   This poor man called; <u>the</u> Lord heard him
   and rescued him from all <u>his</u> distress.

Gospel Acclamation Luke 15:18
*One of the responses Nos 53 to 55 should
be sung before and after this text.*

I will leave this place and go to my <u>father</u> and say:
'Father, I have sinned against heaven and <u>against</u> you.'

Response and Psalm tone: Alan Rees

936 5th Lent (A)

Responsorial Psalm Psalm 129. ℟ v.7

With the Lord there is mer - cy and full -ness of re - demp - tion.

1. Out of the depths I cry to you, O Lord,
   Lord, hear my voice!
   O let your ears be attentive
   to the voice of my pleading.

2. If you, O Lord, should mark our guilt,
   Lord, who would survive?
   But with you is found forgiveness:
   for this we revere you.

3. My soul is waiting for the Lord,
   I count on his word.
   My soul is longing for the Lord
   more than watchman for daybreak.

4. Because with the Lord there is mercy
   and fullness of redemption,
   Israel indeed he will redeem
   from all its iniquity.

Gospel Acclamation John 11:25, 26
*One of the responses Nos 53 to 55 should
be sung before and after this text.*

I am the resurrection and the life, says the Lord;
whoever believes in me will never die.

Response: Alan Rees Psalm tone: Andrew Moore

937 5th Lent (B)

Responsorial Psalm Psalm 50:3-4, 12-15. ℟ v.12

A pure heart cre-ate for me, for me, O God.

1. Have mercy on me, God, <u>in</u> your kindness.
   In your compassion blot out <u>my</u> offence.
   O wash me more and more <u>from</u> my guilt
   and cleanse me <u>from</u> my sin.

2. A pure heart create for <u>me</u>, O God,
   put a steadfast sp<u>ir</u>it within me.
   Do not cast me away <u>from</u> your presence,
   nor deprive me of your <u>ho</u>ly spirit.

3. Give me again the joy <u>of</u> your help;
   with a spirit of fer<u>vour</u> sustain me,
   that I may teach transgre<u>ssor</u>s your ways
   and sinners may re<u>tur</u>n to you.

Gospel Acclamation John 12:26
*One of the responses Nos 53 to 55 should
be sung before and after this text.*

If a man serves me, says the Lord, <u>he</u> must follow me,
wherever I am, my servant will <u>be</u> there too.

Response: Richard Lloyd Psalm tone: Gregory Murray

938 5th Lent (C)

Responsorial Psalm Psalm 125. R℣ v.3

1. When the Lord delivered Zion from bondage,
   it seemed like a dream.
   Then was our mouth filled with laughter,
   on our lips there were songs.

2. The heathens themselves said: 'What marvels
   the Lord worked for them!'
   What marvels the Lord worked for us!
   Indeed we were glad.

3. Deliver us, O Lord, from our bondage
   as streams in dry land.
   Those who are sowing in tears
   will sing when they reap.

4. They go out, they go out, full of tears,
   carrying seed for the sowing;
   they come back, they come back, full of song,
   carrying their sheaves.

Gospel Acclamation Amos 5:14

*One of the responses Nos 53 to 55 should
be sung before and after this text.*

Seek good and not evil so that you may live,
and that the Lord God of hosts may really be with you.

Response: Martin Setchell Psalm tone: Gregory Murray

939 Passion Sunday (A,B,C)

Responsorial Psalm Psalm 21:8-9, 17-20, 23-24. ℞ v.2

1. All who see me deride me,
   they curl their lips, they toss their heads.
   'He trusted in the Lord, let him save him;
   let him release him if this is his friend.'

2. Many dogs have surrounded me,
   a band of the wicked beset me.
   They tear holes in my hands and my feet
   I can count every one of my bones.

3. They divide my clothing among them.
   They cast lots for my robe.
   O Lord, do not leave me alone,
   my strength, make haste to help me!

4. I will tell of your name to my brethren
   and praise you where they are assembled.
   'You who fear the Lord give him praise;
   all sons of Jacob, give him glory.'

Gospel Acclamation Philippians 2:8-9
*One of the responses Nos 53 to 55 should
be sung before and after this text.*

Christ was humbler yet, even to accepting death, death on a cross.
But God raised him high and gave him the name which is above all names.

Response: Gregory Murray Psalm tone: Andrew Moore

940 Holy Thursday -
Evening Mass of the Lord's Supper (A,B,C)

Responsorial Psalm Psalm 115:12-13, 15-18. ℟ cf. 1 Corinthians 10:16

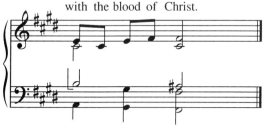

1. How can I repay the Lord
   for his goodness to me?
   The cup of salvation I will raise;
   I will call on the Lord's name.

2. O precious in the eyes of the Lord
   is the death of his faithful.
   Your servant, Lord, your servant am I;
   you have loosened my bonds.

3. A thanksgiving sacrifice I make:
   I will call on the Lord's name.
   My vows to the Lord I will fulfil
   before all his people.

Gospel Acclamation John 13:34
*One of the responses Nos 53 to 55 should
be sung before and after this text.*

I give you a new commandment:
love one another just as I have loved you, says the Lord.

Response: Richard Proulx   Psalm tone: Laurence Bevenot

941 Good Friday -
Celebration of the Lord's Passion (A,B,C)

Responsorial Psalm Psalm 30:2, 6, 12-13, 15-17, 25. ℟ Luke 23:46

Fa - ther, in - to your hands I com-mend my spi - rit.

1. In you, O Lord, I take refuge,
   let me never be put to shame.
   In your justice, set me free.
   It is you who will redeem me, Lord.

2. In the face of all my foes
   I am a reproach,
   an object of scorn to my neighbours
   and of fear to my friends.

3. Those who see me in the street
   run far away from me.
   I am like the dead, forgotten by all,
   like a thing thrown away.

4. But as for me, I trust in you, Lord,
   I say: 'You are my God.'
   My life is in your hands, deliver me
   from the hands of those who hate me.

5. Let your face shine on your servant.
   Save me in your love.
   Be strong, let your heart take courage,
   all who hope in the Lord.

Gospel Acclamation Philippians 2:8-9
*One of the responses Nos 53 to 55 should be
sung before and after this text.*

Christ was humbler yet, even to accepting death, death on a cross.
But God raised him high and gave him the name which is above all names.

Response and Psalm tone: Gregory Murray

After the first Reading

Responsorial Psalm Psalm 103:1-2, 5-6, 10, 12-14, 24, 35. ℟ cf. v.30

1. Bless the <u>Lord</u>, my soul!
   Lord God, how <u>great</u> you are,
   clothed in majes<u>ty</u> and glory,
   wrapped in light as <u>in</u> a robe!

2. You founded the earth <u>on</u> its base,
   to stand firm from <u>age</u> to age.
   You wrapped it with the ocean <u>like</u> a cloak:
   the waters stood higher <u>than</u> the mountains.

3. You make springs gush forth <u>in</u> the valleys:
   they flow in be<u>tween</u> the hills.
   On their banks dwell the <u>birds</u> of heaven;
   from the branches they <u>sing</u> their song.

4. From your dwelling you wa<u>ter</u> the hills;
   earth drinks its fill <u>of</u> your gift.
   You make the grass grow <u>for</u> the cattle
   and the plants to <u>serve</u> our needs.

5. How many are your <u>works</u>, O Lord!
   In wisdom you have <u>made</u> them all.
   The earth is full <u>of</u> your riches.
   Bless the <u>Lord</u>, my soul!

Response and Psalm tone: Andrew Moore

After the second Reading

Responsorial Psalm Psalm 15:5, 8-11. ℟ v.1

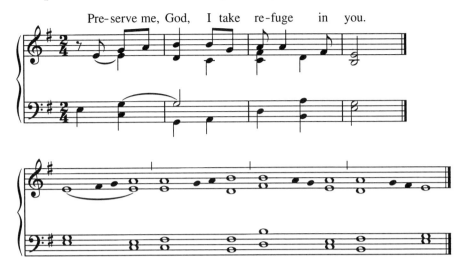

1. O Lord, it is you who are my por<u>tion</u> and cup;
   it is you yourself who <u>are</u> my prize.
   I keep the Lord ever <u>in</u> my sight:
   since he is at my right hand, I <u>shall</u> stand firm.

2. And so my heart rejoices, my <u>soul</u> is glad;
   even my body shall <u>rest</u> in safety.
   For you will not leave my soul <u>among</u> the dead,
   nor let your beloved <u>know</u> decay.

3. O Lord, <u>you</u> will show me
   the <u>path</u> of life,
   the fullness of joy <u>in</u> your presence,
   at your right hand happi<u>ness</u> for ever.

Response: Andrew Moore Psalm tone: Laurence Bevenot

After the third Reading

Responsorial Psalm Exodus 15:1-6, 17-18. ℟ v.1

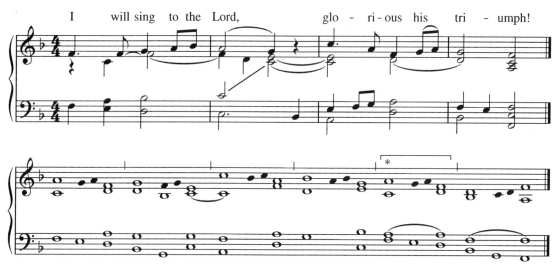

*Omit in verses 1 and 2

1. I will sing to the Lord, glorious his triumph!
   Horse and rider he has thrown into the sea!
   The Lord is my strength, my song, my salvation.
   This is my God and I extol him,
   my father's God and I give him praise.

2. The Lord is a warrior!
   The Lord is his name.
   The chariots of Pharaoh he hurled into the sea,
   the flower of his army is drowned in the sea.
   The deeps hide them; they sank like a stone.

3. Your right hand, Lord, glorious in its power,
   your right hand, Lord, has shattered the enemy.
   In the greatness of your glory you crushed the foe.
   You will lead your people and plant them on your mountain,
   the sanctuary, Lord, which your hands have made.
   The Lord will reign for ever and ever.

Response: Richard Lloyd   Psalm tone: Andrew Moore

After the fourth Reading

Responsorial Psalm Psalm 29:2, 4-6, 11-13. ℞ v.2

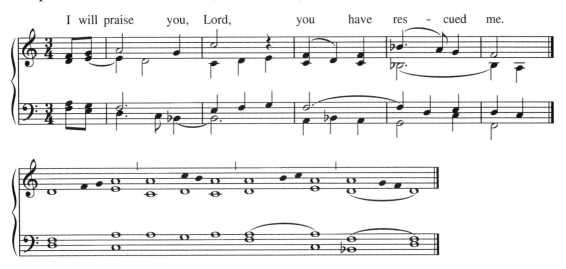

1. I will praise you, Lord, <u>you</u> have rescued me
   and have not let my enemies rejoice <u>over</u> me.
   O Lord, you have raised my soul <u>from</u> the dead,
   restored me to life from those who sink in<u>to</u> the grave.

2. Sing psalms to the Lord, <u>you</u> who love him,
   give thanks to his <u>ho</u>ly name.
   His anger lasts but a moment; his fa<u>vour</u> through life.
   At night there are tears, but joy <u>comes</u> with dawn.

3. The Lord listened <u>and</u> had pity.
   The Lord came <u>to</u> my help.
   For me you have changed my mourning <u>into</u> dancing,
   O Lord my God, I will thank <u>you</u> for ever.

Response: Richard Lloyd   Psalm tone: Alan Rees

After the fifth Reading

Responsorial Psalm Isaiah 12:2-6. ℞ v.3

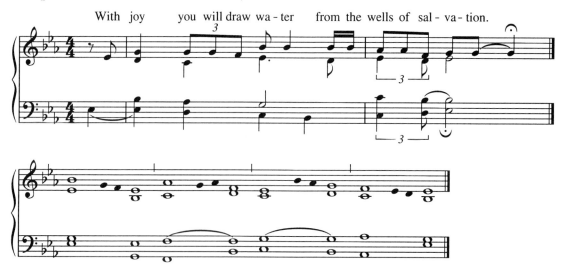

1. Truly God is <u>my</u> salvation,
   I trust, I <u>shall</u> not fear.
   For the Lord is my <u>strength</u>, my song,
   he be<u>came</u> my saviour.

2. Give thanks <u>to</u> the Lord,
   give praise <u>to</u> his name!
   Make his mighty deeds known <u>to</u> the peoples,
   declare the greatness <u>of</u> his name.

3. Sing a psalm to the Lord for he has done glo<u>ri</u>ous deeds,
   make them known to <u>all</u> the earth!
   People of Zion, sing and <u>shout</u> for joy
   for great in your midst is the Holy <u>One</u> of Israel.

Response and Psalm tone: Andrew Moore

After the sixth Reading

Responsorial Psalm Psalm 18:8-11. ℟ John 6:69

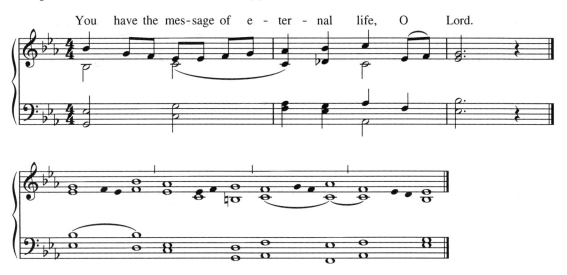

You have the mes-sage of e - ter - nal life, O Lord.

1. The law of the <u>Lord</u> is perfect,
   it re<u>vives</u> the soul.
   The rule of the Lord is <u>to</u> be trusted,
   it gives wisdom <u>to</u> the simple.

2. The precepts of the <u>Lord</u> are right,
   they <u>gladden</u> the heart.
   The command of the <u>Lord</u> is clear,
   it gives light <u>to</u> the eyes.

3. The fear of the <u>Lord</u> is holy,
   a<u>biding</u> for ever.
   The decrees of the <u>Lord</u> are truth
   and all <u>of</u> them just.

4. They are more to be de<u>sired</u> than gold,
   than the pu<u>rest</u> of gold
   and sweeter are <u>they</u> than honey,
   than honey <u>from</u> the comb.

Response and Psalm tone: Andrew Moore

After the seventh Reading

Responsorial Psalm Psalm 41:3, 5; 42:3, 4. ℟ 41:2

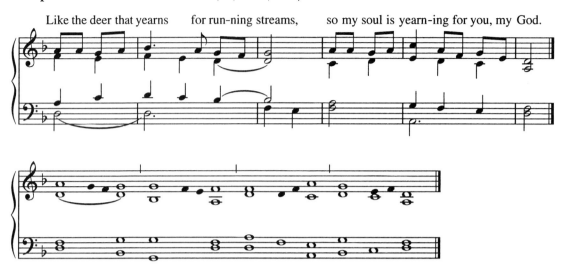

1. My soul is thirsting for God,
   the God of my life;
   when can I enter and see
   the face of God?

2. These things will I remember as I pour out my soul;
   how I would lead the rejoicing crowd into the house of God,
   amid cries of gladness and thanksgiving,
   the throng wild with joy.

3. O send forth your light and your truth;
   let these be my guide.
   Let them bring me to your holy mountain
   to the place where you dwell.

4. And I will come to the altar of God,
   the God of my joy.
   My redeemer, I will thank you on the harp,
   O God, my God.

Response and Psalm tone: Gregory Murray

If a Baptism takes place, the Psalm which follows the fifth Reading is used, or the one that follows here.

Responsorial Psalm Psalm 50:12-15, 18, 19. ℟ v.12

1. A pure heart create for <u>me</u>, O God,
   put a steadfast sp<u>ir</u>it within me.
   Do not cast me away <u>from</u> your presence,
   nor deprive me of your <u>ho</u>ly spirit.

2. Give me again the joy <u>of</u> your help;
   with a spirit of fer<u>vour</u> sustain me,
   that I may teach transgres<u>sors</u> your ways
   and sinners may re<u>turn</u> to you.

3. For in sacrifice you take <u>no</u> delight,
   burnt offering from me you <u>would</u> refuse,
   my sacrifice, a <u>con</u>trite spirit.
   A humbled, contrite heart you <u>will</u> not spurn.

Response: Richard Lloyd   Psalm tone: Gregory Murray

Text © 1963, 1986, 1993 The Grail, England, taken from 'The Psalms, a New Inclusive Language Version', published by HarperCollins Religious. Used by permission of A.P. Watt Ltd, London.
Response © Copyright 1998 Kevin Mayhew Ltd.
Psalm tone © Copyright Downside Abbey, Stratton-on-the-Fosse, Bath BA3 4RH. Used by permission.

943 Easter Sunday - The Mass of Easter Night (A,B,C)

Responsorial Psalm Psalm 117:1-2, 16-17, 22-23

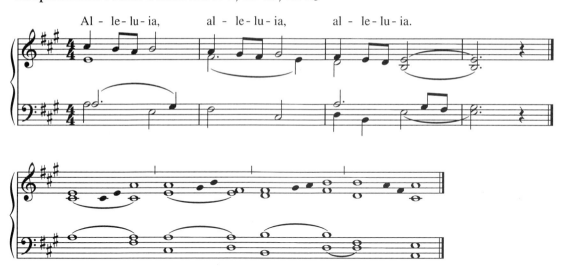

1. Give thanks to the Lord for <u>he</u> is good,
   for his love <u>has</u> no end.
   Let the family of Is<u>ra</u>el say:
   'His love <u>has</u> no end.'

2. The Lord's right <u>hand</u> has triumphed;
   his right hand <u>raised</u> me up.
   I shall not die, <u>I</u> shall live
   and re<u>count</u> his deeds.

3. The stone which the buil<u>ders</u> rejected
   has be<u>come</u> the corner stone.
   This is the work <u>of</u> the Lord,
   a marvel <u>in</u> our eyes.

Response: Martin Setchell   Psalm tone: Alan Rees

944 Easter Sunday - Mass of the Day (A,B,C)

Responsorial Psalm Psalm 117:1-2, 16-17, 22-23. ℟ v.24

This day was made by the Lord; we re-joice and are glad.

1. Give thanks to the Lord for <u>he</u> is good,
   for his love <u>has</u> no end.
   Let the family of Is<u>ra</u>el say:
   'His love <u>has</u> no end.'

2. The Lord's right <u>hand</u> has triumphed;
   his right hand <u>raised</u> me up.
   I shall not die, <u>I</u> shall live
   and re<u>count</u> his deeds.

3. The stone which the buil<u>ders</u> rejected
   has be<u>come</u> the corner stone.
   This is the work <u>of</u> the Lord,
   a marvel <u>in</u> our eyes.

Gospel Acclamation 1 Corinthians 5:7-8
For musical setting see Nos 36 to 47

Alleluia.
Christ, our passover, <u>has</u> been sacrificed;
let us celebrate the feast then, <u>in</u> the Lord.
Alleluia.

Response: Rosalie Bonighton   Psalm tone: Laurence Bevenot

945 2nd Easter (A)

Responsorial Psalm Psalm 117:2-4, 13-15, 22-24. ℟ v.1

Give thanks to the Lord for he is good, give thanks to the Lord for his love has no end.

1. Let the sons of Israel say:
   'His love <u>has</u> no end.'
   Let the sons of Aaron say:
   'His love <u>has</u> no end.'
   Let those who fear <u>the</u> Lord say:
   'His love <u>has</u> no end.'

2. I was thrust down, thrust <u>down</u> and falling
   but the Lord <u>was</u> my helper.
   The Lord is my strength <u>and</u> my song:
   he <u>was</u> my saviour.
   There are shouts of <u>joy</u> and victory
   in the tents <u>of</u> the just.

3. The stone which the bui<u>lders</u> rejected
   has be<u>come</u> the corner stone.
   This is the work <u>of</u> the Lord,
   a marvel <u>in</u> our eyes.
   This day was made <u>by</u> the Lord;
   we rejoice <u>and</u> are glad.

Gospel Acclamation John 20:29
For musical setting see Nos 36 to 47

Alleluia.
Jesus said: 'You believe because <u>you</u> can see me.
Happy are those who have not seen and <u>yet</u> believe.'
Alleluia.

Response: Alan Rees   Psalm tone: Andrew Moore

946 2nd Easter (B)

Responsorial Psalm Psalm 117:2-4, 15-18, 22-24. ℟ v.1

Give thanks to the Lord for he is good, give thanks to the Lord for his love has no end.

1. Let the sons of Israel say:
   'His love has no end.'
   Let the sons of Aaron say:
   'His love has no end.'
   Let those who fear the Lord say:
   'His love has no end.'

2. The Lord's right hand has triumphed;
   his right hand raised me up.
   I shall not die, I shall live
   and recount his deeds.
   I was punished, I was punished by the Lord,
   but not doomed to die.

3. The stone which the builders rejected
   has become the corner stone.
   This is the work of the Lord,
   a marvel in our eyes.
   This day was made by the Lord;
   we rejoice and are glad.

Gospel Acclamation John 20:29
For musical setting see Nos 36 to 47

Alleluia.
Jesus said: 'You believe because you can see me.
Happy are those who have not seen and yet believe.'
Alleluia.

Response: Alan Rees   Psalm tone: Andrew Moore

947 2nd Easter (C)

Responsorial Psalm Psalm 117:2-4, 22-27. ℟ v.1

1. Let the sons of Is<u>ra</u>el say:
   'His love <u>has</u> no end.'
   Let the sons of <u>Aa</u>ron say:
   'His love <u>has</u> no end.'
   Let those who fear <u>the</u> Lord say:
   'His love <u>has</u> no end.'

2. The stone which the bui<u>lders</u> rejected
   has be<u>come</u> the corner stone.
   This is the work <u>of</u> the Lord,
   a marvel <u>in</u> our eyes.
   This day was made <u>by</u> the Lord;
   we rejoice <u>and</u> are glad.

3. O Lord, grant <u>us</u> salvation;
   O Lord, <u>grant</u> success.
   Blessed in the name <u>of</u> the Lord
   is <u>he</u> who comes.
   We bless you from the house <u>of</u> the Lord;
   the Lord God <u>is</u> our light.

Gospel Acclamation John 20:29
For musical setting see Nos 36 to 47

Alleluia.
Jesus said: 'You believe because <u>you</u> can see me.
Happy are those who have not seen and <u>yet</u> believe.'
Alleluia.

Response: Alan Rees   Psalm tone: Andrew Moore

948 3rd Easter (A)

Responsorial Psalm Psalm 15:1-2, 5, 7-11. ℟ v.11

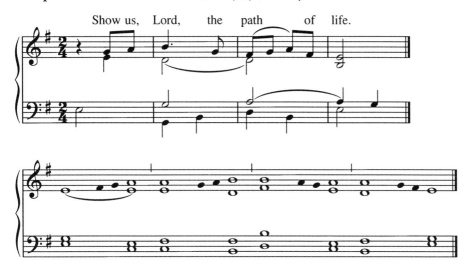

Show us, Lord, the path of life.

1. Preserve me, God, I take re<u>fuge</u> in you.
   I say to the Lord: 'You <u>are</u> my God.
   O Lord, it is you who are my <u>portion</u> and cup;
   it is you yourself who <u>are</u> my prize.'

2. I will bless the Lord who <u>gives</u> me counsel,
   who even at night di<u>rects</u> my heart.
   I keep the Lord ever <u>in</u> my sight:
   since he is at my right hand, I <u>shall</u> stand firm.

3. And so my heart rejoices, my <u>soul</u> is glad;
   even my body shall <u>rest</u> in safety.
   For you will not leave my soul <u>among</u> the dead,
   nor let your beloved <u>know</u> decay.

4. O Lord, <u>you</u> will show me
   the <u>path</u> of life,
   the fullness of joy <u>in</u> your presence,
   at your right hand happi<u>ness</u> for ever.

Gospel Acclamation cf. Luke 24:32
For musical setting see Nos 36 to 47

Alleluia.
Lord Jesus, explain the scrip<u>tures</u> to us.
Make our hearts burn within us <u>as</u> you talk to us.
Alleluia.

Response: Andrew Moore   Psalm tone: Laurence Bevenot

949 3rd Easter (B)

Responsorial Psalm Psalm 4:2, 4, 7, 9. ℟ v.7

Lift up the light of your face on us, O Lord.

1. When I call, answer me, O God of justice;
   from anguish you release me, have mercy and hear me!
   It is the Lord who grants favours to those whom he loves;
   the Lord hears me whenever I call him.

2. 'What can bring us happiness?' many say.
   Lift up the light of your face on us, O Lord.
   I will lie down in peace and sleep comes at once,
   for you alone, Lord, make me dwell in safety.

Gospel Acclamation cf. Luke 24:32
For musical setting see Nos 36 to 47

Alleluia.
Lord Jesus, explain the scriptures to us.
Make our hearts burn within us as you talk to us.
Alleluia.

Response and Psalm tone: Andrew Moore

950 3rd Easter (C)

Responsorial Psalm Psalm 29:2, 4-6, 11-13. ℟ v.2

1. I will praise you, Lord, <u>you</u> have rescued me
   and have not let my enemies rejoice <u>over</u> me.
   O Lord, you have raised my soul <u>from</u> the dead,
   restored me to life from those who sink in<u>to</u> the grave.

2. Sing psalms to the Lord, <u>you</u> who love him,
   give thanks to his <u>holy</u> name.
   His anger lasts but a moment; his fa<u>vour</u> through life.
   At night there are tears, but joy <u>comes</u> with dawn.

3. The Lord listened <u>and</u> had pity.
   The Lord came <u>to</u> my help.
   For me you have changed my mourning <u>into</u> dancing;
   O Lord my God, I will thank <u>you</u> for ever.

Gospel Acclamation cf. Luke 24:32
For musical setting see Nos 36 to 47

Alleluia.
Lord Jesus, explain the scrip<u>tures</u> to us.
Make our hearts burn within us <u>as</u> you talk to us.
Alleluia.

Response: Richard Lloyd   Psalm tone: Alan Rees

951 4th Easter (A)

Responsorial Psalm Psalm 22:1-6. R℣ v.1

The Lord is my shep-herd; there is no-thing I shall want, the Lord is my shep-herd; there is no-thing I shall want.

1. The Lord is my shepherd;
   there is nothing I shall want.
   Fresh and green are the pastures
   where he gives me repose.

2. Near restful waters he leads me
   to revive my drooping spirit.
   He guides me along the right path;
   he is true to his name.

3. If I should walk in the valley of darkness
   no evil would I fear.
   You are there with your crook and your staff;
   with these you give me comfort.

4. You have prepared a banquet for me
   in the sight of my foes.
   My head you have anointed with oil;
   my cup is overflowing.

5. Surely goodness and kindness shall follow me
   all the days of my life.
   In the Lord's own house shall I dwell
   for ever and ever.

Note: verse 3 may be omitted

Gospel Acclamation John 10:14
For musical setting see Nos 36 to 47

Alleluia.
I am the good shepherd, says the Lord;
I know my own sheep and my own know me.
Alleluia.

Response: Andrew Moore   Psalm tone: Alan Rees

952 4th Easter (B)

Responsorial Psalm   Psalm 117:1, 8-9, 21-23, 26, 28-29. ℟ v.22

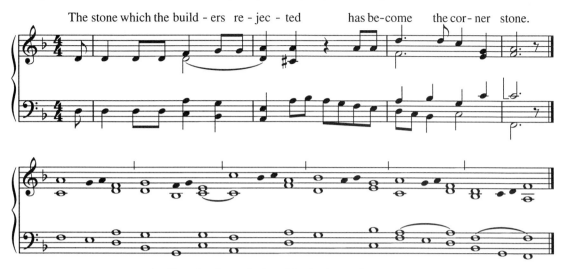

The stone which the build - ers re - jec - ted   has be-come   the cor - ner   stone.

1. Give thanks to the Lord for <u>he</u> is good,
   for his love <u>has</u> no end.
   It is better to take refuge <u>in</u> the Lord
   than to <u>trust</u> in mortals;
   it is better to take refuge <u>in</u> the Lord
   than to <u>trust</u> in rulers.

2. I will thank you for you have <u>given</u> answer
   and you <u>are</u> my saviour.
   The stone which the buil<u>ders</u> rejected
   has be<u>come</u> the corner stone.
   This is the work <u>of</u> the Lord,
   a marvel <u>in</u> our eyes.

3. Blessed in the name of the Lord is <u>he</u> who comes.
   We bless you from the house <u>of</u> the Lord;
   I will thank you for you have <u>given</u> answer
   and you <u>are</u> my saviour.
   Give thanks to the Lord for <u>he</u> is good;
   for his love <u>has</u> no end.

Gospel Acclamation John 10:14
For musical setting see Nos 36 to 47

Alleluia.
I am the good shepherd, <u>says</u> the Lord;
I know my own sheep and my <u>own</u> know me.
Alleluia.

Response: Martin Setchell   Psalm tone: Andrew Moore

953 4th Easter (C)

Responsorial Psalm Psalm 99:1-3, 5. ℟ v.3

1. Cry out with joy to the Lord, all the earth.
   Serve the Lord with gladness.
   Come before him, singing for joy.

2. Know that he, the Lord, is God.
   He made us, we belong to him,
   we are his people, the sheep of his flock.

3. Indeed, how good is the Lord,
   eternal his merciful love.
   He is faithful from age to age.

Gospel Acclamation John 10:14
For musical setting see Nos 36 to 47

Alleluia.
I am the good shepherd, says the Lord;
I know my own sheep and my own know me.
Alleluia.

Response and Psalm tone: Andrew Moore

954 5th Easter (A)

Responsorial Psalm Psalm 32:1-2, 4-5, 18-19. ℟ v.22

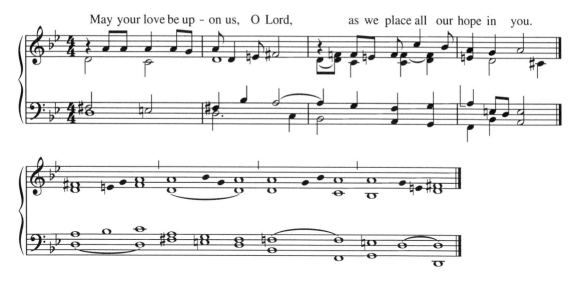

1. Ring out your joy to the Lord, <u>O</u> you just;
   for praise is fitting for <u>loy</u>al hearts.
   Give thanks to the Lord up<u>on</u> the harp,
   with a ten-stringed lute <u>sing</u> him songs.

2. For the word of the <u>Lord</u> is faithful
   and all his works <u>to</u> be trusted.
   The Lord loves jus<u>tice</u> and right
   and fills the earth <u>with</u> his love.

3. The Lord looks on those <u>who</u> revere him,
   on those who hope <u>in</u> his love,
   to rescue their <u>souls</u> from death,
   to keep them a<u>live</u> in famine.

Gospel Acclamation John 14:6
For musical setting see Nos 36 to 47

Alleluia.
Jesus said: 'I am the Way, the Truth <u>and</u> the Life.
No one can come to the Father ex<u>cept</u> through me.'
Alleluia.

Response: Rosalie Bonighton   Psalm tone: Laurence Bevenot

955 5th Easter (B)

Responsorial Psalm Psalm 21:26-28, 30-32. ℟ v.26

You are my praise, O Lord, in the great as-sem-bly.

1. My vows I will pay before <u>those</u> who fear him.
   The poor shall eat and shall <u>have</u> their fill.
   They shall praise the Lord, <u>those</u> who seek him.
   May their hearts live for <u>ever</u> and ever!

2. All the earth shall remember and return <u>to</u> the Lord,
   all families of the nations wor<u>ship</u> before him.
   They shall worship him, all the mighty <u>of</u> the earth;
   before him shall bow all who go down <u>to</u> the dust.

3. And my soul shall live for him, my <u>children</u> serve him.
   They shall tell of the Lord to generations <u>yet</u> to come,
   declare his faithfulness to peoples <u>yet</u> unborn:
   'These things the <u>Lord</u> has done.'

Gospel Acclamation John 15:4-5
For musical setting see Nos 36 to 47

Alleluia.
Make your home in me, as I make <u>mine</u> in you.
Whoever remains in me bears <u>fruit</u> in plenty.
Alleluia.

Response: Andrew Moore   Psalm tone: Gregory Murray

956 5th Easter (C)

Responsorial Psalm Psalm 144:8-13. ℟ cf. v.1

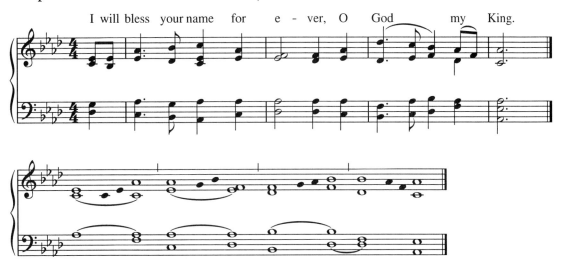

1. The Lord is kind and full of compassion,
   slow to anger, abounding in love.
   How good is the Lord to all,
   compassionate to all his creatures.

2. All your creatures shall thank you, O Lord,
   and your friends shall repeat their blessings.
   They shall speak of the glory of your reign
   and declare your might, O God.

3. They will make known to all your mighty deeds
   and the glorious splendour of your reign.
   Yours is an everlasting kingdom;
   your rule lasts from age to age.

Gospel Acclamation John 13:34
For musical setting see Nos 36 to 47

Alleluia.
Jesus said: 'I give you a new commandment:
love one another, just as I have loved you.'
Alleluia.

Response: Colin Mawby Psalm tone: Alan Rees

957 6th Easter (A)

Responsorial Psalm Psalm 65:1-7, 16, 20. ℟ v.1

Cry out with joy to God all the earth.

1. Cry out with joy to God <u>all</u> the earth,
   O sing to the glory <u>of</u> his name.
   O render him glo<u>ri</u>ous praise,
   say to God: 'How tremen<u>dous</u> your deeds!'

2. 'Before you all the <u>earth</u> shall bow;
   shall sing to you, sing <u>to</u> your name!'
   Come and see the <u>works</u> of God,
   tremendous his deeds <u>among</u> men.

3. He turned the sea in<u>to</u> dry land,
   they passed through the ri<u>ver</u> dry-shod.
   Let our joy then <u>be</u> in him;
   he rules for ever <u>by</u> his might.

4. Come and hear, all <u>who</u> fear God.
   I will tell what he did <u>for</u> my soul:
   Blessed be God who did not re<u>ject</u> my prayer
   nor with<u>hold</u> his love from me.

Gospel Acclamation John 14:23
For musical setting see Nos 36 to 47

   Alleluia.
   Jesus said: 'If anyone loves me they will <u>keep</u> my word,
   and my Father will love them and <u>we</u> shall come to them.'
   Alleluia.

Response: Rosalie Bonighton   Psalm tone: Alan Rees

958 6th Easter (B)

Responsorial Psalm Psalm 97:1-4. ℞ cf.v.2

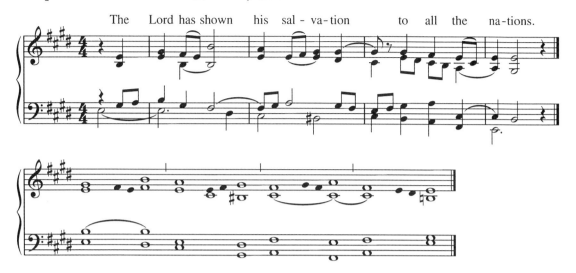

The Lord has shown his sal-va-tion to all the na-tions.

1. Sing a new song to the Lord
   for he has worked wonders.
   His right hand and his holy arm
   have brought salvation.

2. The Lord has made known his salvation;
   has shown his justice to the nations.
   He has remembered his truth and love
   for the house of Israel.

3. All the ends of the earth have seen
   the salvation of our God.
   Shout to the Lord all the earth,
   ring out your joy.

Gospel Acclamation John 14:23
For musical setting see Nos 36 to 47

Alleluia.
Jesus said: 'If anyone loves me they will keep my word,
and my Father will love them and we shall come to them.'
Alleluia.

Response: Richard Proulx   Psalm tone: Andrew Moore

959 6th Easter (C)

Responsorial Psalm Psalm 66:2-3, 5-6, 8. ℟ v.4

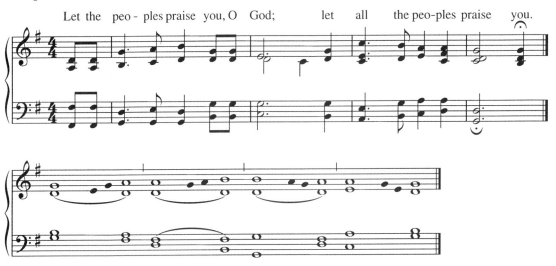

Let the peo - ples praise you, O God; let all the peo-ples praise you.

1. O God, be gracious and bless us
   and let your face shed its light upon us.
   So will your ways be known upon earth,
   and all nations learn your saving help.

2. Let the nations be glad and exult
   for you rule the world with justice.
   With fairness you rule the peoples,
   you guide the nations on earth.

3. Let the peoples praise you, O God;
   let all the peoples praise you.
   May God still give us his blessing
   till the ends of the earth revere him.

Gospel Acclamation John 14:23
For musical setting see Nos 36 to 47

Alleluia.
Jesus said: 'If anyone loves me they will keep my word,
and my Father will love them and we shall come to them.'
Alleluia.

Response: Colin Mawby Psalm tone: Gregory Murray

960 The Ascension of the Lord (A,B,C)

Responsorial Psalm Psalm 46:2-3, 6-9. ℟ v.6

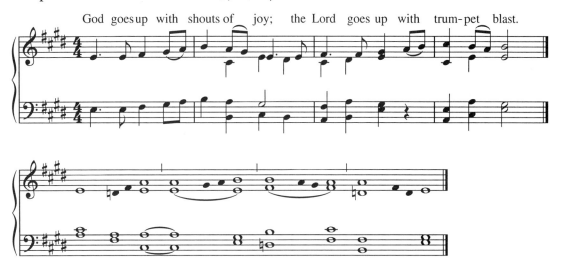

God goes up with shouts of joy; the Lord goes up with trum-pet blast.

1. All peoples, <u>clap</u> your hands,
   cry to God with <u>shouts</u> of joy!
   For the Lord, the Most High, <u>we</u> must fear,
   great king over <u>all</u> the earth.

2. God goes up with <u>shouts</u> of joy;
   the Lord goes up with <u>trum</u>pet blast.
   Sing praise for <u>God</u>, sing praise,
   sing praise to our <u>king</u>, sing praise.

3. God is king of <u>all</u> the earth.
   Sing praise with <u>all</u> your skill.
   God is king <u>over</u> the nations;
   God reigns on his <u>holy</u> throne.

Gospel Acclamation Matthew 28:19, 20
For musical setting see Nos 36 to 47

   Alleluia.
   Go, make disciples of <u>all</u> the nations;
   I am with you always; yes, to the <u>end</u> of time.
   Alleluia.

Response: Andrew Moore   Psalm tone: Laurence Bevenot

961 7th Easter (A)

Responsorial Psalm Psalm 26:1, 4, 7-8. ℟ v.13

1. The Lord is my light <u>and</u> my help;
   whom <u>shall</u> I fear?
   The Lord is the stronghold <u>of</u> my life;
   before whom <u>shall</u> I shrink?

2. There is one thing I ask <u>of</u> the Lord,
   for <u>this</u> I long,
   to live in the house <u>of</u> the Lord,
   all the days <u>of</u> my life.

3. O Lord, hear my voice <u>when</u> I call;
   have mer<u>cy</u> and answer.
   Of you my <u>heart</u> has spoken;
   '<u>Seek</u> his face.'

Gospel Acclamation cf. John 14:18
For musical setting see Nos 36 to 47

Alleluia.
I will not leave you orphans, <u>says</u> the Lord;
I will come back to you, and your hearts will be <u>full</u> of joy.
Alleluia.

Response: Colin Mawby Psalm tone: Alan Rees

962 7th Easter (B)

Responsorial Psalm Psalm 102:1-2, 11-12, 19-20. R℣ v.19

1. My soul, give thanks to the Lord;
   all my being, bless his holy name.
   My soul, give thanks to the Lord
   and never forget all his blessings.

2. For as the heavens are high above the earth
   so strong is his love for those who fear him.
   As far as the east is from the west
   so far does he remove our sins.

3. The Lord has set his sway in heaven
   and his kingdom is ruling over all.
   Give thanks to the Lord, all his angels,
   mighty in power, fulfilling his word.

Gospel Acclamation cf. John 14:18
For musical setting see Nos 36 to 47

Alleluia.
I will not leave you orphans, says the Lord;
I will come back to you, and your hearts will be full of joy.
Alleluia.

Response: Andrew Moore   Psalm tone: Gregory Murray

963 7th Easter (C)

Responsorial Psalm Psalm 96:1-2, 6-7, 9. ℟ vv.1, 9

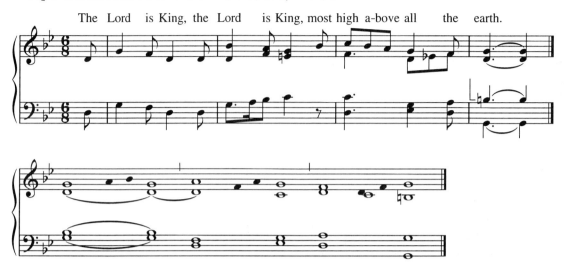

1. The Lord is King, let earth rejoice,
   the many coastlands be glad.
   His throne is justice and right.

2. The skies proclaim his justice;
   all peoples see his glory.
   All you spirits, worship him.

3. For you indeed are the Lord
   most high above all the earth
   exalted far above all spirits.

Gospel Acclamation cf. John 14:18
For musical setting see Nos 36 to 47

Alleluia.
I will not leave you orphans, says the Lord;
I will come back to you, and your hearts will be full of joy.
Alleluia.

Response and Psalm tone: Andrew Moore

964 Pentecost Sunday (A,B,C)

Responsorial Psalm Psalm 103:1, 24, 29-31, 34. R℣ cf.v.30

Send forth your spi - rit, O Lord, and re - new the face of the earth.

1. Bless the <u>Lord</u>, my soul!
   Lord God, how <u>great</u> you are.
   How many are your <u>works</u>, O Lord!
   The earth is full <u>of</u> your riches.

2. You take back your sp<u>ir</u>it, they die,
   returning to the dust from <u>which</u> they came.
   You send forth your spirit, they <u>are</u> created;
   and you renew the face <u>of</u> the earth.

3. May the glory of the Lord <u>last</u> for ever!
   May the Lord rejoice <u>in</u> his works!
   May my thoughts be pleas<u>ing</u> to him.
   I find my joy <u>in</u> the Lord.

Gospel Acclamation
For musical setting see Nos 36 to 47

Alleluia.
Come, Holy Spirit, fill the hearts <u>of</u> your faithful
and kindle in them the fire <u>of</u> your love.
Alleluia.

Response and Psalm tone: Andrew Moore

The Most Holy Trinity (A)

Responsorial Psalm Daniel 3:52-56. ℟ v.22

This Psalm is sung as a Litany. The Response is given out and repeated by all and is then repeated at the end of each line.

1. You are blest, Lord God <u>of</u> our fathers.
   To you glory and praise for evermore.
   Blest your glorious <u>ho</u>ly name.
   To you glory and praise for evermore.

2. You are blest in the temple <u>of</u> your glory.
   To you glory and praise for evermore.
   You are blest on the throne <u>of</u> your kingdom.
   To you glory and praise for evermore.

3. You are blest who gaze in<u>to</u> the depths.
   To you glory and praise for evermore.
   You are blest in the firm<u>ament</u> of heaven.
   To you glory and praise for evermore.

Gospel Acclamation cf. Revelation 1:8
For musical setting see Nos 36 to 47

Alleluia.
Glory be to the Father, and to the Son, and to the <u>Ho</u>ly Spirit,
the God who is, who was, and who <u>is</u> to come.
Alleluia.

Response and Psalm tone: Andrew Moore

The Most Holy Trinity (B)

Responsorial Psalm Psalm 32:4-6, 9, 18-20, 22. ℟ v.12

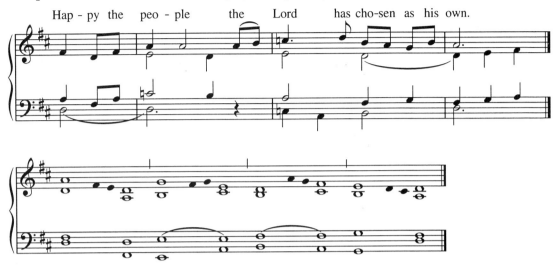

1. The word of the Lord is faithful
   and all his works to be trusted.
   The Lord loves justice and right
   and fills the earth with his love.

2. By his word the heavens were made,
   by the breath of his mouth all the stars.
   He spoke; and they came to be.
   He commanded; they sprang into being.

3. The Lord looks on those who revere him,
   on those who hope in his love,
   to rescue their souls from death,
   to keep them alive in famine.

4. Our soul is waiting for the Lord.
   The Lord is our help and our shield.
   May your love be upon us, O Lord,
   as we place all our hope in you.

Gospel Acclamation cf. Revelation 1:8
For musical setting see Nos 36 to 47

Alleluia.
Glory be to the Father, and to the Son, and to the Holy Spirit,
the God who is, who was, and who is to come.
Alleluia.

Response and Psalm tone: Andrew Moore

The Most Holy Trinity (C)

Responsorial Psalm   Psalm 8:4-9. ℟ v.2

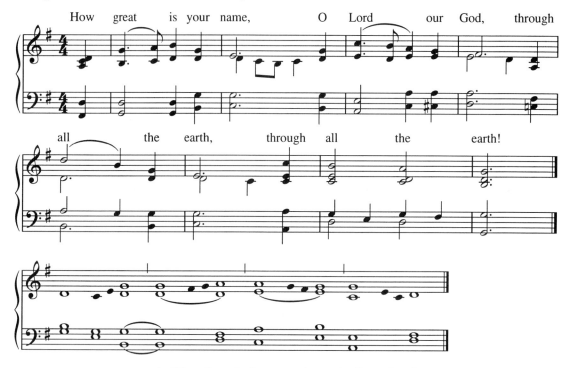

1. When I see the heavens, the work of your hands,
   the moon and the stars which you arranged,
   what are we that you should keep us in mind,
   mortals that you care for us?

2. Yet you have made us little less than gods;
   with glory and honour you crowned us,
   gave us power over the works of your hand,
   put all things under our feet.

3. All of them, sheep and cattle,
   yes, even the savage beasts,
   birds of the air, and fish
   that make their way through the waters.

Gospel Acclamation   cf. Revelation 1:8
For musical setting see Nos 36 to 47

Alleluia.
Glory be to the Father, and to the Son, and to the Holy Spirit,
the God who is, who was, and who is to come.
Alleluia.

Response: Colin Mawby   Psalm tone: Laurence Bevenot

The Body and Blood of Christ (A)

Responsorial Psalm Psalm 147:12-15, 19-20. ℟ v.12

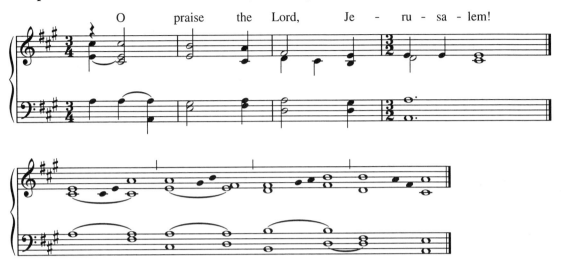

1. O praise the <u>Lord</u>, Jerusalem!
   Zion, <u>praise</u> your God!
   He has strengthened the bars <u>of</u> your gates,
   he has blessed the chil<u>dren</u> within you.

2. He established peace <u>on</u> your borders,
   he feeds you with <u>fin</u>est wheat.
   He sends out his word <u>to</u> the earth
   and swiftly runs <u>his</u> command.

3. He makes his word <u>known</u> to Jacob,
   to Israel his laws <u>and</u> decrees.
   He has not dealt thus with <u>other</u> nations;
   he has not taught them <u>his</u> decrees.

Gospel Acclamation John 6:51-52
For musical setting see Nos 36 to 47

Alleluia.
I am the living bread which has come down from heaven, <u>says</u> the Lord.
Anyone who eats this bread will <u>live</u> for ever.
Alleluia.

Response: Rosalie Bonighton   Psalm tone: Alan Rees

The Body and Blood of Christ (B)

Responsorial Psalm Psalm 115:12-13, 15-18. ℟ v.13

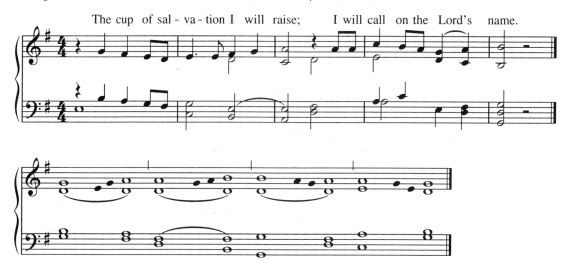

1. How can I repay the Lord
for his goodness to me?
The cup of salvation I will raise;
I will call on the Lord's name.

2. O precious in the eyes of the Lord
is the death of his faithful.
Your servant, Lord, your servant am I;
you have loosened my bonds.

3. A thanksgiving sacrifice I make:
I will call on the Lord's name.
My vows to the Lord I will fulfil
before all his people.

Gospel Acclamation John 6:51-52
For musical setting see Nos 36 to 47

Alleluia.
I am the living bread which has come down from heaven, says the Lord.
Anyone who eats this bread will live for ever.
Alleluia.

Response: Richard Lloyd   Psalm tone: Gregory Murray

The Body and Blood of Christ (C)

Responsorial Psalm Psalm 109:1-4. ℟ v.4

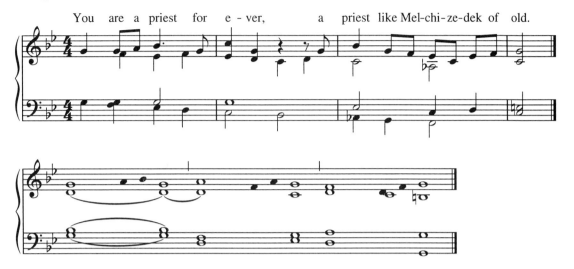

1. The Lord's revelation to my Master:
   'Sit on my right:
   I will put your foes beneath your feet.'

2. The Lord will send from Zion
   your sceptre of power:
   rule in the midst of all your foes.

3. A prince from the day of your birth
   on the holy mountains;
   from the womb before the daybreak I begot you.

4. The Lord has sworn an oath he will not change.
   'You are a priest for ever,
   a priest like Melchizedek of old.'

Gospel Acclamation John 6:51-52
For musical setting see Nos 36 to 47

Alleluia.
I am the living bread which has come down from heaven, says the Lord.
Anyone who eats this bread will live for ever.
Alleluia.

Response: Richard Lloyd   Psalm tone: Andrew Moore

971 2nd in Ordinary Time (A)

Responsorial Psalm Psalm 39:2, 4, 7-10. ℟ vv.8, 9

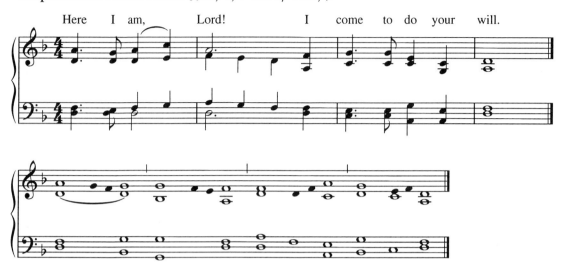

Here I am, Lord! I come to do your will.

1. I waited, I waited for the Lord and
      he stooped down to me;
   he heard my cry.
   He put a new song into my mouth,
   praise of our God.

2. You do not ask for sacrifice and offerings,
   but an open ear.
   You do not ask for holocaust and victim.
   Instead, here am I.

3. In the scroll of the book it stands written
   that I should do your will.
   My God, I delight in your law
   in the depth of my heart.

4. Your justice I have proclaimed
   in the great assembly.
   My lips I have not sealed;
   you know it, O Lord.

Gospel Acclamation

For musical setting see Nos 36 to 47

Alleluia.
Blessings on the King who comes, in the name of the Lord!
Peace in heaven and glory in the highest heavens!
Alleluia.

or John 1:14, 12

Alleluia.
The Word was made flesh and lived among us;
to all who did accept him he gave power to become children of God.
Alleluia.

Response: Colin Mawby   Psalm tone: Gregory Murray

Responsorial Psalm Psalm 26:1, 4, 13-14. ℟ v.1

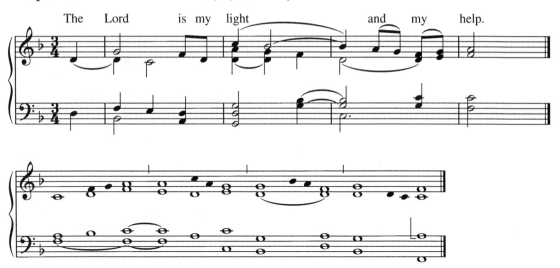

1. The Lord is my light <u>and</u> my help;
   whom <u>shall</u> I fear?
   The Lord is the stronghold <u>of</u> my life;
   before whom <u>shall</u> I shrink?

2. There is one thing I ask <u>of</u> the Lord,
   for <u>this</u> I long,
   to live in the house <u>of</u> the Lord,
   all the days <u>of</u> my life.

3. I am sure I shall see <u>the</u> Lord's goodness
   in the land <u>of</u> the living.
   Hope in him, hold firm <u>and</u> take heart.
   Hope <u>in</u> the Lord!

Gospel Acclamation Matthew 4:23
For musical setting see Nos 36 to 47

Alleluia.
Jesus proclaimed the Good News <u>of</u> the kingdom,
and cured all kinds of sickness a<u>mong</u> the people.
Alleluia.

Response: Richard Lloyd   Psalm tone: Alan Rees

973 4th in Ordinary Time (A)

Responsorial Psalm Psalm 145:7-10. ℟ Matthew 5:3

How hap-py are the poor in spi-rit; for theirs is the king-dom of heav'n.

1. It is the Lord who keeps <u>faith</u> for ever,
   who is just to those who <u>are</u> oppressed.
   It is he who gives bread <u>to</u> the hungry,
   the Lord, who sets pris<u>on</u>ers free.

2. It is the Lord who gives sight <u>to</u> the blind,
   who raises up those who <u>are</u> bowed down,
   the Lord, who pro<u>tects</u> the stranger
   and upholds the wi<u>dow</u> and orphan.

3. It is the Lord who <u>loves</u> the just
   but thwarts the path <u>of</u> the wicked.
   The Lord will <u>reign</u> for ever,
   Zion's God, from <u>age</u> to age.

Gospel Acclamation Matthew 11:25
For musical setting see Nos 36 to 47

Alleluia.
Blessed are you, Father, Lord of Hea<u>ven</u> and earth,
for revealing the mysteries of the kingdom <u>to</u> mere children.
Alleluia.

or Matthew 5:12

Alleluia.
Rejoice <u>and</u> be glad:
your reward will be <u>great</u> in heaven.
Alleluia.

Response: Richard Lloyd   Psalm tone: Andrew Moore

974 5th in Ordinary Time (A)

Responsorial Psalm Psalm 111:4-9. R℣ v.4

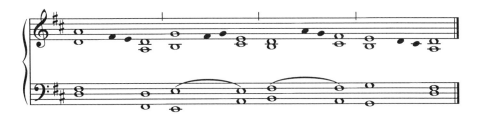

1. They are a light in the darkness <u>for</u> the upright:
   they are generous, merci<u>ful</u> and just.
   The good take pity and lend,
   they conduct their af<u>fairs</u> with honour.

2. The just will <u>nev</u>er waver:
   they will be remem<u>bered</u> for ever.
   They have no fear of <u>e</u>vil news;
   with a firm heart they trust <u>in</u> the Lord.

3. With a steadfast heart they <u>will</u> not fear;
   open-handed, they give <u>to</u> the poor;
   their justice stands <u>firm</u> for ever.
   Their heads will be <u>raised</u> in glory.

Gospel Acclamation John 8:12
For musical setting see Nos 36 to 47

Alleluia.
I am the light of the world, <u>says</u> the Lord,
anyone who follows me will have the <u>light</u> of life.
Alleluia.

Response: Martin Setchell   Psalm tone: Andrew Moore

975 6th in Ordinary Time (A)

Responsorial Psalm Psalm 118:1-2, 4-5, 17-18, 33-34. ℟ v.1

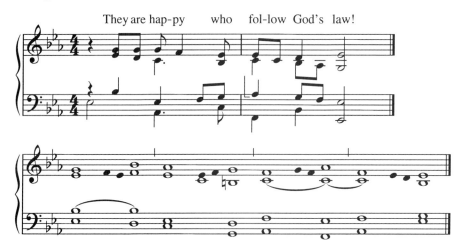

1. They are happy whose <u>life</u> is blameless,
   who fo<u>llow</u> God's law!
   They are happy those who <u>do</u> his will,
   seeking him with <u>all</u> their hearts.

2. You have laid <u>down</u> your precepts
   to be o<u>beyed</u> with care.
   May my foot<u>steps</u> be firm
   to o<u>bey</u> your statutes.

3. Bless your servant and <u>I</u> shall live
   and o<u>bey</u> your word.
   Open my eyes that I <u>may</u> consider
   the wonders <u>of</u> your law.

4. Teach me the demands <u>of</u> your statutes
   and I will keep them <u>to</u> the end.
   Train me to ob<u>serve</u> your law,
   to keep it <u>with</u> my heart.

Gospel Acclamation 1 Samuel 3:9; John 6:68
For musical setting see Nos 36 to 47

Alleluia.
Speak, Lord, your ser<u>vant</u> is listening;
you have the message of e<u>ter</u>nal life.
Alleluia.

Response: Rosalie Bonighton   Psalm tone: Andrew Moore

Text © 1963, 1986, 1993 The Grail, England, taken from 'The Psalms, a New Inclusive Language Version',
published by HarperCollins Religious. Used by permission of A.P. Watt Ltd, London.
Response and Psalm tone © Copyright 1998 Kevin Mayhew Ltd.

976 7th in Ordinary Time (A)

Responsorial Psalm Psalm 102:1-4, 8, 10, 12-13. R℣ v.8

The Lord is com-pas-sion and love, the Lord is com-pas-sion and love.

1. My soul, give thanks <u>to</u> the Lord,
   all my being, bless his <u>holy</u> name.
   My soul, give thanks <u>to</u> the Lord
   and never forget <u>all</u> his blessings.

2. It is he who forgives <u>all</u> your guilt,
   who heals every one <u>of</u> your ills,
   who redeems your life <u>from</u> the grave,
   who crowns you with love <u>and</u> compassion.

3. The Lord is compa<u>ssion</u> and love,
   slow to anger and <u>rich</u> in mercy.
   He does not treat us according <u>to</u> our sins
   nor repay us according <u>to</u> our faults.

4. As far as the east is <u>from</u> the west
   so far does he re<u>move</u> our sins.
   As a father has compassion <u>on</u> his sons,
   the Lord has pity on <u>those</u> who fear him.

Gospel Acclamation John 14:23
For musical setting see Nos 36 to 47

Alleluia.
If anyone loves me they will <u>keep</u> my word,
and my Father will love them and <u>we</u> shall come to them.
Alleluia.

or 1 John 2:5

Alleluia.
When anyone obeys what <u>Christ</u> has said,
God's love comes to perfec<u>tion</u> in him.
Alleluia.

Response: Andrew Moore   Psalm tone: Laurence Bevenot

977 8th in Ordinary Time (A)

Responsorial Psalm Psalm 61:2-3, 6-9. ℟ v.6

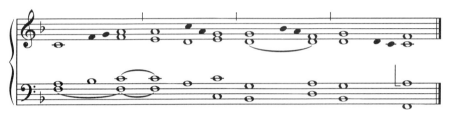

1. In God alone is my soul at rest;
   my help comes from him.
   He alone is my rock, my stronghold,
   my fortress: I stand firm.

2. In God alone be at rest, my soul;
   for my hope comes from him.
   He alone is my rock, my stronghold,
   my fortress: I stand firm.

3. In God is my safety and glory,
   the rock of my strength.
   Take refuge in God all you people.
   Trust him at all times.

Gospel Acclamation John 17:17
For musical setting see Nos 36 to 47

Alleluia.
Your word is truth, O Lord,
consecrate us in the truth.
Alleluia.

or Hebrews 4:12

Alleluia.
The word of God is something alive and active;
it can judge secret emotions and thoughts.
Alleluia.

Response: Rosalie Bonighton   Psalm tone: Alan Rees

978 9th in Ordinary Time (A)

Responsorial Psalm Psalm 30:2-4, 17, 25. ℟ v.3

1. In you, O Lord, I take refuge.
   Let me never be put to shame.
   In your justice, set me free,
   hear me and speedily rescue me.

2. Be a rock of refuge to me,
   a mighty stronghold to save me,
   for you are my rock, my stronghold.
   For your name's sake, lead me and guide me.

3. Let your face shine on your servant.
   Save me in your love.
   Be strong, let your heart take courage,
   all who hope in the Lord.

Gospel Acclamation John 14:23
For musical setting see Nos 36 to 47

Alleluia.
If anyone loves me they will keep my word,
and my Father will love them and we shall come to them.
Alleluia.

or John 15:5

Alleluia.
I am the vine, you are the branches, says the Lord.
Whoever remains in me, with me in him, bears fruit in plenty.
Alleluia.

Response: Andrew Moore   Psalm tone: Alan Rees

979 10th in Ordinary Time (A)

Responsorial Psalm Psalm 49:1, 8, 12-15. ℟ v.23

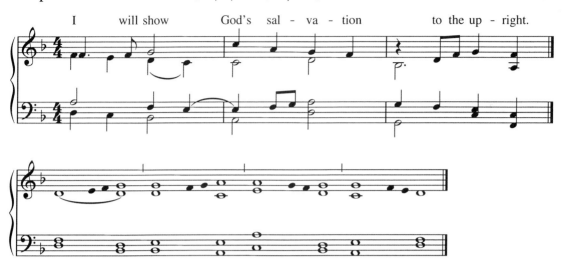

1. The God of gods, the Lord, has spoken and sum<u>mon</u>ed the earth,
   from the rising of the sun <u>to</u> its setting.
   'I find no fault <u>with</u> your sacrifices,
   your offerings are al<u>ways</u> before me.'

2. 'Were I hungry, I <u>would</u> not tell you,
   for I own the world and <u>all</u> it holds.
   Do you think I eat the <u>flesh</u> of bulls,
   or drink the <u>blood</u> of goats?'

3. 'Pay your sacrifice of thanks<u>giv</u>ing to God
   and render him your <u>vo</u>tive offerings.
   Call on me in the day <u>of</u> distress.
   I will free you and <u>you</u> shall honour me.'

Gospel Acclamation cf. Acts 16:14

For musical setting see Nos 36 to 47

Alleluia.
Open our <u>heart</u>, O Lord,
to accept the words <u>of</u> your Son.
Alleluia.

or Luke 4:18

Alleluia.
The Lord has sent me to bring the good news <u>to</u> the poor,
to proclaim liber<u>ty</u> to captives.
Alleluia.

Response: Richard Lloyd   Psalm tone: Laurence Bevenot

Responsorial Psalm Psalm 99:2-3, 5. ℟ v.3

1. Cry out with joy to the Lord, <u>all</u> the earth.
   Serve the <u>Lord</u> with gladness.
   Come before him, sing<u>ing</u> for joy.

2. Know that he, the <u>Lord</u> is God.
   He made us, we be<u>long</u> to him,
   we are his people, the sheep <u>of</u> his flock.

3. Indeed, how good <u>is</u> the Lord,
   eternal his mer<u>ci</u>ful love.
   He is faithful from <u>age</u> to age.

Gospel Acclamation John 10:27
For musical setting see Nos 36 to 47

   Alleluia.
   The sheep that belong to me listen to my voice, <u>says</u> the Lord,
   I know them <u>and</u> they follow me.
   Alleluia.

   or Mark 1:15

   Alleluia.
   The kingdom of God is <u>close</u> at hand.
   Repent, and believe <u>the</u> Good News.
   Alleluia.

Response and Psalm tone: Andrew Moore

981   12th in Ordinary Time (A)

Responsorial Psalm Psalm 68:8-10, 14, 17, 33-35. ℟ v.14

In your great love, in your great love, ans-wer me, O God,
ans-wer me, O God, in your love.

1. It is for you that I <u>suf</u>fer taunts,
   that shame co<u>vers</u> my face,
   that I have become a stranger <u>to</u> my brothers,
   an alien to my own <u>moth</u>er's sons.
   I burn with zeal <u>for</u> your house
   and taunts against you <u>fall</u> on me.

2. This is my <u>prayer</u> to you,
   my prayer <u>for</u> your favour.
   In your great love, answer <u>me</u>, O God,
   with your help that <u>nev</u>er fails:
   Lord, answer, for your <u>love</u> is kind;
   in your compassion, <u>turn</u> towards me.

3. The poor when they see it <u>will</u> be glad
   and God-seeking hearts <u>will</u> revive;
   for the Lord listens <u>to</u> the needy
   and does not spurn his servants <u>in</u> their chains.
   Let the heavens and the earth <u>give</u> him praise,
   the sea and all its <u>liv</u>ing creatures.

Gospel Acclamation John 1:14, 12   or John 15:26, 27
For musical setting see Nos 36 to 47

Alleluia.
The Word was made flesh and <u>lived</u> among us;
to all who did accept him
he gave power to become chil<u>dren</u> of God.
Alleluia

Alleluia.
The Spirit of truth will <u>be</u> my witness;
and you too will <u>be</u> my witnesses.
Alleluia.

Response: Richard Proulx   Psalm tone: Andrew Moore

Responsorial Psalm Psalm 88:2-3, 16-19. ℟ v.2

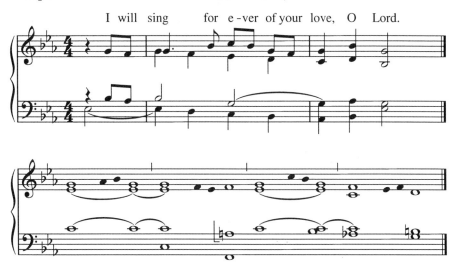

I will sing for e-ver of your love, O Lord.

1. I will sing for ever of your love, O Lord;
   through all ages my mouth will proclaim your truth.
   Of this I am sure, that your love lasts for ever,
   that your truth is firmly established as the heavens.

2. Happy the people who acclaim such a king,
   who walk, O Lord, in the light of your face,
   who find their joy every day in your name,
   who make your justice the source of their bliss.

3. For it is you, O Lord, who are the glory of their strength;
   it is by your favour that our might is exalted;
   for our ruler is in the keeping of the Lord;
   our king in the keeping of the Holy One of Israel.

Gospel Acclamation cf. Acts 16:14
For musical setting see Nos 36 to 47

Alleluia.
Open our heart, O Lord,
to accept the words of your Son.
Alleluia.

or 1 Peter 2:9

Alleluia.
You are a chosen race, a royal priesthood,
   a people set apart to sing the praises of God
who called you out of darkness into his wonderful light.
Alleluia.

Response and Psalm tone: Andrew Moore

983 14th in Ordinary Time (A)

Responsorial Psalm Psalm 144:1-2, 8-11, 13-14. ℟ v.1

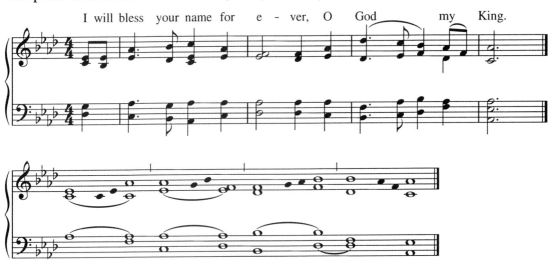

1. I will give you glory, O <u>God</u> my King,
   I will bless your <u>name</u> for ever.
   I will bless you day <u>after</u> day
   and praise your <u>name</u> for ever.

2. The Lord is kind and full <u>of</u> compassion,
   slow to anger, aboun<u>ding</u> in love.
   How good is the <u>Lord</u> to all,
   compassionate to <u>all</u> his creatures.

3. All your creatures shall thank <u>you</u>, O Lord,
   and your friends shall re<u>peat</u> their blessing.
   They shall speak of the glory <u>of</u> your reign
   and declare your <u>might</u>, O God.

4. The Lord is faithful in <u>all</u> his words
   and loving in <u>all</u> his deeds.
   The Lord supports <u>all</u> who fall
   and raises all who <u>are</u> bowed down.

Gospel Acclamation cf. Matthew 11:25
For musical setting see Nos 36 to 47

   Alleluia.
   Blessed are you, Father, Lord of hea<u>ven</u> and earth,
   for revealing the mysteries of the kingdom <u>to</u> mere children.
   Alleluia.

Response: Colin Mawby   Psalm tone: Alan Rees

984 15th in Ordinary Time (A)

Responsorial Psalm Psalm 64:10-14. ℟ Luke 8:8

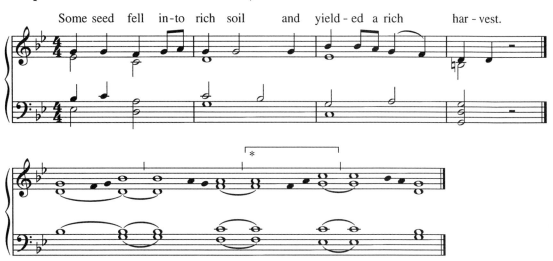

Some seed fell in-to rich soil and yield-ed a rich har - vest.

* Omit in verse 3

1. You care for the earth, <u>give</u> it water,
   you fill <u>it</u> with riches.
   Your river in hea<u>ven</u> brims over
   to pro<u>vide</u> its grain.

2. And thus you provide <u>for</u> the earth;
   you <u>drench</u> its furrows,
   you level it, soften <u>it</u> with showers,
   you <u>bless</u> its growth.

3. You crown the year <u>with</u> your goodness.
   Abundance flows <u>in</u> your steps,
   in the pastures of the wilder<u>ness</u> it flows.

4. The hills are <u>gird</u>ed with joy,
   the meadows co<u>vered</u> with flocks,
   the valleys are <u>decked</u> with wheat.
   They shout for joy, <u>yes</u>, they sing.

Gospel Acclamation 1 Samuel 3:9; John 6:68
For musical setting see Nos 36 to 47

Alleluia.
Speak, Lord, your ser<u>vant</u> is listening;
you have the message of e<u>ter</u>nal life.
Alleluia.

or

Alleluia.
The seed is the word of God, <u>Christ</u> the sower;
whoever finds this seed will re<u>main</u> for ever.
Alleluia.

Response: Richard Lloyd   Psalm tone: Gregory Murray

985   16th in Ordinary Time (A)

Responsorial Psalm Psalm 85:5-6, 9-10, 15-16. ℟ v.5

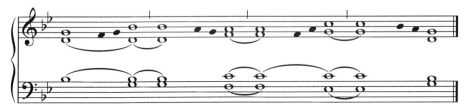

1. O Lord, you are good <u>and</u> forgiving,
   full of love to <u>all</u> who call.
   Give heed, O Lord, <u>to</u> my prayer
   and attend to the sound <u>of</u> my voice.

2. All the nations shall come <u>to</u> adore you
   and glorify your <u>name</u>, O Lord:
   for you are great and do mar<u>vel</u>lous deeds,
   you who a<u>lone</u> are God.

3. But you, God of mercy <u>and</u> compassion,
   slow to an<u>ger</u>, O Lord,
   abounding in <u>love</u> and truth,
   turn and take pi<u>ty</u> on me.

Gospel Acclamation   cf. Ephesians 1:17, 18
For musical setting see Nos 36 to 47

> Alleluia.
> May the Father of our Lord Jesus Christ enlighten the eyes <u>of</u> our mind,
> so that we can see what hope his call <u>holds</u> for us.
> Alleluia.

> or cf. Matthew 11:25

> Alleluia.
> Blessed are you, Father, Lord of hea<u>ven</u> and earth,
> for revealing the mysteries of the kingdom <u>to</u> mere children.
> Alleluia.

Response: Colin Mawby   Psalm tone: Gregory Murray

986 17th in Ordinary Time (A)

Responsorial Psalm Psalm 118:57, 72, 76-77, 127-130. ℟ v.97

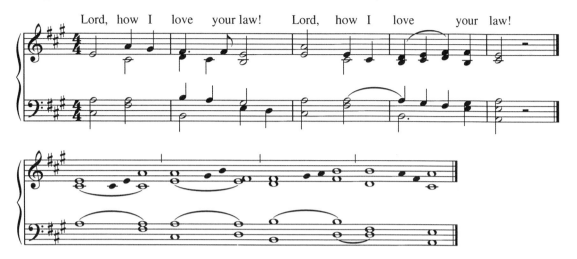

Lord, how I love your law! Lord, how I love your law!

1. My part, I have re<u>solv</u>ed, O Lord,
   is to o<u>bey</u> your word.
   The law from your mouth means <u>more</u> to me
   than sil<u>ver</u> and gold.

2. Let your love be ready <u>to</u> console me
   by your promise <u>to</u> your servant.
   Let your love come to me and <u>I</u> shall live
   for your law is <u>my</u> delight.

3. That is why I love <u>your</u> commands
   more than <u>fin</u>est gold.
   That is why I rule my life <u>by</u> your precepts;
   I <u>hate</u> false ways.

4. Your will is wonder<u>ful</u> indeed;
   therefore <u>I</u> obey it.
   The unfolding of your <u>word</u> gives light
   and tea<u>ches</u> the simple.

Gospel Acclamation John 15:15
For musical setting see Nos 36 to 47

Alleluia.
I call you friends, <u>says</u> the Lord,
because I have made known to you everything I have learnt <u>from</u> my Father.
Alleluia.

or cf. Matthew 11:25

Alleluia.
Blessed are you, Father, Lord of hea<u>ven</u> and earth,
for revealing the mysteries of the kingdom <u>to</u> mere children.
Alleluia.

Response: Richard Lloyd   Psalm tone: Alan Rees

987 18th in Ordinary Time (A)

Responsorial Psalm Psalm 144:8-9, 15-18. ℟ v.16

1. The Lord is kind and full <u>of</u> compassion,
   slow to anger, aboun<u>ding</u> in love.
   How <u>good</u> is the <u>Lord</u> to all,
   compassionate to <u>all</u> his creatures.

2. The eyes of all creatures <u>look</u> to you
   and you give them their food <u>in</u> due time.
   You open <u>wide</u> your hand,
   grant the desires of <u>all</u> who live.

3. The Lord is just in <u>all</u> his ways
   and loving in <u>all</u> his deeds.
   He is close to <u>all</u> who call him,
   call on him <u>from</u> their hearts.

Gospel Acclamation Luke 19:38
For musical setting see Nos 36 to 47

Alleluia.
Blessings on the King who comes in the name <u>of</u> the Lord!
Peace in heaven and glory in the <u>high</u>est heavens!
Alleluia.

or Matthew 4:4

Alleluia.
Man does not live on <u>bread</u> alone,
but on every word that comes from the <u>mouth</u> of God.
Alleluia.

Response: Andrew Moore   Psalm tone: Gregory Murray

988   19th in Ordinary Time (A)

Responsorial Psalm Psalm 84:9-14. ℟ v.8

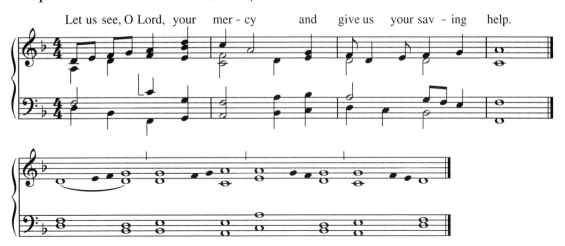

Let us see, O Lord, your mer-cy and give us your sav-ing help.

1. I will hear what the Lord God <u>has</u> to say,
   a voice that <u>speaks</u> of peace.
   His help is near for <u>those</u> who fear him
   and his glory will dwell <u>in</u> our land.

2. Mercy and faithful<u>ness</u> have met;
   justice and peace <u>have</u> embraced.
   Faithfulness shall spring <u>from</u> the earth
   and justice look <u>down</u> from heaven.

3. The Lord will <u>make</u> us prosper
   and our earth shall <u>yield</u> its fruit.
   Justice shall <u>march</u> before him
   and peace shall fo<u>llow</u> his steps.

Gospel Acclamation Luke 19:38
For musical setting see Nos 36 to 47

Alleluia.
Blessings on the King who comes, in the name <u>of</u> the Lord!
Peace in heaven and glory in the <u>high</u>est heavens.
Alleluia.

or Psalm 129:5

Alleluia.
My soul is waiting <u>for</u> the Lord,
I count <u>on</u> his word.
Alleluia.

Response: Stephen Dean   Psalm tone: Laurence Bevenot

989 20th in Ordinary Time (A)

Responsorial Psalm Psalm 66:2-3, 5-6, 8. ℟ v.4

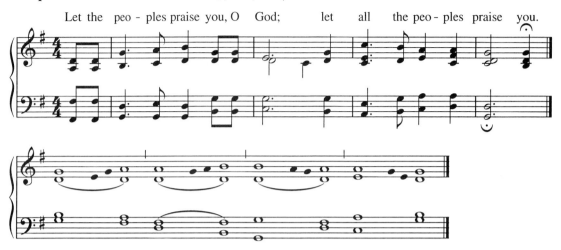

1. O God, be gra<u>cious</u> and bless us
   and let your face shed its <u>light</u> upon us.
   So will your ways be known <u>upon</u> earth
   and all nations learn your <u>saving</u> help.

2. Let the nations be glad <u>and</u> exult
   for you rule the <u>world</u> with justice.
   With fairness you <u>rule</u> the peoples,
   you guide the <u>nations</u> on earth.

3. Let the peoples praise <u>you</u>, O God;
   let all the <u>peoples</u> praise you.
   May God still give <u>us</u> his blessing
   till the ends of the <u>earth</u> revere him.

Gospel Acclamation John 10:27
For musical setting see Nos 36 to 47

    Alleluia.
    The sheep that belong to me listen to my voice, <u>says</u> the Lord,
    I know them <u>and</u> they follow me.
    Alleluia.

    or cf. Matthew 4:23

    Alleluia.
    Jesus proclaimed the Good News <u>of</u> the kingdom,
    and cured all kinds of sickness a<u>mong</u> the people.
    Alleluia.

Response: Colin Mawby   Psalm tone: Gregory Murray

Text © 1963, 1986, 1993 The Grail, England, taken from 'The Psalms, a New Inclusive Language Version',
published by HarperCollins Religious. Used by permission of A.P. Watt Ltd, London.
Response © Copyright 1998 Kevin Mayhew Ltd.
Psalm tone © Copyright McCrimmon Publishing Co. Ltd, 10-12 High St, Great Wakering, Essex SS3 0EQ. Used by permission.

990 21st in Ordinary Time (A)

Responsorial Psalm Psalm 137:1-3, 6, 8. ℟ v.8

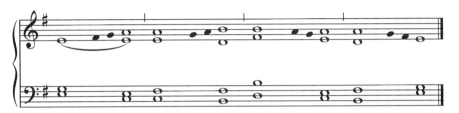

1. I thank you, Lord, with <u>all</u> my heart,
   you have heard the words <u>of</u> my mouth.
   Before the angels <u>I</u> will bless you.
   I will adore before your <u>ho</u>ly temple.

2. I thank you for your faithful<u>ness</u> and love
   which excel all we <u>ev</u>er knew of you.
   On the day I <u>called</u>, you answered;
   you increased the strength <u>of</u> my soul.

3. The Lord is high yet he looks <u>on</u> the lowly
   and the haughty he knows <u>from</u> afar.
   Your love, O Lord, <u>is</u> eternal,
   discard not the work <u>of</u> your hands.

Gospel Acclamation 2 Corinthians 5:19
For musical setting see Nos 36 to 47

Alleluia.
God in Christ was reconciling the world <u>to</u> himself,
and he has entrusted to us the news that <u>they</u> are reconciled.
Alleluia.

or Matthew 16:18

Alleluia.
You are Peter and on this rock I will <u>build</u> my Church.
And the gates of the underworld can never hold <u>out</u> against it.
Alleluia.

Response: Alan Rees   Psalm tone: Laurence Bevenot

991 22nd in Ordinary Time (A)

Responsorial Psalm Psalm 62:2-6, 8-9. ℞ v.2

1. O God, you are my God, for <u>you</u> I long:
   for you my <u>soul</u> is thirsting.
   My body <u>pines</u> for you
   like a dry, weary land <u>with</u>out water.

2. So I gaze on you <u>in</u> the sanctuary
   to see your strength <u>and</u> your glory.
   For your love is be<u>tter</u> than life,
   my lips will <u>speak</u> your praise.

3. So I will bless you <u>all</u> my life,
   in your name I will lift <u>up</u> my hands.
   My soul shall be filled as <u>with</u> a banquet,
   my mouth shall praise <u>you</u> with joy.

4. For you have <u>been</u> my help;
   in the shadow of your wings <u>I</u> rejoice.
   My soul <u>clings</u> to you:
   your right hand <u>holds</u> me fast.

Gospel Acclamation cf. Ephesians 1:17, 18
For musical setting see Nos 36 to 47

Alleluia.
May the Father of our Lord Jesus Christ enlighten the eyes <u>of</u> our mind,
so that we can see what hope his call <u>holds</u> for us.
Alleluia.

Response and Psalm tone: Andrew Moore

992 23rd in Ordinary Time (A)

Responsorial Psalm Psalm 94:1-2, 6-9. ℞ v.8

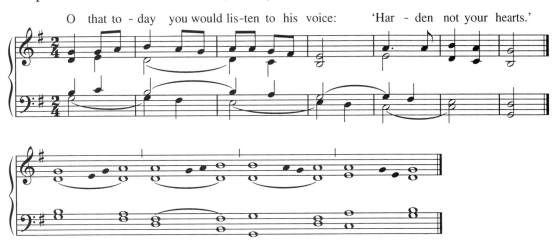

1. Come, ring out our joy to the Lord;
   hail the rock who saves us.
   Let us come before him, giving thanks,
   with songs let us hail the Lord.

2. Come in; let us bow and bend low;
   let us kneel before the God who made us
   for he is our God, and we the people who
       belong to his pasture,
   the flock that is led by his hand.

3. O that today you would listen to his voice!
   Harden not your hearts as at Meribah,
   as on that day at Massah in the desert, when
       your fathers put me to the test;
   when they tried me, though they saw my work.

Gospel Acclamation John 17:17
For musical setting see Nos 36 to 47

Alleluia.
Your word is truth, O Lord,
consecrate us in the truth.
Alleluia.

or 2 Corinthians 5:19

Alleluia.
God in Christ was reconciling the world to himself,
and he has entrusted to us the news that they are reconciled.
Alleluia.

Response and Psalm tone: Gregory Murray

993 24th in Ordinary Time (A)

Responsorial Psalm Psalm 102:1-4, 9-12. R̅ v.8

1. My soul, give thanks <u>to</u> the Lord,
   all my being, bless his <u>holy</u> name.
   My soul, give thanks <u>to</u> the Lord
   and never forget <u>all</u> his blessings.

2. It is he who forgives <u>all</u> your guilt,
   who heals every one <u>of</u> your ills,
   who redeems your life <u>from</u> the grave,
   who crowns you with love <u>and</u> compassion.

3. His wrath will come <u>to</u> an end;
   he will not be an<u>gry</u> for ever.
   He does not treat us according <u>to</u> our sins
   nor repay us according <u>to</u> our faults.

4. For as the heavens are high a<u>bove</u> the earth
   so strong is his love for <u>those</u> who fear him.
   As far as the east is <u>from</u> the west
   so far does he re<u>move</u> our sins.

Gospel Acclamation 1 Samuel 3:9; John 6:68
For musical setting see Nos 36 to 47

> Alleluia.
> Speak, Lord, your ser<u>vant</u> is listening:
> you have the message of e<u>ter</u>nal life.
> Alleluia.

> or John 13:34

> Alleluia.
> I give you a <u>new</u> commandment:
> love one another, just as I have loved you, <u>says</u> the Lord.
> Alleluia.

Response: Andrew Moore   Psalm tone: Laurence Bevenot

994 25th in Ordinary Time (A)

Responsorial Psalm Psalm 144:2-3, 8-9, 17-18. ℟ v.18

1. I will bless you day after day
   and praise your name for ever.
   The Lord is great, highly to be praised,
   his greatness cannot be measured.

2. The Lord is kind and full of compassion,
   slow to anger, abounding in love.
   How good is the Lord to all,
   compassionate to all his creatures.

3. The Lord is just in all his ways
   and loving in all his deeds.
   He is close to all who call him,
   who call on him from their hearts.

Gospel Acclamation Luke 19:38
For musical setting see Nos 36 to 47

    Alleluia.
    Blessings on the King who comes, in the name of the Lord!
    Peace in heaven and glory in the highest heavens!
    Alleluia.

    or cf. Acts 16:14

    Alleluia.
    Open our heart, O Lord,
    to accept the words of your Son.
    Alleluia.

Response: Andrew Moore   Psalm tone: Laurence Bevenot

995 26th in Ordinary Time (A)

Responsorial Psalm Psalm 24:4-9. ℟ v.6

1. Lord, make me <u>know</u> your ways,
   Lord teach <u>me</u> your paths.
   Make me walk in your <u>truth</u>, and teach me;
   for you are <u>God</u> my saviour.

2. Remember your <u>mer</u>cy, Lord,
   and the love you have shown <u>from</u> of old.
   Do not remember the sins <u>of</u> my youth.
   In your <u>love</u> remember me.

3. The Lord is <u>good</u> and upright.
   He shows the path to <u>those</u> who stray,
   he guides the humble in <u>the</u> right path;
   he teaches his way <u>to</u> the poor.

Gospel Acclamation John 14:23
For musical setting see Nos 36 to 47

Alleluia.
If anyone loves me they will <u>keep</u> my word,
and my Father will love them and <u>we</u> shall come to them.
Alleluia.

or John 10:27

Alleluia.
The sheep that belong to me listen to my voice <u>says</u> the Lord,
I know them and <u>they</u> follow me.
Alleluia.

Response: Richard Proulx   Psalm tone: Alan Rees

996 27th in Ordinary Time (A)

Responsorial Psalm Psalm 79:9, 12-16, 19-20. ℟ Isaiah 5:7

The vine-yard of the Lord is the House of Is-ra-el.

1. You brought a vine <u>out</u> of Egypt;
   to plant it you drove <u>out</u> the nations.
   It stretched out its branches <u>to</u> the sea,
   to the Great River it stretched <u>out</u> its shoots.

2. Then why have you broken <u>down</u> its walls?
   It is plucked by all <u>who</u> pass by.
   It is ravaged by the boar <u>of</u> the forest,
   devoured by the beasts <u>of</u> the field.

3. God of hosts, turn again, <u>we</u> implore,
   look down from hea<u>ven</u> and see.
   Visit this vine <u>and</u> protect it,
   the vine your right <u>hand</u> has planted.

4. And we shall never forsake <u>you</u> again:
   give us life that we may call u<u>pon</u> your name.
   God of hosts, <u>bring</u> us back;
   let your face shine on us and we <u>shall</u> be saved.

Gospel Acclamation John 15:15
For musical setting see Nos 36 to 47

Alleluia.
I call you friends, <u>says</u> the Lord,
because I have made known to you everything I have learnt <u>from</u> my Father.
Alleluia.

or cf. John 15:16

Alleluia.
I chose you from the world to go out <u>and</u> bear fruit,
fruit that will last, <u>says</u> the Lord.
Alleluia.

Response: Colin Mawby   Psalm tone: Laurence Bevenot

Text © 1963, 1986, 1993 The Grail, England, taken from 'The Psalms, a New Inclusive Language Version',
published by HarperCollins Religious. Used by permission of A.P. Watt Ltd, London.
Response © Copyright 1998 Kevin Mayhew Ltd.
Psalm tone © Copyright Ampleforth Abbey, York YO6 4EN. Used by permission.

997 28th in Ordinary Time (A)

Responsorial Psalm Psalm 22. ℞ v.6

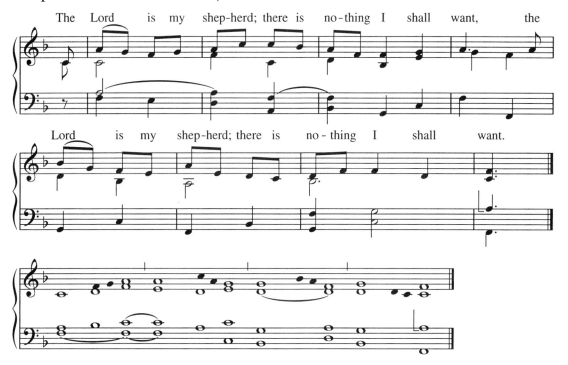

The Lord is my shep-herd; there is no-thing I shall want, the
Lord is my shep-herd; there is no-thing I shall want.

1. The Lord is my shepherd;
   there is nothing I shall want.
   Fresh and green are the pastures
   where he gives me repose.

2. Near restful waters he leads me,
   to revive my drooping spirit.
   He guides me along the right path;
   he is true to his name.

3. If I should walk in the valley of darkness
   no evil would I fear.
   You are there with your crook and your staff;
   with these you give me comfort.

4. You have prepared a banquet for me
   in the sight of my foes.
   My head you have anointed with oil;
   my cup is overflowing.

5. Surely goodness and kindness shall follow me
   all the days of my life.
   In the Lord's own house shall I dwell
   for ever and ever.

Note: verse 3 may be omitted

Gospel Acclamation John 1:12, 14   or cf. Ephesians 1:17, 18
For musical setting see Nos 36 to 47

Alleluia.
The Word was made flesh and lived among us;
to all who did accept him he gave power to
  become children of God.
Alleluia.

Alleluia.
May the Father of our Lord Jesus Christ enlighten
  the eyes of our mind,
so that we can see what hope his call holds for us.
Alleluia.

Response: Andrew Moore   Psalm tone: Alan Rees

998 29th in Ordinary Time (A)

Responsorial Psalm Psalm 95:1, 3-5, 7-10. ℞ v.7

1. O sing a new song to the Lord,
   sing to the Lord all the earth.
   Tell among the nations his glory
   and his wonders among all the peoples.

2. The Lord is great and worthy of praise,
   to be feared above all gods;
   the gods of the heathens are naught.
   It was the Lord who made the heavens.

3. Give the Lord, you families of peoples,
   give the Lord glory and power,
   give the Lord the glory of his name.
   Bring an offering and enter his courts.

4. Worship the Lord in his temple.
   O earth, tremble before him.
   Proclaim to the nations: 'God is king.'
   He will judge the peoples in fairness.

Gospel Acclamation John 17:17
For musical setting see Nos 36 to 47

Alleluia.
Your word is truth, O Lord,
consecrate us in the truth.
Alleluia.

or Phillipians 2:15-16

Alleluia.
You will shine in the world like bright stars
because you are offering it the word of life.
Alleluia.

Response and Psalm tone: Andrew Moore

999 30th in Ordinary Time (A)

Responsorial Psalm Psalm 17:2-4, 47, 51. ℟ v.2

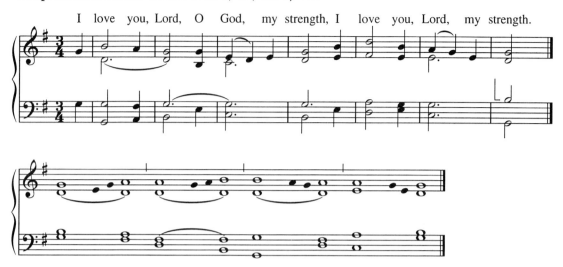

1. My God is the rock where I take refuge;
   my shield, my mighty help, my stronghold.
   The Lord is worthy of all praise.
   When I call I am saved from my foes.

2. Long life to the Lord, my rock!
   Praised be the God who saves me.
   He has given great victories to his king
   and shown his love for his anointed.

Gospel Acclamation cf. Acts 16:14
For musical setting see Nos 36 to 47

Alleluia.
Open our heart, O Lord,
to accept the words of your Son.
Alleluia.

Response:Alan Rees   Psalm tone: Gregory Murray

1000 31st in Ordinary Time (A)

Responsorial Psalm Psalm 130

1. O Lord, my heart <u>is</u> not proud
   nor haugh<u>ty</u> my eyes.
   I have not gone after <u>things</u> too great
   nor mar<u>vels</u> beyond me.

2. Truly I have set my soul in si<u>lence</u> and peace.
   A weaned child on its mother's breast, even so <u>is</u> my soul.
   O Israel, hope <u>in</u> the Lord
   both now <u>and</u> for ever.

Gospel Acclamation 1 Samuel 3:9; John 6:68
For musical setting see Nos 36 to 47

Alleluia.
Speak, Lord, your ser<u>vant</u> is listening;
you have the message of e<u>ter</u>nal life.
Alleluia.

Response: Martin Setchell Psalm tone: Andrew Moore

1001 32nd in Ordinary Time (A)

Responsorial Psalm Psalm 62:2-8. ℟ v.2

For you my soul is thirst - ing, O Lord my God.

1. O God, you are my God, for <u>you</u> I long;
   for you my <u>soul</u> is thirsting.
   My body <u>pines</u> for you
   like a dry, weary land <u>with</u>out water.

2. So I gaze on you <u>in</u> the sanctuary
   to see your strength <u>and</u> your glory.
   For your love is be<u>tter</u> than life,
   my lips will <u>speak</u> your praise.

3. So I will bless you <u>all</u> my life,
   in your name I will lift <u>up</u> my hands.
   My soul shall be filled as <u>with</u> a banquet,
   my mouth shall praise <u>you</u> with joy.

4. On my bed I re<u>member</u> you.
   On you I muse <u>through</u> the night
   for you have <u>been</u> my help;
   in the shadow of your wings <u>I</u> rejoice.

Gospel Acclamation Matthew 24:42, 44
For musical setting see Nos 36 to 47

Alleluia.
Stay awake <u>and</u> stand ready,
because you do not know the hour when the Son of <u>Man</u> is coming.
Alleluia.

Response and Psalm tone: Andrew Moore

1002 33rd in Ordinary Time (A)

Responsorial Psalm Psalm 127:1-5. ℟ v.1

1. O blessed are those who <u>fear</u> the Lord
   and walk <u>in</u> his ways!
   By the labour of your hands <u>you</u> shall eat.
   You will be hap<u>py</u> and prosper.

2. Your wife like a <u>fruit</u>ful vine
   in the heart <u>of</u> your house;
   your children like shoots <u>of</u> the olive,
   <u>around</u> your table.

3. Indeed thus <u>shall</u> be blessed
   those who <u>fear</u> the Lord.
   May the Lord bless <u>you</u> from Zion
   in a hap<u>py</u> Jerusalem.

Gospel Acclamation Revelation 2:10
For musical setting see Nos 36 to 47

Alleluia.
Even if you have to die, <u>says</u> the Lord,
keep faithful, and I will give you the <u>crown</u> of life.
Alleluia.

or John 15:4, 5

Alleluia.
Make your home in me, as I make mine in you, <u>says</u> the Lord.
Whoever remains in me bears <u>fruit</u> in plenty.
Alleluia.

Response: Andrew Moore   Psalm tone: Alan Rees

1003 *Last Sunday in Ordinary Time*
Our Lord Jesus Christ, Universal King (A)

Responsorial Psalm Psalm 22. ℟ v.1

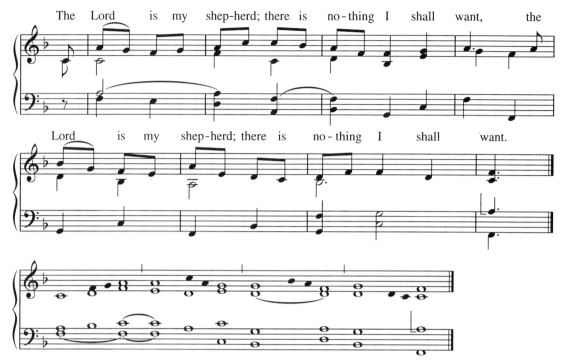

The Lord is my shep-herd; there is no-thing I shall want, the

Lord is my shep-herd; there is no-thing I shall want.

1. The Lord <u>is</u> my shepherd;
   there is nothing <u>I</u> shall want.
   Fresh and green <u>are</u> the pastures
   where he gives <u>me</u> repose.

2. Near restful <u>wat</u>ers he leads me,
   to revive my <u>droop</u>ing spirit.
   He guides me along <u>the</u> right path;
   he is true <u>to</u> his name.

3. If I should walk in the <u>val</u>ley of darkness
   no evil <u>would</u> I fear.
   You are there with your crook <u>and</u> your staff;
   with these you <u>give</u> me comfort.

4. You have prepared a <u>ban</u>quet for me
   in the sight <u>of</u> my foes.
   My head you have <u>anoint</u>ed with oil;
   my cup is <u>over</u>flowing.

5. Surely goodness and <u>kind</u>ness shall follow me
   all the days <u>of</u> my life.
   In the Lord's own house <u>shall</u> I dwell
   for <u>ev</u>er and ever.

   Note: verse 3 may be omitted

Gospel Acclamation Mark 11:10
For musical setting see Nos 36 to 47

Alleluia.
Blessings on him who comes in the name <u>of</u> the Lord!
Blessings on the coming kingdom of our <u>fa</u>ther David!
Alleluia.

Response: Andrew Moore   Psalm tone: Alan Rees

1004 2nd in Ordinary Time (B)

Responsorial Psalm Psalm 39:2, 4, 7-10. ℟ vv.8, 9

Here I am, Lord! I come to do your will.

1. I waited, I waited for the Lord
   and he stooped down to me;
   he heard my cry.
   He put a new song into my mouth,
   praise of our God.

2. You do not ask for sacrifice and offerings,
   but an open ear.
   You do not ask for holocaust and victim.
   Instead, here am I.

3. In the scroll of the book it stands written
   that I should do your will.
   My God, I delight in your law
   in the depth of my heart.

4. Your justice I have proclaimed
   in the great assembly.
   My lips I have not sealed;
   you know it, O Lord.

Gospel Acclamation 1 Samuel 3:9; John 6:68
For musical setting see Nos 36 to 47

Alleluia.
Speak, Lord, your servant is listening:
you have the message of eternal life.
Alleluia.

or

Alleluia.
We have found the Messiah – which means the Christ –
grace and truth have come through him.
Alleluia.

Response: Colin Mawby   Psalm tone: Gregory Murray

1005 3rd in Ordinary Time (B)

Responsorial Psalm Psalm 24:4-9. ℟ v.4

1. Lord, make me <u>know</u> your ways.
   Lord, teach <u>me</u> your paths.
   Make me walk in your <u>truth</u>, and teach me:
   for you are <u>God</u> my saviour.

2. Remember your <u>mer</u>cy Lord,
   and the love you have shown <u>from</u> of old.
   In your <u>love</u> remember me,
   because of your good<u>ness</u>, O Lord.

3. The Lord is <u>good</u> and upright.
   He shows the path to <u>those</u> who stray,
   he guides the humble in <u>the</u> right path;
   he teaches his way <u>to</u> the poor.

Gospel Acclamation Mark 1:15
For musical setting see Nos 36 to 47

Alleluia.
The kingdom of God is <u>close</u> at hand;
believe <u>the</u> Good News.
Alleluia.

Response: Rosalie Bonighton   Psalm tone: Andrew Moore

1006 4th in Ordinary Time (B)

Responsorial Psalm Psalm 94:1-2, 6-9. ℟ v.9

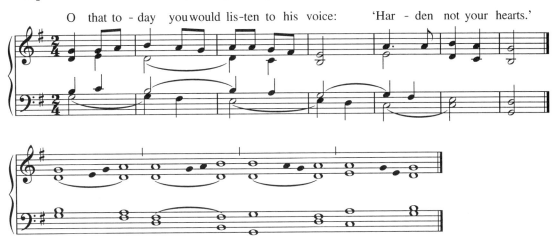

1. Come ring out our joy to the Lord;
   hail the rock who saves us.
   Let us come before him, giving thanks,
   with songs let us hail the Lord.

2. Come in; let us kneel and bend low;
   let us kneel before the God who made us
   for he is our God, and we the people who
      belong to his pasture,
   the flock that is led by his hand.

3. O that today you would listen to his voice!
   'Harden not your hearts as at Meribah,
   as on that day at Massah in the desert, when
      your fathers put me to the test;
   when they tried me, though they saw my work.'

Gospel Acclamation cf. Matthew 11:25
For musical setting see Nos 36 to 47

Alleluia.
Blessed are you, Father, Lord of heaven and earth,
for revealing the mysteries of the kingdom to mere children.
Alleluia.

or Matthew 4:16

Alleluia.
The people that lived in darkness have seen a great light;
on those who dwell in the land and shadow of death a light has dawned.
Alleluia.

Response and Psalm tone: Gregory Murray

1007 5th in Ordinary Time (B)

Responsorial Psalm Psalm 146:1-6. ℟ v.3

Praise the Lord, praise the Lord who heals the bro-ken-heart - ed.

* Omit in verse 1

1. Praise the Lord for <u>he</u> is good;
   sing to our God for <u>he</u> is loving:
   to him our <u>praise</u> is due.

2. The Lord builds <u>up</u> Jerusalem
   and brings back Is<u>rael</u>'s exiles,
   he heals the <u>broken</u>-hearted,
   he binds up <u>all</u> their wounds.

3. Our Lord is great <u>and</u> almighty;
   his wisdom can ne<u>ver</u> be measured.
   The Lord rai<u>ses</u> the lowly;
   he humbles the wicked <u>to</u> the dust.

Gospel Acclamation John 8:12
For musical setting see Nos 36 to 47

Alleluia.
I am the light of the world, <u>says</u> the Lord,
anyone who follows me will have the <u>light</u> of life.
Alleluia.

or Matthew 8:17

Alleluia.
He took our sick<u>nesses</u> away,
and carried our dis<u>eases</u> for us.
Alleluia.

Response: Richard Lloyd   Psalm tone: Gregory Murray

1008 6th in Ordinary Time (B)

Responsorial Psalm Psalm 31:1-2, 5, 11. ℞ v.7

You are my ref-uge, O Lord; you fill me with the joy of sal-va-tion.

1. Happy are those whose offence <u>is</u> forgiven,
   whose sin <u>is</u> remitted.
   O happy are those to <u>whom</u> the Lord
   im<u>putes</u> no guilt.

2. But now I have acknow<u>ledged</u> my sins;
   my guilt I <u>did</u> not hide,
   and you, Lord, <u>have</u> forgiven
   the guilt <u>of</u> my sin.

3. Rejoice, rejoice <u>in</u> the Lord,
   e<u>xult</u>, you just!
   O come, ring <u>out</u> your joy,
   all you up<u>right</u> of heart.

Gospel Acclamation cf. Ephesians 1:17, 18
For musical setting see Nos 36 to 47

   Alleluia.
   May the Father of our Lord Jesus Christ enlighten the eyes <u>of</u> our mind,
   so that we can see what hope his call <u>holds</u> for us.
   Alleluia.

   or Luke 7:16

   Alleluia.
   A great prophet has ap<u>peared</u> among us;
   God has vis<u>ited</u> his people.
   Alleluia.

Response: Colin Mawby   Psalm tone: Gregory Murray

1009 7th in Ordinary Time (B)

Responsorial Psalm Psalm 40:2-5, 13-14. ℟ v.5

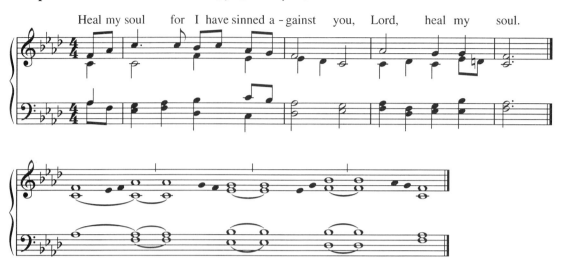

Heal my soul   for I have sinned a-gainst   you,   Lord,   heal my   soul.

1. Happy are those who consider the poor <u>and</u> the weak.
   The Lord will save them in the <u>day</u> of evil,
   will guard them, give them life, make them happy <u>in</u> the land
   and will not give them up to the will <u>of</u> their foes.

2. The Lord will give them strength <u>in</u> their pain,
   he will bring them back from sick<u>ness</u> to health.
   As for me, I said: 'Lord, have mer<u>cy</u> on me,
   heal my soul for I have <u>sinned</u> against you.'

3. If you uphold me I shall <u>be</u> unharmed
   and set in your presence for <u>ev</u>ermore.
   Blessed be the Lord, the <u>God</u> of Israel
   from age to age. A<u>men</u>. Amen.

Gospel Acclamation John 1:12, 14
For musical setting see Nos 36 to 47

Alleluia.
The Word was made flesh and <u>lived</u> among us;
to all who did accept him he gave power to become child<u>ren</u> of God.
Alleluia.

or Luke 4:18

Alleluia.
The Lord has sent me to bring the good news <u>to</u> the poor,
to proclaim liber<u>ty</u> to captives.
Alleluia.

Response: Alan Rees   Psalm tone: Gregory Murray

1010 8th in Ordinary Time (B)

Responsorial Psalm Psalm 102:1-4, 8, 10, 12-13. ℞ v.8

The Lord is com-pas-sion and love, the Lord is com-pas-sion and love.

1. My soul, give thanks to the Lord,
   all my being, bless his holy name.
   My soul, give thanks to the Lord
   and never forget all his blessings.

2. It is he who forgives all your guilt,
   who heals every one of your ills,
   who redeems your life from the grave,
   who crowns you with love and compassion.

3. The Lord is compassion and love,
   slow to anger and rich in mercy.
   He does not treat us according to our sins
   nor repay us according to our faults.

4. As far as the east is from the west
   so far does he remove our sins.
   As a father has compassion on his sons,
   the Lord has pity on those who fear him.

Gospel Acclamation John 10:27
For musical setting see Nos 36 to 47

Alleluia.
The sheep that belong to me listen to my voice, says the Lord,
I know them and they follow me.
Alleluia.

or James 1:18

Alleluia.
By his own choice the Father made us his children by the message of the truth,
so that we should be a sort of first-fruits of all that he created.
Alleluia.

Response: Andrew Moore   Psalm tone: Laurence Bevenot

1011 9th in Ordinary Time (B)

Responsorial Psalm Psalm 80:3-8, 10-11. ℟ v.2

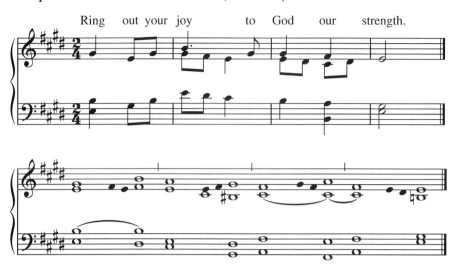

Ring out your joy to God our strength.

1. Raise a song and <u>sound</u> the timbrel,
   the sweet-sounding harp <u>and</u> the lute,
   blow the trumpet at <u>the</u> new moon,
   when the moon is full, <u>on</u> our feast.

2. For this is Is<u>ra</u>el's law,
   a command of the <u>God</u> of Jacob.
   He imposed it as a <u>rule</u> on Joseph,
   when he went out against the <u>land</u> of Egypt.

3. A voice I did not know <u>said</u> to me:
   'I freed your shoulder <u>from</u> the burden;
   your hands were freed <u>from</u> the load.
   You called in distress <u>and</u> I saved you.

4. 'Let there be no foreign <u>god</u> among you,
   no worship of an al<u>ie</u>n god.
   I am the Lord <u>your</u> God,
   who brought you from the <u>land</u> of Egypt.'

Gospel Acclamation cf. John 6:63, 68
For musical setting see Nos 36 to 47

Alleluia.
Your words are spirit, Lord, and <u>they</u> are life:
you have the message of et<u>er</u>nal life.
Alleluia.

or cf. John 17:17

Alleluia.
Your word is <u>truth</u>, O Lord,
consecrate us <u>in</u> the truth.
Alleluia.

Response and Psalm tone: Andrew Moore

1012 10th in Ordinary Time (B)

Responsorial Psalm Psalm 129. ℟ v.7

1. Out of the depths I cry to <u>you</u>, O Lord,
   Lord, <u>hear</u> my voice!
   O let your ears <u>be</u> attentive
   to the voice <u>of</u> my pleading.

2. If you, O Lord, should <u>mark</u> our guilt,
   Lord, who <u>would</u> survive?
   But with you is <u>found</u> forgiveness:
   for this <u>we</u> revere you.

3. My soul is waiting <u>for</u> the Lord,
   I count <u>on</u> his word.
   My soul is longing <u>for</u> the Lord
   more than watch<u>man</u> for daybreak.

4. Because with the Lord <u>there</u> is mercy
   and fullness <u>of</u> redemption,
   Israel indeed he <u>will</u> redeem
   from all <u>its</u> iniquity.

Gospel Acclamation John 14:23
For musical setting see Nos 36 to 47

    Alleluia.
    If anyone loves me they will <u>keep</u> my word,
    and my Father will love them and <u>we</u> shall come to them.
    Alleluia.

    or John 12:31, 32

    Alleluia.
    Now the prince of this world is to be overthrown, <u>says</u> the Lord.
    And when I am lifted up from the earth, I shall draw all men <u>to</u> myself.
    Alleluia.

Response: Alan Rees   Psalm tone: Andrew Moore

1013 11th in Ordinary Time (B)

Responsorial Psalm Psalm 91:2-3, 13-16. ℟ v.2

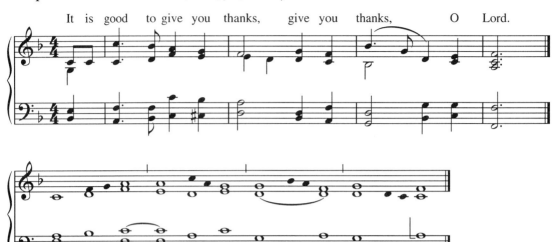

1. It is good to give thanks <u>to</u> the Lord
   to make music to your name, <u>O</u> Most High,
   to proclaim your love <u>in</u> the morning
   and your truth in the watches <u>of</u> the night.

2. The just will flourish <u>like</u> the palm-tree
   and grow like a Le<u>ba</u>non cedar.
   Planted in the house <u>of</u> the Lord
   they will flourish in the courts <u>of</u> our God.

3. Still bearing fruit when <u>they</u> are old,
   still full of <u>sap</u>, still green,
   they will proclaim that the <u>Lord</u> is just.
   In him, my rock, there <u>is</u> no wrong.

Gospel Acclamation John 15:15
For musical setting see Nos 36 to 47

Alleluia.
I call you friends, <u>says</u> the Lord,
because I have made known to you everything I have learnt <u>from</u> my Father.
Alleluia.

or

Alleluia.
The seed is the word of God, <u>Christ</u> the sower;
whoever finds the seed will re<u>main</u> for ever.
Alleluia.

Response: Colin Mawby   Psalm tone: Alan Rees

1014 12th in Ordinary Time (B)

Responsorial Psalm Psalm 106:23-26, 28-31. ℟ v.1

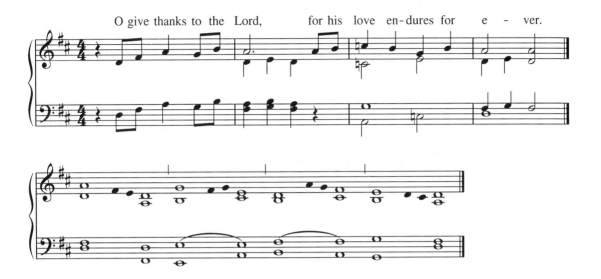

O give thanks to the Lord, for his love en-dures for e - ver.

Response and Psalm tone:Andrew Moore

1. Some sailed to the <u>sea</u> in ships
   to trade on the <u>migh</u>ty waters.
   These have seen <u>the</u> Lord's deeds,
   the wonders he does <u>in</u> the deep.

2. For he spoke; he sum<u>moned</u> the gale,
   tossing the waves <u>of</u> the sea
   up to heaven and back in<u>to</u> the deep;
   their soul melted away in <u>their</u> distress.

3. Then they cried to the Lord <u>in</u> their need
   and he rescued them from <u>their</u> distress.
   He stilled the storm <u>to</u> a whisper:
   all the waves of the <u>sea</u> were hushed.

4. They rejoiced because <u>of</u> the calm
   and he led them to the haven <u>they</u> desired.
   Let them thank the Lord <u>for</u> his love,
   the wonders he does <u>for</u> his people.

Gospel Acclamation cf. Ephesians 1:17, 18
For musical setting see Nos 36 to 47

Alleluia.
May the Father of our Lord Jesus Christ enlighten the eyes <u>of</u> our mind,
so that we can see what hope his call <u>holds</u> for us.
Alleluia.

or Luke 7:16

Alleluia.
A great prophet has ap<u>peared</u> among us;
God has vis<u>ited</u> his people.
Alleluia.

1015　13th in Ordinary Time (B)

Responsorial Psalm Psalm 29:2, 4-6, 11-13. ℟ v.2

1. I will praise you, Lord, <u>you</u> have rescued me
   and have not let my enemies rejoice <u>o</u>ver me.
   O Lord, you have raised my soul <u>from</u> the dead,
   restored me to life from those who sink in<u>to</u> the grave.

2. Sing psalms to the Lord, <u>you</u> who love him,
   give thanks to his <u>ho</u>ly name.
   His anger lasts but a moment; his fa<u>vour</u> through life.
   At night there are tears, but joy <u>comes</u> with dawn.

3. The Lord listened <u>and</u> had pity.
   The Lord came <u>to</u> my help.
   For me you have changed my mourning <u>into</u> dancing,
   O Lord my God, I will thank <u>you</u> for ever.

Gospel Acclamation cf. John 6:63, 68
For musical setting see Nos 36 to 47

> Alleluia.
> Your words are spirit, Lord, and <u>they</u> are life:
> you have the message of e<u>ter</u>nal life.
> Alleluia.

Response: Richard Lloyd　Psalm tone: Alan Rees

1016 14th in Ordinary Time (B)

Responsorial Psalm Psalm 122. ℟ v.2

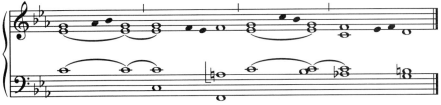

1. To you have I lifted <u>up</u> my eyes,
   you who dwell <u>in</u> the heavens:
   my eyes, like the <u>eyes</u> of slaves
   on the hand <u>of</u> their lords.

2. Like the eyes <u>of</u> a servant
   on the hand <u>of</u> his mistress,
   so our eyes are on the <u>Lord</u> our God
   till he show <u>us</u> his mercy.

3. Have mercy on us, <u>Lord</u>, have mercy.
   We are filled <u>with</u> contempt.
   Indeed all too full <u>is</u> our soul
   with the scorn <u>of</u> the rich.

Gospel Acclamation John 1:12, 14
For musical setting see Nos 36 to 47

Alleluia.
The Word was made flesh and <u>lived</u> among us;
to all who did accept him he gave power to become chil<u>dren</u> of God.
Alleluia.

or Luke 4:18

Alleluia.
The Lord has sent me to bring the good news <u>to</u> the poor,
to proclaim liber<u>ty</u> to captives.
Alleluia.

Response and Psalm tone: Andrew Moore

1017 15th in Ordinary Time (B)

Responsorial Psalm Psalm 84:9-14. ℞ v.8

1. I will hear what the Lord God <u>has</u> to say,
   a voice that <u>speaks</u> of peace.
   His help is near for <u>those</u> who fear him
   and his glory will dwell <u>in</u> our land.

2. Mercy and faithful<u>ness</u> have met;
   justice and peace <u>have</u> embraced.
   Faithfulness shall spring <u>from</u> the earth
   and justice look <u>down</u> from heaven.

3. The Lord will <u>make</u> us prosper
   and our earth shall <u>yield</u> its fruit.
   Justice shall <u>march</u> before him
   and peace shall fo<u>llow</u> his steps.

Gospel Acclamation cf. John 6:63, 68
For musical setting see Nos 36 to 47

Alleluia.
Your words are spirit, Lord, and <u>they</u> are life:
you have the message of e<u>ter</u>nal life.
Alleluia.

or cf. Ephesians 1:17, 18

Alleluia.
May the Father of our Lord Jesus Christ enlighten the eyes <u>of</u> our mind,
so that we can see what hope his call <u>holds</u> for us.
Alleluia.

Response: Stephen Dean   Psalm tone: Laurence Bevenot

1018 16th in Ordinary Time (B)

Responsorial Psalm Psalm 22. ℞ v.2

The Lord is my shep-herd; there is no-thing I shall want, the

Lord is my shep-herd; there is no-thing I shall want.

1. The Lord is my shepherd;
   there is nothing I shall want.
   Fresh and green are the pastures
   where he gives me repose.

2. Near restful waters he leads me
   to revive my drooping spirit.
   He guides me along the right path;
   he is true to his name.

3. If I should walk in the valley of darkness
   no evil would I fear.
   You are there with your crook and your staff;
   with these you give me comfort.

4. You have prepared a banquet for me
   in the sight of my foes.
   My head you have anointed with oil;
   my cup is overflowing.

5. Surely goodness and kindness shall follow me
   all the days of my life.
   In the Lord's own house shall I dwell
   for ever and ever.

Note: verse 3 may be omitted

Gospel Acclamation John 10:27
For musical setting see Nos 36 to 47

Alleluia.
The sheep that belong to me listen to my voice, says the Lord,
I know them and they follow me.
Alleluia.

Response: Andrew Moore   Psalm tone: Alan Rees

1019 17th in Ordinary Time (B)

Responsorial Psalm Psalm 144:10-11, 15-18. ℞ v.16

1. All your creatures shall thank <u>you</u>, O Lord,
   and your friends shall re<u>peat</u> their blessing.
   They shall speak of the glory <u>of</u> your reign
   and declare your <u>might</u>, O God.

2. The eyes of all creatures <u>look</u> to you
   and you give them their food <u>in</u> due time.
   You open <u>wide</u> your hand,
   grant the desires of <u>all</u> who live.

3. The Lord is just in <u>all</u> his ways
   and loving in <u>all</u> his deeds.
   He is close to <u>all</u> who call him,
   who call on him <u>from</u> their hearts.

Gospel Acclamation cf. John 6:63, 68
For musical setting see Nos 36 to 47

Alleluia.
Your words are spirit, Lord, and <u>they</u> are life:
you have the message of e<u>ter</u>nal life.
Alleluia.

or Luke 7:16

Alleluia.
A great prophet has <u>appeared</u> among us;
God has vis<u>ited</u> his people.
Alleluia.

Response: Andrew Moore   Psalm tone: Gregory Murray

1020 18th in Ordinary Time (B)

Responsorial Psalm Psalm 77:3-4, 23-25, 54. R℣ v.24

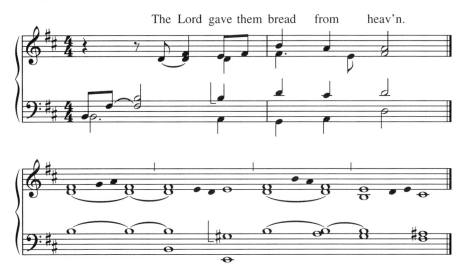

The Lord gave them bread from heav'n.

1. The things we have heard and <u>under</u>stood,
   the things our fore<u>bears</u> have told us,
   we will tell to the next <u>gen</u>eration:
   the glories of the Lord <u>and</u> his might.

2. He commanded the <u>clouds</u> above
   and opened the <u>gates</u> of heaven.
   He rained down manna <u>for</u> their food,
   and gave them <u>bread</u> from heaven.

3. Mere mortals ate the <u>bread</u> of angels.
   He sent them abun<u>dance</u> of food.
   He brought them to his <u>holy</u> land,
   to the mountain which his right <u>hand</u> had won.

Gospel Acclamation John 14:5
For musical setting see Nos 36 to 47

Alleluia.
I am the Way, the Truth and the Life, <u>says</u> the Lord;
no one can come to the Father ex<u>cept</u> through me.
Alleluia.

or Matthew 4:4

Alleluia.
Man does not live on <u>bread</u> alone,
but on every word that comes from the <u>mouth</u> of God.
Alleluia.

Response: Rosalie Bonighton   Psalm tone: Andrew Moore

1021 19th in Ordinary Time (B)

Responsorial Psalm Psalm 33:2-9. R̸ v.9

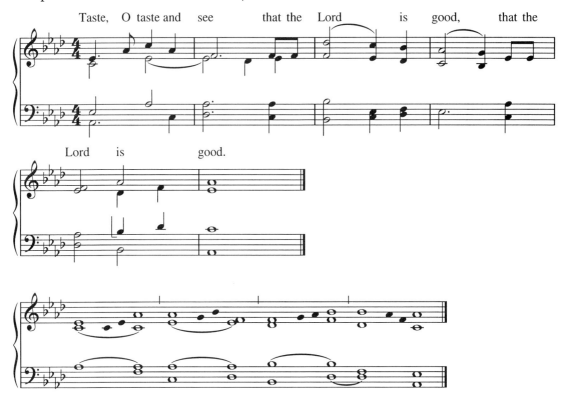

1. I will bless the Lord at all times,
   his praise always on my lips;
   in the Lord my soul shall make its boast.
   The humble shall hear and be glad.

2. Glorify the Lord with me.
   Together let us praise his name.
   I sought the Lord and he answered me;
   from all my terrors he set me free.

3. Look towards him and be radiant;
   let your faces not be abashed.
   When the poor cry out the Lord hears them
   and rescues them from all their distress.

4. The angel of the Lord is encamped
   around those who revere him, to rescue them.
   Taste and see that the Lord is good.
   They are happy who seek refuge in him.

Gospel Acclamation John 14:23
For musical setting see Nos 36 to 47

Alleluia.
If anyone loves me they will keep my word,
and my Father will love them, and we shall
come to them.
Alleluia.

or John 6:51

Alleluia.
I am the living bread which has come down
   from heaven, says the Lord.
Anyone who eats this bread will live for ever.
Alleluia.

Response and Psalm tone: Alan Rees

1022 20th in Ordinary Time (B)

Responsorial Psalm Psalm 33:2-3, 10-15. ℞ v.9

Taste, O taste and see that the Lord is good, that the Lord is good.

1. I will bless the Lord <u>at</u> all times,
   his praise always <u>on</u> my lips;
   in the Lord my soul shall <u>make</u> its boast.
   The humble shall hear <u>and</u> be glad.

2. Revere the Lord, <u>you</u> his saints.
   They lack nothing, those <u>who</u> revere him.
   Strong lions suffer want <u>and</u> go hungry
   but those who seek the Lord <u>lack</u> no blessing.

3. Come, chil<u>dren</u>, and hear me
   that I may teach you the fear <u>of</u> the Lord.
   Who are they who <u>long</u> for life
   and many days, to enjoy <u>their</u> prosperity?

4. Then keep your <u>tongue</u> from evil
   and your lips from spea<u>king</u> deceit.
   Turn aside from evil <u>and</u> do good;
   seek and strive <u>after</u> peace.

Gospel Acclamation John 1:12, 14
For musical setting see Nos 36 to 47

    or John 6:56

Alleluia.
The Word was made flesh and <u>lived</u> among us;
to all who did accept him he gave power to
  become chil<u>dren</u> of God.
Alleluia.

Alleluia.
They who eat my flesh and <u>drink</u> my blood
live in me, and I live in them, <u>says</u> the Lord.
Alleluia.

Response and Psalm tone: Alan Rees

1023 21st in Ordinary Time (B)

Responsorial Psalm Psalm 33:2-3, 16-23. ℟ v.9

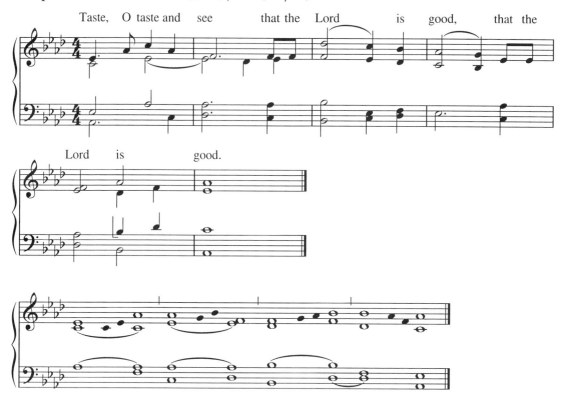

1. I will bless the Lord at all times,
   his praise always on my lips;
   in the Lord my soul shall make its boast.
   The humble shall hear and be glad.

2. The Lord turns his face against the wicked
   to destroy their remembrance from the earth.
   The Lord turns his eyes to the just
   and his ears to their appeal.

3. They call and the Lord hears
   and rescues them in all their distress.
   The Lord is close to the broken-hearted;
   those whose spirit is crushed he will save.

4. Evil brings to the wicked;
   those who hate the good are doomed.
   The Lord ransoms the souls of his servants.
   Those who hide in him shall not be condemned.

Gospel Acclamation cf. John 6:63, 68
For musical setting see Nos 36 to 47

Alleluia.
Your words are spirit, Lord, and they are life:
you have the message of eternal life.
Alleluia.

Response and Psalm tone: Alan Rees

1024 22nd in Ordinary Time (B)

Responsorial Psalm Psalm 14:2-5. ℟ v.1

1. Lord, who shall dwell on your <u>ho</u>ly mountain?
   Those who walk <u>with</u>out fault;
   those who <u>act</u> with justice
   and speak the truth <u>from</u> their hearts.

2. Those who do no wrong <u>to</u> their kindred,
   who cast no slur <u>on</u> their neighbours,
   who hold the godless <u>in</u> disdain,
   but honour those who <u>fear</u> the Lord.

3. Those who keep their pledge, <u>come</u> what may;
   who take no interest <u>on</u> a loan
   and accept no bribes a<u>gainst</u> the innocent.
   Such people will stand <u>firm</u> for ever.

Gospel Acclamation cf. John 6:63, 68
For musical setting see Nos 36 to 47

> Alleluia.
> Your words are spirit, Lord, and <u>they</u> are life:
> you have the message of e<u>ter</u>nal life:
> Alleluia.

> or James 1:18

> Alleluia.
> By his own choice the Father made us his children by the
>   message <u>of</u> the truth,
> so that we should be a sort of first-fruits of all that <u>he</u> created.
> Alleluia.

Response: Richard Proulx   Psalm tone: Gregory Murray

1025 23rd in Ordinary Time (B)

Responsorial Psalm Psalm 145:7-10. ℟ v.1

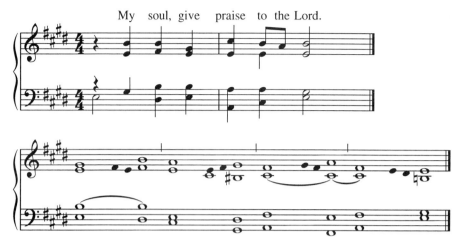

1. It is the Lord who keeps <u>faith</u> for ever,
   who is just to those who <u>are</u> oppressed.
   It is he who gives bread <u>to</u> the hungry,
   the Lord, who sets pris<u>on</u>ers free.

2. It is the Lord who gives sight <u>to</u> the blind,
   who raises up those who <u>are</u> bowed down,
   the Lord who <u>loves</u> the just,
   the Lord, who pro<u>tects</u> the stranger.

3. The Lord upholds the wi<u>dow</u> and orphan,
   but thwarts the path <u>of</u> the wicked.
   The Lord will <u>reign</u> for ever,
   Zion's God, from <u>age</u> to age.

Gospel Acclamation 1 Samuel 3:9; John 6:68
For musical setting see Nos 36 to 47

Alleluia.
Speak, Lord, your ser<u>vant</u> is listening:
you have the message of et<u>er</u>nal life.
Alleluia.

or cf. Matthew 4:23

Alleluia.
Jesus proclaimed the Good News <u>of</u> the kingdom,
and cured all kinds of sickness a<u>mong</u> the people.
Alleluia.

Response: Rosalie Bonighton   Psalm tone: Andrew Moore

1026 24th in Ordinary Time (B)

Responsorial Psalm Psalm 114:1-6, 8-9. ℟ v.9

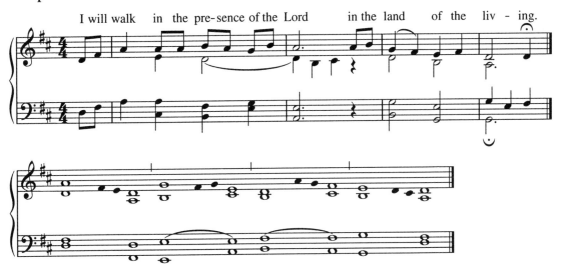

I will walk in the pre-sence of the Lord in the land of the liv - ing.

1. I love the Lord for <u>he</u> has heard
   the cry of <u>my</u> appeal;
   for he <u>turned</u> his ear to me
   in the day <u>when</u> I called him.

2. They surrounded me, the <u>snares</u> of death,
   with the anguish <u>of</u> the tomb;
   they caught me, sorrow <u>and</u> distress.
   O Lord my <u>God</u>, deliver me!

3. How gracious is the <u>Lord</u>, and just;
   our God <u>has</u> compassion.
   The Lord protects the <u>simple</u> hearts;
   I was helpless <u>so</u> he saved me.

4. He has kept my soul from death, my <u>eyes</u> from tears
   and my <u>feet</u> from stumbling.
   I will walk in the presence <u>of</u> the Lord
   in the land <u>of</u> the living.

Gospel Acclamation John 14:5
For musical setting see Nos 36 to 47

Alleluia.
I am the Way, the Truth and the Life, <u>says</u> the Lord;
no one can come to the Father ex<u>cept</u> through me.
Alleluia.

or Galatians 6:14

Alleluia.
The only thing I can boast about is the cross <u>of</u> our Lord,
through whom the world is crucified to me, and I <u>to</u> the world.
Alleluia.

Response and Psalm tone: Andrew Moore

1027 25th in Ordinary Time (B)

Responsorial Psalm Psalm 53:3-6, 8. ℟ v.6

* Omit in verse 2

1. O God, save me <u>by</u> your name;
   by your power, up<u>hold</u> my cause.
   O God, <u>hear</u> my prayer;
   listen to the words <u>of</u> my mouth.

2. For the proud have ri<u>sen</u> against me,
   ruthless foes <u>seek</u> my life.
   They have no re<u>gard</u> for God.

3. But I have God <u>for</u> my help.
   The Lord up<u>holds</u> my life.
   I will sacrifice to you with <u>willing</u> heart
   and praise your name for <u>it</u> is good.

Gospel Acclamation John 8:12
For musical setting see Nos 36 to 47

Alleluia.
I am the light of the world, <u>says</u> the Lord,
anyone who follows me will have the <u>light</u> of life.
Alleluia.

or cf. 2 Thessalonians 2:14

Alleluia.
Through the Good News <u>God</u> has called us
to share the glory of our Lord <u>Jesus</u> Christ.
Alleluia.

Response: Colin Mawby Psalm tone: Gregory Murray

1028 26th in Ordinary Time (B)

Responsorial Psalm Psalm 18:8, 10, 12-14. ℟ v.9

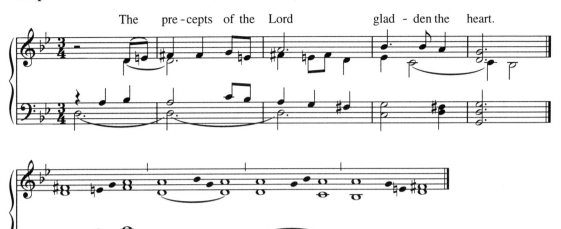

The pre-cepts of the Lord glad - den the heart.

1. The law of the <u>Lord</u> is perfect,
   it re<u>vives</u> the soul.
   The rule of the Lord is <u>to</u> be trusted,
   it gives wisdom <u>to</u> the simple.

2. The fear of the <u>Lord</u> is holy,
   abi<u>ding</u> for ever.
   The decrees of the <u>Lord</u> are truth
   and all <u>of</u> them just.

3. So in them your servant <u>finds</u> instruction;
   great reward is <u>in</u> their keeping.
   But who can detect <u>all</u> their errors?
   From hidden <u>faults</u> acquit me.

4. From presumption re<u>strain</u> your servant
   and let <u>it</u> not rule me.
   Then shall <u>I</u> be blameless,
   clean <u>from</u> grave sin.

Gospel Acclamation cf. John 17:17
For musical setting see Nos 36 to 47

Alleluia.
Your word is <u>truth</u>, O Lord
consecrate us <u>in</u> the truth.
Alleluia.

Response: Richard Lloyd   Psalm tone: Laurence Bevenot

1029 27th in Ordinary Time (B)

Responsorial Psalm Psalm 127. R℣ v.5

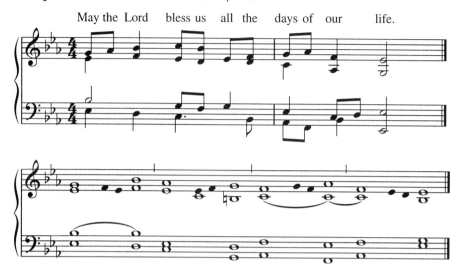

May the Lord bless us all the days of our life.

1. O blessed are those who <u>fear</u> the Lord
   and walk <u>in</u> his ways!
   By the labour of your hands <u>you</u> shall eat.
   You will be hap<u>py</u> and prosper.

2. Your wife will be like a <u>fruit</u>ful vine
   in the heart <u>of</u> your house;
   your children like shoots <u>of</u> the olive,
   a<u>round</u> your table.

3. Indeed thus <u>shall</u> be blessed
   those who <u>fear</u> the Lord.
   May the Lord bless <u>you</u> from Zion
   in a hap<u>py</u> Jerusalem.

Gospel Acclamation cf. John 17:17
For musical setting see Nos 36 to 47

Alleluia.
Your word is <u>truth</u>, O Lord,
consecrate us <u>in</u> the truth.
Alleluia.

or 1 John 4:12

Alleluia.
As long as we love <u>one</u> another
God will live in us and his love will be com<u>plete</u> in us.
Alleluia.

Response: Rosalie Bonighton   Psalm tone: Andrew Moore

1030 28th in Ordinary Time (B)

Responsorial Psalm Psalm 89:12-17. ℟ v.14

1. Make us know the shortness of our life
   that we may gain wisdom of heart.
   Lord, relent! Is your anger for ever?
   Show pity to your servants.

2. In the morning, fill us with your love;
   we shall exult and rejoice all our days.
   Give us joy to balance our affliction
   for the years when we knew misfortune.

3. Show forth your work to your servants;
   let your glory shine on their children.
   Let the favour of the Lord be upon us:
   give success to the work of our hands.

Gospel Acclamation cf. Matthew 11:25
For musical setting see Nos 36 to 47

Alleluia.
Blessed are you, Father, Lord of heaven and earth,
for revealing the mysteries of the kingdom to mere children.
Alleluia.

or Matthew 5:3

Alleluia,
How happy are the poor in spirit;
theirs is the kingdom of heaven.
Alleluia.

Response: Andrew Moore   Psalm tone: Alan Rees

1031 29th in Ordinary Time (B)

Responsorial Psalm Psalm 32:4-5, 18-20, 22. ℟ v.22

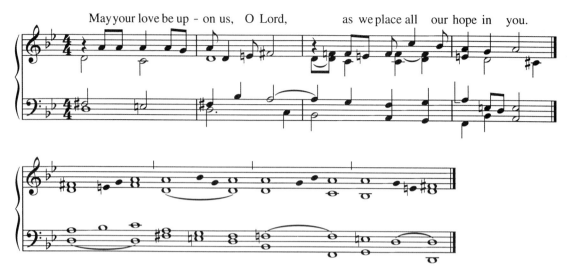

May your love be up-on us, O Lord, as we place all our hope in you.

1. The word of the Lord is faithful
   and all his works to be trusted.
   The Lord loves justice and right
   and fills the earth with his love.

2. The Lord looks on those who revere him,
   on those who hope in his love,
   to rescue their souls from death,
   to keep them alive in famine.

3. Our soul is waiting for the Lord.
   The Lord is our help and our shield.
   May your love be upon us, O Lord,
   as we place all our hope in you.

Gospel Acclamation John 14:15
For musical setting see Nos 36 to 47

Alleluia.
I am the Way, the Truth and the Life, says the Lord;
no one can come to the Father except through me.
Alleluia.

or Mark 10:45

Alleluia.
The Son of Man came to serve,
and to give his life as a ransom for many.
Alleluia.

Response: Rosalie Bonighton   Psalm tone: Laurence Bevenot

1032 30th in Ordinary Time (B)

Responsorial Psalm Psalm 125. ℟ v.3

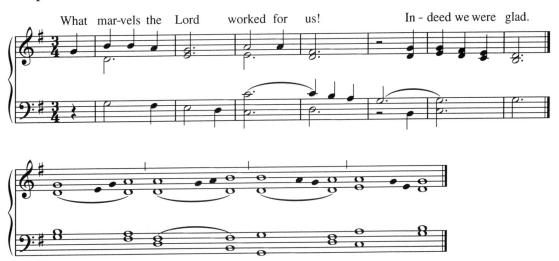

1. When the Lord delivered Zi<u>on</u> from bondage,
   it seemed <u>like</u> a dream.
   Then was our mouth <u>filled</u> with laughter,
   on our lips <u>there</u> were songs.

2. The heathens themselves <u>said</u>: 'What marvels
   the Lord <u>worked</u> for them!'
   What marvels the Lord <u>worked</u> for us!
   Indeed <u>we</u> were glad.

3. Deliver us, O Lord, <u>from</u> our bondage
   as streams <u>in</u> dry land.
   Those who are so<u>wing</u> in tears
   will sing <u>when</u> they reap.

4. They go out, they go out, <u>full</u> of tears,
   carrying seed <u>for</u> the sowing:
   they come back, they come back, <u>full</u> of song,
   carry<u>ing</u> their sheaves.

Gospel Acclamation John 8:12
For musical setting see Nos 36 to 47

Alleluia.
I am the light of the world, <u>says</u> the Lord,
anyone who follows me will have the <u>light</u> of life.
Alleluia.

Response: Martin Setchell   Psalm tone: Gregory Murray

1033 31st in Ordinary Time (B)

Responsorial Psalm Psalm 17:2-4, 47, 51. ℟ v.2

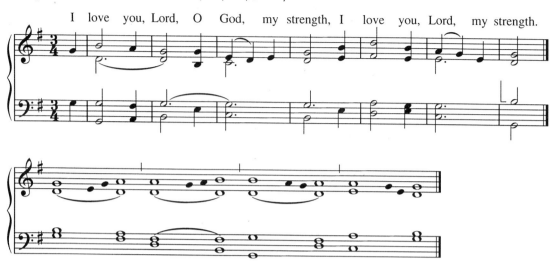

1. I love you, Lord, my strength,
   my rock, my for<u>tress</u>, my saviour.
   My God is the rock where <u>I</u> take refuge;
   my shield, my mighty <u>help</u>, my stronghold.

2. The Lord is worthy <u>of</u> all praise:
   when I call I am saved <u>from</u> my foes.
   Long life to the <u>Lord</u>, my rock!
   Praised be the <u>God</u> who saves me.

Gospel Acclamation cf. John 6:63, 68
For musical setting see Nos 36 to 47

Alleluia.
Your words are spirit, Lord, and <u>they</u> are life:
you have the message of et<u>er</u>nal life.
Alleluia.

or John 14:23

Alleluia.
If anyone loves me they will <u>keep</u> my word,
and my Father will love them and <u>we</u> shall come to them.
Alleluia.

Response: Alan Rees   Psalm tone: Gregory Murray

1034 32nd in Ordinary Time (B)

Responsorial Psalm Psalm 145:7-10. ℟ v.2

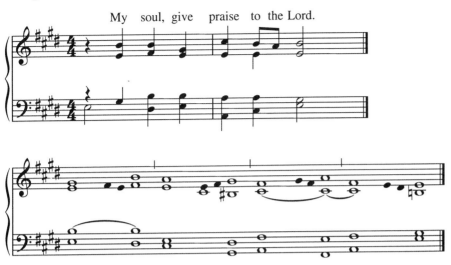

My soul, give praise to the Lord.

1. It is the Lord who keeps <u>faith</u> for ever,
   who is just to those who <u>are</u> oppressed.
   It is he who gives bread <u>to</u> the hungry,
   the Lord, who sets pris<u>on</u>ers free.

2. It is the Lord who gives sight <u>to</u> the blind,
   who raises up those who <u>are</u> bowed down.
   It is the Lord who <u>loves</u> the just,
   the Lord, who pro<u>tects</u> the stranger.

3. The Lord upholds the wi<u>dow</u> and orphan
   but thwarts the path <u>of</u> the wicked.
   The Lord will <u>reign</u> for ever,
   Zion's God, from <u>age</u> to age.

Gospel Acclamation Revelation 2:10
For musical setting see Nos 36 to 47

Alleluia.
Even if you have to die, <u>says</u> the Lord,
keep faithful, and I will give you the <u>crown</u> of life.
Alleluia.

or Matthew 5:3

Alleluia.
How happy are the <u>poor</u> in spirit;
theirs is the king<u>dom</u> of heaven.
Alleluia.

Response: Rosalie Bonighton   Psalm tone: Andrew Moore

1035 33rd in Ordinary Time (B)

Responsorial Psalm Psalm 15:5, 8-11. ℟ v.1

Pre-serve me, God, I take ref-uge in you.

1. O Lord, it is you who are my <u>por</u>tion and cup;
   it is you yourself who <u>are</u> my prize.
   I keep the Lord ever <u>in</u> my sight:
   since he is at my right hand, I <u>shall</u> stand firm.

2. And so my heart rejoices, my <u>soul</u> is glad;
   even my body shall <u>rest</u> in safety.
   For you will not leave my soul a<u>mong</u> the dead,
   nor let your beloved <u>know</u> decay.

3. O Lord, <u>you</u> will show me
   the <u>path</u> of life,
   the fullness of joy <u>in</u> your presence,
   at your right hand happi<u>ness</u> for ever.

Gospel Acclamation Matthew 24:42, 44
For musical setting see Nos 36 to 47

Alleluia.
Stay awake <u>and</u> stand ready,
because you do not know the hour when the Son of <u>Man</u> is coming.
Alleluia.

or Luke 21:36

Alleluia.
Stay awake, praying <u>at</u> all times
for the strength to stand with confidence before the <u>Son</u> of Man.
Alleluia.

Response: Andrew Moore   Psalm tone: Laurence Bevenot

Our Lord Jesus Christ, Universal King (B)

Responsorial Psalm Psalm 92:1-2, 5. ℟ v.1

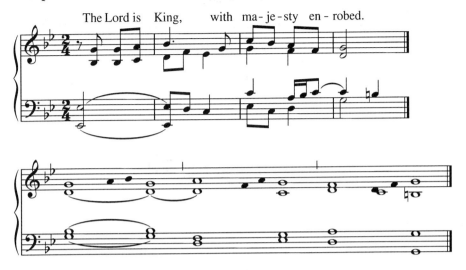

1. The Lord is King, with majes<u>ty</u> enrobed;
   the Lord has robed him<u>self</u> with might,
   he has girded him<u>self</u> with power.

2. The world you made firm, not <u>to</u> be moved;
   your throne has stood firm <u>from</u> of old.
   From all eternity, O <u>Lord</u>, you are.

3. Truly your decrees are <u>to</u> be trusted.
   Holiness is fitting <u>to</u> your house,
   O Lord, until the <u>end</u> of time.

Gospel Acclamation Mark 11:9, 10
For musical setting see Nos 36 to 47

   Alleluia.
   Blessings on him who comes in the name <u>of</u> the Lord!
   Blessings on the coming kingdom of our <u>father</u> David!
   Alleluia.

Response and Psalm tone: Andrew Moore

1037 2nd in Ordinary Time (C)

Responsorial Psalm Psalm 95:1-3, 7-10. R̸ v.3

1. O sing a new song <u>to</u> the Lord,
   sing to the Lord <u>all</u> the earth.
   O sing to the Lord, <u>bless</u> his name.

2. Proclaim his help <u>day</u> by day,
   tell among the <u>nations</u> his glory
   and his wonders among <u>all</u> the peoples.

3. Give the Lord, you fam<u>ilies</u> of peoples,
   give the Lord <u>glory</u> and power,
   give the Lord the glory <u>of</u> his name.

4. Worship the Lord <u>in</u> his temple.
   O earth, trem<u>ble</u> before him.
   Proclaim to the nations: '<u>God</u> is king.'

Gospel Acclamation cf. John 6:63, 68
For musical setting see Nos 36 to 47

> Alleluia.
> Your words are spirit, Lord, and <u>they</u> are life:
> you have the message of e<u>ter</u>nal life.
> Alleluia.

> or cf. 2 Thessalonians 2:14

> Alleluia.
> Through the Good News <u>God</u> has called us
> to share the glory of our Lord <u>Jesus</u> Christ.
> Alleluia.

Response and Psalm tone: Andrew Moore

1038 3rd in Ordinary Time (C)

Responsorial Psalm Psalm 18:8-10, 15. ℟ John 6:63

1. The law of the <u>Lord</u> is perfect,
   it re<u>vives</u> the soul.
   The rule of the Lord is <u>to</u> be trusted,
   it gives wisdom <u>to</u> the simple.

2. The precepts of the <u>Lord</u> are right,
   they gla<u>dden</u> the heart.
   The command of the <u>Lord</u> is clear,
   it gives light <u>to</u> the eyes.

3. The fear of the <u>Lord</u> is holy,
   abi<u>ding</u> for ever.
   The decrees of the <u>Lord</u> are truth
   and all <u>of</u> them just.

4. May the spoken words <u>of</u> my mouth,
   the thoughts <u>of</u> my heart,
   win favour in your <u>sight</u>, O Lord,
   my rescu<u>er</u>, my rock!

Gospel Acclamation Luke 4:18
For musical setting see Nos 36 to 47

Alleluia.
The Lord has sent me to bring the good news <u>to</u> the poor,
to proclaim liber<u>ty</u> to captives.
Alleluia.

Response and Psalm tone: Andrew Moore

1039 4th in Ordinary Time (C)

Responsorial Psalm Psalm 70:1-6, 15, 17. ℟ v.15

1. In you, O Lord, I take refuge;
   let me never be put to shame.
   In your justice rescue me, free me;
   pay heed to me and save me.

2. Be a rock where I can take refuge,
   a mighty stronghold to save me;
   for you are my rock, my stronghold.
   Free me from the hand of the wicked.

3. It is you, O Lord, who are my hope,
   my trust, O Lord, since my youth.
   On you I have leaned from my birth,
   from my mother's womb you have been my help.

4. My lips will tell of your justice
   and day by day of your help.
   O God, you have taught me from my youth
   and I proclaim your wonders still.

Gospel Acclamation John 14:5
For musical setting see Nos 36 to 47

Alleluia.
I am the Way, the Truth and the Life, says the Lord;
no one can come to the Father except through me.
Alleluia.

or Luke 4:18

Alleluia.
The Lord has sent me to bring the good news to the poor,
to proclaim liberty to captives.
Alleluia.

Response: Colin Mawby   Psalm tone: Gregory Murray

1040 5th in Ordinary Time (C)

Responsorial Psalm Psalm 137:1-5, 7-8. ℟ v.1

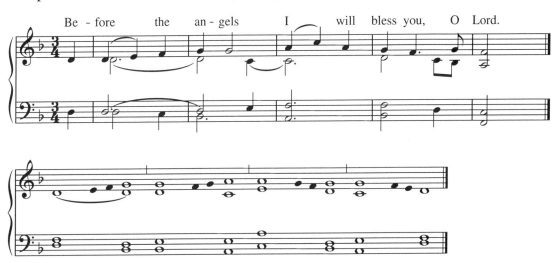

1. I thank you, Lord, with all my heart,
   you have heard the words of my mouth.
   Before the angels I will bless you
   I will adore before your holy temple.

2. I thank you for your faithfulness and love
   which excel all we ever knew of you.
   On the day I called, you answered;
   you increased the strength of my soul.

3. All earth's kings shall thank you
   when they hear the words of your mouth.
   They shall sing of the Lord's ways:
   'How great is the glory of the Lord!'

4. You stretch out your hand and save me,
   your hand will do all things for me.
   Your love, O Lord, is eternal,
   discard not the work of your hand.

Gospel Acclamation John 15:15
For musical setting see Nos 36 to 47

Alleluia.
I call you friends, says the Lord,
because I have made known to you everything I have learnt from my Father.
Alleluia.

or Matthew 4:19

Alleluia.
Follow me, says the Lord,
and I will make you fishers of men.
Alleluia.

Response: Richard Lloyd   Psalm tone: Laurence Bevenot

1041 6th in Ordinary Time (C)

Responsorial Psalm Psalm 1:1-4, 6. ℟ Psalm 39:5

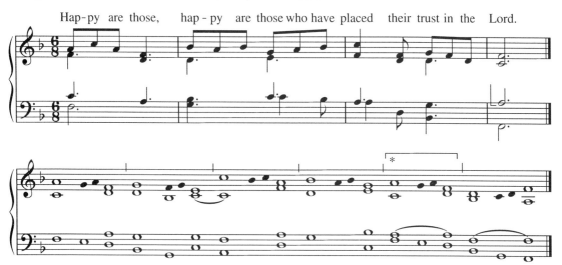

* Omit in verses 2 and 3

1. Happy indeed are those
   who follow not the counsel of the wicked;
   nor linger in the way of sinners
   nor sit in the company of scorners,
   whose delight is the law of the Lord
   and who ponder his law day and night.

2. They are like a tree that is planted
   beside the flowing waters,
   that yields its fruit in due season
   and whose leaves shall never fade;
   and all that they do shall prosper.

3. Not so are the wicked, not so!
   For they like winnowed chaff
   shall be driven away by the wind.
   For the Lord guards the way of the just
   but the way of the wicked leads to doom.

Gospel Acclamation cf. Matthew 11:25
For musical setting see Nos 36 to 47

Alleluia.
Blessed are you, Father, Lord of heaven and earth,
for revealing the mysteries of the kingdom to mere children.
Alleluia.

or Luke 6:23

Alleluia.
Rejoice and be glad:
your reward will be great in heaven.
Alleluia.

Response: Alan Rees   Psalm tone: Andrew Moore

1042 7th in Ordinary Time (C)

Responsorial Psalm Psalm 102:1-4, 8, 10, 12-13. ℟ v.8

The Lord is com-pas-sion and love, the Lord is com-pas-sion and love.

1. My soul, give thanks <u>to</u> the Lord,
   all my being, bless his <u>holy</u> name.
   My soul, give thanks <u>to</u> the Lord
   and never forget <u>all</u> his blessings.

2. It is he who forgives <u>all</u> your guilt,
   who heals every one <u>of</u> your ills,
   who redeems your life <u>from</u> the grave,
   who crowns you with love <u>and</u> compassion.

3. The Lord is compas<u>sion</u> and love,
   slow to anger and <u>rich</u> in mercy.
   He does not treat us according <u>to</u> our sins
   nor repay us according <u>to</u> our faults.

4. As far as the east is <u>from</u> the west
   so far does he re<u>move</u> our sins.
   As a father has compassion <u>on</u> his sons,
   the Lord has pity on <u>those</u> who fear him.

Gospel Acclamation cf. Acts 16:14
For musical setting see Nos 36 to 47

> Alleluia.
> Open our <u>heart</u>, O Lord,
> to accept the words <u>of</u> your Son.
> Alleluia.

> or John 13:34

> Alleluia.
> I give you a new commandment: love <u>one</u> another,
> just as I have loved you, <u>says</u> the Lord.
> Alleluia.

Response: Andrew Moore   Psalm tone: Laurence Bevenot

1043 8th in Ordinary Time (C)

Responsorial Psalm Psalm 91:2-3, 13-16. ℟ cf. v.2

It is good to give you thanks, give you thanks, O Lord.

1. It is good to give thanks to the Lord
   to make music to your name, O Most High,
   to proclaim your love in the morning
   and your truth in the watches of the night.

2. The just will flourish like the palm-tree
   and grow like a Lebanon cedar.
   Planted in the house of the Lord
   they will flourish in the courts of our God.

3. Still bearing fruit when they are old,
   still full of sap, still green,
   they will proclaim that the Lord is just.
   In him, my rock, there is no wrong.

Gospel Acclamation cf. Acts 16:14
For musical setting see Nos 36 to 47

Alleluia.
Open our heart, O Lord,
to accept the words of your Son.
Alleluia.

or Philippians 2:15-16

Alleluia.
You will shine in the world like bright stars
because you are offering it the word of life.
Alleluia.

Response: Colin Mawby Psalm tone: Alan Rees

1044 9th in Ordinary Time (C)

Responsorial Psalm Psalm 116:1-2. ℟ Mark 16:15

1. O praise the Lord, <u>all</u> you nations,
   acclaim him <u>all</u> you peoples!

2. Strong is his <u>love</u> for us;
   he is faith<u>ful</u> for ever.

Gospel Acclamation John 1:14, 12
For musical setting see Nos 36 to 47

Alleluia.
The Word was made flesh and <u>lived</u> among us;
to all who did accept him he gave power to become chil<u>dren</u> of God.
Alleluia.

or John 3:16

Alleluia.
God loved the world so much that he gave his <u>only</u> Son
so that everyone who believes in him may have e<u>ter</u>nal life.
Alleluia.

Response and Psalm tone: Andrew Moore

1045 10th in Ordinary Time (C)

Responsorial Psalm Psalm 29:2, 4-6, 11-13. ℟ v.2

1. I will praise you, Lord, <u>you</u> have rescued me
   and have not let my enemies rejoice <u>o</u>ver me.
   O Lord, you have raised my soul <u>from</u> the dead,
   restored me to life from those who sink in<u>to</u> the grave.

2. Sing psalms to the Lord, <u>you</u> who love him,
   give thanks to his <u>ho</u>ly name.
   His anger lasts a moment; his fa<u>vour</u> through life.
   At night there are tears, but joy <u>comes</u> with dawn.

3. The Lord listened <u>and</u> had pity.
   The Lord came <u>to</u> my help.
   For me you have changed my mourning <u>into</u> dancing;
   O Lord my God, I will thank <u>you</u> for ever.

Gospel Acclamation cf. Ephesians 1:17, 18
For musical setting see Nos 36 to 47

Alleluia.
May the Father of our Lord Jesus Christ enlighten the eyes <u>of</u> our mind,
so that we can see what hope his call <u>holds</u> for us.
Alleluia.

or Luke 7:16

Alleluia.
A great prophet has ap<u>peared</u> among us;
God has vis<u>ited</u> his people.
Alleluia.

Response: Richard Lloyd   Psalm tone: Alan Rees

1046 11th in Ordinary Time (C)

Responsorial Psalm Psalm 31:1-2, 5, 7, 11. ℟ cf. v.5

For - give, Lord, the guilt of my sin.

1. Happy are those whose offence is forgiven
   whose sin is remitted.
   O happy are those to whom the Lord
   imputes no guilt.

2. But now I have acknowledged my sins:
   my guilt I did not hide.
   And you, Lord, have forgiven
   the guilt of my sin.

3. Rejoice, rejoice in the Lord,
   exult, you just!
   O come, ring out your joy,
   all you upright of heart.

Gospel Acclamation John 14:5
For musical setting see Nos 36 to 47

Alleluia.
I am the Way, the Truth and the Life, says the Lord;
no one can come to the Father except through me.
Alleluia.

or 1 John 4:10

Alleluia.
God so loved us when he sent his Son
to be the sacrifice that takes our sins away.
Alleluia.

Response: Martin Setchell   Psalm tone: Alan Rees

1047 12th in Ordinary Time (C)

Responsorial Psalm Psalm 62:2-6, 8-9. R℣ v.2

For you my soul is thirst - ing, O Lord my God.

1. O God, you are my God, for <u>you</u> I long;
   for you my <u>soul</u> is thirsting.
   My body <u>pines</u> for you
   like a dry, weary land <u>without</u> water.

2. So I gaze on you <u>in</u> the sanctuary
   to see your strength <u>and</u> your glory.
   For your love is bet<u>ter</u> than life,
   my lips will <u>speak</u> your praise.

3. So I will bless you <u>all</u> my life,
   in your name I will lift <u>up</u> my hands.
   My soul shall be filled as <u>with</u> a banquet,
   my mouth shall praise <u>you</u> with joy.

4. For you have <u>been</u> my help;
   in the shadow of your wings <u>I</u> rejoice.
   My soul <u>clings</u> to you;
   your right hand <u>holds</u> me fast.

Gospel Acclamation John 8:12
For musical setting see Nos 35 to 39 and 39 to 47

Alleluia.
I am the light of the world, <u>says</u> the Lord,
anyone who follows me will have the <u>light</u> of life.
Alleluia.

or John 10:27

Alleluia.
The sheep that belong to me listen to my voice, <u>says</u> the Lord,
I know them <u>and</u> they follow me.
Alleluia.

Response and Psalm tone: Andrew Moore

1050 15th in Ordinary Time (C)

Responsorial Psalm Psalm 68:14, 17, 30-31, 33-34, 36-37. ℟ cf. v.33

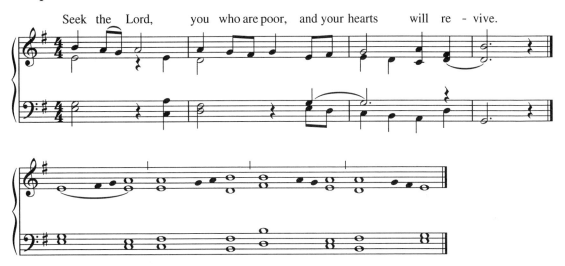

Seek the Lord, you who are poor, and your hearts will re-vive.

1. This is my prayer to you, my prayer <u>for</u> your favour.
   In your great love, answer <u>me</u>, O God,
   with your help that <u>ne</u>ver fails:
   Lord, answer, for your <u>love</u> is kind.

2. As for me in my pover<u>ty</u> and pain
   let your help, O God, <u>lift</u> me up.
   I will praise God's name <u>with</u> a song;
   I will glorify him <u>with</u> thanksgiving.

3. The poor when they see it <u>will</u> be glad
   and God-seeking hearts <u>will</u> revive;
   for the Lord listens <u>to</u> the needy
   and does not spurn his servants <u>in</u> their chains.

4. For God will bring <u>help</u> to Zion
   and rebuild the ci<u>ties</u> of Judah.
   The sons of his servants <u>shall</u> inherit it;
   those who love his <u>name</u> shall dwell there.

The Gospel Acclamation is to be found on the next page.

Response: Andrew Moore   Psalm tone: Laurence Bevenot

Alternative Responsorial Psalm Psalm 18:8-11. R℣ v.9

The pre-cepts of the Lord glad - den the heart.

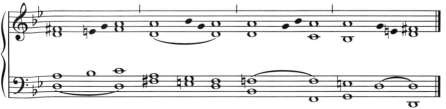

1. The law of the <u>Lord</u> is perfect,
   it re<u>vives</u> the soul.
   The rule of the Lord is <u>to</u> be trusted,
   it gives wisdom <u>to</u> the simple.

2. The precepts of the <u>Lord</u> are right,
   they glad<u>den</u> the heart.
   The command of the <u>Lord</u> is clear,
   it gives light <u>to</u> the eyes.

3. The fear of the <u>Lord</u> is holy,
   abi<u>ding</u> for ever.
   The decrees of the <u>Lord</u> are truth
   and all <u>of</u> them just.

4. They are more to be de<u>sired</u> than gold,
   than the pur<u>est</u> of gold
   and sweeter are <u>they</u> than honey,
   than honey <u>from</u> the comb.

Gospel Acclamation John 10:27
For musical setting see Nos 36 to 47

Alleluia.
The sheep that belong to me listen to my voice, <u>says</u> the Lord,
I know them <u>and</u> they follow me.
Alleluia.

or cf. John 6:63, 68

Alleluia.
Your words are spirit, Lord, and <u>they</u> are life:
you have the message of e<u>ter</u>nal life.
Alleluia.

Response: Richard Lloyd   Psalm tone: Laurence Bevenot

1051 16th in Ordinary Time (C)

Responsorial Psalm Psalm 14:2-5. ℟ v.1

1. Lord, who shall dwell on your <u>ho</u>ly mountain?
   Those who walk <u>with</u>out fault;
   those who <u>act</u> with justice
   and speak the truth <u>from</u> their hearts.

2. Those who do no wrong <u>to</u> their kindred
   who cast no slur <u>on</u> their neighbour,
   who hold the godless <u>in</u> disdain,
   but honour those who <u>fear</u> the Lord.

3. Those who keep their pledge, <u>come</u> what may;
   who take no interest <u>on</u> a loan
   and accept no bribes a<u>gainst</u> the innocent.
   Such people will stand <u>firm</u> for ever.

Gospel Acclamation cf. Acts 16:14
For musical setting see Nos 36 to 47

Alleluia.
Open our <u>heart</u>, O Lord,
to accept the words <u>of</u> your Son.
Alleluia.

or cf. Luke 8:15

Alleluia.
Blessed are those who, with a noble and gen<u>e</u>rous heart,
take the word of God to themselves and yield a harvest
    through their <u>per</u>severance.
Alleluia.

Response: Richard Proulx   Psalm tone: Gregory Murray

Responsorial Psalm Psalm 137:1-3, 6-8. ℟ v.8

1. I thank you, Lord, with all my heart,
   you have heard the words of my mouth.
   Before the angels I will bless you.
   I will adore before your holy temple.

2. I thank you for your faithfulness and love
   which excel all we ever knew of you.
   On the day I called, you answered;
   you increased the strength of my soul.

3. The Lord is high yet he looks on the lowly
   and the haughty he knows from afar.
   Though I walk in the midst of affliction
   you give me life and frustrate my foes.

4. You stretch out your hand and save me,
   your hand will do all things for me.
   Your love, O Lord, is eternal,
   discard not the work of your hands.

Gospel Acclamation John 1:12, 14
For musical setting see Nos 36 to 47

Alleluia.
The Word was made flesh and lived among us;
to all who did accept him he gave power to become children of God.
Alleluia.

or Romans 8:15

Alleluia.
The spirit you recieved is the spirit of children,
and it makes us cry out, 'Abba, Father!'
Alleluia.

Response: Richard Lloyd   Psalm tone: Laurence Bevenot

1053 18th in Ordinary Time (C)

Responsorial Psalm Psalm 89:3-6, 12-14, 17. ℟ v.1

O Lord, you have been our ref - uge from

one gen-er-a - tion to the next.

1. You turn us back into dust
   and say: 'Go back children of the earth.'
   To your eyes a thousand years are like
       yesterday, come and gone,
   no more than a watch in the night.

2. You sweep us away like a dream,
   like grass which springs up in the morning.
   In the morning it springs up and flowers:
   by evening it withers and fades.

3. Make us know the shortness of our life
   that we may gain wisdom of heart.
   Lord, relent! Is your anger for ever?
   Show pity to your servants.

4. In the morning, fill us with your love;
   we shall exult and rejoice all our days.
   Let the favour of the Lord be upon us:
   give success to the work of our hands.

The Gospel Acclamation is to be found on the next page.

Response: Rosalie Bonighton   Psalm tone: Andrew Moore

Alternative Responsorial Psalm Psalm 94:1-2, 6-9. ℟ vv.7-8

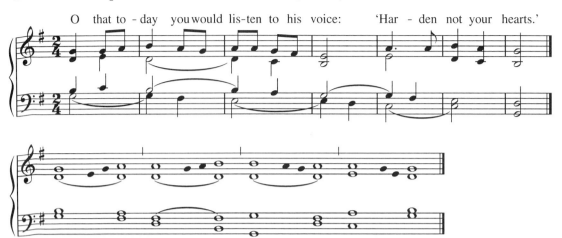

O that to-day you would lis-ten to his voice: 'Har - den not your hearts.'

1. Come, ring out our joy <u>to</u> the Lord;
   hail the <u>rock</u> who saves us.
   Let us come before him, <u>gi</u>ving thanks,
   with songs let us <u>hail</u> the Lord.

2. Come in; let us bow <u>and</u> bend low;
   let us kneel before the <u>God</u> who made us
   for he is our God, and we the people who
      belong <u>to</u> his pasture,
   the flock that is led <u>by</u> his hand.

3. O that today you would listen <u>to</u> his voice!
   'Harden not your hearts as <u>at</u> Meribah,
   as on that day at Massah in the desert, when
      your fathers put me <u>to</u> the test;
   when they tried me, though they <u>saw</u> my work.'

Gospel Acclamation cf. John 17:17
For musical setting see Nos 36 to 47

Alleluia.
Your word is <u>truth</u>, O Lord,
consecrate us <u>in</u> the truth.
Alleluia.

or Matthew 5:3

Alleluia.
How happy are the <u>poor</u> in spirit;
theirs is the <u>king</u>dom of heaven.
Alleluia.

Response and Psalm tone: Gregory Murray

1054 19th in Ordinary Time (C)

Responsible Psalm Psalm 32:1, 12, 18-20, 22. Ry v.12

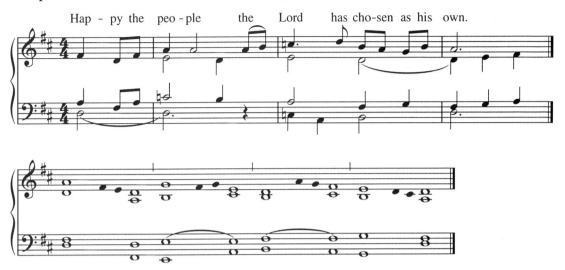

1. Ring out your joy to the Lord, O you just;
   for praise is fitting for loyal hearts.
   They are happy, whose God is the Lord,
   the people he has chosen as his own.

2. The Lord looks on those who revere him,
   on those who hope in his love,
   to rescue their souls from death,
   to keep them alive in famine.

3. Our soul is waiting for the Lord.
   The Lord is our help and our shield.
   May your love be upon us, O Lord,
   as we place all our hope in you.

Gospel Acclamation cf. Matthew 11:25
For musical setting see Nos 36 to 47

Alleluia.
Blessed are you, Father, Lord of heaven and earth,
for revealing the mysteries of the kingdom to mere children.
Alleluia.

or Matthew 24:42, 44

Alleluia.
Stay awake and stand ready,
because you do not know the hour when the Son of Man is coming.
Alleluia.

Response and Psalm tone: Andrew Moore

1055 20th in Ordinary Time (C)

Responsorial Psalm Psalm 39:2-4, 18. ℟ v.14

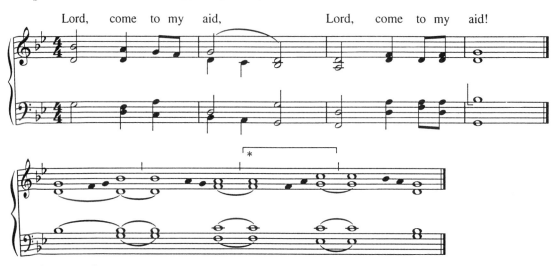

*Omit in verse 1

1. I waited, I waited for the Lord
   and he stooped down to me;
   he heard my cry.

2. He drew me from the deadly pit,
   from the miry clay.
   He set my feet upon a rock
   and made my footsteps firm.

3. He put a new song into my mouth,
   praise of our God.
   Many shall see and fear
   and shall trust in the Lord.

4. As for me, wretched and poor,
   the Lord thinks of me.
   You are my rescuer, my help,
   O God, do not delay.

Gospel Acclamation cf. Acts 16:14
For musical setting see Nos 36 to 47

Alleluia.
Open our heart, O Lord,
to accept the words of your Son.
Alleluia.

or John 10:27

Alleluia.
The sheep that belong to me listen to my voice, says the Lord,
I know them and they follow me.
Alleluia.

Response: Colin Mawby   Psalm tone: Gregory Murray

1056 21st in Ordinary Time (C)

Responsorial Psalm Psalm 116. ℟ Mark 16:15

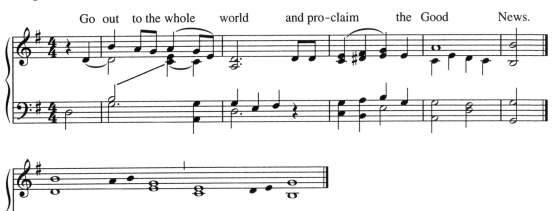

1. O praise the Lord, <u>all</u> you nations,
   acclaim him <u>all</u> you peoples!

2. Strong is his <u>love</u> for us;
   he is faith<u>ful</u> for ever.

Gospel Acclamation John 14:23
For musical setting see Nos 36 to 47

Alleluia.
If anyone loves me they will <u>keep</u> my word,
and my Father will love them and <u>we</u> shall come to them.
Alleluia.

or John 14:6

Alleluia.
I am the Way, the Truth and the Life, <u>says</u> the Lord;
no one can come to the Father ex<u>cept</u> through me.
Alleluia.

Response and Psalm tone: Andrew Moore

Responsorial Psalm Psalm 67:4-7, 10-11. ℟ cf. v.11

In your good - ness, O God, you pre - pared a home for the poor.

1. The just shall rejoice at the presence of God,
   they shall exult and dance for joy.
   O sing to the Lord, make music to his name;
   rejoice in the Lord, exult at his presence.

2. Father of the orphan, defender of the widow,
   such is God in his holy place.
   God gives the lonely a home to live in;
   he leads the prisoners forth into freedom.

3. You poured down, O God, a generous rain:
   when your people were starved you gave them new life.
   It was there that your people found a home,
   prepared in your goodness, O God, for the poor.

Gospel Acclamation John 14:23
For musical setting see Nos 36 to 47

Alleluia.
If anyone loves me they will keep my word,
and my Father will love them and we shall come to them.
Alleluia.

or Matthew 11:29

Alleluia.
Shoulder my yoke and learn from me,
for I am gentle and humble in heart.
Alleluia.

Response: Richard Proulx   Psalm tone: Andrew Moore

1058 23rd in Ordinary Time (C)

Responsorial Psalm Psalm 89:3-6, 12-14, 17. ℟ v.1

O Lord, you have been our ref - uge from one gen-er-a-tion to the next.

1. You turn us back <u>into</u> dust
   and say: 'Go back, children <u>of</u> the earth!'
   To your eyes a thousand years are like
      yesterday, <u>come</u> and gone,
   no more than a watch <u>in</u> the night.

2. You sweep us away <u>like</u> a dream,
   like grass which springs up <u>in</u> the morning.
   In the morning it springs <u>up</u> and flowers:
   by evening it wi<u>thers</u> and fades.

3. Make us know the shortness <u>of</u> our life
   that we may gain wis<u>dom</u> of heart.
   Lord, relent! Is your <u>anger</u> for ever?
   Show pity <u>to</u> your servants.

4. In the morning, fill us <u>with</u> your love;
   we shall exult and rejoice <u>all</u> our days.
   Let the favour of the Lord <u>be</u> upon us:
   give success to the work <u>of</u> our hands.

Gospel Acclamation John 15:15
For musical setting see Nos 36 to 47

Alleluia.
I call you friends, <u>says</u> the Lord,
because I have made known to you everything I have learnt <u>from</u> my Father.
Alleluia.

or Psalm 118:135

Alleluia.
Let your face shine <u>on</u> your servant,
and teach me <u>your</u> decrees.
Alleluia.

Response: Rosalie Bonighton   Psalm tone: Andrew Moore

1059 24th in Ordinary Time (C)

Responsorial Psalm Psalm 50:3-4, 12-13, 17, 19. ℟ Luke 15:18

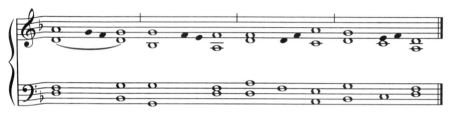

1. Have mercy on me, God, <u>in</u> your kindness.
   In your compassion blot out <u>my</u> offence.
   O wash me more and more <u>from</u> my guilt
   and cleanse me <u>from</u> my sin.

2. A pure heart create for <u>me</u>, O God,
   put a steadfast sp<u>irit</u> within me.
   Do not cast me away <u>from</u> your presence,
   nor deprive me of your <u>hol</u>y spirit.

3. O Lord, <u>open</u> my lips
   and my mouth shall de<u>clare</u> your praise.
   My sacrifice is a <u>con</u>trite spirit;
   a humbled, contrite heart you <u>will</u> not spurn.

Gospel Acclamation cf. Ephesians 1:17, 18
For musical setting see Nos 36 to 47

Alleluia.
May the Father of our Lord Jesus Christ enlighten the eyes <u>of</u> our mind,
so that we can see what hope his call <u>holds</u> for us.
Alleluia.

or 2 Corinthians 5:19

Alleluia.
God in Christ was reconciling the world <u>to</u> himself,
and he has entrusted to us the news that <u>they</u> are reconciled.
Alleluia.

Response: Alan Rees Psalm tone: Gregory Murray

1062 27th in Ordinary Time (C)

Responsorial Psalm Psalm 94:1-2, 6-9. ℟ v.9

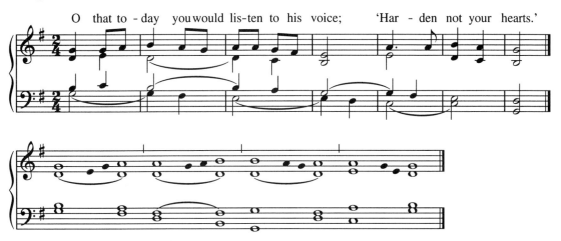

1. Come, ring out our joy to the Lord;
   hail the rock who saves us.
   Let us come before him, giving thanks,
   with songs let us hail the Lord.

2. Come in; let us bow and bend low;
   let us kneel before the God who made us
   for he is our God, and we the people who
      belong to his pasture,
   the flock that is led by his hand.

3. O that today you would listen to his voice!
   'Harden not your hearts as at Meribah,
   as on that day at Massah in the desert, when
      your fathers put me to the test;
   when they tried me, though they saw my work.'

Gospel Acclamation 1 Samuel 3:9; John 6:68
For musical setting see Nos 36 to 47

Alleluia.
Speak, Lord, your servant is listening:
you have the message of eternal life.
Alleluia.

or 1 Peter 1:25

Alleluia.
The word of the Lord remains for ever:
What is this word? It is the Good News that has been brought to you.
Alleluia.

Response and Psalm tone: Gregory Murray

1063 28th in Ordinary Time (C)

Responsorial Psalm Psalm 97:1-4. ℟ cf.v.2

1. Sing a song <u>to</u> the Lord
   for he <u>has</u> worked wonders.
   His right hand and his <u>holy</u> arm
   have <u>brought</u> salvation.

2. The Lord has made known <u>his</u> salvation;
   has shown his justice <u>to</u> the nations.
   He has remembered his <u>truth</u> and love
   for the <u>house</u> of Israel.

3. All the ends of the <u>earth</u> have seen
   the salvation <u>of</u> our God.
   Shout to the Lord <u>all</u> the earth,
   ring <u>out</u> your joy.

Gospel Acclamation cf. John 6:63, 68
For musical setting see Nos 36 to 47

   Alleluia.
   Your words are spirit, Lord, and <u>they</u> are life;
   you have the message of et<u>ern</u>al life.
   Alleluia.

   or cf. 1 Thessalonians 5:18

   Alleluia.
   For all <u>things</u> give thanks,
   because this is what God expects you to do <u>in</u> Christ Jesus.
   Alleluia.

Response: Richard Proulx   Psalm tone: Andrew Moore

1064 29th in Ordinary Time (C)

Responsorial Psalm Psalm 120. ℟ cf. v.2

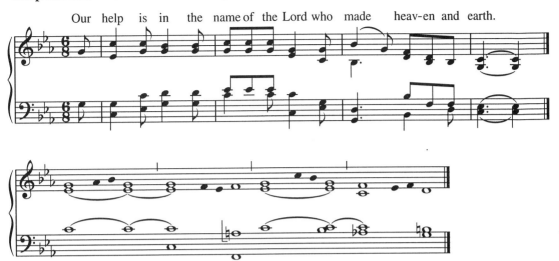

Our help is in the name of the Lord who made heav-en and earth.

1. I lift up my eyes <u>to</u> the mountains:
   from where shall <u>come</u> my help?
   My help shall come <u>from</u> the Lord
   who made hea<u>ven</u> and earth.

2. May he never allow <u>you</u> to stumble!
   Let him sleep <u>not</u>, your guard.
   No, he sleeps <u>not</u> nor slumbers,
   Is<u>ra</u>el's guard.

3. The Lord is your guard <u>and</u> your shade;
   at your right <u>side</u> he stands.
   By day the sun <u>shall</u> not smite you
   nor the moon <u>in</u> the night.

4. The Lord will guard <u>you</u> from evil,
   he will <u>guard</u> your soul.
   The Lord will guard your <u>going</u> and coming
   both now <u>and</u> for ever.

Gospel Acclamation cf. Ephesians 1:17, 18
For musical setting see Nos 36 to 47

Alleluia.
May the Father of our Lord Jesus Christ enlighten the eyes <u>of</u> our mind,
so that we can see what hope his call <u>holds</u> for us.
Alleluia.

or Hebrews 4:12

Alleluia.
The word of God is something <u>alive</u> and active;
it can judge secret em<u>otions</u> and thoughts.
Alleluia.

Response: Colin Mawby   Psalm tone: Andrew Moore

1065 30th in Ordinary Time (C)

Responsorial Psalm Psalm 32:2-3, 17-19, 23. ℟ v.7

The Lord hears the cry of the poor.

1. I will bless the Lord <u>at</u> all times,
   his praise always <u>on</u> my lips;
   in the Lord my soul shall <u>make</u> its boast.
   The humble shall hear <u>and</u> be glad.

2. The Lord turns his face <u>against</u> the wicked
   to destroy their remembrance <u>from</u> the earth.
   The just call and <u>the</u> Lord hears
   and rescues them in all <u>their</u> distress.

3. The Lord is close to the <u>broken</u>-hearted;
   those whose spirit is crushed <u>he</u> will save.
   The Lord ransoms the souls <u>of</u> his servants.
   Those who hide in him shall not <u>be</u> condemned.

Gospel Acclamation cf. Matthew 11:25
For musical setting see Nos 36 to 47

Alleluia.
Blessed are you, Father, Lord of hea<u>ven</u> and earth,
for revealing the mysteries of the kingdom <u>to</u> mere children.
Alleluia.

or 2 Corinthians 5:19

Alleluia.
God in Christ was reconciling the world <u>to</u> himself,
and he has entrusted to us the news that <u>they</u> are reconciled.
Alleluia.

Response: Andrew Moore   Psalm tone: Laurence Bevenot

1066 31st in Ordinary Time (C)

Responsorial Psalm Psalm 144:1-2, 8-11, 13-14. ℟ cf. v.1

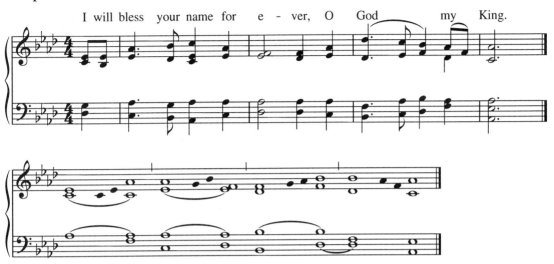

1. I will give you glory, O God my King,
   I will bless your name for ever.
   I will bless you day after day
   and praise your name for ever.

2. The Lord is kind and full of compassion,
   slow to anger, abounding in love.
   How good is the Lord to all,
   compassionate to all his creatures.

3. All your creatures shall thank you, O Lord,
   and your friends shall repeat their blessing.
   They shall speak of the glory of your reign
   and declare your might, O God.

4. The Lord is faithful in all his words
   and loving in all his deeds.
   The Lord supports all who fall
   and raises all who are bowed down.

Gospel Acclamation Luke 19:38
For musical setting see Nos 36 to 47

Alleluia.
Blessings on the King who comes in the name of the Lord!
Peace in heaven and glory in the highest heavens!
Alleluia.

or John 3:16

Alleluia.
God loved the world so much that he gave his only Son,
so that everyone who believes in him may have eternal life.
Alleluia.

Response: Colin Mawby   Psalm tone: Alan Rees

1067 32nd in Ordinary Time (C)

Responsorial Psalm Psalm 16:1, 5-6, 8, 15. ℟ v.15

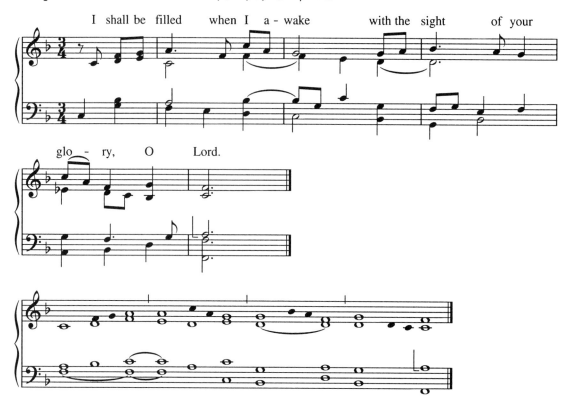

1. Lord, hear a cause <u>that</u> is just,
   pay heed <u>to</u> my cry.
   Turn your ear <u>to</u> my prayer:
   no deceit is <u>on</u> my lips.

2. I kept my feet firmly <u>in</u> your paths;
   there was no faltering <u>in</u> my steps.
   I am here and I call, you will hear <u>me</u>, O God.
   Turn your ear to me; <u>hear</u> my words.

3. Guard me as the apple <u>of</u> your eye.
   Hide me in the shadow <u>of</u> your wings.
   As for me, in my justice I shall <u>see</u> your face
   and be filled, when I awake, with the sight <u>of</u> your glory.

Gospel Acclamation Luke 21:36   or Revelation 1:5, 6
For musical setting see Nos 36 to 47

Alleluia.
Stay awake, praying <u>at</u> all times
for the strength to stand with confidence
  before the <u>Son</u> of Man.
Alleluia.

Alleluia.
Jesus Christ is the First-born <u>from</u> the dead;
to him be glory and power for <u>ev</u>er and ever.
Alleluia.

Response: Richard Proulx   Psalm tone: Alan Rees

1068 33rd in Ordinary Time (C)

Responsorial Psalm Psalm 97:5-9. ℞ cf. v.9

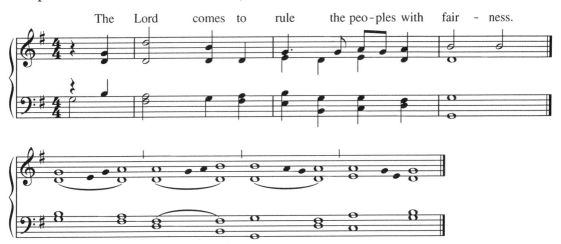

1. Sing psalms to the Lord <u>with</u> the harp
   with the <u>sound</u> of music.
   With trumpets and the sound <u>of</u> the horn
   acclaim the <u>King</u>, the Lord.

2. Let the sea and all with<u>in</u> it, thunder;
   the world, and <u>all</u> its peoples.
   Let the rivers <u>clap</u> their hands
   and the hills ring <u>out</u> their joy.

3. Rejoice at the presence <u>of</u> the Lord,
   for he comes to <u>rule</u> the earth.
   He will rule the <u>world</u> with justice
   and the peo<u>ples</u> with fairness.

Gospel Acclamation Luke 21:36
For musical setting see Nos 36 to 47

Alleluia.
Stay awake, praying <u>at</u> all times
for the strength to stand with confidence before the <u>Son</u> of Man.
Alleluia.

or Luke 21:28

Alleluia.
Stand erect, hold <u>your</u> heads high,
because your liberation is <u>near</u> at hand.
Alleluia.

Response: Rosalie Bonighton   Psalm tone: Gregory Murray

Our Lord Jesus Christ, Universal King (C)

Responsorial Psalm Psalm 121:1-5. ℟ cf. v.2

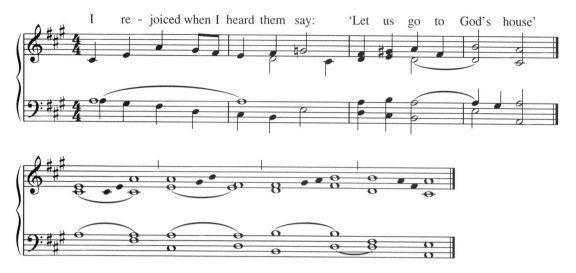

1. I rejoiced when I <u>heard</u> them say:
   'Let us go <u>to</u> God's house.'
   And now our <u>feet</u> are standing
   within your gates, <u>O</u> Jerusalem.

2. Jerusalem is built <u>as</u> a city
   strong<u>ly</u> compact.
   It is there that the <u>tribes</u> go up,
   the tribes <u>of</u> the Lord.

3. For Israel's <u>law</u> it is,
   there to praise <u>the</u> Lord's name.
   There were set the <u>thrones</u> of judgement
   of the <u>house</u> of David.

Gospel Acclamation Mark 11:9, 10
For musical setting see Nos 36 to 47

Alleluia.
Blessings on him who comes in the name <u>of</u> the Lord!
Blessings on the coming kingdom of our <u>father</u> David!
Alleluia.

Response: Andrew Moore Psalm tone: Alan Rees

1070 *2 February*

The Presentation of the Lord (A,B,C)

Responsorial Psalm Psalm 23:7-10. ℞ v.8

1. O gates, lift up your heads;
   grow higher, ancient doors.
   Let him enter, the King of Glory!

2. Who is the King of Glory?
   The Lord, the mighty, the valiant,
   the Lord, the valiant in war.

3. O gates, lift high your heads;
   grow higher, ancient doors.
   Let him enter, the King of Glory!

4. Who is he, the King of Glory?
   He, the Lord of armies,
   he is the King of Glory.

Gospel Acclamation Luke 2:32
For musical setting see Nos 36 to 47

Alleluia.
The light to enlighten the Gentiles
and give glory to Israel, your people.
Alleluia.

Response and Psalm tone: Andrew Moore

1071 *24 June*
The Birth of St John the Baptist (A,B,C)

Responsorial Psalm Psalm 138:1-3, 13-15. ℟ v.14

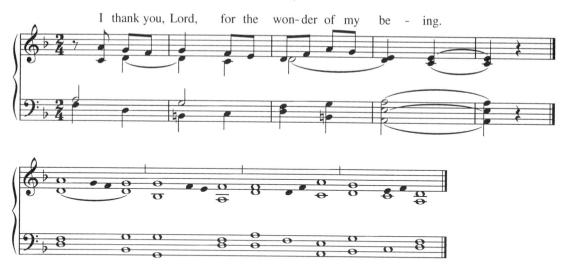

1. O Lord, you search me and you know me,
    you know my resting <u>and</u> my rising,
    you discern my purpose <u>from</u> afar.
    You mark when I walk <u>or</u> lie down,
    all my ways lie <u>open</u> to you.

2. For it was you who cre<u>ated</u> my being,
    knit me together in my <u>mother's</u> womb.
    I thank you for the wonder <u>of</u> my being,
    for the wonders of all <u>your</u> creation.

3. Already you <u>knew</u> my soul,
    my body held no <u>secret</u> from you
    when I was being <u>fashioned</u> in secret
    and moulded in the depths <u>of</u> the earth.

Gospel Acclamation cf. Luke 1:76
For musical setting see Nos 36 to 47

Alleluia.
As for you, little child, you shall be called a prophet
    of God, <u>the</u> Most High.
You shall go ahead of the Lord to prepare his <u>ways</u> before him.
Alleluia.

Response: Richard Proulx   Psalm tone: Gregory Murray

SS Peter and Paul, Apostles (A,B,C)

Responsorial Psalm Psalm 33:2-9. ℟ v.5. Alt. ℟ v.8

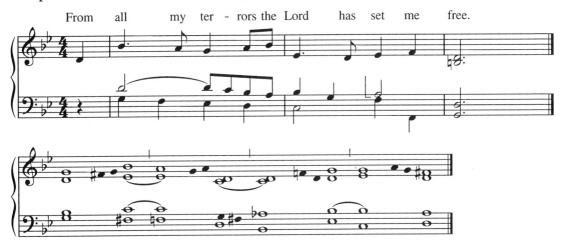

From all my ter - rors the Lord has set me free.

1. I will bless the Lord <u>at</u> all times,
   his praise always <u>on</u> my lips;
   in the Lord my soul shall <u>make</u> its boast.
   The humble shall hear <u>and</u> be glad.

2. Glorify the <u>Lord</u> with me.
   Together let us <u>praise</u> his name.
   I sought the Lord <u>and</u> he answered me;
   from all my terrors he <u>set</u> me free.

3. Look towards him <u>and</u> be radiant;
   let your faces not <u>be</u> abashed.
   When the poor cry out <u>the</u> Lord hears them,
   and rescues them from all <u>their</u> distress.

4. The angel of the Lord <u>is</u> encamped
   around those who revere <u>him</u>, to rescue them.
   Taste and see that the <u>Lord</u> is good.
   They are happy who seek <u>refuge</u> in him.

Gospel Acclamation Matthew 16:18
For musical setting see Nos 36 to 47

Alleluia.
You are Peter and on this rock I will <u>build</u> my church.
And the gates of the underworld can never hold <u>out</u> against it.
Alleluia.

Response and Psalm tone: Andrew Moore

1073 *6 August*

The Transfiguration of the Lord (A,B,C)

Responsorial Psalm Psalm 96:1-2, 5-6, 9. ℟ vv.1, 9

1. The Lord is King, let <u>earth</u> rejoice,
   let all the coast<u>lands</u> be glad.
   His throne, jus<u>tice</u> and right.

2. The mountains <u>melt</u> like wax
   before the Lord of <u>all</u> the earth.
   All peoples <u>see</u> his glory.

3. For you indeed <u>are</u> the Lord
   most high above <u>all</u> the earth
   exalted far a<u>bove</u> all spirits.

Gospel Acclamation Matthew 17:5
For musical setting see Nos 36 to 47

Alleluia.
This is my Son, <u>the</u> Beloved,
he enjoys my favour; lis<u>ten</u> to him.
Alleluia.

Response and Psalm tone: Andrew Moore

The Assumption of the Blessed Virgin Mary (A,B,C)

Responsorial Psalm Psalm 44:10-12, 16. ℟ v.10

On your right hand stands the queen, in gar - ments of gold.

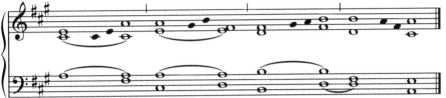

1. The daughters of kings are a<u>mong</u> your loved ones.
   On your <u>right</u> stands the queen in <u>gold</u> of Ophir.
   Listen, O daughter, give ear <u>to</u> my words:
   forget your own people and your <u>fa</u>ther's house.

2. So will the king de<u>sire</u> your beauty.
   He is your lord, pay ho<u>mage</u> to him.
   They are escorted amid glad<u>ness</u> and joy;
   they pass within the palace <u>of</u> the king.

Gospel Acclamation
For musical setting see Nos 36 to 47

Alleluia.
Mary has been taken up <u>into</u> heaven;
all the choirs of angels <u>are</u> rejoicing.
Alleluia.

Response: Colin Mawby   Psalm tone: Alan Rees

1075 *14 September*

The Triumph of the Cross (A,B,C)

Responsorial Psalm Psalm 77:1-2, 34-38. ℟ v.7

1. Give heed, my people, <u>to</u> my teaching;
   turn your ear to the words <u>of</u> my mouth.
   I will open my mouth <u>in</u> a parable
   and reveal hidden lessons <u>of</u> the past.

2. When he slew them then <u>they</u> would seek him,
   return and seek <u>him</u> in earnest.
   They would remember that God <u>was</u> their rock,
   God the Most High <u>their</u> redeemer.

3. But the words they spoke <u>were</u> mere flattery;
   they lied to him <u>with</u> their lips.
   For their hearts were not <u>truly</u> with him;
   they were not faithful <u>to</u> his covenant.

4. Yet he who is full <u>of</u> compassion
   forgave their <u>sin</u> and spared them.
   So often he held <u>back</u> his anger
   when he might have stirred <u>up</u> his rage.

Gospel Acclamation
For musical setting see Nos 36 to 47

Alleluia.
We adore you, O Christ, <u>and</u> we bless you;
because by your cross you have re<u>deemed</u> the world.
Alleluia.

Response: Richard Lloyd   Psalm tone: Alan Rees

All Saints (A,B,C)

Responsorial Psalm Psalm 23:1-6. ℟ cf. v.6

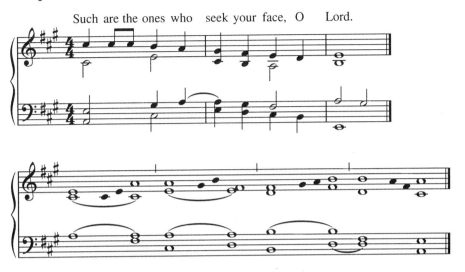

Such are the ones who seek your face, O Lord.

1. The Lord's is the earth <u>and</u> its fullness,
   the world and <u>all</u> its peoples.
   It is he who set it <u>on</u> the seas;
   on the waters he <u>made</u> it firm.

2. Who shall climb the mountain <u>of</u> the Lord?
   Who shall stand in his <u>ho</u>ly place?
   Those with clean hands <u>and</u> pure heart,
   who desire not <u>worth</u>less things.

3. They shall receive blessings <u>from</u> the Lord
   and reward from the <u>God</u> who saves them.
   Such are the <u>ones</u> who seek him,
   seek the face of the <u>God</u> of Jacob.

Gospel Acclamation Matthew 11:28
For musical setting see Nos 36 to 47

Alleluia.
Come to me, all you who labour and are <u>over</u>burdened,
and I will give you rest, <u>says</u> the Lord.
Alleluia.

Response: Rosalie Bonighton   Psalm tone: Alan Rees

The Commemoration of all the Faithful Departed (A,B,C)

Responsorial Psalm Psalm 26:1, 4, 7-9, 13-14. ℟ v.1. Alt. ℟ v.13

1. The Lord is my light <u>and</u> my help;
   whom <u>shall</u> I fear?
   The Lord is the stronghold <u>of</u> my life;
   before whom <u>shall</u> I shrink?

2. There is one thing I ask <u>of</u> the Lord,
   for <u>this</u> I long,
   to live in the house <u>of</u> the Lord,
   all the days <u>of</u> my life.

3. O Lord, hear my voice <u>when</u> I call;
   have mer<u>cy</u> and answer.
   It is your face, O Lord, <u>that</u> I seek;
   hide <u>not</u> your face.

4. I am sure I shall see <u>the</u> Lord's goodness
   in the land <u>of</u> the living.
   Hope in him, hold firm <u>and</u> take heart.
   Hope <u>in</u> the Lord!

Gospel Acclamation John 6:39
For musical setting see Nos 36 to 47

> Alleluia.
> It is my Father's will, says the Lord, that I should lose nothing of all that <u>he</u> has given me,
> and that I should raise it up on <u>the</u> last day.
> Alleluia.

Response: Colin Mawby   Psalm tone: Alan Rees

1078 The Dedication of a Church

Responsorial Psalm Psalm 45:2-3, 5-6, 8-9. ℟ v.5

The wa-ters of a ri-ver give joy, give joy to God's ci-ty.

1. God is for us a re<u>fuge</u> and strength,
   a helper close at hand, in time <u>of</u> distress:
   so we shall not fear though the <u>earth</u> should rock,
   though the mountains fall into the depths <u>of</u> the sea.

2. The waters of a river give joy <u>to</u> God's city,
   the holy place where the <u>Most</u> High dwells.
   God is within, it can<u>not</u> be shaken;
   God will help it at the dawning <u>of</u> the day.

3. The Lord of <u>hosts</u> is with us:
   the God of Jacob <u>is</u> our stronghold.
   Come, consider the works <u>of</u> the Lord
   the redoubtable deeds he has done <u>on</u> the earth.

Gospel Acclamation 2 Chronicles 7:16
For musical setting see Nos 36 to 47

   Alleluia.
   I have chosen and consecrated this house, <u>says</u> the Lord,
   for my name to be <u>there</u> for ever.
   Alleluia.

Response: Rosalie Bonighton   Psalm tone: Laurence Bevenot

Eucharist Adoration with Benediction

1079 O salutaris *O saving victim* (Tune 1)

MELCOMBE LM

1. O sa - lu - ta - ris ho - sti - a, quae
2. U - ni tri - no - que Do - mi - no sit

cæ - li pan - dis os - ti - um, bel - la pre - munt ho -
sem - pi - ter - na glo - ri - a, qui vi - tam si - ne

sti - li - a, da ro - bur, fer au - xi - li - um.
ter - mi - no no - bis do - net in pa - tri - a. A - men.

1. O saving victim, op'ning wide
   the gate of heav'n to man below;
   our foes press on from ev'ry side;
   thine aid supply, thy strength bestow.

2. To thy great name be endless praise,
   immortal Godhead, One in Three;
   O grant us endless length of days
   in our true native land with thee. Amen.

Text: St. Thomas Aquinas (1227-1274) trans. John Mason Neale (1818-1866)
Music: Samuel Webbe (1740-1816)

1080 O salutaris *O saving victim* (Tune 2)

O SALUTARIS LM

1. O sa - lu - ta - ris ho - sti - a, quae
2. U - ni tri - no - que Do - mi - no sit

cæ - li pan - dis os - ti - um, bel - la pre - munt ho -
sem - pi - ter - na glo - ri - a, qui vi - tam si - ne

sti - li - a, da ro - bur, fer au - xi - li - um.
ter - mi - no no - bis do - net in pa - tri - a. A - men.

1. O saving victim, op'ning wide
   the gate of heav'n to man below;
   our foes press on from ev'ry side;
   thine aid supply, thy strength bestow.

2. To thy great name be endless praise,
   immortal Godhead, One in Three;
   O grant us endless length of days
   in our true native land with thee. Amen.

Text: St. Thomas Aquinas (1227-1274) trans. John Mason Neale (1818-1866)
Music: Abbé Duguet (c.1767)

1081 O salutaris *O saving victim* (Tune 3)

COCKFIELD GREEN LM

1. O sa - lu - ta - ris ho - sti - a, quae cæ - li pan - dis os - ti - um, bel - la pre - munt ho - sti - li - a, da ro - bur, fer au - xi - li - um.

2. U - ni tri - no - que Do - mi - no sit sem - pi - ter - na glo - ri - a, qui vi - tam si - ne ter - mi - no no - bis do - net in pa - tri - a. A - men.

1. O saving victim, op'ning wide
the gate of heav'n to man below;
our foes press on from ev'ry side;
thine aid supply, thy strength bestow.

2. To thy great name be endless praise,
immortal Godhead, One in Three;
O grant us endless length of days
in our true native land with thee. Amen.

Text: St. Thomas Aquinas (1227-1274) trans. John Mason Neale (1818-1866)
Music: unknown

1082 O salutaris *O saving victim* (Tune 4)

1. O sa - lu - ta - ris ho - sti - a,
2. U - ni tri - no - que Do - mi - no

quae cæ - li pan - dis os - ti - um, bel - la pre - munt ho - sti - li - a,
sit sem - pi - ter - na glo - ri - a, qui vi - tam si - ne ter - mi - no

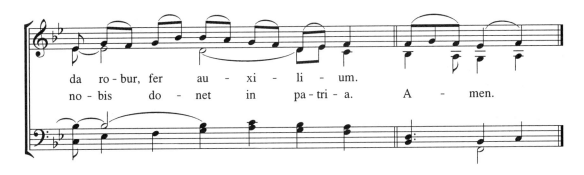

da ro - bur, fer au - xi - li - um.
no - bis do - net in pa - tri - a. A - men.

1. O saving victim, op'ning wide
   the gate of heav'n to man below;
   our foes press on from ev'ry side;
   thine aid supply, thy strength bestow.

2. To thy great name be endless praise,
   immortal Godhead, One in Three;
   O grant us endless length of days
   in our true native land with thee. Amen.

Text: St. Thomas Aquinas (1227-1274) trans. John Mason Neale (1818-1866)
Music: Plainsong, accompaniment by Gregory Murray (1905-1992)

1083 Tantum ergo *Come adore* (Tune 1)

ST THOMAS 87 87 87

1. Tan - tum er - go Sa - cra - men - tum ve - ne - re - mur cer - nu - i:
2. Gen - i - tor - i, gen - i - to - que laus et ju - bi - la - ti - o,

et an - ti - quum do - cu - men - tum no - vo ce - dat ri - tu - i;
sal - us, ho - nor, vir - tus, quo - que sit et be - ne - di - cti - o;

præ - stet fi - des sup - ple - men - tum sen - su - um de - fe - ctu - i.
pro - ce - den - ti ab u - tro - que com - par sit lau - da - ti - o. A - men.

1. Come, adore this wondrous presence,
   bow to Christ, the source of grace.
   Here is kept the ancient promise
   of God's earthly dwelling-place.
   Sight is blind before God's glory,
   faith alone may see his face.

2. Glory be to God the Father,
   praise to his co-equal Son,
   adoration to the Spirit,
   bond of love, in Godhead one.
   Blest be God by all creation
   joyously while ages run.

A lower setting will be found at No. 509

Text: St Thomas Aquinas (1227-1274) trans. James Quinn (b.1919)
Music: Samuel Webbe (1740-1816)

1084 Tantum ergo *Come adore* (Tune 2)

PANGE LINGUA 87 87 87

1. Tan-tum er-go Sa-cra-men-tum ve-ne-re-mur cer-nu-i:
2. Gen-i-tor-i, gen-i-to-que laus et ju-bi-la-ti-o,

et an-ti-quum do-cu-men-tum no-vo ce-dat ri-tu-i;
sa-lus, ho-nor, vir-tus, quo-que sit et be-ne-di-cti-o;

præ-stet fi-des sup-ple-men-tum sen-su-um de-fe-ctu-i.
pro-ce-den-ti ab u-tro-que com-par sit lau-da-ti-o. A-men.

1. Come, adore this wondrous presence,
   bow to Christ, the source of grace.
   Here is kept the ancient promise
   of God's earthly dwelling-place.
   Sight is blind before God's glory,
   faith alone may see his face.

2. Glory be to God the Father,
   praise to his co-equal Son,
   adoration to the Spirit,
   bond of love, in Godhead one.
   Blest be God by all creation
   joyously while ages run.

Text: St Thomas Aquinas (1227-1274) trans. James Quinn (b.1919)
Music: Plainsong, accompaniment by Andrew Moore (b.1954)

1085 Adoremus in æternum

Refrain
Unison   Fine

A - do - re - mus   in   æ - ter - num   san - ctis - si - mum   sa - cra - men - tum.

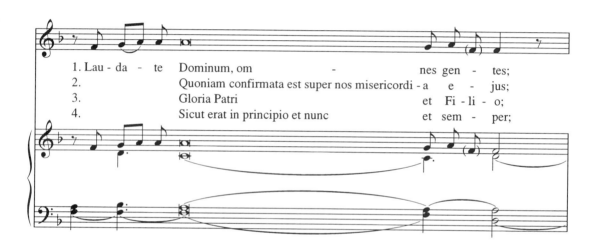

1. Lau - da - te   Dominum, om   -   nes gen - tes;
2.   Quoniam confirmata est super nos misericordi - a   e - jus;
3.   Gloria Patri   et Fi - li - o;
4.   Sicut erat in principio et nunc   et sem - per;

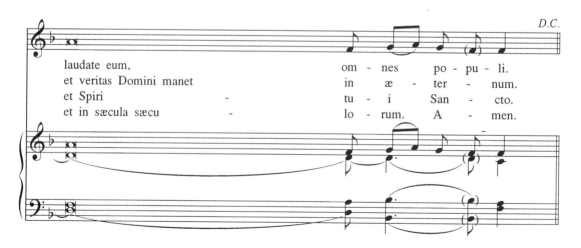

D.C.

laudate eum,   om - nes   po - pu - li.
et veritas Domini manet   in   æ - ter - num.
et Spiri   -   tu - i   San - cto.
et in sæcula sæcu -   lo - rum.   A - men.

Text: Psalm 116
Music: Plainsong, accompaniment by Gregory Murray (1905-1992)

Index of Composers, Arrangers and Sources of Music

Alphabetical Index of Tunes

Metrical Index of Tunes

Some modern tunes, because of their free rhythmic patterns, are not listed in this index.

4 6 6 5
Plaisir d'amour 560

4 6 88 4
Laurence 553

4 6 886
Edgbaston 627

4 10 4 10 and Refrain
Deep calls to deep 235

55 53 D
Bunessan 193, 194, 476, 680

65 63
Grace in Essence 181

65 65
Caswall 19, 280
Holy Cross 402

65 65 66 65
Monks Gate 331

65 65 and Refrain
Lourdes 360
Make peace 738

65 65 D
Evelyns 147
Laudes 313
Princethorpe 247, 392

65 65 D and Refrain
St Gertrude 544

664 6664
Moscow 689

666 66 and Refrain
Personent Hodie (Theodoric) 290

66 8 D and Refrain
The old rugged cross 535

66 11 D
Down Ampney 209

66 65 D and Refrain
This is your God 475

66 66
Ave Maris Stella 632
Ravenshaw 454

66 66 44 44
Darwall's 148th 589
Love unknown 487

66 66 88 6
Divine Mysteries 635
Sanctissimum 635

66 66 and Refrain
Gopsal 591

66 84 D
Leoni 291

66 86 SM (Short Metre)
Bellwoods 648
Carlisle 182
Franconia 174, 648
Narenza 692
Southwell (Damon) 448

66 86 66 86 DSM (Double Short Metre)
Corona 229, 281
Diademata 229, 292, 323
Donnybrook 211

67 67
Love came down 460

67 67 66 66
Nun Danket 497, 586

67 67 and Refrain
This joyful Eastertide (Vreuchten) 686

74 74
Michael row the boat 773, 774, 775

74 74 D
Gwalchmai 408

75 75 44 75
Living God 630

76 76
Mary's child 179

76 76 77 76
Kelvingrove 740

76 76 676
Es ist ein' ros' entsprungen 136

76 76 and Refrain
St Theodulph 113

76 76 and Refrain
All things bright and beautiful 125
Cor Jesu 693
Royal Oak 125
Vaughan 442

76 76 D
Aurelia 647, 513, 521
Crüger 314

Ellacombe 393, 649
Ewing 387
Hatherop Castle 522
King's Lynn 512
O King of Might 523
Passion Chorale 551, 552
Pinner 517
Tempus adest floridum 301
Thornbury 517, 690
Turris Davidica 358
Willsbridge 512

76 76 D and Refrain
Wir pflügen 718

76 77
Puer nobis 698

76 86 Irregular and Refrain
The holly and the ivy 653

77 74 D and Refrain
Here I am 376

77 75 D
Benedicite 102

77 77
Aus der Tiefe (Heinlein) 264
Culbach 269
Lübeck 466
Monkland 428
Orientis partibus 478
The Call 215

77 77 77
Dix 144

77 77 and Alleluias
Easter Hymn 389
Llanfair 311

77 77 and Refrain
Bransle de L'Official 238
Christmas morn 601
Humulity (Oxford) 601
Iris 135
King Divine 310
Westminster Old 188

77 77 D
Easter Hymn 199
St George's Windsor 226
Salzburg 146

77 77 D and Refrain
Mendelssohn 317

777 11
Resonet in laudibus 399

777 D
Veni Sancte Spiritus 341

77 87 87 6 and Refrain
Battle Hymn 271

78 76 and Refrain
Venez, Divin Messie 216

78 78 77
Grosser Gott 333

7 8 9 8 and Refrain
Reproaches 534

84 84
Lord for tomorrow (Providence) 445

84 84 88 84
Ar hyd y nos 115, 232, 233, 334, 456, 736

84 84 888 4
East Acklam 261

85 85 and Refrain
Guiting Power 200

86 86 CM (Common Metre)
Amazing Grace 131, 491
Antioch 404
Belmont 479
Billing 582, 704
Brixton 433
Crimond 661
Dundee 665
Farrant 130
Horsley 666
Irish 516
Miles Lane 116
St Anne 514
St Bernard 127, 130
St Flavian 458
St Fulbert 665, 746
St Magnus 652
Tallis's Ordinal 210
Tozer 400
Westminster 481
Winchester Old 739

86 86 86 and Refrain
God rest you merry 296

86 86 86 86 DCM (Double Common Metre)
Ellacombe 675
Forest Green 526
Noel 375
St Andrew 727

86 86 87 86
Iver 685

86 86 88
Verbum Dei 347

Index of Authors and Sources of Text

Scriptural Index

Index of Uses

Index of Sunday and Feastday Themes

9th SUNDAY

Year A *Building on rock*
119 All my hope on God is founded
448 Lord Jesus, think on me
514 O God, our help in ages past
647 The Church's one foundation
847 The wise man

Year B *Freedom from slavery*
266 Freedom for my people
299 Go in peace
355 If I am lacking love
711 We behold the splendour of God
717 We hold a treasure

Year C *Outsiders are welcome*
139 As bread my Lord comes to me
164 Be still and know that I am God
197 Christ is made the sure foundation
240 Do not be afraid
395 Jesus is Lord! In love he came

10th SUNDAY

Year A *I want love not ritual*
355 If I am lacking love
376 I, the Lord of sea and sky
462 Love is his word
463 Love is patient
562 Our hearts were made for you

Year B *Adam and Satan*
168 Be thou my vision
186 Brother, sister, let me serve you
299 Go in peace
582 Praise to the Holiest
746 Ye choirs of new Jerusalem

Year C *The dead raised to life*
220 Come, praise the Lord
348 I am the bread of life (Konstant)
520 O, how good is the Lord
561 Our God sent his Son long ago
564 Ours were the sufferings he bore

11th SUNDAY

Year A *Spread the Good News*
206 Come and praise him
286 God forgave my sin
289 God is love
303 Go, the Mass is ended
546 Open your ears, O Christian people

Year B *Growth of the Kingdom*
120 All over the world
123 All the earth proclaim the Lord
180 Bread from the earth
226 Come, ye thankful people, come
351 I cannot tell

Year C *God forgives*
131 Amazing grace
237 Deep within my heart
258 Firmly I believe
620 Sing, my soul
862 Bless the Lord, my soul

12th SUNDAY

Year A *Do not be afraid*
240 Do not be afraid
370 In your coming and going
378 I watch the sunrise
582 Praise to the Holiest
688 Though the mountains may fall

Year B *The Conqueror of chaos*
166 Be still, my soul
416 Lead us, heavenly Father, lead us

435 Listen, let your heart keep seeking
647 The Church's one foundation
706 Walk with me, O my Lord

Year C *Take up the cross*
189 By the cross
259 Follow me, follow me
429 Lift high the cross
483 My God said to me, 'Follow'
538 One bread, one body

13th SUNDAY

Year A *Cups of water are rewarded*
259 Follow me, follow me
429 Lift high the cross
483 My God said to me, 'Follow'
667 There is a river
753 You have been baptised in Christ

Year B *Victory over death*
325 He is Lord
352 I come like a beggar
447 Lord Jesus Christ
862 Bless the Lord, my soul
880 Nada te turbe

Year C *Follow me*
259 Follow me, follow me
266 Freedom for my people
350 I am the Light
585 Praise to you, O Christ, our Saviour
754 You have called us

14th SUNDAY

Year A *Humility*
127 All you who seek a comfort sure
223 Come to me, all who labour
224 Come to me, come, my people
377 I, the Servant-Lord
725 What kind of greatness

Year B *Speak out*
168 Be thou my vision
194 Christ be beside me
240 Do not be afraid
297 God's Spirit is in my heart
331 He who would valiant be

Year C *Make peace*
263 Forth in the peace of Christ we go
286 God forgave my sin
572 Peace is flowing like a river
573 Peace is the gift
731 When I survey the wondrous cross

15th SUNDAY

Year A *The prodigal Sower*
140 As earth that is dry
350 I am the Light
435 Listen, let your heart keep seeking
565 Out of darkness
639 Take my hands

Year B *Go and preach*
172 Blessed be the God of Jesus Christ
270 From the sun's rising
286 God forgave my sin
297 God's Spirit is in my heart
303 Go, the Mass is ended

Year C *God's Word is near you*
214 Come, Lord Jesus, come
362 In bread we bring you, Lord
444 Lord, enthroned in heavenly splendour
464 Love is the only law
726 Whatsoever you do

16th SUNDAY

Year A *The lenient Judge*
226 Come, ye thankful people, come
261 For the fruits of his creation
527 O living water
540 One Father
670 The seed is Christ's

Year B *The Shepherd*
407 Keep in mind
486 My shepherd is the Lord
656 The King of love my shepherd is
661 The Lord's my shepherd
677 The wandering flock of Israel

Year C *God in the midst*
194 Christ be beside me
235 Deep calls to deep
369 In you, my God
557 O, the love of my Lord
691 To be in your presence

17th SUNDAY

Year A *Discernment*
94 Abba, Abba, Father
369 In you, my God
567 O Word, in uncreated light
670 The seed is Christ's
717 We hold a treasure

Year B *The hungry are fed*
139 As bread my Lord comes to me
169 Bind us together, Lord
272 Gather around, for the table is spread
362 In bread we bring you, Lord
690 Thy hand, O God, has guided

Year C *Never stop asking*
83-87 Our Father
286 God forgave my sin
423 Let the heavens declare
604 Seek ye first
897 Wait for the Lord

18th SUNDAY

Year A *God's pity*
140 As earth that is dry
354 If God is for us
504 O, come to the water
525 O let all who thirst
667 There is a river

Year B *Bread from Heaven*
348 I am the bread of life (Konstant)
349 I am the bread of life (Toolan)
500 O bread of heaven
743 Word made flesh
865 Eat this bread

Year C *Rich before God*
194 Christ be beside me
262 For the healing of the nations
311 Hail the day that sees him rise
512 O God of earth and altar
779 Do not worry over what to eat

19th SUNDAY

Year A *Calm after the storm*
234 Dear Lord and Father of mankind
243 Eternal Father, strong to save
379 I will be with you
706 Walk with me, O my Lord
863 Calm me, Lord

Year B *The Bread of Life*
139 As bread my Lord comes to me

30th SUNDAY

Year A *Loving neighbours is like loving God*
133 A new commandment
464 Love is the only law
658 The Lord hears the cry of the poor
726 Whatsoever you do
762 All of my heart

Year B *Lord that I may see*
131 Amazing grace
320 Healer of the sick
444 Lord, enthroned in heavenly splendour
658 The Lord hears the cry of the poor
870 Jesus, remember me

Year C *God prefers sinners*
97 Abide with me
255 Fight the good fight
318 Have mercy on us, O Lord
436 Listen to me, Yahweh
437 Listen to my voice

31st SUNDAY

Year A *A warning for priests*
174 Blest are the pure in heart
304 Grant to us, O Lord
338 Holy Jesus, in our likeness born
377 I, the Servant-Lord
1000 O Lord, my heart is not proud

Year B *Loving God and neighbour*
119 All my hope on God is founded
133 A new commandment
362 In bread we bring you, Lord
583 Praise to the Lord, the Almighty
726 Whatsoever you do

Year C *God saves the lost*
131 Amazing grace
290 God is love: his the care
583 Praise to the Lord, the Almighty
857 Zacchaeus was a very little man
1066 I will give you glory

32nd SUNDAY

Year A *Keep watch*
153 Awake, awake: fling off the night
154 Awake from your slumber
274 Give me joy in my heart
566 O Wisdom, source of harmony
704 Waken, O sleeper, wake and rise

Year B *Giving one's all*
213 Come, Lord Jesus
286 God forgave my sin
639 Take my hands
652 The head that once was crowned
with thorns
1034 It is the Lord who keeps faith

Year C *Always alive before God*
220 Come, praise the Lord
348 I am the bread of life (Konstant)
451 Lord of life
649 The day of resurrection
659 The Lord is alive

33rd SUNDAY

Year A *Using our talents*
122 All that I am
251 Father, I place into your hands
639 Take my hands
705 Wake up, O people
726 Whatsoever you do

Year B *Saved from disaster*
286 God forgave my sin
438 Lo, he comes with clouds descending
467 Lumen Christi
521 O Jesus Christ, remember
759 You who dwell in the shelter of the Lord

Year C *Don't give in*
370 In your coming and going
567 O Word, in uncreated light
648 The coming of our God
757 You shall cross the barren desert
1068 Sing psalms to the Lord

34th SUNDAY (CHRIST THE KING)

Year A *Bandaging the wounded*
228 Creator of the day
311 Hail the day that sees him rise
390 Jesus Christ is waiting
466 Loving shepherd of thy sheep
726 Whatsoever you do

Year B *Christ Supreme*
124 All the ends of the earth
229 Crown him with many crowns
336 Holy, holy, holy is the Lord
469 Majesty, worship his majesty
652 The head that once was crowned
with thorns

Year C *A place for us in the Kingdom*
201 Christus vincit
314 Hail to the Lord's anointed
423 Let the heavens declare
444 Lord, enthroned in heavenly splendour
870 Jesus, remember me

Responsorial Psalm Index

A complete set of Responsorial Psalms will be found at numbers 900-1078.

Those suggested below are either alternative translations, paraphrases or songs based on the appropriate psalm.

The Lectionary also provides for common psalms for each season which are also noted here.

Index of First Lines

This index is in five parts:
1. Mass Music
2. Hymns and Songs
3. Children's Hymns and Songs
4. Chants
5. Eucharistic Adoration with Benediction

Responsorial Psalms at numbers 900-1078 are not included in this index.

This index gives the first line of each hymn. If a hymn is known also by a title (e.g. As gentle as silence) this is given as well, but indented and in italic.

MASS MUSIC

A New People's Mass (Murray) 1
A Simple Mass (Moore) 2
Mass of the spirit (Mayhew) 3
Mass of the Bread of Life (Rizza) 4
Missa de Angelis (Plainsong) 5
Mass XVIII (Plainsong) 6
American Eucharist 7
Hopwood Mass 8
Israeli Mass 9

Penitential Rite

Lord, have mercy (Missa de Angelis) 10
Lord, have mercy (Orbis Factor) 11
Lord, have mercy (Alme Pater) 12
Kyrie eleison (Haugen) 13
Lord, have mercy (Archer) 14
Lord, have mercy (Rock) 15
Kyrie eleison (Rizza) 16
Kyrie (Mawby) 17
Kyrie (Taizé) 18
Lord, have mercy on us (Filitz) 19

Gloria

Coventry 20
Rees 21
Archer 22
Taizé 23
Daniels 24
Anderson 25
Salazar 26
Duffy 27
Lourdes 28
Leftley 29
Peruvian 30
Country Gardens 31
Ash Grove 32

Gospel Acclamation

Advent (Joncas) 33
Alleluia (Lloyd) 34
Scottish (Kelly) 35
Irish 36
Celtic 37
Eightfold 38
Easter (Moore) 39
Berthier 40
Archer 41
Plainsong 42
Moore No. 1 43
Moore No. 2 44
White 45

Moore No. 3 46
Bevenot 47
Lundy 48
Alleluia! Magnificat! 49
Alleluia: We will hear your Word 50
Halle, halle, halle 51
Sing praises to the Lord 52
Lent and Holy Week (Lundy) 53
Lent and Holy Week (Walsh) 54
Lent and Holy Week (Moore) 55

Creed

Credo 3 56
Lourdes 57
Fitzpatrick 58

Sanctus

MacMillan 59
Celtic Liturgy 60
Donnelly 61
Deutsche Messe 62
Taizé 63
Lourdes 64
Holy, holy, holy is the Lord 65
Slane 66
Ash Grove 67

Memorial Acclamation

Christ has died

Celtic Liturgy 68
Duffy 69
Donnelly 70
Hill 71
Wise 72

Dying you destroyed our death (Duffy) 73

When we eat this bread

Irish 74
MacMillan 75
Proulx 76

Great Amen

Mayhew 77
Lourdes 78
Plainsong 79
Hill 80
Proulx 81
South African 82

Lord's Prayer

White 83
Wiener 84
Rimsky-Korsakov 85
Echo 86
Caribbean 87

Agnus Dei

Fitzpatrick 88
Archer 89
Rees 90
Inwood 91
Duffy 92
Repton 93

HYMNS and SONGS

A

Abba, Abba, Father 94
Abba Father, from your hands 95
Abba, Father, send your Spirit 96
Abide with me 97
A child is born in Bethlehem 98
Across the years there echoes still 99
Adeste fideles 100
Advent acclamations 721
Advent song 213
A healing song 437
A hymn of glory let us sing! 101
All creation, bless the Lord 102
All creatures of our God and King 103
Alleluia: All the earth 104
Alleluia, alleluia, give thanks to the risen Lord 105
Alleluia, I will praise the Father 106
Alleluia: Let us sing of the Lord 107
Alleluia: My soul praises the glory – see
Alleluia: Sing, my soul 109
Alleluia: Praise God 108
Alleluia: Sing, my soul 109
Alleluia, sing to Jesus 110
Alleluia, thank you for fathers 111
All for Jesus! 112
All glory, laud and honour 113
All glory to you, Redeemer and Lord 114
All God's people, here together 115
All hail the power of Jesus' name 116
All heaven declares 117
All I once held dear 118
All my hope on God is founded 119
All over the world 120
All people that on earth do dwell 121
All that I am 122
All the earth proclaim the Lord 123
All the ends of the earth 124
All things bright and beautiful 125
All you nations, sing out your joy 126
All you who seek a comfort sure 127
Alma redemptoris mater 128
Almighty Father, Lord most high 129
Almighty Father, take this bread 130
Amazing grace 131
And did those feet in ancient time 132
A new commandment 133
Angels we have heard in heaven 134
Angels we have heard on high 135
A noble flower of Judah 136
Arise, come to your God 137
Arise to greet the Lord of light 138
As bread my Lord comes to me 139
As earth that is dry 140
As gentle as silence 557
As I kneel before you 141
As the deer pants for the water 142
As we are gathered 143
As with gladness men of old 144
A touching place 198
At the cross her station keeping 145
At the Lamb's high feast we sing 146

At the name of Jesus 147
At your feet 148
Ave Maria, O maiden, O mother 149
Ave, Regina caelorum 150
Ave verum corpus 151
Awake, awake and greet the new morn 152
Awake, awake: fling off the night 153
Awake from your slumber 154
Away in a manger 155

B

Battle is o'er, hell's armies flee 156
Beauty for brokenness 157
Be blessed, pure of heart 158
Before the light of evening fades 159
Behold, the Lamb of God 160
Behold, the Saviour of the nations 161
Be humble of heart 224
Beloved, let us love 162
Be not afraid 757
Be still and know I am with you 163
Be still and know that I am God 164
Be still, for the presence of the Lord 165
Be still, my soul 166
Bethlehem, of noblest cities 167
Be thou my vision 168
Bind us together, Lord 169
Blessed assurance 170
Blessed be God 171
Blessed be God 175
Blessed be the God of Jesus Christ 172
Bless the Lord, my soul 173
Blest are the pure in heart 174
Blest are you, Lord 175
Blest are you, Lord of creation 176
Blest are you, O God 177
Blest be the Lord 178
Born in the night, Mary's child 179
Bread from the earth 180
Bread is blessed and broken 181
Breathe on me, Breath of God 182
Breath of God, O Holy Spirit 183
Bridegroom and bride 288
Bring, all ye dear-bought nations 184
Bring flowers of the rarest 185
Bring forth the kingdom 749
Brother, sister, let me serve you 186
By his grace 187
By the blood that flowed from thee 188
By the cross 189
By the waters of Babylon 190

C

Called to be servants 191
Change my heart, O God 192
Child in the manger 193
Christ be beside me 194
Christ be our light 439
Christians, lift up your hearts 195
Christ is King of earth and heaven 196
Christ is made the sure foundation 197